LICHENS

An Illustrated Guide to the British and Irish Species

Frank S. Dobson

This edition is dedicated to Jeremy Gray and Peter James
for their help and advice with this book and many other projects.

First edition 1979
Second revised edition 1981
Third enlarged edition 1992
Fourth revised colour edition 2000

ISBN 0 85546 094 6 Paper
ISBN 0 85546 093 8 Hardcovers

Published by The Richmond Publishing Co. Ltd
P.O. Box 963, Slough, SL2 3RS, England

Tel: +44 (0)1753 643104
Fax: +44 (0)1753 646553
email rpc@richmond.co.uk

Printed by
Cambrian Printers, Aberystwyth, Wales

CONTENTS

Cover illustration: *Caloplaca aurantia*
Spine illustation: *Cladonia caespiticia*

ACKNOWLEDGMENTS

I am grateful to all the readers of the previous editions of this book who have made suggestions to improve its usefulness. I have, where possible, incorporated these ideas in this edition. In addition there have been many people who have assisted and have put up with me questioning them closely over various aspects of the subject. In particular I would like to mention Tom Chester, Dr. Brian Coppins, Peter Earland-Bennett, Peter Lambley, Jack Laundon, Ivan Pedley, Dr. William Purvis, Dr. Francis Rose and other members of the British Lichen Society and students on courses run by the Field Studies Council who have all been very helpful with suggestions and in testing out the keys.

I am also indebted to the British Lichen Society for permission to use data collected for their mapping scheme and to Prof. Mark Seaward for his assistance in seeing that I obtained the relevant information and assisting with many other suggestions.

Special thanks must be given to Peter James and Jeremy Gray for checking all the proofs and suggesting many valuable alterations, Prof. Rosmarie Honnegger for her help with the section on lichen algae and Prof. David Hawksworth for the assistance that he has given me and for allowing me to use his microphotographs. The Natural History Musuem must be thanked for the loan of of a number of specimens used in producing of this book.

Many of the translations of the generic names are derived from *Etymologie der Wissenschaftlichen Gattungsnamen der Flechten* by Prof. Dr G.-B. Feige and I am grateful to him for permission to use this information.

I am extremely grateful for all this assistance, without which it would have been almost impossible to produce this book. However, I must stress that any errors contained in this book are mine alone, as is the rather personal choice of rarer species included. I live in the south of Britain and despite efforts to include northern species I suspect that it still has a slight bias in species towards the South.

Photographs by:

J. M. Grey: *Arthonia spadicia, Blarneya hibernica, Collema nigricans, Leptogium britannicum, L. cyanescens, Micarea adnata,, Rhizocarpon lecanorinum.*

D. Hawksworth: *Ephebe lanata, Rinodina teichophila*

INTRODUCTION

Lichens are stable, consistent and identifiable combinations between algae and/or cyanobacteria (the photobiont) and a fungus (the mycobiont). It is, however, difficult to define them more closely than this; indeed, a number of species are studied by lichenologists even though there is evidence that the fungal 'element' exists without any associated alga. On the other hand, some stable relationships between fungi and algae are traditionally ignored by lichenologists. The field of study is circumscribed by tradition rather than by science and a lichen is a biological rather than a taxonomic category.

One useful definition is 'A lichen is a stable self-supporting association of a mycobiont and a photobiont in which the mycobiont is the exhabitant' (Hawksworth 1988). The last phrase of this definition eliminates those seaweeds and other algae which almost invariably contain a symbiotic fungus but in which the alga forms the outside layer. In a lichen the alga is normally on the inside, the exception being in the gelatinous lichens.

The problem of definition has produced difficulties for botanists for many centuries and lichens were at one time classified with the mosses, algae or liverworts. As a 'dual organism' it cannot be named under the Botanic Code and it is, therefore, actually only the fungal partner to which the name is applied. It should be noted that a different fungus occurs in each lichen species but that the same algal species may occur in many different lichens.

For the most part, the nomenclature used in this book follows that of the comprehensive *Lichen Flora of Great Britain and Ireland;* Purvis *et al.* (1992). Names used in the Flora appear in this book as synonyms where there have been changes since its publication in 1992.

The form of the lichen thallus is a result of the interaction between the fungal partner and the photobiont. If cultured alone the mycobiont simply forms a rather shapeless mass. In some cases, where two or more photobionts are present in one lichen (usually a cyanobacterium and a green alga), these produce very different forms, even in the same thallus. However, as only one fungus is involved, only one name may be used for the lichen. These differing forms with different algae are now referred to as 'phases' of the lichen. Normally the fungus forms up to 95% of a lichen with the alga contained in a thin inner layer (heteromerous). In most of the lichens that include only a cyanobacterium the photobiont differs and is distributed throughout the thickness of the lichen (homoiomerous), the mycobiont and the cyanobacterial cell being supended in a gelatinous matrix. In the case of the filamentous lichens the thread-like chain of algal cells comprises the core around which the fungus forms an outer sheath.

It has been said that most lichens are ascomycetes with an unusual mode of nutrition, but out of over 30,000 species forming the *Ascomycota,* almost half of them are lichenized; indeed lichenization is probably the most common single life-style of the ascomycetes. The vast majority of the approximately 1,700 lichenized fungi in the United Kingdom and Ireland are ascomycetes producing their spores in sac-like asci and there are but few *basidiomycete, coelomycete, hyphomycete* and *phycomycete* lichens. In common with other fungi, the fungal partner is unable to photosynthesize and produce its own food in order to survive. Non-lichenized fungi overcome this problem by breaking down living or dead organic material, or forming alternative mutualistic associations such as mycorrhizas. In the case of lichens, an example of mutualistic symbiosis, the fungus stimulates the algal partner to release the sugars needed to provide the energy for survival, growth and reproduction. The alga obtains protection from the extremes of temperature, light and moisture and probably obtains mineral salts leached by the fungus from the substrate, but more importantly this enables the alga to survive in habitats where it would be unable to exist in its free-living state.

For many years the algal cells were not recognized as such by botanists and were often thought to be the reproductive cells of the lichen. When Schwendener in the 1860s suggested the true nature of a lichen he was reviled and his views of a fungal/algal relationship were not accepted by some people for a considerable period. Almost all the fungi and some of the algae in lichens have never been found alone; the co-evolved mutualism is therefore self-evident. The shape assumed by a lichen species is such that the algal cells are displayed to maximum advantage of the lichen for that particular ecological niche. Whatever the final outcome of research into the relationship, it is clear that it is evolutionarily very successful. Indeed lichens have been able to colonize many habitats from below sea-level to the tops of mountains, and from the cold polar regions to the baking heat of deserts, vastly outnumbering the flowering plants in many harsh environments such as Antarctica or arctic tundra where they may form the majority of the biomass present. Many species grow less than a millimetre a year, but nevertheless some may survive for many hundreds of years.

Very many lichens produce fruiting bodies. The shape and structure of these, the asci, spores, and other reproductive parts which they contain, form the basis of most lichen classification. Unlike many other fungi, these fruiting bodies are long-lived and can often produce very large numbers of spores over several years. Where there is a combination of different organisms there is often a problem of dispersal and propagation. In the case of lichens these fruiting bodies are only produced by the fungal partner and, with a few specialized exceptions, they do not contain any reproductive element from the alga. This means that after dispersal and before the spore can develop after germination, it must quickly obtain suitable algal cells to incorporate into the potential lichen or it will die. Lichens employ various strategies to help minimize this difficulty. Some produce very many small spores to increase the chances of one of them landing at a suitable site for germination. These small spores may have a short life as there is no room for a large reserve of food. Other species produce a smaller number of large spores which may have a thick wall and are thus able to remain viable for a longer period during which they may come in contact with a suitable alga. Some other lichens produce spores with many nuclei, each of which is capable of germination. In many species the germinating spore develops by parasitizing another lichen which contains a suitable alga and then taking over this alga for its own use. It also appears that, in the early stages, some lichens may develop by associating with an alga that is not the preferred one for that species. The alga may not be able to survive in this association but it does mean that the period is extended during which the correct alga may be contacted. However, despite the considerable number of spores produced, the odds are still against frequent successful reproduction by this means.

In many species the importance of vegetative means of dispersal is high, indeed some species have never been found with sexual fruiting bodies.

Vegetative propagules may consist of algal cells and fungal hyphae that are simply broken fragments of thallus or they may be formed in special structures (such as soralia and isidia). These propagules are dispersed by many means, such as wind, rain, insects or other animals. If they arrive on a suitable substratum it may then be possible for them to develop, forming a new complete lichen.

The ecology of lichens is complex and there is still much that is not fully understood. Some species are able to occupy a wide range of habitats; others require very precise conditions in order to survive and this variation can provide a very useful guide to identification. These requirements are noted in this book under 'habitat' in the species entries. For example, some species require a degree of nutrient enrichment from birds whilst others may only be found in Scotland above 700 metres in nutrient-poor sites. Grazing animals and walkers may affect the habitat to the benefit of the lichens by keeping an area open and preventing these species from being shaded out by the higher plants. The type of rock on which they grow may be important, with acid and basic rock types each supporting a different range of species. The pH and water absorbency of bark also affect the colonization by certain species.

A range of specialized lichens may be found by the seashore, occupying a niche in this hostile, salt-laden environment where few other organisms are able to survive. The height at which they grow above the low tide line is a useful aid in identifying these species. Yet other species appear to have a poor ability to spread any distance and are only found in ancient woodlands. The absence of certain lichens in an apparently old wood may indicate that the wood was clear-felled well over 100 years ago but that these lichens have never been able to re-establish themselves. We are fortunate in having a wide range of climatic conditions in the British Isles allowing a number of more Mediterranean species to colonize the extreme South and West. Conversely, some arctic-alpine species may be found in the northern uplands. The effect of air pollution on lichens is profound and is considered later in this introduction.

Of the 1,700 or so lichen species in Britain this book covers about 700 of them. They are the majority of those found commonly in the British Isles. Many of the other species are very rare, having been identified only once or twice, or in a very limited area.

The study of lichens has the advantage over the study of most British plants in that they have the same form throughout the year and may be collected in winter or summer alike. Care should, however, be taken not to remove the very rare species and even the common ones may only be collected if a viable number of specimens can be left at any particular site. Lichens should only be collected for scientific purposes and not merely to swell a private collection. Permission from the landowner should always be obtained before collecting in any area, and the 'Country Code' must be followed. In some circumstances it is now an offence to collect without the owner's permission.

Collecting requires only simple equipment and as long as the specimens are dried fairly quickly, perhaps over a warm radiator, and are then kept dry, they are seldom subject to attack by insects or moulds. The following equipment should be obtained by anyone taking a serious interest in lichenology.

A hand-lens giving a magnification of x 8–12 is essential and another of x 15–20 is useful for inspecting small details.

A stout knife for removing specimens from trees, wood, etc. (not folding, as these can cause an accident if they close up whilst in use).

A hammer (preferably a geological hammer or at least a hammer with a flat head).
Well-sharpened cold chisels and a pair of protective glasses or goggles and gloves.
Sheets of paper or packets in which to place the specimens after collection (damp specimens in polythene bags become mouldy very quickly).
Other equipment as required, such as secateurs for collecting twigs.

As specimens are collected they should be individually wrapped as they can very easily become valueless through damage caused by rubbing against each other, especially when dry. Details of where and when the specimen was collected should be written on the packet as soon as it has been collected.

When the specimen has been identified the following is the minimum information that will be required if the specimen is to have any future scientific use:

Name of species.
Place collected (if possible including the grid references, or at least the name of the vice-county) and nearest town or village.
Substratum.
Date collected.
Name of collector and, if different, the name of the person who identified the specimen.

When identifying a specimen bear in mind that the thallus colour described is usually of a dry material and that this often changes when it is wet, in some species from a silvery grey to almost black, or from a greenish grey to golden yellow or green. After a period in an herbarium many species become a light buff colour. Some of the specimens collected will be seen to be distorted and atypical making them almost impossible to identify. It must be accepted that not every specimen collected can be identified without using advanced techniques such as thin layer chromatography. When some specimens are found, especially if in a poor condition, they may have become covered in green algae or, if dead or dying, may turn white or even bright red from the breakdown of the lichen substances that they contain. Many lichens require specific lighting conditions. Broken branches brought down by the wind may afford the only opportunity of studying those which require the high light levels of the upper canopy. Such lichens soon die when exposed to the very different conditions on the ground and may rapidly change colour and form making identification difficult.

It will soon be found that the ascus, spores and other reproductive parts form such an important part of classification that in order to examine these minute bodies, access to a compound microscope capable of giving a magnification of at least x 400 and ideally x 1000 is essential for any serious lichenologist. As well as this microscope, a binocular dissecting microscope with a magnification of x 10–40 is very useful for examining and preparing specimens, but is not essential.

In order to examine the spores a 'squash' must be made. This is done by choosing a good, well-formed fruiting body, wetting it to soften it, cutting a thin vertical sliver from the centre of this fruit, placing it on a microscope slide, then adding a small drop of water which is left for a minute or two to be absorbed. A cover slip is lowered gently on top and the blunt end of a pencil is dropped lightly but repeatedly onto it from a height of about one centimetre. This will usually squash the specimen sufficiently to show the detailed structure and release some of the spores. If needed, more pressure can be applied to the cover slip by thumb or forefinger (covered by a tissue to keep grease off) to spread the specimen on the slide. If the slide is prepared on a white surface it is possible to judge progress during this process more easily. The slide should be examined under the microscope as the squashing progresses as it is a simple matter to continue the process but it cannot be reversed. When required, a specimen will often soften more easily and rapidly in K solution (see page 10) which should not be allowed to come into contact with the microscope lens.

The secret of a good squash is to take the smallest vertical slice possible of the fruit body and to use the least amount of liquid. In examining certain structures (e.g. perithecia) a very thin slice is vital as squashing will disturb the arrangement of the parts needed for identification.

When examining spores a number of them should be carefully studied on the slide before deciding the spore type as some may have only developed septa or colour as they matured. Be aware that some brown spores look greenish in a K solution squash, and measure only those which have been discharged from the ascus. The K solution may cause some spores to swell slightly and should not be used if spore size is critical.

Much modern taxonomy of lichens uses the reaction of various parts of the ascus to iodine (K/I test) and it is important to be able to perform this test as follows:

1. Moisten with water and place a section of a fruiting body on a microscope slide as described above.
2. Add a drop of 10% potassium hydroxide solution (K) to the section and after 1–3 minutes absorb the excess onto a tissue held at the edge of the drop of liquid.
3. Add a drop of Lugol's iodine and then absorb the iodine onto a tissue.
4. Repeat stage 3 twice more but do not soak up the final iodine.
5. Place a cover slip on the specimen and examine under a microscope at x 100 for colour changes to any parts of the hymenium (the tissues around the ascus).
6. Examine the ascus at about x 400 magnification and note carefully any areas which have turned blue.

If the outer coat of the ascus or the whole tip turns blue it may be difficult to determine the appearance of any of the inner structures With practice this problem may be alleviated by omitting step 4. This leaves a small quantity of K in the tissues which has the effect of slowly bleaching the iodine and as it disappears it is often possible to see, fleetingly, if any of the inner structures have turned blue. The addition of further iodine will turn the parts blue again. It is easy to misplace the very small piece of lichen on the slide whilst absorbing the liquids onto a tissue.

Many lichens contain very stable substances. Fresh material and even specimens in collections 200 or more years old will react with several different chemicals to show colour changes. These changes are very valuable in identification, but it must be remembered that although a positive result can be considered conclusive, a negative one can mean that the specimen may have a low percentage of the substance for which the test is made. In this case the test should be repeated on another part of the thallus. The substances being tested for are sometimes most concentrated just behind the growing point. Rather than adding the chemical to the whole specimen a small piece should be removed for testing which should then be discarded. If it is the cortex that is to be tested, and in this book this is the case unless otherwise stated, a drop of chemical is placed on the upper surface of the thallus. The chemicals are only used in very small quantities and are best applied with a glass rod or a clean cocktail stick, but they often change the colour of the lichen by turning the cortex translucent, making the alga visible. This may look like a positive result. If there is any doubt about a colour change, take up the liquid onto a small piece of white tissue or filter paper and examine this. Sometimes it is the medulla and not the cortex which should be tested. To expose the medulla, which is white in most species, cut or scrape away the upper cortex of the lichen with a razor blade or scalpel held at a shallow angle. It is sometimes possible to obtain different reactions to the same chemical in separate specimens of the same species. These 'chemotypes' are referred to in the species notes. In the past the importance given to these differences has varied but they are now generally considered to be insignificant. In many cases it may only be the lack of a single gene that prevents the build-up at a certain stage, of more complex chemicals by the lichen.

The following are the most commonly used of the simple thalline chemical tests. All chemicals are poisonous and should be handled with great care, but Pd is thought to be possibly carcinogenic and extra care should be taken in using it.

K: potassium hydroxide. A 10% solution is required but the concentration is not too critical. This forms a stable solution that will keep for many months in a closed bottle. Many of the yellow reactions obtained using this solution are best seen by taking up the drop of chemical from the thallus under test onto white tissue or filter paper.

C: calcium hypochlorite. This is the main constituent of many household bleaches although a number of them now contain sodium hypochlorite. This is equally effective for a spot test. C remains active for only a few weeks but it is inexpensive and can be replaced at regular intervals. It should be tested frequently (e.g. *Ochrolechia androgyna* or *O. tartarea* turn red). The reaction to C is often fleeting and may only last a few seconds, so tests should be performed while the specimen is being examined under a lens.

KC: K is applied to the specimen. After about 30 seconds it can be taken up onto white filter paper. A drop of C is then placed on the paper next to the K. The colour change, which is often fleeting, occurs where they intermingle.

CK: This is the reverse of the previous test with C being applied followed by K. This test is important in identifying diffractaic acid, but is rarely used.

P or **Pd**: Paraphenylenediamine (crystals). As far as possible its use should be avoided. It is unstable and is used by wetting a crystal with alcohol and applying the liquid to the specimen. If even a minute crystal falls on paper it will, over a period, produce a strong brown stain. A fairly stable solution may be made as Steiner's Solution (1 g paraphenylenediamine, 10 g sodium sulphite, two or three drops of wetting agent (domestic liquid detergent) in 100 ml water). This solution should last for up to three months but should be tested at intervals (the medulla of *Parmelia sulcata* turns yellow then red). The reaction with Pd often takes two or three minutes to develop and a specimen should be tested several times before a negative result is declared.

I: Iodine is used in a number of tests under the microscope where the presence or absence of particular carbohydrates such as isolichenin (a starch-like product) is important. Lugol's iodine (1 g iodine with 2 g potassium iodine in 300 ml of water) is ideal for these tests. The squash may be made in the iodine solution but frequently a better result will be obtained by using K to make the slide and then drawing the Lugol's solution under the cover slip with a piece of filter paper held at the opposite side. Meltzer's reagent (0.5 g iodine in 1 g potassium iodide plus 20 gm chloralhydrate and 25 ml water) can be used in squash preparations when it is important to see the septa of spores more clearly. It may be tested on the spores of *Graphis* which turn blue-purple. As mentioned earlier iodine is used to examine some of the detailed structure of the ascus.

UV: Ultraviolet light is becoming an important aid to identification. Under it, chemicals in the lichen fluoresce showing a range of colours which may be used to identify substances both in thin layer chromatography and in direct examination of a specimen in a darkened room. A UV lamp with a wavelength of about 350 µm is suitable and is also the wavelength used in many lamps sold for philately or for checking bank notes. Most paper now has substances added which fluoresce bright ice-blue and care should be taken to shield the specimen from this bright light which will otherwise swamp the subtle colours from the lichen. If a specimen is mounted on such paper, it can be examined by viewing it through a small hole cut in a mask of black paper. All UV lamps emit a certain amount of white light and care must be taken not to confuse the pale reflection of this with the brighter fluorescence from a lichen. The amount of fluorescent substance in a lichen can vary greatly so that, where possible, a negative result should be confirmed by testing further specimens. The cortex, medulla and/or soredia should be tested as different chemicals may be found in each.

N: 50% Nitric acid reacts with some pigments in the apothecia to give useful colour changes.

The lichen photobiont

Until very recently, both algologists and lichenologists have tended to give scant attention to the more detailed aspects of the algal partner (the photobiont) in the symbiotic relationship. This has meant that our knowledge of the taxonomy and ecology or, indeed, any other aspect of the alga, has been fairly limited. It is hoped that the following notes will assist in identifying some of the commoner species of algae and cyanobacteria found in lichens.

As already mentioned, every lichen species has a different fungus and these fungi belong to very many different genera. In Britain alone about 270 fungal genera include lichenized species, and there are very many more lichenized genera world-wide. However, the situation is very different with the photobiont where there is a total of only about 40 genera world-wide that associate with fungi to form lichens. Some of these have been misreported or are very rare so that the true number of genera which are commonly lichenized is probably fewer than thirty. About two-thirds of these genera are green algae and one-third are cyanobacteria.

The cells of the green algae resemble those of the higher plants in their ability to photosynthesize by means of chloroplasts (the bodies that contain the pigment molecules needed for photosynthesis). Inside the chloroplasts there may be dark-staining pyrenoids (small masses of protein and starch and associated with the synthesis of starch by the alga). Unlike cyanobacteria the nucleus is contained within a membrane.

The cyanobacteria differ from the green algae in several ways, especially in the lack of membrane-bound organelles such as a nucleus, pyrenoids or chloroplasts. The carbohydrate they produce is glucose whereas green algae produce sugar alcohols such as ribitol, erythritol, etc. All these sugars are converted into mannitol by the fungus. This substance is also important to the fungus for protecting membranes and organelles from desiccation during drought. Most cyanobacterial photobionts have the ability to fix nitrogen. This process takes place in structures called heterocysts. These are specialized cells that provide the anaerobic condition in which the reaction with the enzyme nitrogenase can take place. In lichens these heterocysts may be five times as numerous and be larger than those found in free-living cyanobacteria. It has been calculated that, in lichens world-wide, about 60% contain unicellular green algae, of which the most common is *Trebouxia*, found in over half of all lichen species. About 30% contain the orange-pigmented green alga *Trentepohlia* that forms chains of cells and fewer than 10% contain cyanobacteria of which the commonest is *Nostoc* but even this is found in fewer than 5% of lichen species.

A number of lichen species consistently contain both green algae and cyanobacteria. The greater part of the photobiont in these lichens consists of the green alga with the cyanobacteria restricted to a thin layer or contained in delimited stuctures called cephalodia. These cephalodia may be either within the thickness of the thallus, or as external protrusions that often differ in appearance from the rest of the thallus, e.g. *Lobaria amplissima*. A number of other lichens are sometimes very loosely associated with cyanobacteria. This is often the case in their younger stages.

The identification of lichen algae is often difficult as their appearance can be very different when incorporated in a lichen as opposed to when they are free-living. When in a lichen, the algae often have thinner walls, larger chloroplasts and, in cyanobacteria, may be surrounded by a thinner layer of mucilage. Indeed some lichens, such as the *Endocarpon* species, overcome the problem of a spore only dispersing the fungus, by having small cells of their green alga *Stichococcus* mixed amongst the contents of the hymenium. When a spore is discharged it may well carry some of these small algal cells with it. The *Stichococcus* cells in the thallus of this lichen are much larger than those in the hymenium.

When *Trebouxia* cells reach a diameter of about 10 µm they divide and the clusters formed are pushed apart by the extending fungal hyphae and, in filamentous algae, the chains of cells may be broken apart. This happens most frequently near the growing tip or edge of the lichen. As the older algal cells become further from the growing point they divide less frequently but become larger and, in the case of cyanobacteria, most nitrogen fixation takes place in these older cells.

The fungal hyphae spreading amongst the algal cells often produce a substance that causes the alga to leak the majority of the sugar it produces, which is then available to the fungus. To do this the fungus must come into very close contact with the algae or cyanobacteria. In leprose, crustose and many filamentous species it may actually perforate the algal cell wall with structures called haustoria (these are also found in plant pathogenic fungi). It is mainly the older cells that are penetrated in this manner. After such an attack the cell usually dies or, as the inner membrane is still intact, it divides. However, the cells of *Trentepohlia* appear to be penetrated at any age. In foliose and fruticose species the algal cells are not normally entered but the fungal hyphae lie in intimate contact with the algal cells. With many cyanobacteria, although the haustoria may push in the cell wall, they do not actually cross through it or the inner membrane. Instead they push them in, like a finger being pushed into an inflated balloon. They may also be in less intimate contact with the cells and only grow into the gelatinous matrix

The fungal hyphae which form the medulla and spread into the algal layer are hydrophobic (water repellent) and this prevents the lichen from becoming waterlogged, thus enabling adequate gaseous exchange. In contrast to the medulla, the upper cortex is hydophilic (water absorbing). This becomes translucent as it takes up moisture, allowing the light and sufficient moisture through to permit photosynthesis by the alga. Green algae are able to utilize humid conditions to photosynthesize. *Trentepohlia* is able to retain more water and thus is able to continue producing sugars at much lower external humidity than is the case with most other green algae. Conversely, cyanobacteria need liquid water to photosynthesize as humid conditions do not provide sufficient moisture. The gelatinous sheath around the colony is hydrophilic and thereby often holds enough moisture to permit photosynthesis to take place.

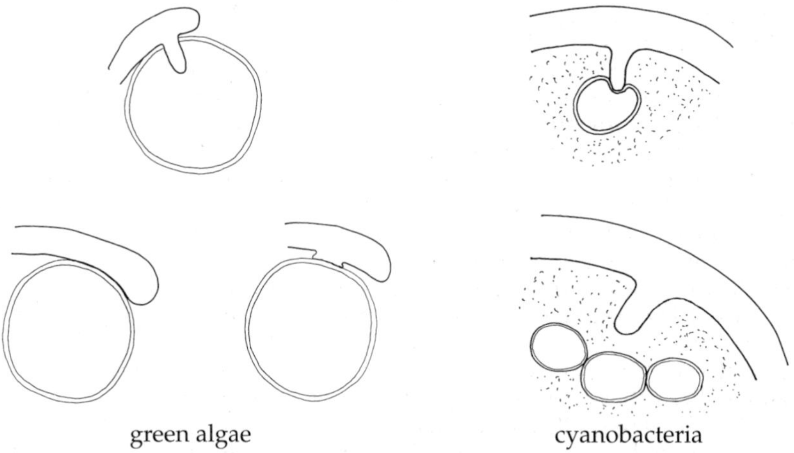

Fungal contacts between green algae and cyanobacterial cells
(after Honegger, R., 1988).

Some common algae and cyanobacteria

Green Algae

Trebouxia including ***Pseudotrebouxia*:** These genera are the commonest algae found in lichens and a number of different algal species are included, each having a slightly different appearance, especially in the shape of the large chloroplast. The cells are spherical, 5-15 µm long, or in a few species ellipsoid, and the lobate chloroplast containing a single pyrenoid fills most of the interior. The cell nucleus is often contained inside a fold of the chloroplast. This genus is not frequently found in the free-living state but is very common and widespread in lichens. Mattock and Stewart have shown that it is so similar to the free-living filamentous alga *Pleurastrum* that it is probably this genus which has become modified by living in a lichen.

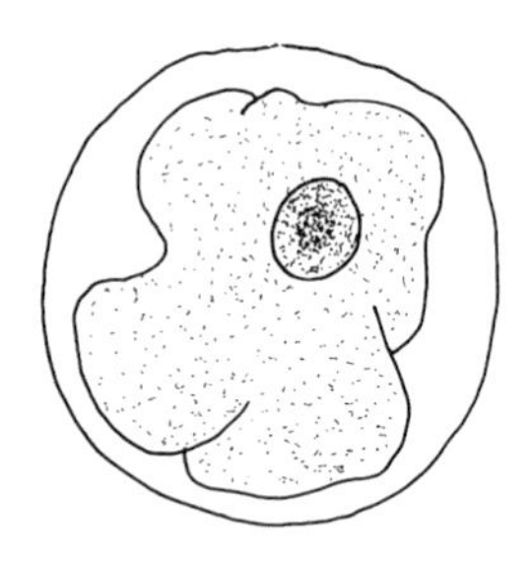

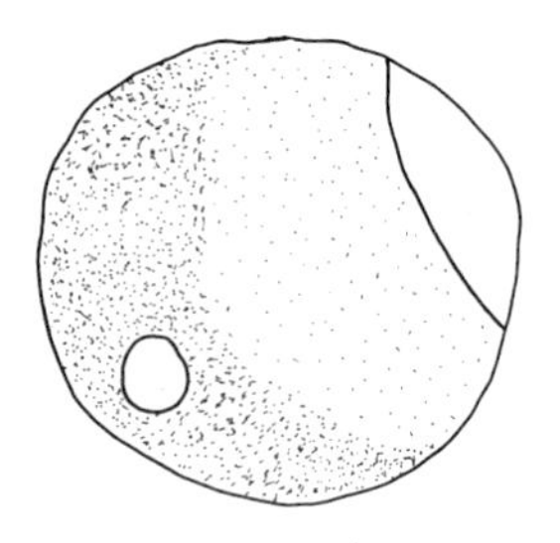

***Chlorella*:** The cells are spherical and only about 10 µm diameter. They contain a cup-shaped parietal (around the edge) chloroplast, with a pyrenoid. When the cells divide they form a figure of 8 shape.

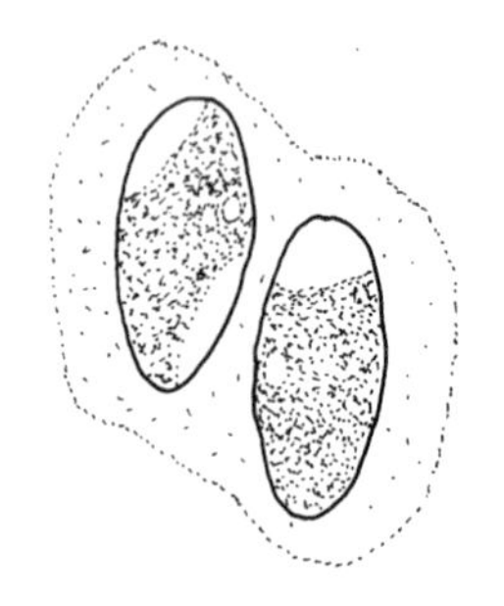

***Coccomyxa*:** The cells are usually rather spindle-shaped, up to 15 µm in length with a parietal chloroplast. There are often clear areas lacking cytoplasm. The cells are surrounded by a layer of mucilage. This mucilage can be much reduced in quantity when the alga is in a lichen.

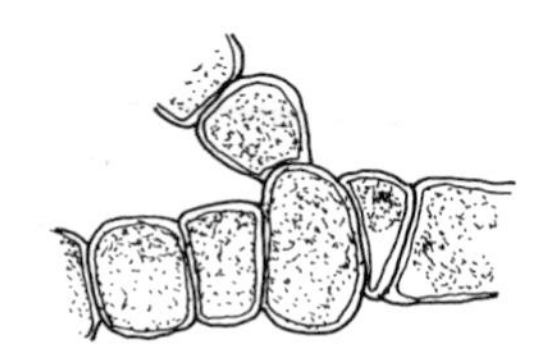

***Leptosira*:** This consists of a web of dicotomously branched, yellow-green filaments with somewhat square cells 10–15 µm long. It is found in *Thrombium* and *Vezdaea* species.

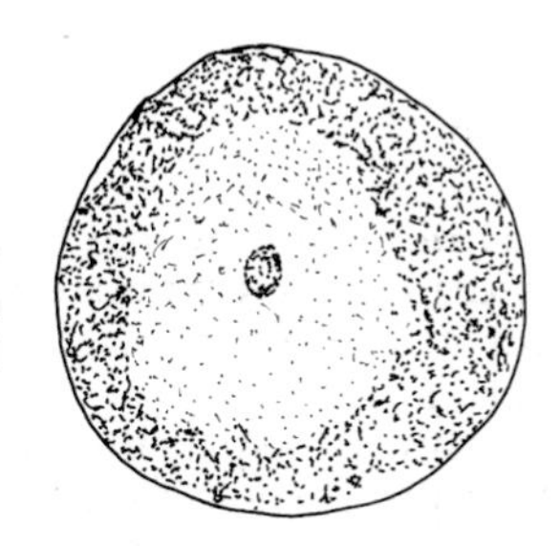

***Myrmecia*:** The cells are irregularly spherical to ellipsoid, about 15 µm diam. It differs from *Trebouxia* in the smooth chloroplast and the central nucleus.

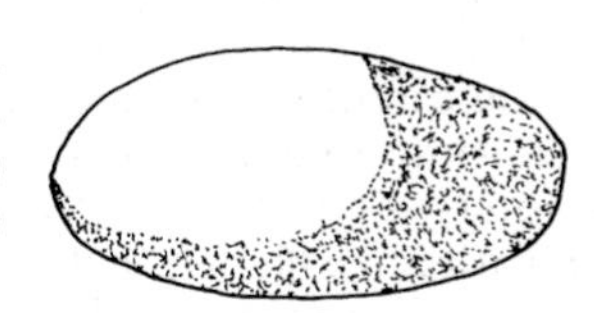

***Stichococcus*:** The cells are bacilliform, about 8 µm long with a parietal chloroplast which often leaves large clear areas in the cell. The cells found in the hymenium of *Endocarpon* species are often more rounded and are 3–5(7) µm long.

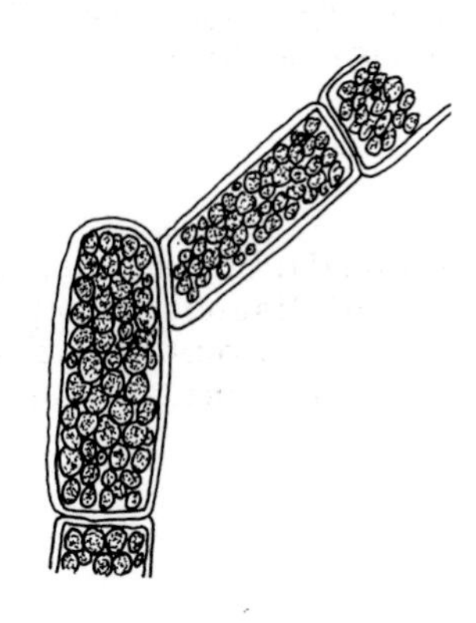

Trentepohlia: This is a green filamentous alga that may appear orange due to the carotinoid pigments that it contains. It forms filaments of thick-walled cells about 20–50 µm long and joined by rather square ends, slightly constricted at the joints. The cells are filled with many discoid chloroplasts. It is frequently found free-living as minute, fluffy, orange balls on the damp, shaded side of trees and rocks. In lichens it is found in many of the crustose species that grow in shaded sites. It can often be identified by scratching the surface of the lichen when the orange colour will become apparent. The only non-crustose genus in the British Isles containing this alga is *Roccella*.

Cyanobacteria

Note that the filamentous structure (in cyanobacteria the chain of cells inside the sheath is called a trichome) is often broken up by the fungal hyphae.

***Calothrix*:** This consists of filaments, often grouped together at the base which are whip-like, tapering to the tip and with a slightly 'hairy' sheath. The cells are wider than they are long. The heterocysts, which are often difficult to see, are situated at the lower end of each filament.

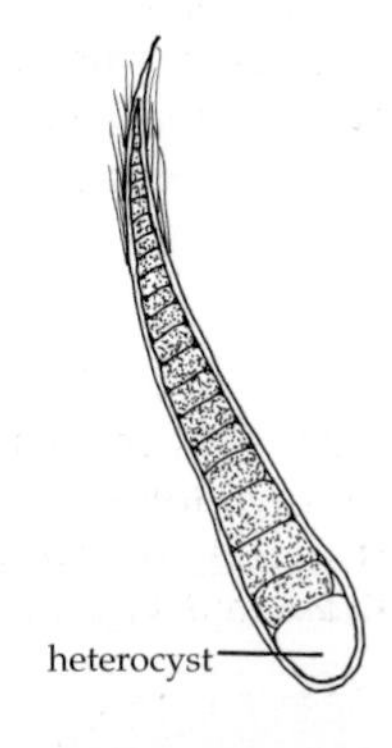

'Chroococcoid' cyanobacteria are rare in British lichens but common in the lichens of other countries. The individual cells are 10–20 µm long (but less than 6 µm in *Chroococcidiopsis*) . The outer sheath is soft and breaks down when the colony reaches 2–4, or rarely more, individuals.

laminated sheath

***Gloeocapsa*:** The cells are about 10 µm long, usually several enclosed in a gelatinous sheath about 40 µm wide which is red-violet or brownish (seen only when mounted in water).

***Nostoc*:** The commonest cyanobacterium in lichens and often found free-living as brown gelatinous sheets on damp soil etc. The cells form 'pearl necklace' chains of globose cells about 6 µm diameter interspersed by the colourless heterocysts. These chains are embedded in a brownish gelatinous sheath, although this may be much reduced when it is incorporated in a lichen.

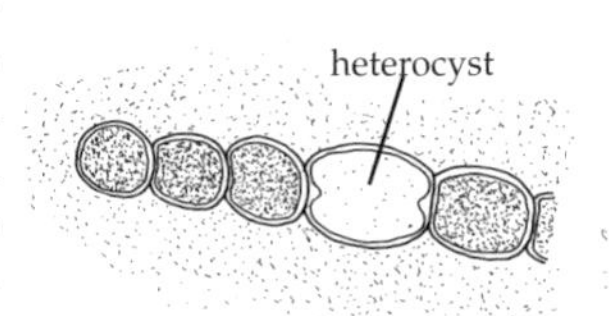

***Scytonema*:** This forms chains which are covered with a brownish stratified sheath. It exhibits 'false branching' where the trichome is interupted (often at a heterocyst) and pushes out through the sheath in a new direction (but it is often broken up by the fungus). This gives this species a distinctive paired appearance. The indidvidual cells are 3–12 µm long and rather variable in shape.

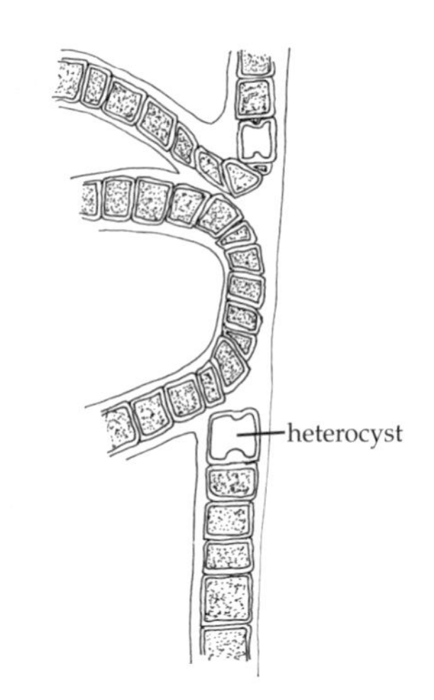

***Stigonema*:** This is a large species. Each filament is up to 100 µm wide and contains continuous clusters of brown-green cells 5–15 µm diameter within the yellow-brown sheath. The side branches are produced at about 90° to the main filaments mainly containing only single cells uniseriately arranged in the side filament .

LAYOUT OF THE ENTRIES

The main body of the book is laid out in alphabetical order according to genus. Each genus commences with its main characteristics together with illustrations of spores, paraphyses and other reproductive parts. Many of the illustrations, which should be used for general guidance only, have been drawn directly from specimens under the microscope but in other cases details have been derived from many sources. The information in this section is not usually repeated under each species and it should always be consulted when undertaking identification.

There then follows a table of characteristics or a key which should agree only with species described in this book. It is possible that the data given may also agree with rare species not included in this book. If a specimen is found that clearly belongs to a particular genus, but will not key out, again, it may be one of the rarer species not included in this book. *The Lichen Flora of Great Britain and Ireland* should then be consulted. The descriptions and photographs are of average specimens such as are commonly found in the British Isles, rather than of superb but rare examples. To aid recognition the entries are sometimes subdivided into groups relating to habitat or prominent characters. A description is given of any simple chemical reactions of importance which, unless otherwise mentioned, refer to the reactions of the cortex. The final section gives details of the preferred habitat of that species. In most instances a photograph is also provided which, as far as possible, will have been chosen to show the more important features.

The colour changes in the reactions given in this book are sometimes abbreviated for reasons of space as follows: y = yellow, o = orange, r = red, c = crimson, p = purple, y–r = yellow first then turning red, b = blue, f = faint.

Where a species is frequently referred to by a synonym this is shown in round brackets ( ). This name is often an earlier one used in *The Lichen Flora of Great Britain and Ireland* (1992). Square brackets [ ] indicate a more recent name that may, or may not, be generally accepted.

AIR POLLUTION ZONES

The following table uses the 'Hawksworth and Rose' scale proposed in 1970 but which remains broadly correct, especially for lowland England. In many parts of the country the mean levels of sulphur dioxide are falling and lichens are recolonizing areas where they have not been seen for many years. The ability to recolonize depends not only on the level of pollution but also on a number of other factors. A lichen with a low rate of recolonization may be absent from an area although other species, less able to stand pollution but better at re-establishing themselves, may be present. Where levels of sulphur dioxide pollution are dropping rapidly a number of species in the middle zones 5 and 6, which need a rather acid bark, may never reappear because the substrate has already become too basic to support them. This phenomenon is known as 'zone-skipping'.

All these factors must be considered when deciding, from the above scales, the zone which is appropriate for any particular site. It will be realized that these scales are most reliable where levels of sulphur dioxide pollution are stable or rising. Great caution is needed where levels are falling.

Hawksworth and Rose Zone scale for the estimation of mean winter

Zone	Acid bark
0	Epiphytes absent.
1	*Desmococcus viridis* s.l. present but confined to base.
2	*Desmococcus viridis* s.l. extends up the trunk; *Lecanora conizaeoides* present but confined to the bases.
3	*Lecanora conizaeoides* extends up the trunk; *Lepraria incana* s.l. becomes frequent on the bases.
4	*Hypogymnia physodes* and/or *Parmelia saxatilis* or *P. sulcata* appear on the bases, do not extend up the trunks. *Hypocenomyce scalaris, Lecanora expallens* and *Chaenotheca ferruginea* often present.
5	*Hypogymnia physodes* or *P. saxatilis* extends up the trunk to 2.5 m or more; *P. glabratula, P. subrudecta, Parmeliopsis ambigua* and *Lecanora chlarotera* appear; *Calicium viride, Chrysothrix candelaris* and *Pertusaria amara* may occur; *Ramalina farinacea* and *Evernia prunastri* if present largely confined to the bases; *Platismatia glauca* may be present on horizontal branches.
6	*Parmelia caperata* present at least on the base; rich in species of *Pertusaria* (e.g. *P. albescens, P. hymenea*) and *Parmelia* (e.g. *P. revoluta* (except in N.E.), *P. tiliacea, P. exasperatula* (in N.)); *Graphis elegans* appearing; *Pseudevernia furfuracea* and *Bryoria fuscescens* present in upland areas.
7	*Parmelia caperata, P. revoluta* (except in N.E.), *P. tiliacea, P. exasperatula* (in N.) extend up the trunk; *Usnea subfloridana, Pertusaria hemisphaerica, Rinodina roboris* (in S.) and *Arthonia impolita* (in E.) appear.
8	*Usnea ceratina, Parmelia perlata,* or *P. reticulata* (S. and W.) appear; *Rinodina roboris* extends up the trunk (in S.); *Normandina pulchella* and *U. rubicunda* (in S.) usually present.
9	*Lobaria pulmonaria, L. amplissima, Pachyphiale cornea, Dimerella lutea,* or *Usnea florida* present; if these absent, crustose flora well developed with often more than 25 species on larger well-lit trees.
10	*L. amplissima, L. scrobiculata, Sticta limbata, Pannaria* spp., *Usnea articulata, U. filipendula*, or *Teloschistes flavicans* present to locally abundant.

sulphur dioxide levels in England and Wales

Basic or nutrient-enriched bark	Mean winter SO_2 µg/m³)
Epiphytes absent.	?
Desmococcus viridis s.l. extends up the trunk.	> 170
Lecanora conizaeoides abundant; *L. expallens* occurs occasionally on the bases.	About 150
Lecanora expallens and *Amandinea punctata* abundant, *Diploicia canescens* appears.	About 125
Diploicia canescens common; *Physcia adscendens* and *Xanthoria parietina* appear on the bases; *Physcia tribacia* appears in S.	About 70
Physconia grisea, Diplotomma alboatrum, Phaeophyscia orbicularis, Physcia tenella, Ramalina farinacea, Haematomma ochroleucum var. *porphyrium, Schismatomma decolorans, Xanthoria candelaria, Opegrapha varia* and *O. vulgata* appear; *Diploicia canescens* and *X. parietina* common; *Parmelia acetabulum* appears in E.	About 60
Pertusaria albescens, Physconia distorta, Hyperphyscia adglutinata, Acrocordia gemmata, Caloplaca luteoalba, Xanthoria polycarpa and *Lecania cyrtella* appear; *Phaeophyscia orbicularis, Opegrapha varia* and *O. vulgata* become abundant.	About 50
Physcia aipolia, Anaptychia ciliaris, Bacidia rubella, Ramalina fastigiata, Candelaria concolor and *Anisomeridium biforme* appear.	About 40
Physcia aipolia abundant; *Anaptychia ciliaris* occurs in fruit; *Parmelia perlata, P. reticulata* (in S and W), *Gyalecta flotowii, Ramalina canariensis,* and *R. pollinaria* appear.	About 35
Ramalina calicaris, R. fraxinea, R. subfarinacea, Physcia leptalea and *Caloplaca cerina* appear.	Under 30
As 9 (above).	'Pure'

HOW TO USE THE MAPS

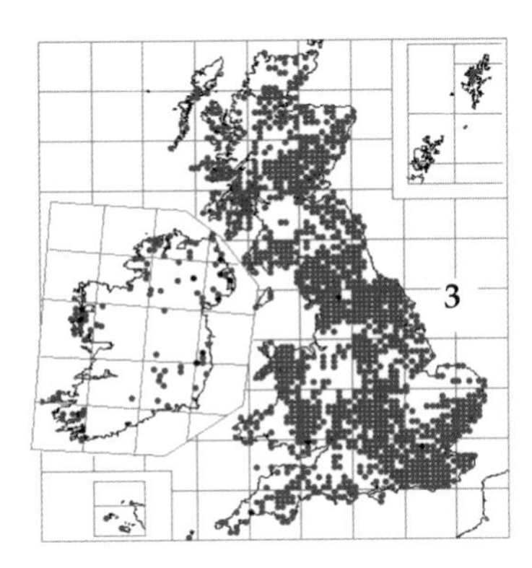

The dots on the maps show 10 km squares where a species has been recorded, frequently indicating a clear pattern of distribution, but the lack of a black dot may simply be due to an area being under-recorded. The BLS mapping scheme has been recording data for almost 40 years and it is only in Ireland that under-recording is still important, but it should be noted that the maps are only intended to act as an aid to identification. Note that the presence of a dot might mean that only one specimen has been found. Therefore, a group of dots does not necessarily mean that a species is common in that area.

Many factors such as a lack of a suitable substratum or too high a pollution level will lead to the absence of a species. An estimate of the maximum zone level of sulphur dioxide air pollution that can be tolerated by a species is given in the scale (1 to 10) in the right-hand side of the map (see pages 17–19 for an explanation of this scale). In some cases, such as where a species grows on the coastline or there is considerable doubt over the pollution tolerance, this code is not given.

The distribution maps included in this book are based on the latest information available and are reproduced by kind permission of The British Lichen Society. A great deal has still to be learnt regarding the distribution of British lichens, and this is an aspect of lichenology where the amateur can be of much assistance. It should be noted that the maps are based on data supplied to the mapping scheme by members of the Society and that some records may need verification. A further problem is caused by the changes that have occurred in the concept of the status of certain species. It is often difficult to know to which of the new species concepts some older records relate. It is hoped that readers of this book will aid the Society's mapping scheme by supplying records. Further information may be obtained from the Society's Mapping Recorder: Prof. M.R.D. Seaward, The Department of Environmental Science, University of Bradford, Bradford, West Yorkshire BD7 1DP.

NOTES ON USING THE GENERIC KEY

This key is designed for use only for those species that are included in this book. It may not 'key-out' correctly for other species. If a rare species is found that is not included in this book, the genus can, in many cases, be deduced from the group key and then from the main key by using the spore details.

Note that a number of species will be found to spread from their normal substrate to overgrow adjacent moss, etc.

The chemical tests listed should be made on the surface of the lichen unless otherwise stated. + or – refers to all species in that group that are included in the book. The absence of an entry means that the test is unimportant or variable.

GROUP KEY

The first part of the key (1 to 7) covers the basic lichen thallus forms. A decision has to be made as to which group a specimen to be identified belongs. These entries terminate in a letter (A to D or T) indicating the section of the main key that should be used. If an entry terminates in a figure (8, 9 or 10), refer to the section with that number in this group key. Here a further decision is required to provide the letter indicating the section of the main key that should be used.

MAIN KEY

When experience has been gained it will be possible to go straight to the main key using the Synopsis. This key is used by comparing alternatives at each level of indentation of the text and then using, in the same way, the further indented alternatives given immediately under the chosen answer

A number of genera resemble those of a different group. In these cases the genus will key-out in both groups. The symbol ! after the name indicates that the genus does not belong scientifically in that group.

The additional notes at the end of each entry refer to all members of that genus included in the book, but are not necessarily exclusive to that entry.

In most cases it should be possible to key-out a specimen to its genus but if due to lack of spores, etc., it can only be reduced to two or three possible genera, the details and photographs of each of these genera should be consulted in the main text. This should enable the user to determine the genus.

SPORE TYPES

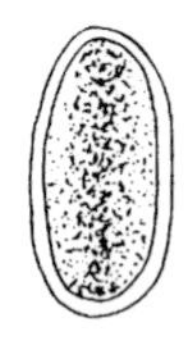

SIMPLE

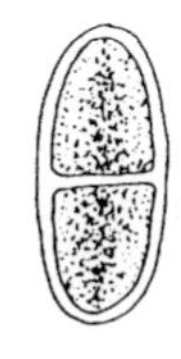

1-SEPTATE

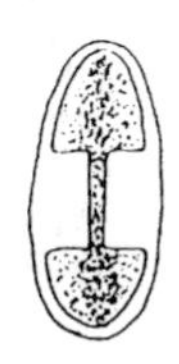

POLARILOCULAR

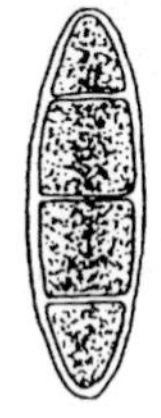

MULTI-SEPTATE

MURIFORM

GROUP KEY

1. LEPROSE

Consisting of a more or less diffuse powdery mass (or, in this key, crustose but entirely covered in soredia) **Key A**

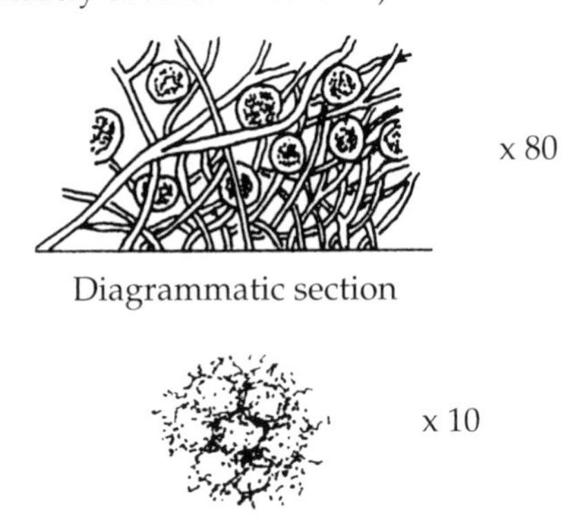

Diagrammatic section

View from above

---

2. FILAMENTOUS

Very fine, soft, hair-like or gathered into a felt-like mat of fine filaments. Fungal hyphae enveloping the algal filaments or chains. (If longer than 3 cm, see 7) **Key B**

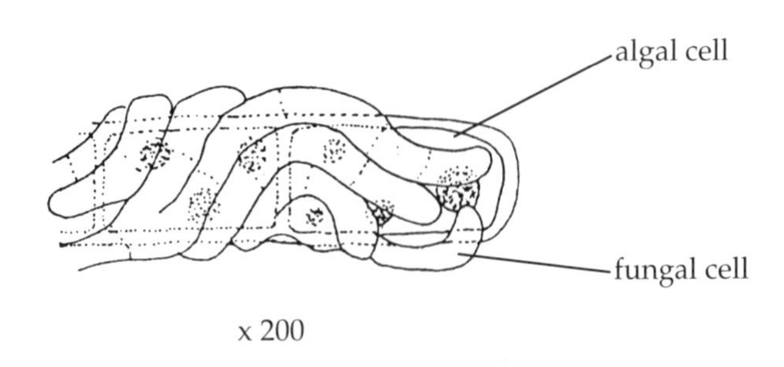

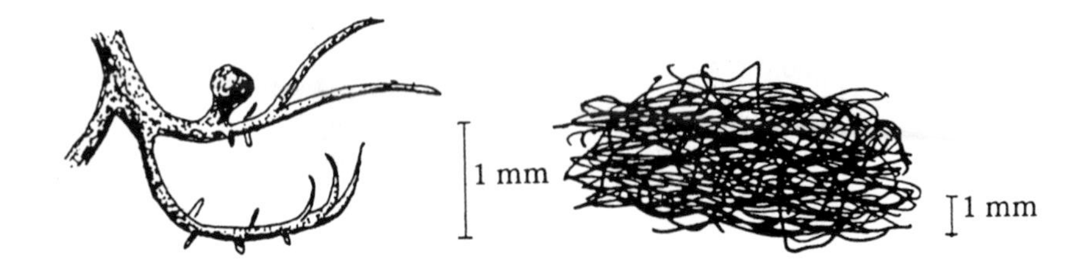

3. CRUSTOSE — Forming a crust which usually can only be removed with part of the substratum. Thallus in some cases thin or inside the substratum with only the apothecia showing at the surface. Fruiting bodies present **8**

or — Not fertile but with delimited soralia, isidia, or white-pruinose pycnidia **Key T**

x 100

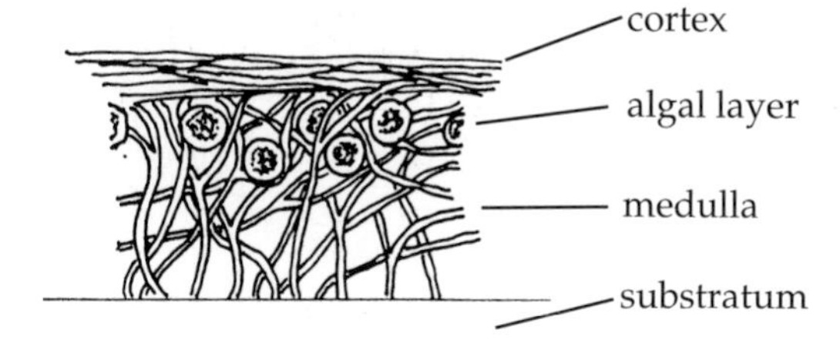

---

4. PLACODIOID — Crustose but appearing lobed towards the margin. Usually can only be removed with part of the substratum **Key C**

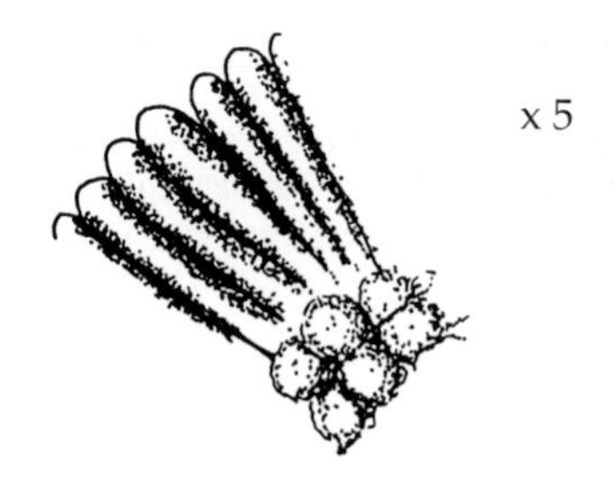

---

5. SQUAMULOSE — Consisting of small (to about 1 cm long) leaf-like squamules, crustose at the base but free at the edges and/or tips, often overlapping and forming mats. Fruiting bodies often podetia **Key D**

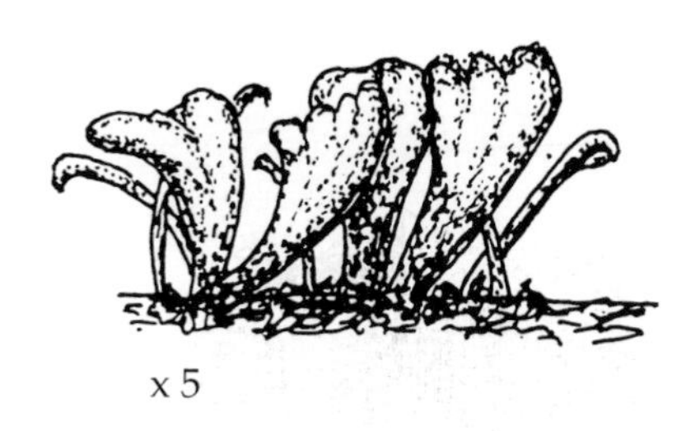

x 5

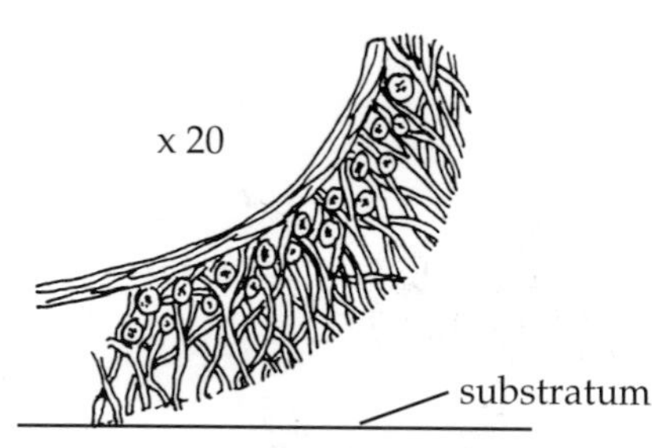

6. FOLIOSE (leaflike)

Flattened and leaf-like, often large. Distinctly dorsiventral species belong here (excluding squamulose). May be thin and papery when dry, swelling considerably when wet. Can usually be removed without part of the substratum, may be attached by rhizines **9**

x 2

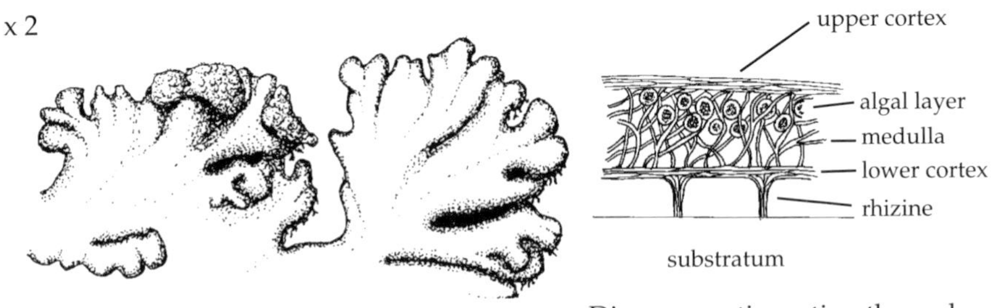

Diagrammatic section through a foliose lichen with rhizinae

---

7. FRUTICOSE (shrubby)

Radially symmetrical, coarse, lacking a distinct upper and lower surface, branches in transverse section rounded or flattened. (If dorsiventral go to 9.) Attached to the substratum at one point only, or unattached. Algal layer just inside the cortex; there is a central core in *Usnea* **10**

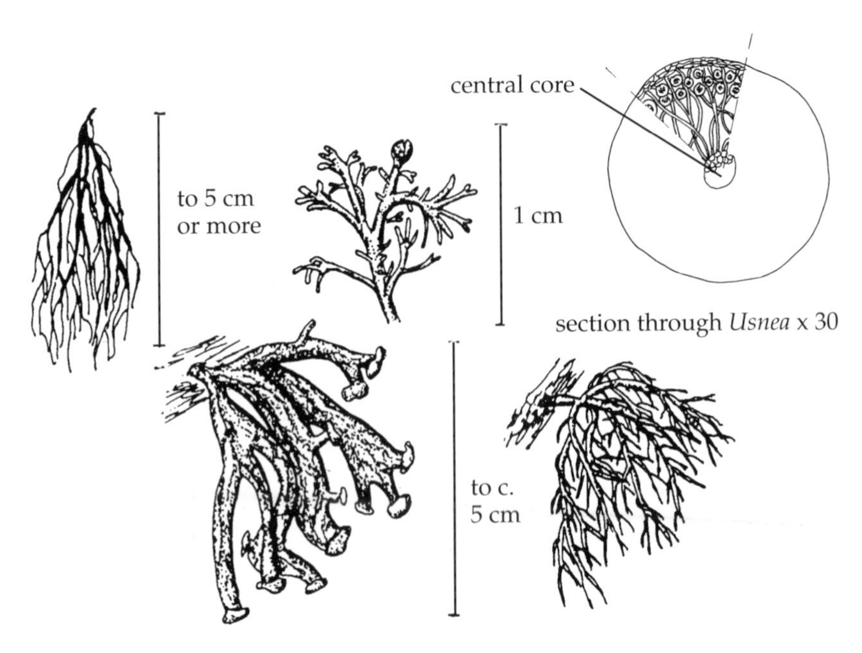

section through *Usnea* x 30

8. CRUSTOSE
FRUITING BODIES

(i) Stalked	To 3 mm high, indian-club or golf-tee shaped, lacking algal cells in the thin stalk	**Key E**

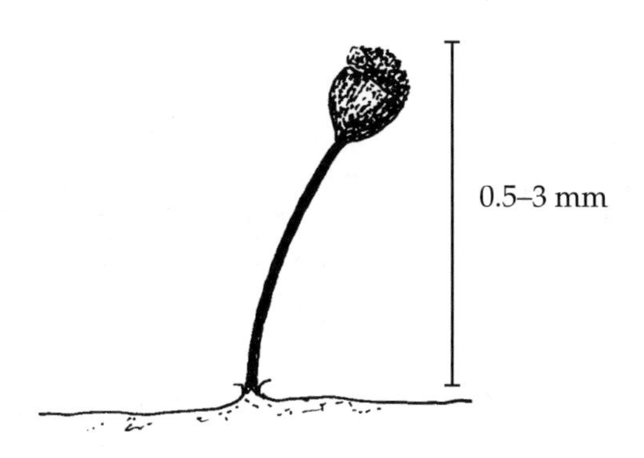

(ii) Podetia or mushroom-shaped	Apothecia borne on hollow or solid stalks, or like small mushrooms to 5 mm tall	**Key F**

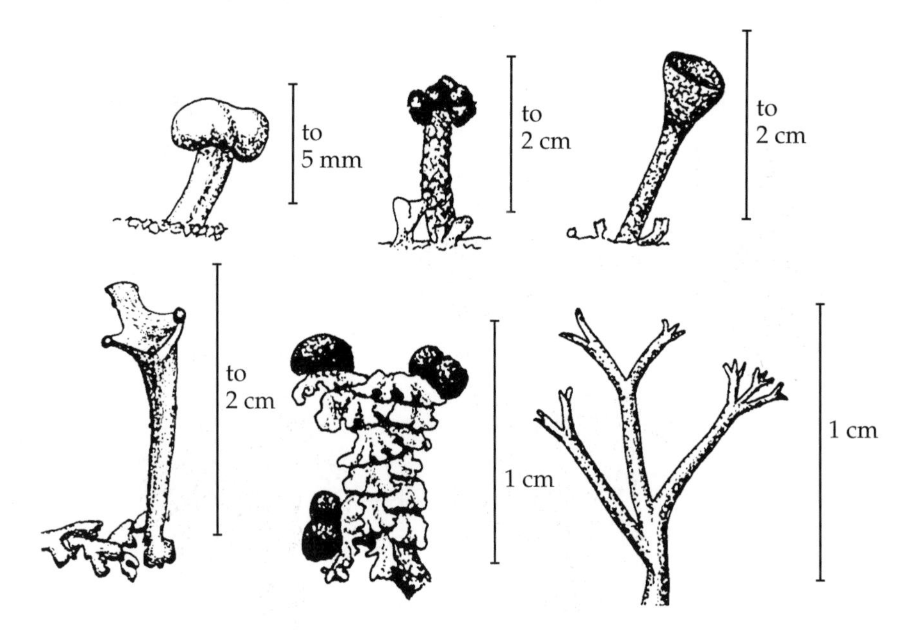

(iii) Lirellate

Fruiting bodies more than twice as long as wide, often with black carbonaceous margins **Key G**

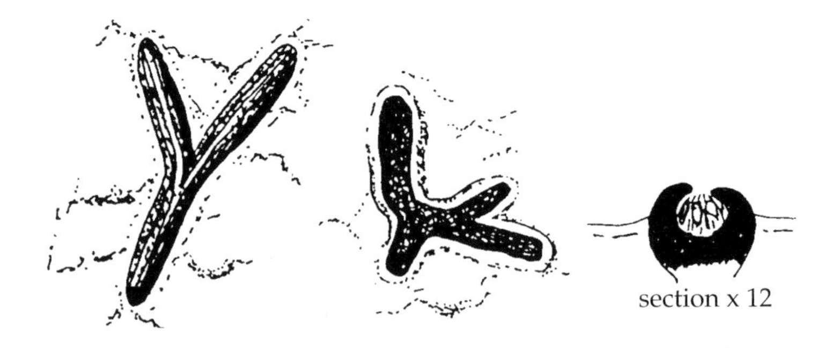

(iv) Lecanorine

Apothecia disc-shaped, with a margin containing algal cells. The margin is usually of the same colour as the thallus (at least when young); sometimes sunk into the thallus when it may be confused with (v) **Key H**

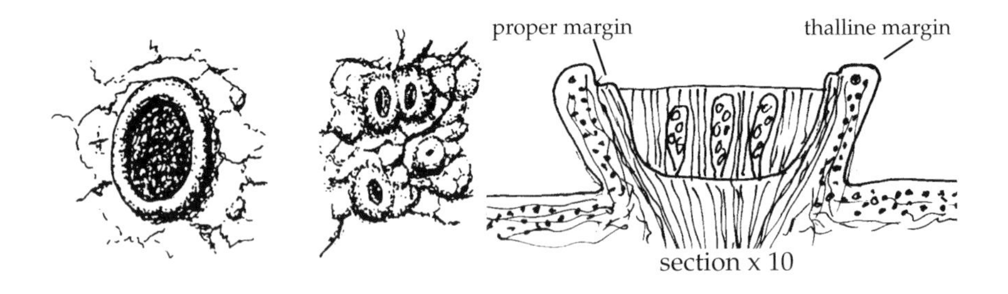

(v) Lecideine

Apothecia disc-shaped, but lacking the thalline margin found in species in group H; the proper margin usually distinct and raised and often the same colour as the disc **Key J**

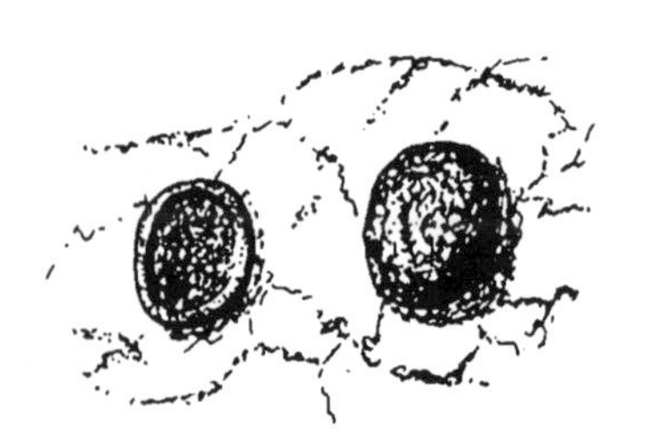

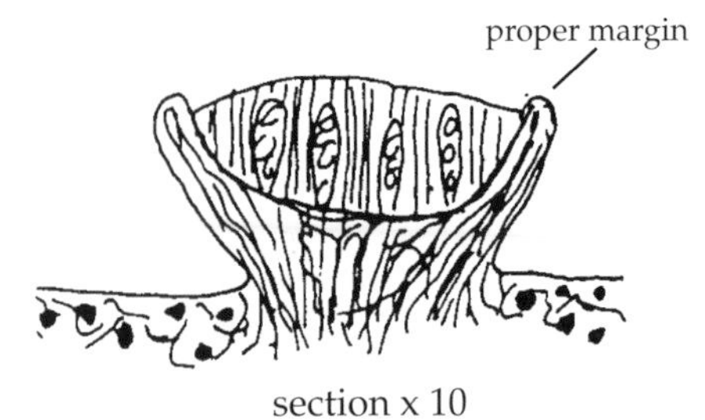

(vi) Perithecia — A flask-shaped fruiting body with a small opening at the tip, often cone-shaped, superficial, or may be immersed in the thallus or substrate; sometimes united in compact groups **Key J**

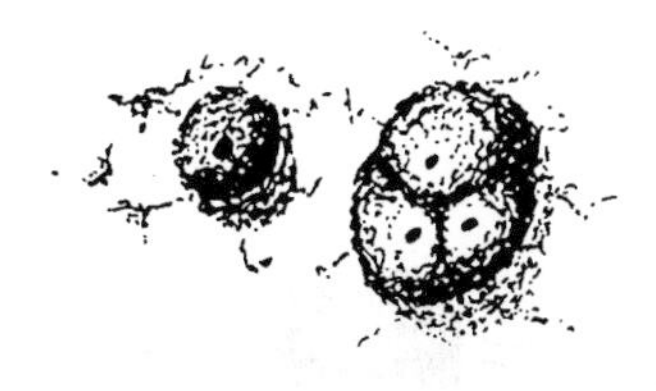

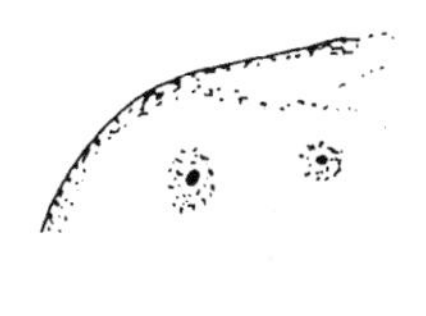

section x 10

(vii) Arthonioid — Apothecia poorly delimited and lacking a proper margin, often flat and irregular in outline and not in groups E–J **Key K**

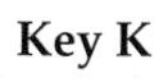

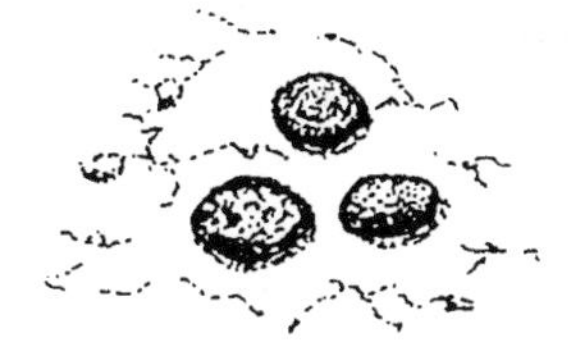

section x 10

---

9 (i) Thallus and apothecia orange **Key L**

(ii) Thallus inflated **Key M**

(iii) Thallus attached only at the centre or at a single basal holdfast **Key N**

(iv) Lower surface tomentose **Key O**

(v) Not in groups L–O and attached to the substrate by rhizines. Not noticeably swollen when wet **Key P**

(vi) Not in groups L–O and attached to the substrate either directly or by adhesive pads. Swollen or not when wet **Key Q**

---

10 (i) Thallus hollow, or orange **Key R**

(ii) Thallus solid, not orange **Key S**

Abbreviations used in sections **A–S** of the main key

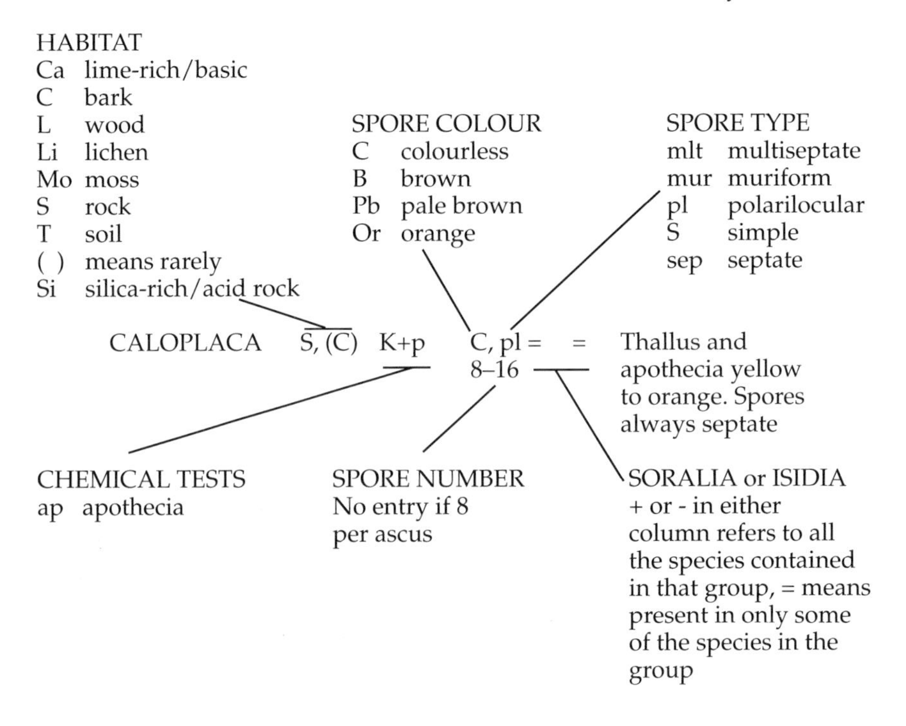

T. CRUSTOSE. Hyphomycete or not fertile but with delimited soralia or with isidia

GENUS OR SPECIES	THALLUS COLOUR	HABITAT	REACTIONS	NOTES
OCHROLECHIA androgyna	Grey	Trees and moss	C+o	Pale yellow, globose soralia

MAIN KEY
Synopsis

GENUS OR SPECIES	HABITAT	REACTION	SPORES	Sl	Is	NOTES
A. Leprose						
(Note: a number of other species often form sorediate crusts. See also key T)						
LEPRARIA	All	K–/fy				Thallus white to green-grey forming a loose mat or dispersed granules
LEPROPLACA	Ca	K+p				Thallus yellow (one species more or less marginally lobate)
LEPROLOMA!	C, S	Neg				White medulla with slight marginal lobes
PSILOLECHIA lucida!	S	Neg				Yellow-green. Found on walls and vertical rocks and in cracks
SCHISMATOMMA!	C	K–/fy				White to mauve-grey sorediate crust on rough bark
LECANORA expallens!	C, L	K–, C+o				Yellow to yellowish grey. Very common especially on trees and fences (see also *Pyrrhospora*)
DIRINA!	S	C+r				Soft pinkish grey, orange when scratched, on limestone and calcium-rich walls
B. Filamentous						
EPHEBE lanata	Si	Neg	C,1(2) sep 8–16	–	–	Forms brown-black mats to c. 1 cm across on rocks by water. Filaments much divided with fine points
CYSTOCOLEUS	Si	Neg		–	–	Black and felted, on vertical shaded siliceous rock. Fungal hyphae contorted and surrounding algal strands. If fungal hyphae straight see *Racodium*
LICHINA!	S	Neg	C, S	–	–	Dark brown to black, shrubby, to 1 cm high. Found around HWM. Apothecia spherical at branch tips
BRYORIA!	C, Mo, Si		C, S	=	–	Forms rather wiry brown mats or festoons in well-lit situations. If a mat to 1 cm high see *Pseudephebe*. See table page 53
C. Placodioid						
ASPICILIA	S		C, S4–8	–	=	Thallus white to grey and large
LECANORA muralis	S	Neg	C,S	–	–	Greenish grey lobes with white edges. Common on man-made substrates
CANDELARIELLA medians	Ca	K–	C, S	–	–	Yellow lobes, greyish on centre. Apothecia rare, yellow
SOLENOPSORA candicans	Ca	K–, P–	C, 1 sep	–	–	Chalk-white. Disc brownish black and pruinose. On hard maritime limestone
DIPLOICIA canescens	S, C	K+y	B, 1 sep	+	–	Nutrient-rich substrates. White-pruinose lobes. Apothecia rare except in South
PLACOPSIS gelida	Si	K+y, C+r	C, S	+	–	Mainly upland. Pink-brown cephalodia, reddish discs

GENUS OR SPECIES	HABITAT	REACTION	SPORES	Sl	Is	NOTES
FULGENSIA	Ca, T	K+p	C, S	–	–	Thallus egg-yellow. Apothecia common, orange red. Spores usually simple
CALOPLACA	S, (C)	K+p	C, pl 8–16	=	=	Thallus and apothecia yellow to orange. Spores always septate in placodioid species
CALOPLACA teicholyta	Ca	ap K+p	C, pl	–	–	Thallus white to bluish grey and scurfy in centre
PHYSCIA!	S, C		B, 1-pl	=	–	Discs black. With care the lobate structure can be seen at the centre of the thallus Key page 301.

D. Squamulose

GENUS OR SPECIES	HABITAT	REACTION	SPORES	Sl	Is	NOTES
HYPOCENOMYCE scalaris	C, L, walls	C+r	C, S	–	–	Grey-brown overlapping squamules to 1.5 mm wide
PSORA	Ca, T		C, S	–	–	Squamules to 5 mm wide with apothecia to 1.5 mm with black discs
SQUAMARINA	Ca, T		C, S	–	–	Grey-brown with pruinose edges. Apothecia lecanorine, discs brown
PSOROMA hypnorum	C, S, T	Neg	C,S	–	–	Green to orange-brown, with rhizines. In damp shade in upland areas. Discs red-brown
CATAPYRENIUM	Ca, Mo	Neg	C, S	–	–	With sunken dot-like perithecia
PANNARIA	C, S		C, S	–	–	Apothecia lecanorine. Lower surface sometimes with a dark felted hypothallus
PARMELIELLA jamesii	C, Mo	Neg	C, S	+	+	Squamules blue-grey, 1–2 mm long. soredia marginal but may form a crust
PHYLLOPSORA rosei	C, Mo	P+r	C, S, 1 sep	–	–	Grey-green squamules to 0.15 mm diam. White prothallus. Found in old woodlands
ACAROSPORA	S		C, S, 50+	–	–	Areolate to squamulose. Apothecia often immersed and indistinct
SOLENOPSORA	S	Neg	C, 1 sep	=	–	Overlapping small squamules, mainly on coastal rocks
DEGELIA!	C, S		C, S-1 sep	–	=	Apothecia reddish, lecideine. Plate-like circular thallus. Lower surface a dark felted hypothallus
CLADONIA	C,T		C, S-1 sep	=	–	Green, yellowish-green or grey mats of squamules, often erect and overlapping and bearing hollow podetia
TONINIA	Ca, T, S		C, 1–3 sep	–	–	Lobes very convex, usually grey and often pruinose. Apothecia lecideine, large, black and globose. Discs often pruinose
AGONIMIA	Mo, T	Neg	C, mur 1–2	–	–	Squamules about 0.5 mm grey-brown to green. Black prominent perithecia
NORMANDINA pulchella	Mo, C, T	Neg	–	+	–	Green oyster shell-shaped with raised slightly paler, sometimes sorediate margins. To 3 mm across
OMPHALINA	T	Neg	C, S 2–4	–	–	Blue-green, granular to shell-shaped thallus. On peat. Fruits a small mushroom

GENUS OR SPECIES	HABITAT	REACTION	SPORES	Sl	Is	NOTES
			CRUSTOSE			
			(If a *Hyphomycete* or infertile but sorediate or isidiate see key T)			
			E. Pin-stalked or Indian-club shaped			
CHAENOTHECA	S, L, C, T		B, S	=	–	Spore mass orange to very dark brown. Stalks to 3 mm
STENOCYBE	C	Neg	B, 1–3 sep	–	–	Fruits Indian-club shaped, usually on holly or alder. No distinct thallus
CALICIUM	C	Neg	B, 1 sep	–	–	Stalks to 2 mm. Spores constricted at septum. Often with a green to grey thallus
			F. Podetia, pseudopodetia or mushroom-shaped			
			Podetia (Stems hollow)			
CLADONIA	All		C, S–1 sep	+	–	Red or brown apothecia. Podetia often much branched and interwoven. Basal squamules may form a mat or disappear
PYCNOTHELIA papillaria	Peat	K+y	C,S	–	–	Podetia to 1.5 cm high, grey-brown, darker tips, unbranched cylindrical, often densely packed
THAMNOLIA vermicularis	T	K+y P+y		–	–	White, mainly unbranched pointed tubes. Usually found above c. 700 m. Apothecia unknown
			Pseudopodetia (Stems solid)			
STEREOCAULON	Si, Mo	K+y	C, 3–7 sep	–	–	Often with dark cephalodia. Phyllocladia flattened
SPHAEROPHORUS	T, S		B,S	–	–	Podetia solid. Apothecia rare, globose at tips, spores in a powdery mass. Branchlets rounded
LEPROCAULON microscopicum	Ca, T, S	K–		+	–	Yellow-green, to 3 cm high. Pseudopodetia becoming sorediate
			Mushroom-shaped			
BAEOMYCES	S, T	K+y	C, S–1 sep	–	–	Thallus granular to squamulose. Apothecia pink to brown, on stalks
PILOPHORUS strumaticus	Si	K+y	C, S	+	–	Grey almost squamulose thallus. Apothecia rather rare
OMPHALINA	T	Neg	C, S 2–4	–	–	A basidiomycete with the spores borne on the gills of the mushroom
			G. Lirellate			
XYLOGRAPHA abietina	L	Neg (P+o)	C, S	–	–	Lirellae brown, often following the grain of wood. If K+y, P+o see *X. vitiligo*
ARTHONIA!	C		C, 3 sep	–	–	Brownish thallus. Apothecia irregular without margins
OPEGRAPHA	C, S	Neg	C, 3+ sep	=	–	Lirellae usually prominent to 5 mm long. Ascus not extending at discharge

GENUS OR SPECIES	HABITAT	REACTION	SPORES	Sl	Is	NOTES
GRAPHIS	C	Neg	C, mlt	–	–	Emergent and often furrowed margins, lirellae to 2 cm long. Ascus tips with K/I+ blue ring, extending at discharge
ENTEROGRAPHA!	C, (S)	Neg	C, mlt	–	–	Apothecia minute, immersed and in lines so as to appear lirellate. Black prothallus
GRAPHINA	C	Neg	C, mur	–	–	Usually with flat margins, disc often leprose. Asci as in *Graphis*
PHAEOGRAPHIS	C	K+y–r or K–	B, mlt	–	–	Disc erupting through the bark and often pruinose. Asci as in *Graphis*

H. Lecanorine

Spores colourless, simple

Thallus yellow, brown or orange

GENUS OR SPECIES	HABITAT	REACTION	SPORES	Sl	Is	NOTES
PROTOPARMELIA badia	Si	KC+ pink	C,S	–	–	Grey-brown to chestnut, thick thallus on hard mainly coastal rocks
CANDELARIELLA	S, C, L	K–	C, S 8–32	–	–	Thallus and apothecia lemon or mustard-yellow. Some spores may appear septate
FULGENSIA	Ca, T	K+p	C. S	–	–	Yellow thallus. Some spores may look septate due to contents collecting at ends
HYMENELIA lacustris	Si	Neg	C, S	–	–	Orange thallus. Innate concave apothecia. On rocks by water

Thallus white, grey or yellowish green to green

Only found on stone

GENUS OR SPECIES	HABITAT	REACTION	SPORES	Sl	Is	NOTES
TEPHROMELA atra	Si	K+y	C, S	–	–	White to grey thallus with large (up to 4 mm) apothecia with distorted margins and black discs
ASPICILIA	S		C,S 4–8	–	=	Thallus grey (*A. laevata* olive green). Areolate becoming placodioid
IONAPSIS	S	Neg	C,S	–	–	Photobiont *Trentepohlia* (often scratches orange). Spores rather globose
PLACOPSIS gelida	Si	K+y, C+r	C, S	+	–	Upland species with wart-like pink to brown cephalodia

Found on stone, soil wood or trees

GENUS OR SPECIES	HABITAT	REACTION	SPORES	Sl	Is	NOTES
LECANORA	C, S, L		C, S	=	–	Thallus white, grey or yellowish green
OCHROLECHIA	S, C	C±	C, S	=	–	Thallus white, grey or greenish and often warted. Spores very large and thin-walled. Discs pinkish and often pruinose. Margin of thallus often limited by concentric rings
PERTUSARIA	S, C		C, S 1–8	=	=	Apothecia often ± in warts. Spores very large and thick-walled. Margin of thallus often limited by concentric rings
MEGASPORA verrucosa	Ca, Mo	Neg	C, S	–	–	Thallus of grey, pruinose, swollen granules. On calcareous soils and plant remains

Spores polarilocular

GENUS OR SPECIES	HABITAT	REACTION	SPORES	Sl	Is	NOTES
CALOPLACA	S, C	ap K+p	C, pl 8–16	=	=	Thallus yellow, orange, grey or white. Apothecia mainly orange or red, K+p, apothecia rarely black

GENUS OR SPECIES	HABITAT	REACTION	SPORES	Sl	Is	NOTES
RINODINA	C, S		B, pl Pl-3 sep	–	–	Mainly grey or greenish grey thallus with black discs
MOELLEROPSIS nebulosa (rare)	T	Neg	C, S	–	–	On soil on wall tops in the west. Chestnut-coloured discs

Spores septate

Apothecia flesh-pink or blood-red

GENUS OR SPECIES	HABITAT	REACTION	SPORES	Sl	Is	NOTES
HAEMATOMMA	S, C		C, 1–7 sep	=	–	Discs blood-red and K+p
ICMADOPHILA ericetorum	Peat	K+y	C, 1–3 sep	–	–	Apothecia flesh-pink becoming convex K+o, C+o. Thallus greenish white. Rarely on rotting wood

Apothecia fawn to black

GENUS OR SPECIES	HABITAT	REACTION	SPORES	Sl	Is	NOTES
LECANIA	S, C	Neg	C, 1–7 sep	=	–	Apothecia fawn to black minute to small, becoming very convex
RINODINA	C, S		B, pl-3 sep	–	–	Mainly grey or greenish grey thallus with black discs
CYPHELIUM	L, C	K+y P+y	B, 1 sep	–	–	Apothecia irregular in outline, black. Spores in powdery mass which leaves a sooty mark on the finger
THELOTREMA subtile	C	Neg	C, 8–12 sep	–	–	In West in damp shade on smooth bark especially on hazel in N.W. Scotland

Spores becoming muriform

GENUS OR SPECIES	HABITAT	REACTION	SPORES	Sl	Is	NOTES
PHLYCTIS	C	K+y/r	C, mur 1–2	=	–	Thallus white to grey. Apothecia immersed with whitish margins
THELOTREMA lepadinum	C, (Si)	Neg	C, 10–18 sep/mur	–	–	Apothecia with a visible inner margin, barnacle-like
DIPLOSCHISTES	S, Mo, lichen	C+r	B, 5–10 sep/mur	–	–	Overarching margins to the discs, at least when young

I. Lecideine

Spores colourless, simple

8 spores per ascus

Apothecia yellow, orange or red

GENUS OR SPECIES	HABITAT	REACTION	SPORES	Sl	Is	NOTES
PSILOLECHIA lucida	S	Neg	C, S	+	–	Sulphur yellow granules with small yellow apothecia. On rocks and walls
PROTOBLASTENIA	Ca	ap K+ p	C, S	–	–	Apothecia convex, orange
PYRROSPORA quernea	C	C+o	C, S	+	–	Red-brown irregular shaped apothecia on a buff sorediate thallus

Apothecia fawn to black

GENUS OR SPECIES	HABITAT	REACTION	SPORES	Sl	Is	NOTES
LECIDEA s. lat.	All		C, S	=	–	Usually dark-coloured discs. Includes; *Lecidea, Lecidella, Carbonea, Clauzadea, Fuscidia, Herteliana, Hypocenomye, Lecidoma, Porpidia, Schaereria, Trapelia, Trapeliopsis*. For a group table see page 204
TREMOLECIA atrata	Si	Neg	C, S	–	–	Rust-red thallus with innate black fruits. Found on metal-rich rocks
PLACYNTHIELLA	L, T	Neg	C, S	–	+	Thallus of minute coralloid or spherical, chocolate-brown or brown-green granules

GENUS OR SPECIES	HABITAT	REACTION	SPORES	Sl	Is	NOTES
CLAUZADEA	Ca	Neg	C, S	–	–	Apothecia brown to black, pruinose in many species
XYLOGRAPHA abietina	L	Neg	C, S	–	–	Apothecia brown and becoming lirellate in appearance, following the grain of the wood
MICAREA bauschiana	S, T	Neg	C, S	–	–	Greenish grey thallus on dry underhangs. Apothecia 0.3 mm globose, grey to black.
MIRIQUIDICA leucophaea	Si, L	ap C± pink	C, S	–	–	Variable. Areoles grey to brown, glossy. Often on metal-rich rocks
			Spores 1–3 or more than 8 per ascus			
MYCOBLASTUS sanguinarius	S, Mo	K+y	C, S 1–3	–	–	Medulla with red patches. Spores with many nuclei
SARCOGYNE	S	Neg	C, S 50+	–	–	Usually endolithic, discs chestnut to black, often with convoluted margins
POLYSPORINA simplex	Ca	Neg	C, S 50+	–	–	Usually endolithic, apothecia dark red to black with a gyrose margin
ACAROSPORA	S		C, S 50+	–	–	Areolate to squamulose with small innate fruits
STEINIA geophana	T, L	Neg	C, S 16	–	–	Thallus gelatinous, grey to green. On moist metal-rich or disturbed soil etc. Ephemeral
			Spores colourless, septate to muriform Spores 1-septate			
CATILLARIA	C, S	Neg	C, 1 sep	–	–	Spores usually slightly bent. Apothecia black or brown
CLIOSTOMUM griffithii	C	K+y	C, 1 sep	–	–	With many 0.2 mm black pycnidia. Common in moderately polluted areas.
FUSCIDEA lightfootii	C	neg	C, (1 sep) +			Spores constricted in centre to appear 1-septate. On ± horizontal branches, often near water
FELLHANERA	Twigs, leaves	Neg	C, 1 sep	–	–	On well-lit leaves and twigs on evergreen trees
DIMERELLA	C, Mo	K–	C, 1 sep	–	–	Thallus grey or evanescent. Apothecia translucent pinkish or yellow-orange
MEGALARIA grossa	C, (Ca)	Neg	C, 1 sep large	–	–	Apothecia black, up to 2 mm
MICAREA denigrata, prasina	L, C, T	C+o/–	C, 1 sep	–	–	Buff to olive-green granular thallus. Apothecia becoming globose, to 0.5 mm
BIATORA	C, Mo, Si	Neg	C, 1 sep rarely 0	–	–	Damp mossy trees and rocks, granular thallus. Buff to orange apothecia
			Spores becoming multi-septate			
LECANIA	S, C	Neg	C, 1(3)sep	–	–	Apothecia fawn to black, very small, becoming convex. Actually lecanorine
PLACYNTHIUM nigrum	Hard Ca	Neg	1–3 sep	–	–	Brown to black coralloid granules. Blue-black prothallus
VEZDAEA	Mo	Neg	C, 1–3	–	–	Develops inside moss or lichens. Has small, short-lived grey to reddish brown apothecia

GENUS OR SPECIES	HABITAT	REACTION	SPORES	Sl	Is	NOTES
TONINIA	Ca, S, T	Neg	C, 1–3 sep	–	–	Often with deep 'roots', pruinose. Discs black, convex, often pruinose
CRYPTOLECHIA carneolutea	C, (Ca)	Neg	C, 3 sep	–	–	Mainly on shaded ash and elm. Apothecia translucent yellow with dentate margins
DIPLOTOMMA alboatrum	C, Ca	Neg	3 sep	–	–	Black but very pruinose apothecia, on a white to pale grey thallus
PETRACTIS clausa	Hard Ca	Neg	C, 3 sep	–	–	Pale orange disc 0.5 mm, with whitish toothed margins
MICAREA	C, Mo, S, T		C, 3–7 sep	=	–	Thallus granular to slightly areolate. Apothecia becoming globose
SCOLICIOSPORUM	C, S	Neg	C, 3–7 sep	–	–	Dark brown to black apothecia. Thallus bright to dark green on trees or black and widely cracked on rocks and tombs
LECANACTIS	C		C, 3–7 sep	–	–	Shaded rough bark. Carbonaceous sometimes pruinose apothecia. Pycnidia C+ red in one species
DIRINA	Ca	C+r	C, 3–8 sep	=	–	Thallus orange when scratched in fresh material. On vertical shaded rocks and walls
ARTHRORHAPHIS citrinella	S	Neg	C, 3–7 sep	+	–	Yellow to yellow-green granules. Mainly montane
BACIDIA	C, C		C, 3–16 sep	–	–	Apothecia usually convex and rubbery when wet
PACHYPHIALE carneola	C	Neg	C, 9–16 sep	–	–	Apothecia to 0.5 mm reddish brown, 'wine-gum' shaped. On rough-barked deciduous trees
			Spores becoming muriform			
RHIZOCARPON	S, Ca		C, 1–mlt usually mur	–	–	Thallus areolate with a black or grey prothallus evident. Apothecia dark brown or black, immersed, often angular
GYALECTA	C, Ca	Neg	C, 3–7 sep/mur	–	–	Apothecia orange or yellow with dentate or crenulate margins
DIPLOTOMMA alboatrum	C, Ca	Neg	3 sep /mur	–	–	Black but very pruinose apothecia on a white to pale grey thallus
GYALIDEOPSIS anastomosans	C	Neg	C, mur	–	+	Grey-green patches up to 1 cm on damp usually inclined branches
			Spores brown, septate to muriform			
SCLEROPHYTON circumscriptum	S	K+y P+o	B, 5–7 sep	=	–	Under overhangs. Thallus orange when scratched. Apothecia in lines
AMANDINEA	S		B, 1			Discs black. Conidia thread-like
BUELLIA	S, C		B, 1–3 sep to mur	=	–	Discs black. Conidia not thread-like
RHIZOCARPON	S		B, 1–mlt usually mur	–	–	Thallus areolate with a black prothallus evident as lines giving the margin a mosaic-like appearance. Apothecia dark brown or black, immersed, often angular

GENUS OR SPECIES	HABITAT	REACTION	SPORES	Sl	Is	NOTES

J. Perithecia (sometimes immersed)

GENUS OR SPECIES	HABITAT	REACTION	SPORES	Sl	Is	NOTES
			Spores colourless, simple			
VERRUCARIA	S	Neg	C, S	–	–	Paraphyses and other filaments absent in mature perithecium except in neck
DERMATOCARPON	S, T	Neg	C, S	–	–	Attached by a central holdfast or rhizinae. Perithecia reddish, immersed
PERTUSARIA pertusa!	C, (S)	K+y P+o	C, S 2	–	–	Apothecia look like perithecia grouped in grey thalline warts
CATAPYRENIUM	Ca, Mo	Neg	C, S	–	–	Thallus squamulose. Perithecia brown-black, immersed
			Spores colourless, septate			
ARTHOPYRENIA	C		C, 1 sep	–	–	Spores often clavate. Found on smooth bark. Involucrellum often well-developed
PYRENOCOLLEMA halodytes	S	Neg	C, 1 sep	–	–	Around HWM. Immersed on shells and limestone. Has small black perithecia
MYCOPORUM quercus	C	Neg	C 1 sep	–	–	Faint stain on young oak or hazel. Apothecia up to 0.3 mm but often grouped in a stroma
ACROCORDIA	Ca, C		C, 1–3 sep	–	–	Thallus white or ± absent, scratches orange. Pseudoparaphyses anastomosing. Spore septum central
ANISOMERIDIUM	C		C, 1–3 sep	–	–	Thallus white to light grey. Perithecia up to 0.5 mm. Spore septum often not central
LEPTORHAPHIS epidermidis	Birch trees	Neg	C, 3 sep	–	–	Thallus endophloedal. Spores curved
TOMASELLIA	C	Neg	C, 1–3 sep	–	–	Thallus inapparent, immersed. Perithecia grouped in a stroma. Found mainly on hazel, alder or holly
THELOPSIS rubella	C	Neg	C, (1)3 sep	–	–	Thallus grey-green, diffuse. Found on old trees, often in rain tracks
PORINA	C, S	Neg	C, 3(1) sep	–	–	Perithecia often pinkish yellow to black. Thallus grey to green-brown or absent. Spores in rarer species up to 7-septate
THELIDIUM	Ca, S	Neg	C, 1–3 sep	–	–	Spores often slightly muriform, slightly clavate. Thallus white to grey or evanescent or immersed
PYRENULA	C	K+y	C, 3 (1–5) sep	–	–	Forming mosaics. Spores loculate. Thallus looks waxy with white flecks
ZAMENHOFIA	C	Neg	3 or 9–11 sep	–	±	On old trees. Photobiont *Trentepohlia*. Perithecia rare
			Spores colourless becoming muriform			
POLYBLASTIA	S	Neg	C, mur 2–8	–	–	Thallus often immersed. Perithecia simple or grouped
THELIDIUM	Ca, S	Neg	C, mur	–	–	Spores slightly clavate. Thallus white to grey or evanescent

GENUS OR SPECIES	HABITAT	REACTION	SPORES	Sl	Is	NOTES
MYCOPORUM quercus	C	Neg	C, mur	–	–	Faint stain on young oak or hazel. Apothecia up to 0.3 mm but often grouped in a stroma

Spores brown, septate or muriform

GENUS OR SPECIES	HABITAT	REACTION	SPORES	Sl	Is	NOTES
TOMASELLIA	C	Neg	Pale B 1–3 sep	–	–	Thallus inapparent, immersed. Perithecia grouped in stroma. Found on hazel, alder or holly
MYCOGLAENA myricae!	C	Neg	B, 3 sep	–	–	On smooth bark, mainly *Myrica*. Second cell of spore enlarged
POLYBLASTIA	S	Neg	C, mur 2–8	–	–	Thallus often immersed. Perithecia simple or grouped
STAUROTHELE	S	Neg	B, mur 2–8	–	–	Pale grey, green-grey or brown. Perithecia with hymenial algae

K. Arthonioid

GENUS OR SPECIES	HABITAT	REACTION	SPORES	Sl	Is	NOTES
ARTHONIA	C, Li, Si		C, 1–5 sep	–	–	Spores slightly clavate. Apothecia often stellate, reddish orange or black, to 3 mm

FOLIOSE

L. Thallus and apothecia yellow or orange

GENUS OR SPECIES	HABITAT	REACTION	SPORES	Sl	Is	NOTES
XANTHORIA	C, S	K+p	C, pl	–	=	Lobes wider than 1 mm (if less then not sorediate). Nutrient-rich sites
CANDELARIA concolor	C, S	K–	C, S8+	+	–	Lobes to 1 mm wide, erect. Soredia on lobe tops

M. Thallus inflated

GENUS OR SPECIES	HABITAT	REACTION	SPORES	Sl	Is	NOTES
HYPOGYMNIA	C, S	K+y med KC+r	C, S	+	–	Attached by adhesive pads. Common even in moderate pollution. Upper surface not perforated by small holes
CAVERNULARIA	C	K+y	C, S	+	–	Thallus partially hollow, no rhizines, lower surface with pits. Not fertile in Britain
MENEGAZZIA	C, S	K+y med P+o	C, S 2–4	+	–	Upper surface perforated by small, neat circular holes

N. Thallus attached only at the centre or by single basal holdfast

Spores simple

GENUS OR SPECIES	HABITAT	REACTION	SPORES	Sl	Is	NOTES
EVERNIA prunastri	C, S, T	K+y	C, S	+	–	Looks fruticose. Upper surface yellowish-green, lower surface white. Lobes less than 10 mm wide with faint net-like white lines. Becomes sorediate. Apothecia very rare
PSEUDEVERNIA furfuracea	Si, C, L	K+y	C, S	–	+	Looks fruticose. Upper surface grey, under surface black or white. Isidiate.
PLATISMATIA glauca	C, Si	K+y	C, S	+	=	Erect with, rarely, a very few coarse rhizinae. Lobes thin and papery often with small white flecks on the upper surface. Apothecia usually absent
DERMATOCARPON	S	Neg	C, S	–	–	Thallus grey or brown. Perithecia immersed, with brown-black ostioles visible

GENUS OR SPECIES	HABITAT	REACTION	SPORES	Sl	Is	NOTES
			Spores septate to muriform			
PHYSCIA s. lat.	C, S	K+y	C, 1 sep	=	–	Lobes less than 2 mm wide often with long marginal cilia *Hyperphyscia* has lobes to 0.5 mm wide with minute greenish soredia. These genera together with *Physconia* and *Phaeophyscia* are keyed out on page 301.
LASALLIA pustulata	S	Med C+r	B, mur)	–	–	Brown to 5 cm across pustulate surface usually pruinose in centre. Rarely fertile
ANAPTYCHIA ciliaris	C, S	Neg	B, 1 sep	–	–	Lobes to 4 mm wide and 4 cm long with long marginal cilia
UMBILICARIA	S		C–B S–mur 1–8	–	=	Thallus papery when dry. Apothecia often convoluted

O. Lower surface tomentose or loosely hairy

GENUS OR SPECIES	HABITAT	REACTION	SPORES	Sl	Is	NOTES
UMBILICARIA! polyrrhiza	Si	C+r	C, S 1–8	–	–	Lower surface a dense mass of fine, black, forked rhizinae
SOLORINA	T, S	Med K+p	B, 1 sep 2–8	–	–	Apothecia innate, lecideine, reddish. Lower surface with rhizinae
STICTA	C, S		C	=	=	Lower surface with neat white circular depressions (cyphellae). Not usually fertile
LOBARIA	C, S		C–B 1–3 sep	=	=	Large and spreading. No cyphellae on lower surface. Found on unpolluted regions in old forested areas
PSEUDO-CYPHELLARIA	C, S		B 1–3 sep	+	–	Apothecia rare. Soralia mauve-grey or greenish-yellow. Lower surface with distinct pseudocyphellae. Oceanic, western
PELTIGERA	C, S		C, 3–7 sep (c. 8)	=	=	Apothecia red-brown on upper surface of lobe tips. Thallus large and spreading

P. Not in groups L–O and attached by rhizines

GENUS OR SPECIES	HABITAT	REACTION	SPORES	Sl	Is	NOTES
CETRELIA olivetorum	C, S, Mo	K–		+	–	Large grey thallus, sorediate margins with small white pseudocyphellae on upper surface
			Spores colourless, simple			
PARMELIA	C, S	Most K+y	C, S 2–8	=	=	Thallus often large and spreading. Lower surface with rhizinae
PLATISMATIA glauca	C, Si	K+y	C, S	+	=	Erect with only very few coarse rhizines. Lobes thin and papery often with small white flecks on the upper surface. Apothecia rare
CETRARIA	C, S		C, S	=	=	Lobes often long and erect, often only a few coarse rhizines present
IMSHAUGIA aleurites	C, (S)	C–P+o	C, S	–	+	Like a small *Parmelia*, closely adpressed to the substrate. Apothecia rare. Lower surface pale brown
PARMELIOPSIS	C	C–	C, S	+	–	Differs from *Imshaugia* in the curved spores. Lower surface dark

GENUS OR SPECIES	HABITAT	REACTION	SPORES	Sl	Is	NOTES
UMBILICARIA polyrrhiza	S	C+r	C, S	–	–	Upper surface brown when dry, greenish brown when wet. Lower surface a dense mat of fine black rhizines

Spores colourless, septate to muriform

GENUS OR SPECIES	HABITAT	REACTION	SPORES	Sl	Is	NOTES
MASSALONGIA carnosa	Si	Neg	C, 1(3) sep	–	+	Dark rosettes to 2 cm across, amongst mosses in or near water
PELTIGERA	C, S		C, 3–7sep	=	=	Usually large and loosely attached, often by coarse rhizinaes Apothecia with red-brown discs.
LEPTOGIUM	S, C, T	Neg	C, 3 sep/ mur 4–8	–	=	Thin and papery and often blue-grey when dry, swollen, green or brown when wet. Rhizines fine or absent. Apothecia with red-brown discs

Spores brown, 1-septate

GENUS OR SPECIES	HABITAT	REACTION	SPORES	Sl	Is	NOTES
PHYSCIA s. lat.	C, S		B, 1 sep	=	=	Narrow lobes often with white pseudocyphellae and/or marginal cilia. Discs dark but often pruinose. For a key to this group see page 301
SOLORINA	T, Ca		B, 1 sep 2–8	–	–	Apothecia innate in upper surface, reddish, lecideine
HETERODERMIA (rare)	Mo, C, Si	K+y/o	B, 1 sep	=	–	Not greatly adpressed. Lobes white to pale grey, up to 3 mm wide
HYPERPHYSCIA adglutinata	C, Si	Neg	B, 1 sep	+	–	Thallus up to 1.5 cm diam. Lobes under 0.5 mm wide. Surface splits to give greenish soralia
ANAPTYCHIA runcinata	S, (C)	K–	B, 1 sep	–	–	Large brown thallus. Bleaches with the application of C. Maritime

Q. Attached directly or by adhesive pads

Not swelling greatly when wet

GENUS OR SPECIES	HABITAT	REACTION	SPORES	Sl	Is	NOTES
PLATISMATIA glauca	C, Si	K+y	C, S	+	+	Erect with sorediate/isidiate margins, lobes thin and papery often with white flecks on upper surface. Apothecia rare, with brown discs
CAVERNULARIA hultenii	C	K+y	C, S	+	–	Grey above with deep depressions on the dark lower surface. Lobes to 1 mm wide with sorediate tops. Found in Scotland
ALLANTO-PARMELIA	Si	K+y med C+r	C, S	–	–	Dark brown to black. Found on well-lit rocks, usually above 600 metres
DERMATOCARPON	S	Neg	C, S	–	–	Perithecia immersed with only the brown ostioles visible
NEPHROMA	C, S		C, 3 sep	=	–	Apothecia on lower surface of lobe tips. Medulla often yellow
PLACYNTHIUM flabellosum	Si	Neg	–	–	–	Brown to olive-green with marginal lobes to 0.5 mm wide. Flattened isidia in centre. In or near water

GENUS OR SPECIES	HABITAT	REACTION	SPORES	Sl	Is	NOTES

Swelling greatly when wet

GENUS OR SPECIES	HABITAT	REACTION	SPORES	Sl	Is	NOTES
LEPTOGIUM	C, S, T	Neg	C, 3–mur 6–8	–	=	Thin and papery, grey to dark brown when dry, swollen, brown or green when wet Discs red-brown
COLLEMA	C, S, T	Neg	C, mlt/mur	–	=	Thin and papery dark brown to black when dry, very swollen and gelatinous greenish black when wet. Discs red-brown

FRUTICOSE

R. Thallus hollow or orange

GENUS OR SPECIES	HABITAT	REACTION	SPORES	Sl	Is	NOTES
TELOSCHISTES	C, S	K+p	C, pl	=	–	Thallus greenish orange to orange. More or less maritime
CLADONIA	T, C, L		C, S–1 sep	=	–	Tangled mat of greyish or yellowish green branches, or hollow podetia that often grow from basal squamules
ALECTORIA	C, S		Pale B 2–8	–	–	Greenish yellow to grey-black. Erect tufts, prostrate or pendent, round or flattened. See table on page 53 for this group
BRYORIA	C, Mo, Si		C, S	=	–	Grey-green to black rather wiry thallus
COELOCAULON	T, S	Neg	C, S	–	–	Glossy brown, spiky mats on soil; or erect, matt and brown-black. If fertile see *Cornicularia*
THAMNOLIA vermicularis	T	K+y, P+y		–	–	White or yellowish sparsely branched tubes. Found above c. 750 metres on acid heathland

S. Thallus appears solid and not orange

Spores colourless, simple

GENUS OR SPECIES	HABITAT	REACTION	SPORES	Sl	Is	NOTES
LICHINA	S	Neg	C, S	–	–	Dark brown to black, shrubby, to 1 cm high. Found around and below HWM. Apothecia spherical, at branch tips
CETRARIA!	T, S	Neg	C, S	–	–	Glossy brown, spiky mats on soil; or erect, matt and brown-black. If fertile see *Cornicularia*
EVERNIA prunastri!	C, S, T	K+y	C, S	+	–	Upper surface yellowish-green, lower surface white. Lobes less than 10 mm wide with faint net-like lines. Actually foliose
PSEUDEVERNIA furfuracea!	Si, C, L	Med K+y	C, S	–	+	Upper surface grey, under-surface black or white. Apothecia very rare. Actually foliose
USNEA	C, S, L		C, S	=	=	Branches round with a tough elastic central core. Bushy to pendant. Attached by a single often blackened holdfast
BRYORIA	C, Mo, Si		C, S	=	–	Grey-green to black rather wiry thallus. Table on page 53

Spores colourless, septate

GENUS OR SPECIES	HABITAT	REACTION	SPORES	Sl	Is	NOTES
RAMALINA	C, S	C–	C, 1 sep	=	–	Fawn to green-grey. More or less flattened, with no central core

GENUS OR SPECIES	HABITAT	REACTION	SPORES	Sl	Is	NOTES
ROCCELLA	S	C+r	C, 3 sep	+	–	Cortex or soralia C+r. Thallus bluish grey. Apothecia very rare. Found in the south and west in maritime situations
STEREOCAULON	Si, L	K+y	C, 3–7 sep	–	–	Branchlets pale grey, coralloid, small and flattened. Cephalodia often present. Found on heathland and acid rocks. If blue-green and not more than 3 mm high see *Leprocaulon microscopicum*
			Spores pale brown to brown, simple			
SPHAEROPHORUS	S, T, (C)		B, S	–	–	Bushy, branches more or less terete. Apothecia globose at branch tips
ALECTORIA!	C, S		Pale B 2–8	–	–	Greenish yellow to grey-black. No central core. Erect tufts, prostrate or pendent, round or flattened. See table on page 53 for this group

T. CRUSTOSE Hyphomycete or not fertile but with soredia or isidia

(see also section A)

GENUS OR SPECIES	THALLUS COLOUR	HABITAT	REACTIONS	NOTES
		ISIDIATE		
PERTUSARIA coccodes	Grey	Trees	K+o, P+o	Grey to brown isidia
P. corallina	Pale grey	Rocks	K+y	Isidia concolorous or brownish tipped. If thallus is K+y turning red then *P. pseudocorallina*
P. flavida	Yellow-green	Trees	C+o	Densed massed globose often eroded isidia
OCHROLECHIA subviridis	Grey	Old trees	Isidia C+r or –	Dense cylindrical isidia. If C– see *O. turneri*
ZAMENHOFIA	Orange-brown	Trees	Neg	On old trees. Photobiont *Trentepohlia*
PLACYNTHIUM nigrum	Black	Calc. rock	Neg	Brown to black coralloid granules. Blue-black prothallus
		SOREDIATE or HYPHOMYCETE		
		On rocks or soil, sometimes on moss		
		Cortex or soralia C+ orange to red		
TRAPELIOPSIS granulosa	Grey-green or green	Soil or stumps	C+r	Green-grey, yellow or reddish soralia. If K+p orange patches see *T. pseudogranulosa*. If with greenish soralia see *T. flexuosa*
OCHROLECHIA androgyna	Grey	Rocks	C+r	Pale yellow, globose soralia
OPEGRAPHA gyrocarpa	Red-brown	Acid rocks	C+r	Orange soralia. In shade and under overhangs of rocks and tombs
PERTUSARIA lactea	Grey	Rocks	Soralia C+r	Punctiform, concolorous soralia

GENUS OR SPECIES	THALLUS COLOUR	HABITAT	REACTIONS	NOTES
LECIDELLA scabra	Green-grey	Rock	C+o	Punctiform, concolorous soralia
PERTUSARIA flavicans	Yellow	Acid rocks	Soralia C+o	On well-lit rocks in the north and west
DIRINA	Warm grey	Calc. rocks	C+r	Soralia concolorous, becoming confluent. Thallus scratches yellow
		Cortex and soralia C–		
		Thallus grey		
PORPIDIA tuberculosa	Grey	Acid rocks	Neg	Blue-grey punctiform soralia
LECANIA erysibe	Grey	Calc. rock	Neg	Small yellow-green punctiform soralia. Pollution tolerant
HAEMATOMMA ochroleucum	Pale grey	Rocks, walls	K+y, P+y ap K+p	On dry rock. Wide white fimbriate prothallus
		Thallus yellow, yellow-grey or yellow-green		
LECANORA soralifera	Yellow-green	Rocks	Neg	Yellow-green soralia spreading from centre of areolae. If from margins see *L. handelii*. If thallus green see *L. epanora*
LECANORA orosthea	Yellow-grey	Rocks	Neg	Yellow-grey soralia spreading from the edges of the areolae
CALOPLACA citrina!	Yellow	Calc. rocks	K+p	Very common, pollution resistant
PSILOLECIA lucida	Yellow	Rocks walls	Neg	Common on slightly damp rocks and brick walls. If on shaded soil or trees see *Chaenotheca furfuracea*
ARTHRORHAPHIS citrinella	Yellow	Acid rocks	Neg	In upland regions. Often associated with *Baeomyces rufus*
		Thallus blue-green or orange-red		
LEPROCAULON microscopicum	Blue-green	Soil, acid rocks	Neg	Rather coastal. Usually very small pseudopodetia are present
BELONIA nidarosiensis	Orange-red	Calc. rocks	Neg	Powdery orange-brown to red crust with white flecks
		On trees, wood or moss or lichen		
		Cortex or soralia C+ orange or red		
		Thallus grey		
OCHROLECHIA androgyna	Grey	Trees, moss	C+r	Yellowish grey soralia
O. inversa	Grey	Acid bark	C+o	Yellow-grey soralia that may become confluent
ARTHONIA impolita	Grey	Trees	C+r	Thallus thick and on dry side of trees

GENUS OR SPECIES	THALLUS COLOUR	HABITAT	REACTIONS	NOTES
BLARNEYA hibernica	Pale pink	Lichen	C+r	Grows on *Enterographa* and *Lecanactis*. A *Hyphomycete*
PERTUSARIA hemisphaerica	Grey	Trees	C+ rose	White to grey delimited, convex soralia
MYCOBLASTUS sterilis	Grey	Smooth trees	K+y medK+r	Punctiform bluish soralia which may become confluent. If P– see *Buellia griseovirens*
		Thallus yellow to greenish grey or green-brown		
TRAPELIA corticola (rare)	Green-brown	Trees	C+r	Buff balls of soredia on trees in high rainfall areas
LECIDELLA elaeochroma	Green-grey	Trees	Soralia C+o	Small yellow-green punctiform soralia
LECANORA expallens	Yellow-green	Trees	K+y, C+o	Concolorous soralia that become confluent
PYRRHOSPORA quernea	Dull yellow	Trees	C+o	On old nutrient-enriched trees, more buff-coloured than *Lecanora expallens*
		Cortex and soralia C–		
		Thallus white or grey		
PERTUSARIA amara	Grey	Trees (rocks)	Soralia KC+v	White delimited soralia with a bitter taste. If KC– and a mild taste *P. albescens*
PERTUSARIA multipuncta	Grey	Trees (rocks)	K+y, P+y	Large white soralia which become confluent
MICARIA adnata!	Grey-green	Trees, wood	Negative	Has apothecia but white convex sporodocia more obvious
HAEMATOMMA elatinum	Grey	Trees	K+y, P+y	Globose yellow-green soralia. If bluish grey with discrete grey soralia see *H. caesium*
LECANORA jamesii	Grey	Smooth bark	Soralia K–	Yellow-green, small punctiform soralia. Found in damp shade
PHLYCTIS argena	Pale grey	Trees	Soralia K+o–r	Soralia in lines and patches, erupting out of the thallus
SCHISMATOMMA	White to warm grey	Trees	Various	Soredia concolorous or paler and becoming confluent
		Thallus yellow, green, green-grey or rust-coloured		
CHRYSOTHRIX	Yellow to green	Bark cracks, wood	K–	Golden-yellow or greenish granules. If bright green sorediate on wood see *C. chrysophthalma*
CHAENOTHECA ferruginea	Yellow, buff, or rusty	Bark cracks	K–. Any orange areas K+r	A species of rough-barked trees on polluted areas
FUSCIDEA lightfootii	Green-grey	Trees	C–, P–	Forms neat patches to 2 cm across
THELOPSIS rubella	Greenish grey	Trees	Neg	Thallus diffuse.Found on old, trees, often in rain tracks

DESCRIPTIONS OF GENERA AND SPECIES

ACAROSPORA ('inconspicuous spores'). **Thallus** crustose to areolate, often squamulose. **Photobiont** chlorococcoid. **Apothecia** immersed or sessile. **Asci** contain up to 200 minute, spherical to oval spores. **Paraphyses** simple and often conglutinate. **Conidia** globose to ellipsoid. **Habitat** found on nutrient-enriched, siliceous rocks (but see *A. umbilicata* and *A. glaucocarpa*).

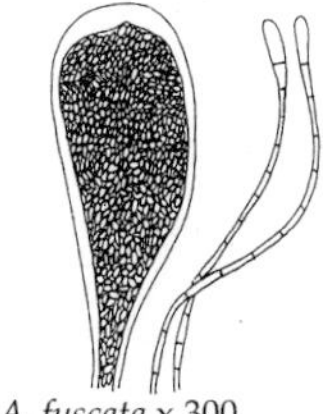

A. fuscata x 300.

1.	On calcareous rocks	2
–	On siliceous rocks	3
2.	C+ red	**6. A. umbilicata**
–	C–	**2. A. glaucocarpa**
3.	C+ red, K–	**1. A. fuscata**
–	C–, K– or K+ red	4
4.	Thallus dark red to black, K–	**3. A. impressula**
–	Thallus cream to rust-red, K– or K+ red	5
5.	Thallus cream to brown, K+ red (usually)	**5. A. smaragdula**
–	Thallus bright rust-red, K–	**4. A. sinopica**

1. Acarospora fuscata Thallus matt, yellow-brown to dark reddish brown, thick with angular areoles that are raised at the edges like dried mud. Apothecia 0.2–1 mm, sunken in the areoles and a darker reddish brown, one or several in each areole. Spores 4–6 x 1–1.5 µm.
KC+ red, C+ red.
Habitat: A common species on nutrient-rich, hard, siliceous rocks and also found in other areas where there are suitable churchyards or monuments. It appears to reach its best development in slightly polluted sites.

A. fuscata x 6.

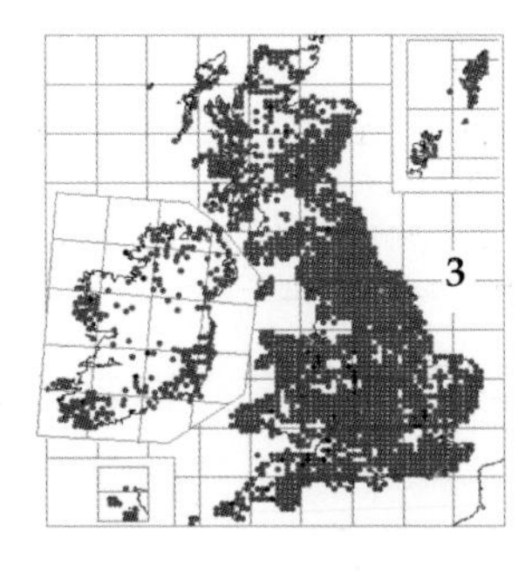

2. A. glaucocarpa (A. cervina) A variable species of separate to imbricate squamules, light grey to tan with white raised margins, often covered in a thick grey pruina. The apothecia (0.7–2 mm) are pruinose with a thick, contorted margin that may become lobulate. They may almost fill the squamule so that in some specimens only apothecia appear to be present. Spores 4–8 x 1.5–3 µm.

Reactions: negative.
Habitat: Hard calcareous rocks, mainly in upland Britain.

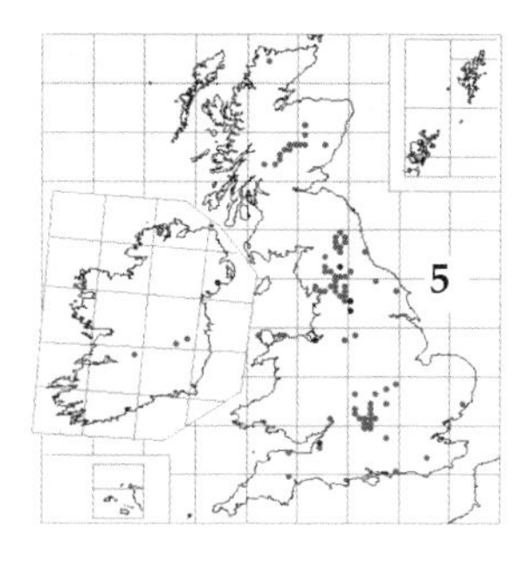

A. glaucocarpa x 6.

3. A. impressula (A. atrata) Thallus dark red-brown to almost black, thin, with small, angular areoles (less than 2 mm) forming colonies up to 3 cm across. Apothecia 0.2–0.4 mm, almost black, innate. Spores 3–4 x 2–2.5 µm.
Reactions: negative.
Habitat: Well-lit siliceous rocks, especially granite and also metal-rich sites, scarce, mainly near the coast in the West.

4. A. sinopica Differs from *A. smaragdula* in having a bright rust-red thallus, and normally convex squamules. It is usually only fertile towards the centre of the thallus. Spores 3–3.5 x 1–1.5 µm.
Reactions: negative.
Habitat. Fairly common on iron-rich, acid rocks, often with *Tremolechia atrata, Rhizocarpon oederi* and *Lecanora epanora.*

A. sinopica x 10.

5. A. smaragdula Thallus variable, usually creamy brown to yellow-green. Distinguished from *A. fuscata* by the flat to convex, more scattered squamules and by the C–, K+ red, P± yellow reactions (often patchy and hard to obtain). Apothecia several per areole, 0.2–0.3 mm diam. Spores 2–5 x 1–2 µm.
Habitat: Fairly common on siliceous rocks. It is also found in metal-rich situations as on walls, under metal grids and in run-off from copper fittings.

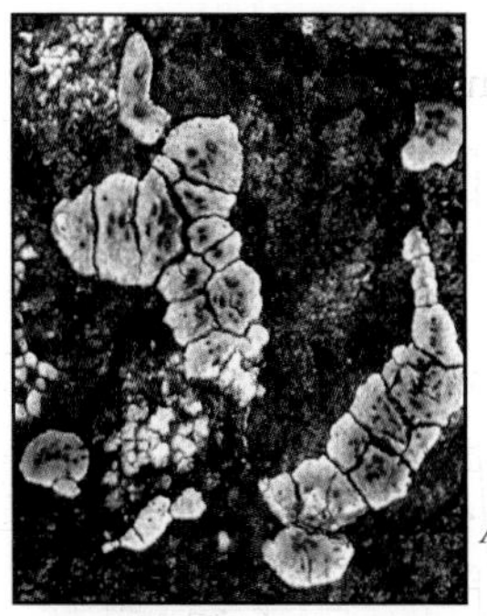

A. smaragdula x 6.

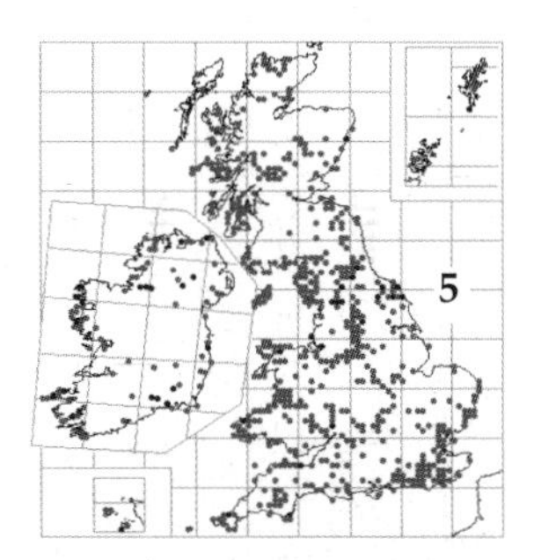

6. A. umbilicata Areoles convex and white-pruinose, less than 1.5 mm wide. Apothecia to 0.5 mm wide and arising from the edges of areoles. Spores 4–5 x 1.5–2 µm.
KC+ red, C+ red.
Habitat: Found mainly on acid rocks and walls in seepage tracks from mortar and calcareous substrates.

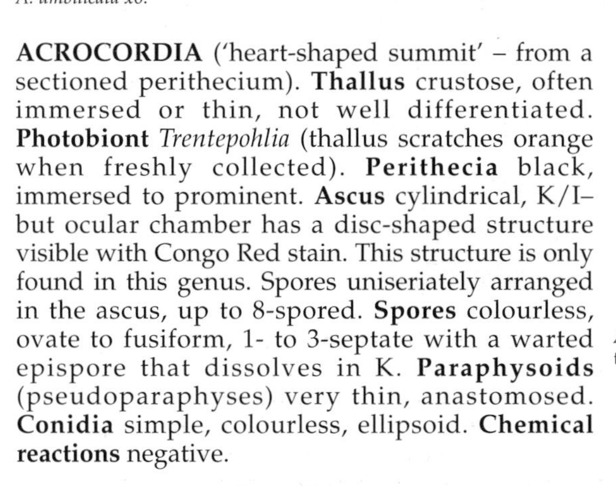

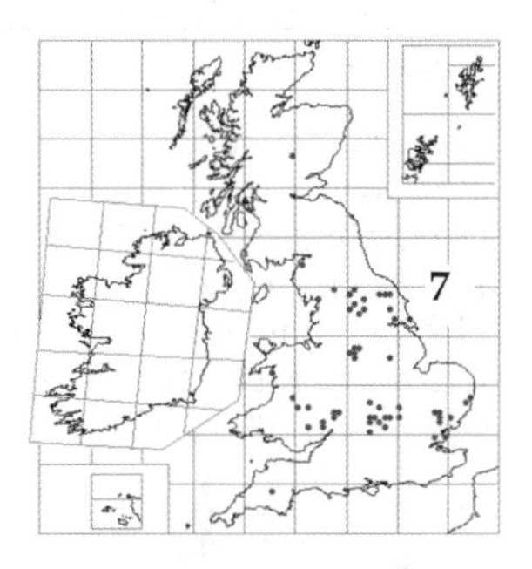

A. umbilicata x6.

ACROCORDIA ('heart-shaped summit' – from a sectioned perithecium). **Thallus** crustose, often immersed or thin, not well differentiated. **Photobiont** *Trentepohlia* (thallus scratches orange when freshly collected). **Perithecia** black, immersed to prominent. **Ascus** cylindrical, K/I– but ocular chamber has a disc-shaped structure visible with Congo Red stain. This structure is only found in this genus. Spores uniseriately arranged in the ascus, up to 8-spored. **Spores** colourless, ovate to fusiform, 1- to 3-septate with a warted epispore that dissolves in K. **Paraphysoids** (pseudoparaphyses) very thin, anastomosed. **Conidia** simple, colourless, ellipsoid. **Chemical reactions** negative.

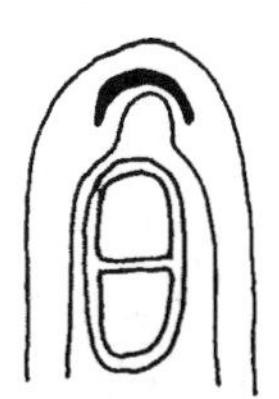

Acrocordia ascus tip x 1000.

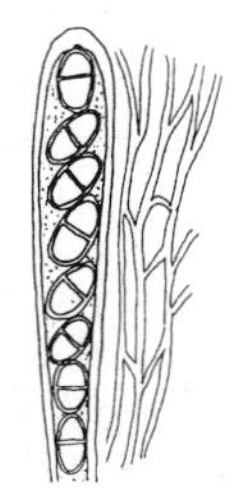

A. conoidia x 250.

1. Corticolous **1. A. gemmata**
– Saxicolous 2
2. Perithecia to 1 mm diam, conical 3
– Perithecia to 2 mm, very prominent, hemispherical. On soft calcareous substrates, especially mortar **4. A. salweyi**
3. Mainly on hard limestone. Spores 10–20 x 6–9 µm **2. A. conoidea**
– On hard acid or slightly basic rock. Spores 19–26 x 9–12 mm **3. A. macrospora**

1. Acrocordia gemmata Thallus thin, white to light grey and cracked. Perithecia black, hemispherical, 0.5–1 mm diam, often with the ostiole off-centre and sometimes papillate. Spores ellipsoid, 18–30 x 8–12 µm. Pycnidia scattered. Conidia 3–5 x 0.8–1 µm. May be confused with *Anisomeridium biforme* but that species has perithecia less than 0.5 mm diam and more numerous pycnidia.
Habitat: Common on rough bark of old trees. Rarely found on smooth bark.

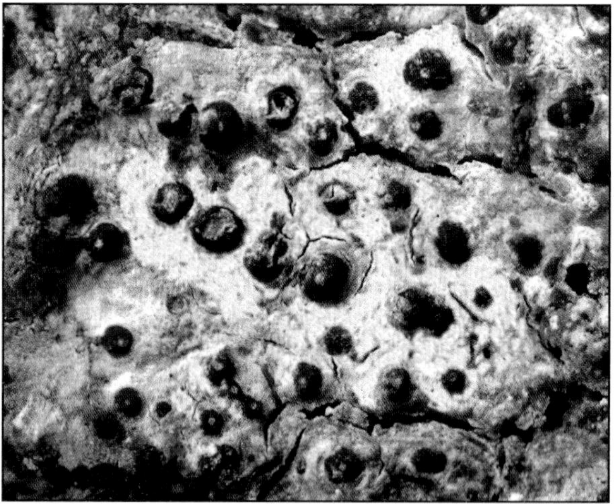

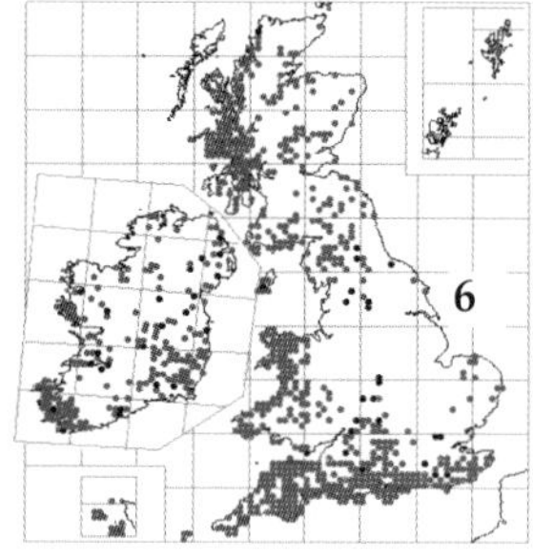

A. gemmata x 8.

2. A. conoidea Thallus pink-grey, thin, powdery or immersed. Perithecia prominent, conical and spreading, large (up to 1 mm), evenly distributed, leaving shallow, empty pits when they fall out. Ostioles not very apparent, flattened or with very small papillae. Spores 1-septate (rarely with a thin longitudinal septum), colourless, 10–20 x 6–9 µm. Pycnidia often present, up to 0.2 mm diam.
Habitat: Frequent on hard limestones and other hard calcareous substrates, especially where moist and sheltered.

3. A. macrospora Similar to *A. conoidea* but with a grey-brown thallus. The perithecia are about 1 mm wide with rounded, but never papillose, ostioles. Spores larger, 19–26 x 9–12 µm.
Habitat: on sheltered, acid or slightly basic rocks, coastal, especially in the North and West.

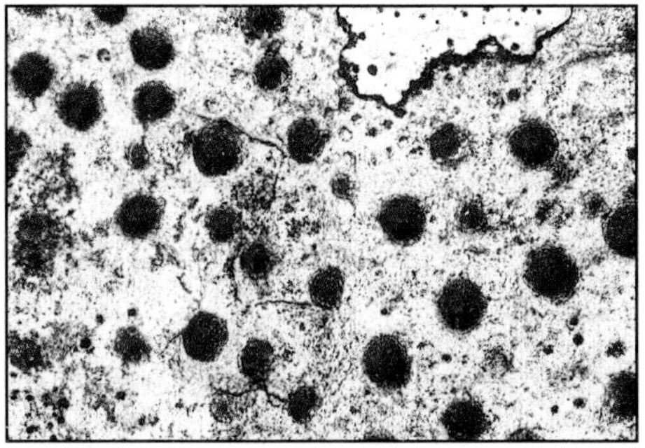

A. conoidea x 8.

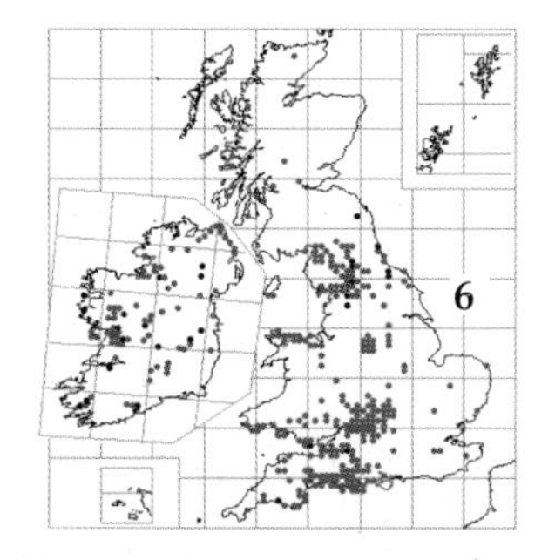

4. A. salweyi Larger perithecia than the previous two species, up to almost 2 mm diam, not spreading but appearing almost spherical and rather randomly distributed, usually leaving a black base in the pit when a perithecium dies. Spores 20–35 x 10–15 µm.
Habitat: As *A. conoidea* but usually on softer rocks and more common, especially in the South-East. on man-made substrates such as mortar in old walls.

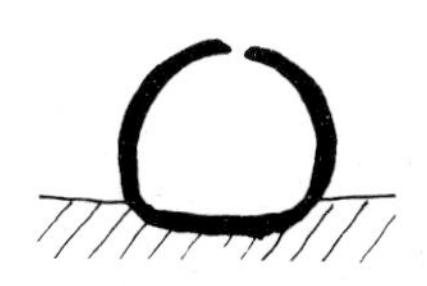

Section through a perithecium of *A. salweyi*.

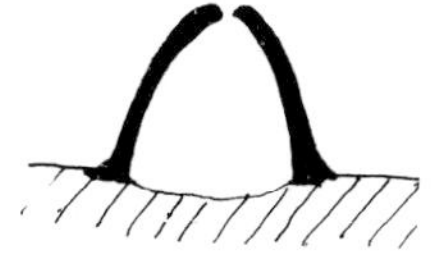

Section through a perithecium of *A. conoidea*.

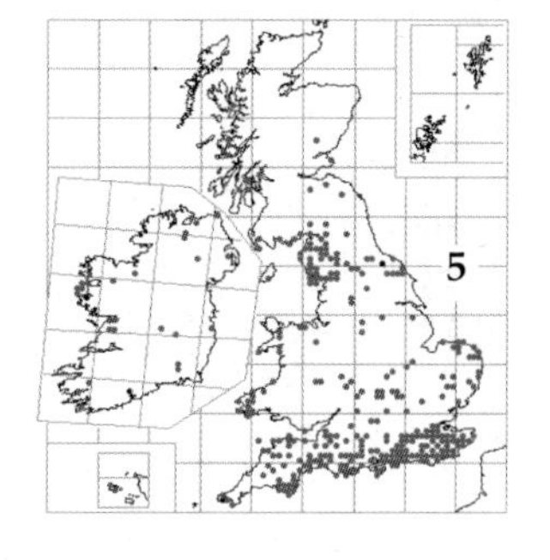

AGONIMIA ('without sex organs' – it has no photobiont in hymenium, unlike *Endocarpon*). **Thallus** minutely squamulose or granular, very small with papillae on the upper surface. **Photobiont** chlorococcoid. **Perithecia** superficial or often buried between the squamules. **Periphyses** simple or evanescent. **Ascus** 2- to 8-spored, K/I–. **Spores** colourless to light brown, muriform. **Chemical reactions** negative.

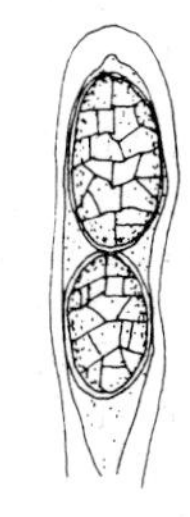

A. tristicula x 150.

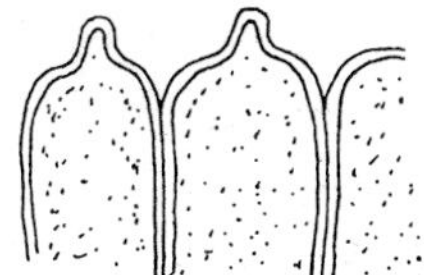

Papillate cortical cells x 2000.

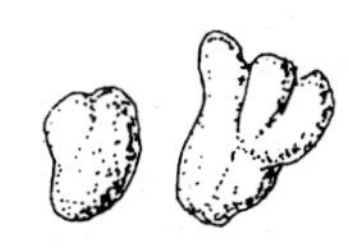

Squamules x 35.

Agonimia tristicula Thallus pale grey-brown, green when wet, consisting of very small flattened squamules (about 0.3 mm diam). The squamules have minute projections on the upper surface (use microscope). Perithecia 0.3–0.5 mm diam,

barrel-shaped, usually prominent but sometimes more or less hidden amongst the squamules. Spores colourless, becoming yellow-brown when mature, 1–2 per ascus. Spores 70–120 x 25–50 µm.
Habitat: Frequent throughout Britain, but especially in the South and West. On mosses on the mortar of old walls, base-rich soils and occasionally on the damp bark of trees, especially ash.

A. *tristicula* (wet) x 10.

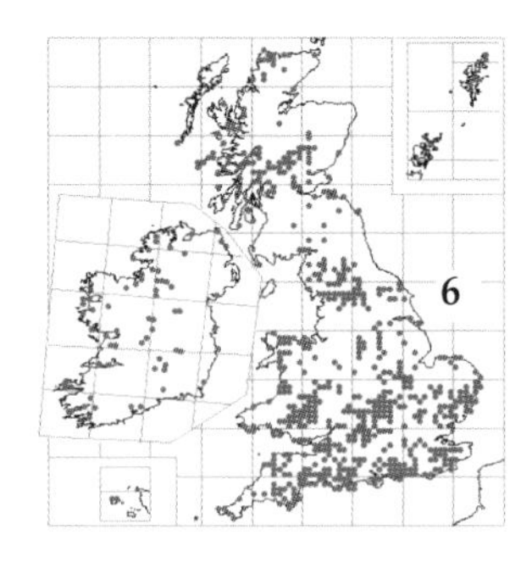

The rare **A. octospora** has smaller (to 0.25 mm) white squamules and 8 spores per ascus. It is found in old woodlands in South and West.

ALECTORIA (from the Greek for 'hair', or alternatively 'unwedded' due to the scarcity of fruiting bodies). It has been said to enhance the colour of hair; black hair from the darker species (these species are now in *Bryoria*) and blond from the yellow species. **Thallus** fruticose, erect, pendent or prostrate. Branches rounded, up to 2 mm diam, becoming flattened and expanded in some species. Medulla randomly orientated with no solid core. **Photobiont** *Trebouxia*. **Apothecia** are found in Britain only in *A. sarmentosa*. **Ascus** 2- to 4-spored, *Lecanora*-type. **Spores** simple, ellipsoid, colourless to brown. Soralia and isidia absent in British species but pseudocyphellae are always present and usually conspicuous. Many species have been transferred to *Bryoria* or *Pseudephebe* and these species are compared in the branching patterns and table on pages 52 and 53.

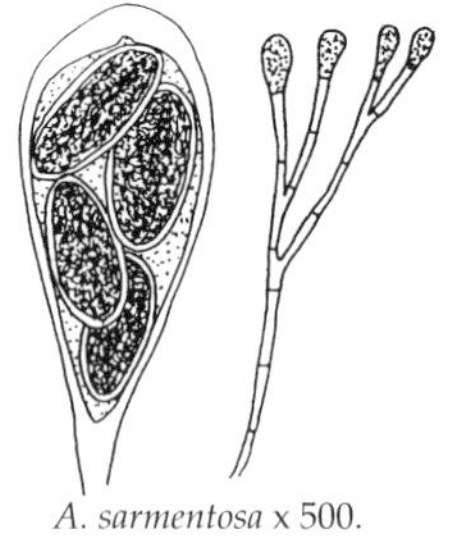

A. sarmentosa x 500.

1. A. nigricans Forms dense tufted to decumbent mats up to 5 cm high, the main branches up to 1.5 mm diam. Usually matt, pale pink or brown, becoming darker towards the apices which are often dull black, becoming paler in the herbarium (where it is inclined to stain the paper reddish brown after a long period). Distinct pseudocyphellae present, white, fusiform, up to 0.8 mm long. Soralia and apothecia absent in Britain. This species may be recognized by the large pseudocyphellae, matt thallus, paler at the base and by the C+ reaction. Thallus K+ yellow, KC+ red (fades fast), C+ rose-red (fades fast), P+ yellow.

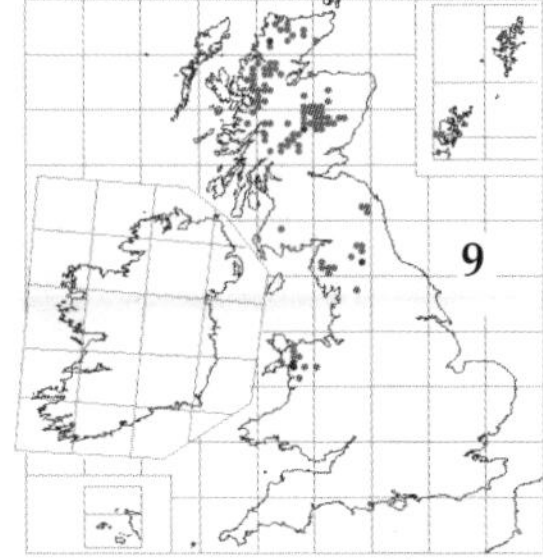

Habitat: Common locally in arctic-alpine heathland above 700 m.

A. *nigricans* x 2.

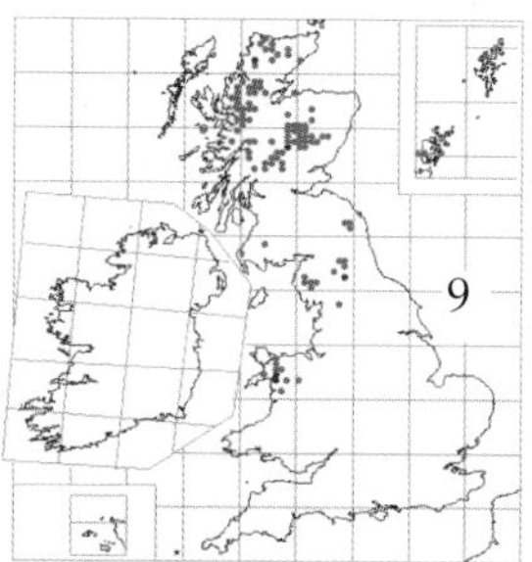

2. A. ochroleuca Thallus erect to somewhat decumbent, up to 8 cm long, greenish yellow fading to yellow. Branches up to 2 mm diam. This is a very variable species but it may be distinguished from *A. sarmentosa* by being usually erect and more neatly branched. It differs from *A. nigricans* in its colour, the C– reaction of the cortex and the CK+ deep yellow of the medulla and from *A. sarmentosa* subsp. *vexillifera* by its habit, branching pattern and by the consistently KC–, CK+ deep yellow and UV– reaction.
Habitat: Rare and decreasing, mainly above 750 m in the Cairngorms.

3. A. sarmentosa subsp. vexillifera Prostrate, up to 30 cm long. Greenish yellow to yellow. Main stems frequently very dorsiventrally flattened and pitted, up to 8 mm wide. The base is inclined to die away leaving the thallus attached to the substrate by hapters. Pseudocyphellae abundant, white, fusiform about 1.0 x 0.2 mm. Soralia absent. Apothecia rare, to 5 mm diam with an orange to black disc.
Habitat: Decumbent on low vegetation between 300–1000 m. The subsp. ***sarmentosa*** is the only British yellow pendent *Alectoria*, branches to 2.5 mm wide. It is rare, found on trees and rock in the Scottish Highlands.
The spot reactions of this and subsp. *vexillifera* are: cortex K– or + faint yellow, C–, P–; medulla KC+ red or –, CK–, P–, UV+ ice-blue.

A. sarmentosa subsp. *vexillifera* x 2.

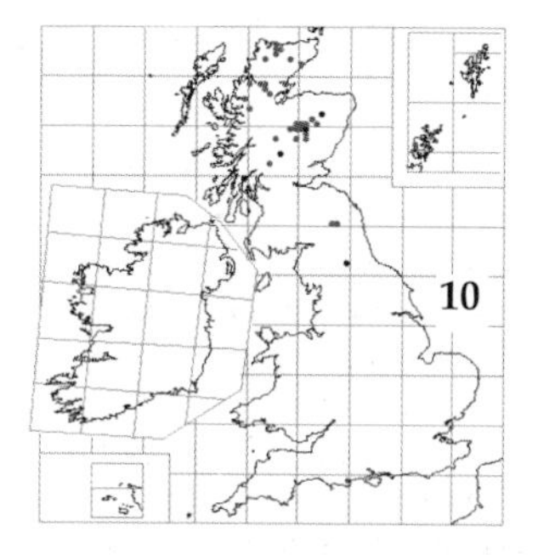

A. sarmentosa subsp. *vexillifera*.

Bryoria, *Alectoria* and *Pseudephebe* branching patterns x 4 approx.

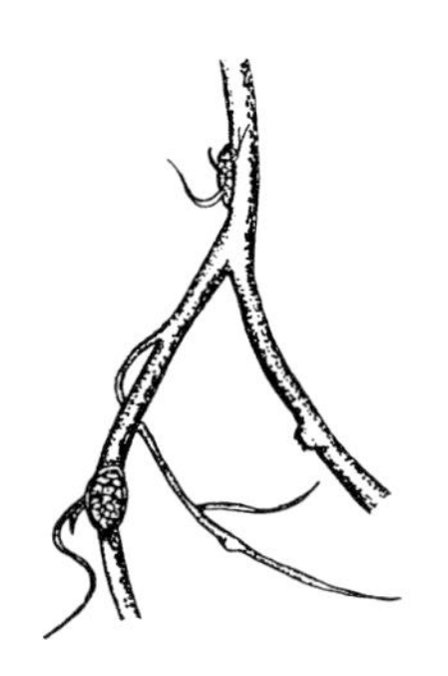

B. fuscescens

B. bicolor

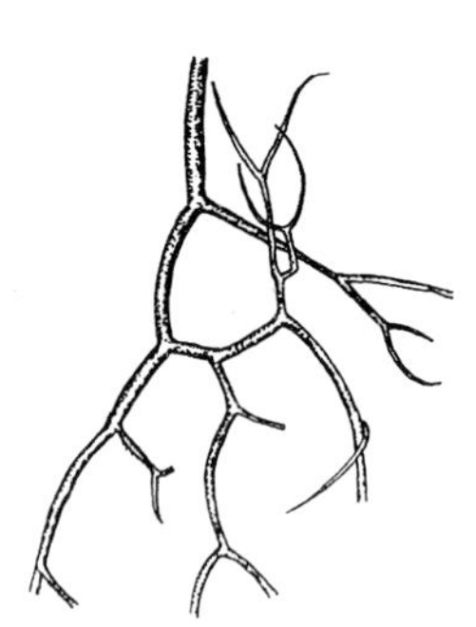

B. capillaris

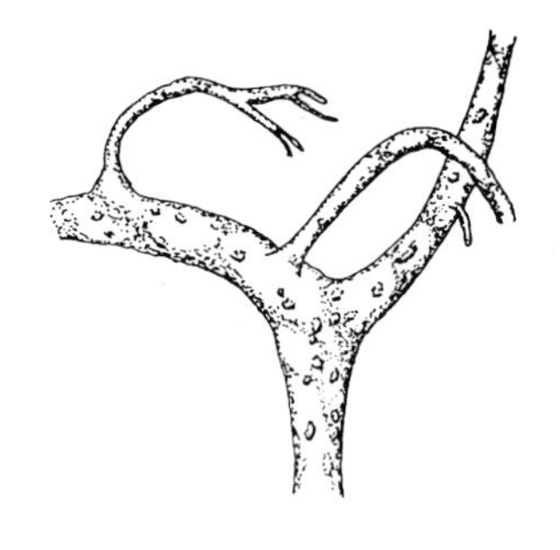

A. sarmentosa subsp. *vexillifera*

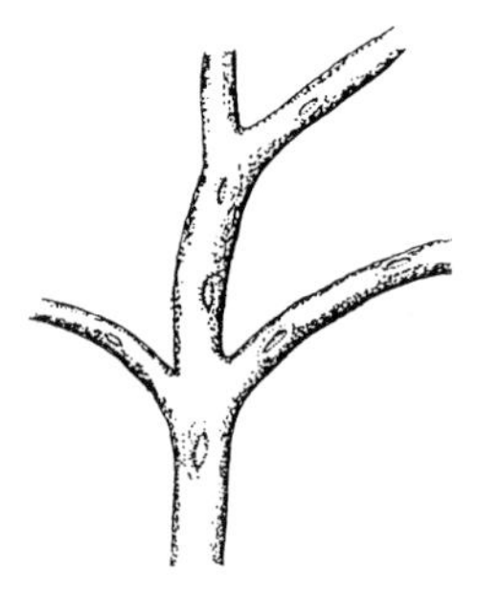

A. nigricans

P. pubescens x 8

Species	Colour	Form	Habitat	Key Reactions	Pseudo-cyphellae	Soralia	Remarks
A. nigricans	Blackish tips pinkish base	Erect	Arctic-alpine heathland	K+fy, KC+red	+	–	Stains paper pink in time
A. ochroleuca	Greenish yellow	Erect	Arctic-alpine heathland	Cort. KC+y Med CK+y, KC–	+	–	Rare in Scottish Highlands
A. sarmentosa* subsp. *sarmentosa	Greenish yellow	Pendent	Rocks and trees	Medulla CK– KC– or + red	+	–	Very rare in Scotland
A. sarmentosa* subsp. *vexillifera	Greenish yellow	Prostrate, dorsiventrally flattened	Arctic-alpine heathland	Medulla KC+ or –, CK–	+	–	
B. bicolor	Base black, tips brown	Erect tufts	Mossy rocks and trees	Medulla in parts P+red	–	–	Abundant spinules
B. capillaris	Grey-green to grey-brown	Pendent	Trees	K+y, KC+rose P+y-o	+ (Very minute)	±	Scottish Highlands
B. chalybeiformis	Brown to black	Prostrate	Rocks	Medulla P– Soralia P+red	–	–	Uplands
B. fuscescens	Brown, paler at base	Pendent or prostrate	Trees, fences, rocks and soil	Cortex P+red (–)	(±)	+	Very common in Scotland
B. subcana	Ash grey-green	Pendent	Trees	P+ intense orange to red	–	+	Northern and western
P. pubescens	Dark brown	Prostrate mat	Rocks	All negative	–	–	Fertile on high ground

Note. Yellow species tend to be yellow-green in the field becoming yellow in the herbarium. ***A*** = *Alectoria*; ***B*** = *Bryoria*; ***P*** = *Pseudephebe.*

ALLANTOPARMELIA ('sausage-shaped parmelia' – from the inrolled lobes). **Thallus** foliose and closely adpressed, subcrustose towards the centre. **Photobiont** chlorococcoid. **Apothecia** lecanorine, sessile, with dark-coloured discs. **Ascus** 8-spored. **Spores** simple, colourless. **Hymenium** colourless. The genus has only one British species which was separated from *Parmelia* due to the lack of rhizinae on the lower surface and from *Hypogymnia* by its chemistry.

Allantoparmelia alpicola Thallus foliose, dark brown to black with narrow (up to 1.5 mm wide) lobes, contorted and closely adpressed to the substrate to which it is attached by the lower surface in a similar manner to *Hypogymnia* species. Without soralia or isidia but frequently fertile. Apothecia to 5 mm wide. Disc brown. Spores 7–10 x 5–7 μm. The lack of pseudocyphellae and rhizinae help to separate it from *Parmelia stygia.*
Cortex: K+ yellow. Medulla: K+ yellow, C+ red, P+ yellow, KC+ red.
Habitat: Well-lit acid rocks in mountainous regions, usually above 600 metres.

A. alpicola x 1.

AMANDINEA (after the French botanist Amand). Separated from *Buellia* mainly by the long, curved, thread-like conidia. In *Buellia* they are ellipsoid to fusiform. This division of the two genera is still controversial. **Thallus** crustose, cracked or areolate. **Photobiont** chlorococcoid. **Apothecia** black, lecideine. **Paraphyses** unbranched except sometimes just below the dark expanded tip. **Ascus** clavate, 8-spored, *Lecanora*-type. **Spores** brown, 1-septate.

A. punctata (Buellia punctata) Thallus dark green-grey, greener on nutrient-enriched sites, very variable, from smooth to areolate. Usually fertile with many small, black, convex apothecia up to 0.5 mm diam. The young fruits have indistinct margins. Spores ellipsoid, 10–18 x 5–10 μm.
K– rarely faint yellow.
Habitat: Common on trees, posts, especially when nutrient-enriched. It is occasionally found on acid rocks (particularly bird perches), when it is often probably more correctly named **A. lecideina** (**Rinodina lecideina**).

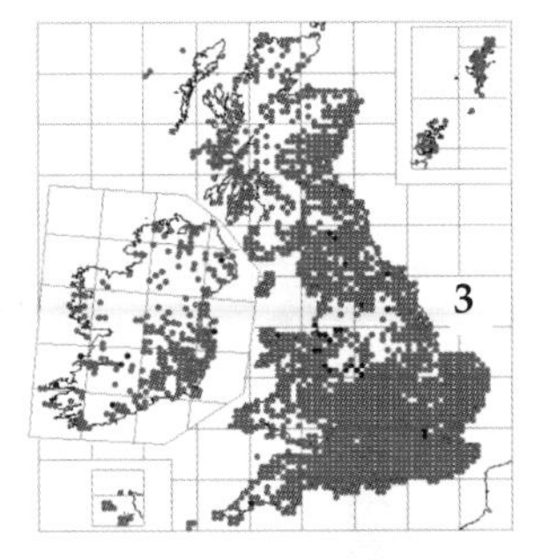

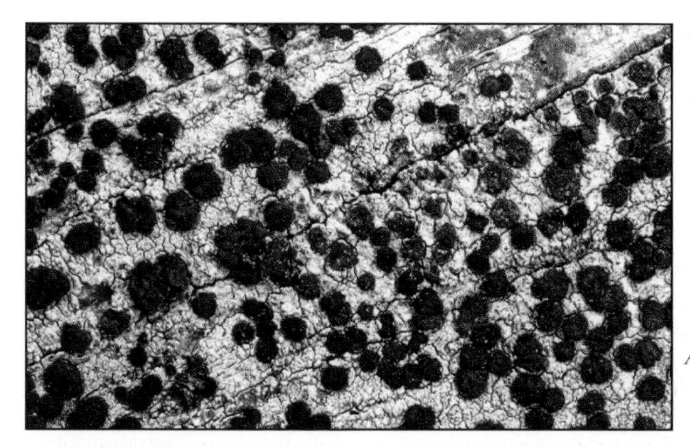

A. punctata x 8.

ANAPTYCHIA ('folded back'). **Thallus** shrubby or foliose. **Photobiont** trebouxioid, lacking soralia or isidia. **Apothecia** lecanorine and stalked. **Ascus** 8-spored, *Lecanora*-type. **Spores** brown, 1-septate. **Conidia** colourless, bacilliform. Resembles *Physcia* and *Physconia* from which it may be distinguished by the hyphae in the upper cortex which run parallel to the surface, whilst in *Physcia* and *Physconia* they are at right angles to the surface. *Heterodermia* has thicker-walled spores than *Anaptychia*.

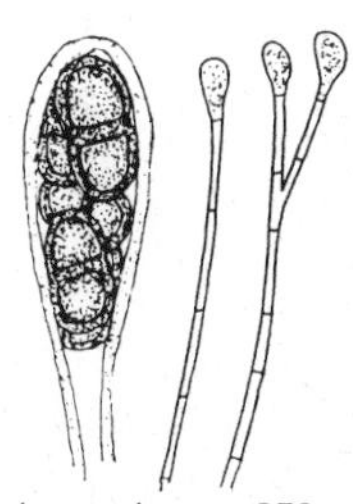

A. runcinata x 250.

1. Thallus grey to brownish, with marginal cilia **1. A. ciliaris**
– Thallus golden to red-brown, no marginal cilia **2. A. runcinata**

1. Anaptychia ciliaris Thallus has long narrow lobes widening at the tips with long concolorous or dark marginal cilia, some of which attach the thallus by discs to the substratum. Lobes to 5 cm long, grey, tipped with brown, the surface appearing furry (handlens). The lower surface is concave and white, lacking a lower cortex with the hyphae forming a loose mat. Apothecia are common in unpolluted areas, borne on short stalks, disc black, frequently pruinose, to 5 mm diam with thick margins which become crenulate. Spores 40–45 x 18–24 µm.
Reactions: negative.
Habitat: Local on well-lit, nutrient-rich wayside trees, more rarely on mossy calcareous rocks and walls. Found in unpolluted areas. A declining species.

A. ciliaris x 3.

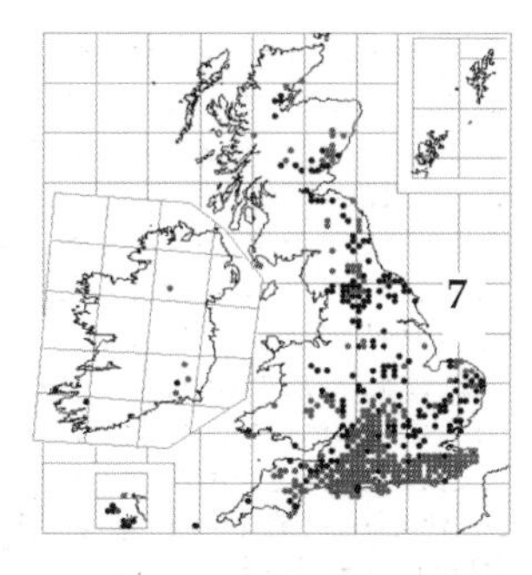

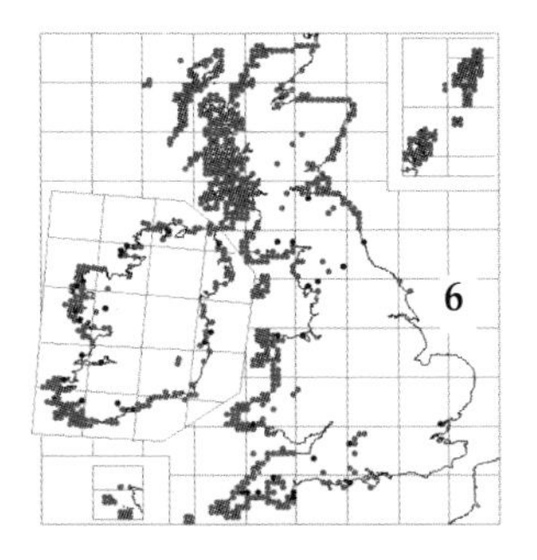

2. A. runcinata (A. fusca) Thallus matt, golden to dark red-brown, dark, oily brown-green when wet. Closely adpressed to the substratum, orbicular with long narrow imbricate lobes that widen towards the tips. Under-surface brown. Frequently fertile, apothecia up to 3 mm or more with contorted crenulate margins. Spores 30–36 x 15–18 µm.
K–, C bleaches thallus to pale yellow.
Habitat: Common on maritime rocks down to sea-level, rarely found on inland rocks, stone walls, and sometimes on trees in the West.

A. runcinata x 3.

ANISOMERIDIUM ('not in the middle' – refers to the often non-central spore septum). **Thallus** white to light grey but frequently immersed in the bark of the host. **Photobiont** *Trentepohlia*. **Perithecia** small and superficial. **Ascus** cylindrical, with a short ocular chamber, K/I–. **Paraphyses** slender, anastomosing. **Spores** 8 per ascus, colourless, 1- to 3-septate. **Conidia** separate macro- and microconidia produced. **Chemical reactions** negative.

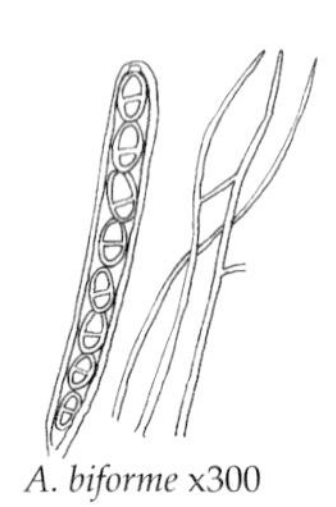

A. biforme x300

1. Perithecia larger than 0.25 mm, spores 1-septate — **1. A. biforme**
- Perithecia smaller than 0.25 mm, spores 1–3-septate — **2. A. polypori**

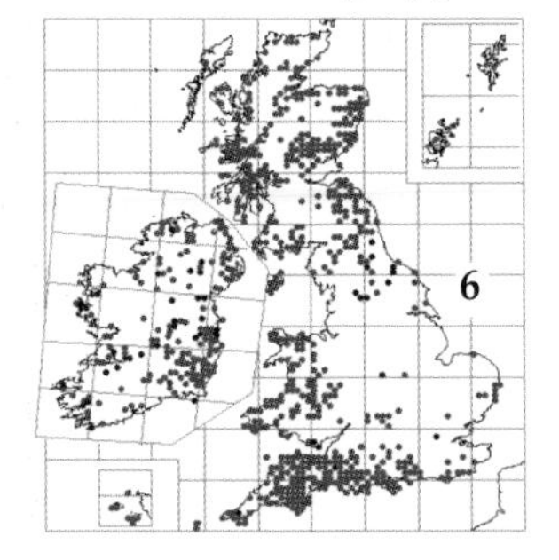

1. Anisomeridium biforme (Arthopyrenia biformis) Thallus pale grey, thin, prothallus dark. Perithecia 0.3–0.5 mm diam more or less immersed and leaving pits when they fall out. Spores 1-septate, 12–16 x 5–7 µm. Pycnidia frequent, 0.1–0.2 mm diam or less than 2–4 µm (these may exude a white jelly containing the conidia). Macroconidia 40–100 µm diam. Microconidia 1–2 µm diam.
Habitat: Common on trees (mainly on smooth bark) in light shade.

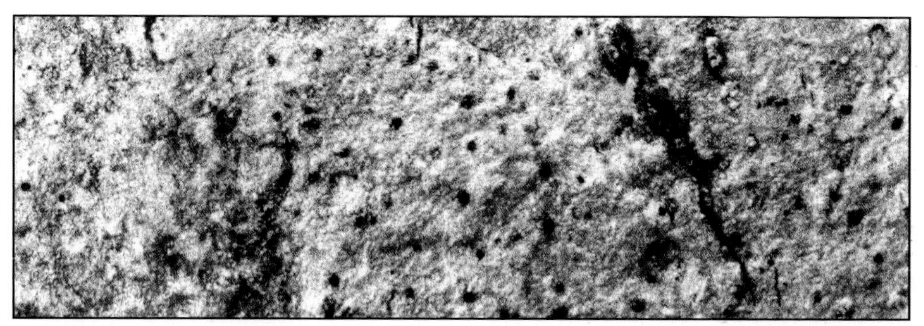

A. biforme x 5.

2. A. polypori (A. nyssaegenum, A. juistense) Thallus very thin and inconspicuous, scarcely distinguishable from the bark. Perithecia up to 0.25 mm diam, frequently absent when the species may be recognized by the usually abundant, small (0.1–0.2 mm) pycnidia which are conical and with nipple- or peg-like tips. Conidia 3-4 x 2 µm. Ascospores 1- to 3- septate, 15–20 x 4–5 µm.
Habitat: Frequent but overlooked, on rough bark in damp shaded areas.

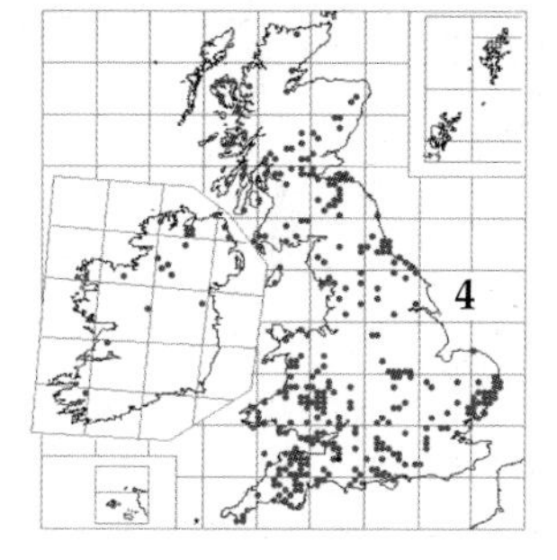

A. polypori x 8.

Pycnidium of *A. polipori* x 100.

ARTHONIA (Greek 'to sprinkle', – referring to the scattered apothecia). **Thallus** crustose or immersed, sometimes growing on other lichens. **Photobiont** usually *Trentepohlia*. **Apothecia** rounded, or elongate to stellate, more or less immersed, immarginate with a rubbed-down appearance, scarlet to black, sometimes pruinose. **Asci** clavate to globose, 8-spored, K/I–, or blue at top of ocular chamber. **Paraphyses** branched and anastomosing. **Hymenium** K/I blue. **Ascus** 8-spored, K/I– or as diagram. **Spores** colourless or pale brown, oblong to fusiform. **Pycnidia** common but inconspicuous. **Habitat** The common British species are corticolous and found mostly only at low altitude.

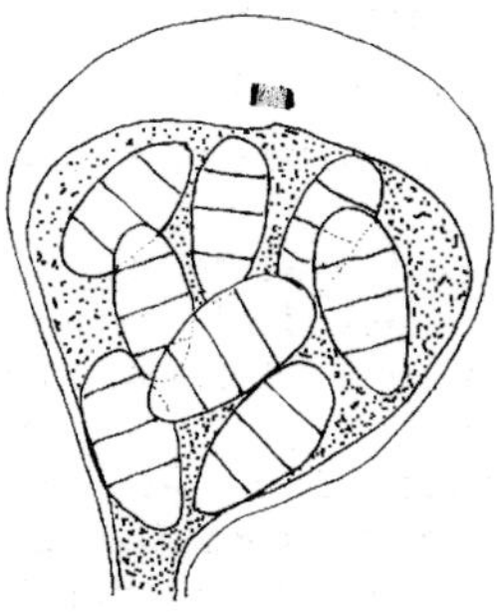

A. radiata ascus x 700.
Note K/I blue area around ocular chamber.

1. Thallus absent. In apothecia of *Lecanora rupicola* **10. A. varians**
– Thallus usually present. Not in lichen apothecia 2

2. Thallus and apothecia C– 3
– Thallus and apothecia C+ red **4. A. impolita**

3. Apothecia K+ orange, red or purple 4
– Apothecia K– 6

4. Apothecia orange, light to dark brown 5
– Apothecia purple-brown to black 9

5. Apothecia orange to dark brown. On old trees. Spores 1-septate **11. A. vinosa**
– Apothecia bright orange. On smooth-barked trees. Spores 3–5-septate **1. A. cinnabarina**

6. On rocks 7
– On smooth-barked trees 8

7. On hard acid rocks above high water mark **6. A. phaeobaea**
– On calcareous rocks often in metal run-off **5. A. lapidicola**

8. Apothecia black, up to 2 mm long 11
– Apothecia orange to dark brown, up to 0.3 mm long **2. A. didyma**

9. Spores 1-septate 10
– Spores 3–4-septate **3. A. elegans**

10. Apothecia to 1.5 mm long. Like tar spots **9. A. spadicea**
– Apothecia to 0.3 mm long. Fleck-like **2. A. didyma**

11. Apothecia up to 0.4 mm long. Not lichenized **7. A. punctiformis**
– Apothecia up to 2 mm long. Photobiont *Trentepohlia* **8. A. radiata**

1. Arthonia cinnabarina (A. tumidula) Thallus light grey or frequently pale orange-brown with orange flecks. Brown prothallus. Often forms mosaics. Apothecia up to 0.5 mm diam, white to red-pruinose, often with bright orange margins, becoming dark red-brown when old, many of the apothecia growing in small groups. Spores 3- to 5-septate, clavate, 20–28 x 7–10 µm. Old spores often become brown. Orange areas and apothecia K+ purple.
Habitat: Common in shaded areas on smooth-barked trees.

A. cinnabarina x 6.

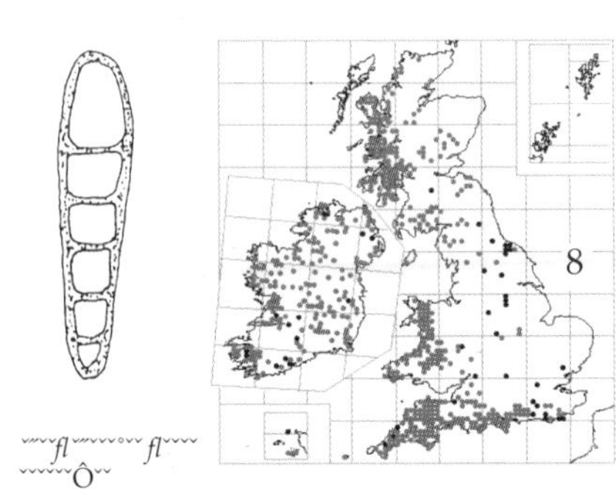

2. A. didyma Thallus fawn to pinkish or grey evanescent. Apothecia red-brown to purple-black, small (up to 0.3 mm long), fleck-like. Spores 1-septate, 12–15 x 4–6 µm, ellipsoid and becoming brown when old.
Apothecia K+ purple or K–.
Habitat: Locally common on smooth-barked trees, especially hazel. Found throughout Britain but most frequent in sheltered western valleys. Differs in the field from *A. vinosa* in its flat, very small apothecia.

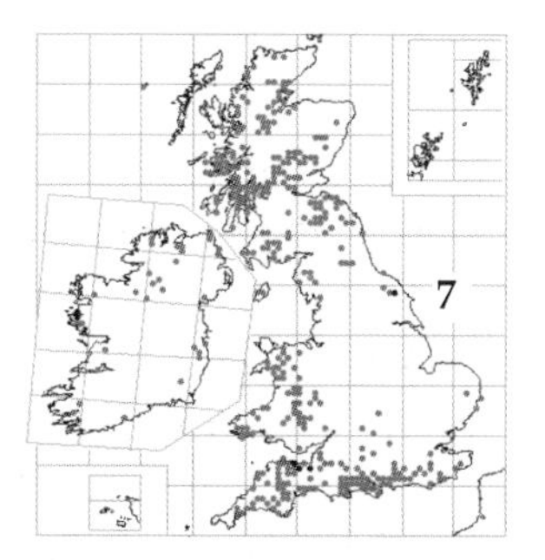

3. A. elegans Yellow to brown often limited by an orange-brown prothallus. Apothecia purple-brown, usually reddish pruinose along the margins. Up to about 1.5 mm long and often branched. Occasionally with red pruina on the margins on the apothecia. Spores 3- to 4-septate, 15–20 x 5–7 µm.
Apothecia K+ purple.
Habitat: Locally common especially in the West on shaded, mainly smooth-barked trees, normally hazel.

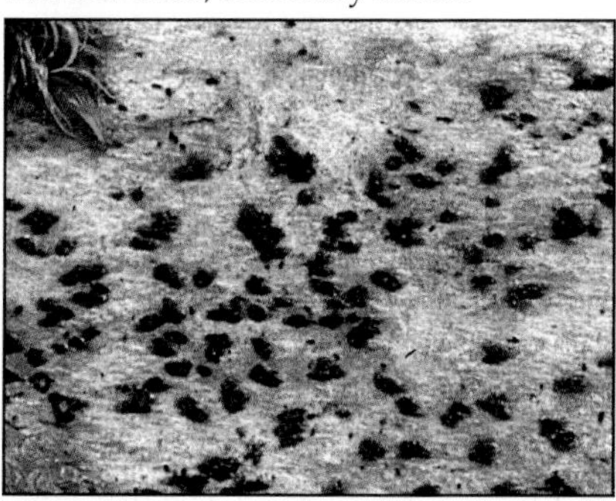

A. elegans x 4.

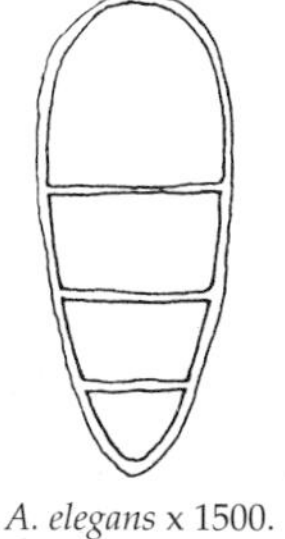

A. elegans x 1500.

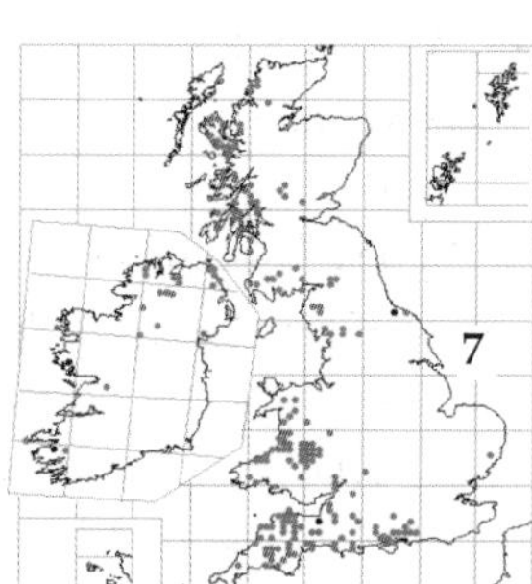

4. A. impolita Thallus light grey to pale, warm brown and often thick (when infertile it may resemble *Schismatomma decolorans* which is C– and sorediate). Apothecia round or irregular in shape, up to about 1 mm across, innate, brown but usually with thick, light grey pruina. Spores 3- to 5-septate, 10–22 x 5–8 µm.
Thallus and apothecia C+ red.
Habitat: Locally common on the dry side of old trees, especially in the South.

A. impolita x 3.

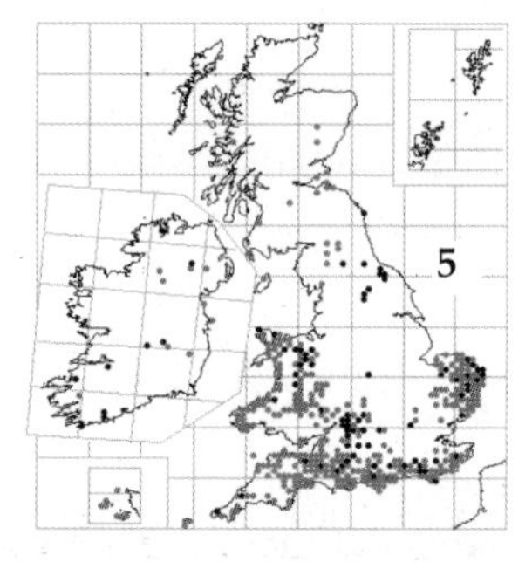

5. A. lapidicola Thallus thin, granular or evanescent. Grey to dark green-brown. Apothecia very dark brown to black, 0.2–0.5 mm diam, globose, often looking like a lecideine apothecium. Spores 1-septate, 10–15 x 4–7 µm, constricted at the septum and with the upper cell enlarged.
Reactions: negative.
Habitat: Found on well-lit, calcareous rocks and stones. Especially frequent on church walls and sills in run-off from metal grilles.

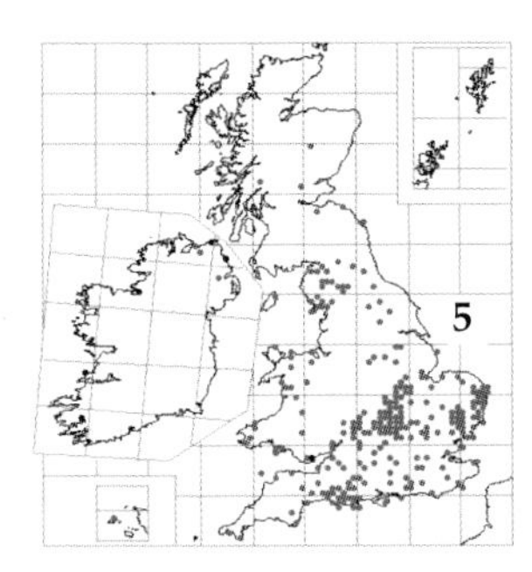

6. A. phaeobaea Thallus light brown-grey, smooth, in distinct patches. The photobiont is not *Trentepohlia* but is probably trebouxioid. Apothecia small (less than 0.3 mm), dark brown and rarely dark pruinose. Spores 3- to 5-septate, 18–25 x 5–7 µm. Numerous minute black pycnidia help identify sterile specimens. Conidia oblong, 4–6 x 1–2 µm.
Reactions: negative.
Habitat: Frequent in North Britain but often overlooked. On hard acid rocks above the high water mark.

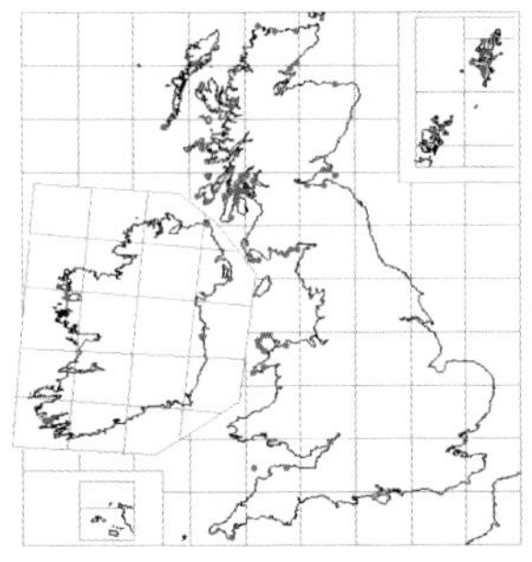

7. A. punctiformis Thallus immersed with no prothallus. It does not appear to be lichenized. Apothecia up to about 0.25 mm diam; irregular rounded or somewhat elongate, at first immersed and then pushing the bark apart as they emerge. Spores 3-septate, 13–23 x 5–7 µm, upper cell not enlarged.
Reactions: negative.
Habitat: Very common on smooth-barked trees. A primary colonizer of twigs. Common but overlooked, found even in moderately polluted areas.

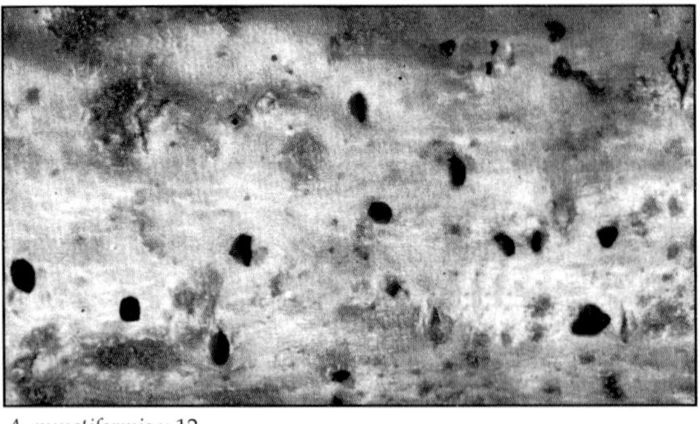

A. punctiformis x 12.

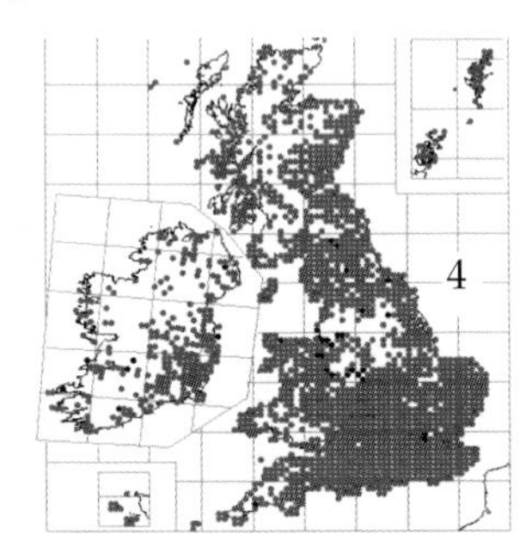

8. A. radiata Thallus fawn-grey to brown or immersed, up to 3 cm across, the junction between it and other lichens showing the black prothallus. Apothecia crowded, black, rounded or rather stellate, only slightly raised, not pruinose, up to 2 mm long but usually smaller. Spores 3-septate, upper cell not enlarged, 15–20 x 5–7 µm.
Reactions: negative.
Habitat: Very common, on smooth-barked trees and shrubs.

A. radiata x 3.

A. radiata x 2250.

9. A. spadicea Thallus immersed or shades of greenish grey. Apothecia rounded (up to 1.5 mm diam), flat to convex, black and usually shiny, giving it the name of 'tar spot' lichen. Spores 1-septate, 7–10 x 3–4 µm. Pycnidia frequent, 0.1 mm diam.
Apothecia and pycnidia K+ purple.
Habitat: Fairly common on rough-barked trees in shaded situations. Often near the base. When present it is often abundant.

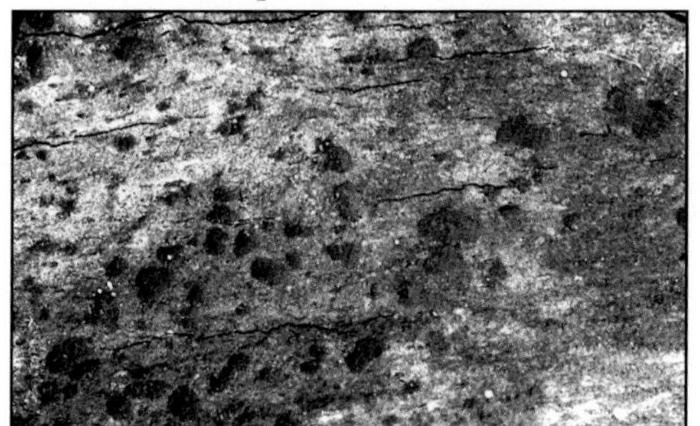

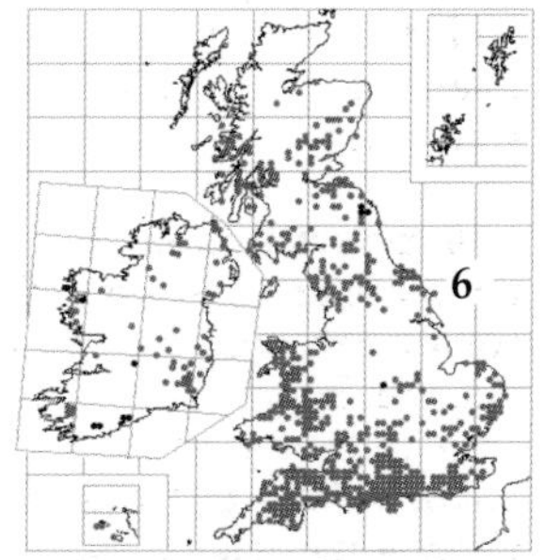

A. spadicea x 3.

10. A varians (A. glaucomaria) This species lacks a thallus and develops in the hymenium of apothecia of *Lecanora rupicola* where it forms black areas. These are normally immersed and level with the epithecium of the host. Spores 2- or 3-septate, 10–17 x 5–7 µm.
Habitat: Very common on host. Where *L. rupicola* is present many apothecia are usually infected.

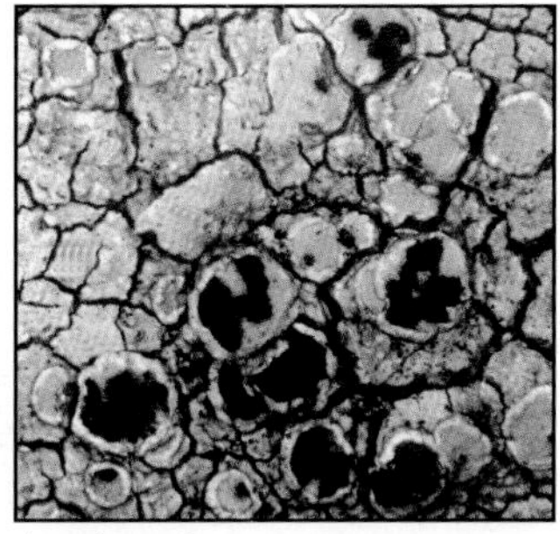

A. varians x 8.

11. A. vinosa Thallus creamy yellow to orange, often with darker orange patches. Apothecia convex, rounded, orange to dark brown, not pruinose, up to about 0.5 mm, irregular in shape. Spores usually 1-septate, slightly clavate, 10–15 x 4–5 µm.
Apothecia and darker patches of thallus K+ purple.
Habitat: Fairly common on shaded trees (especially oak) in old woodland sites.

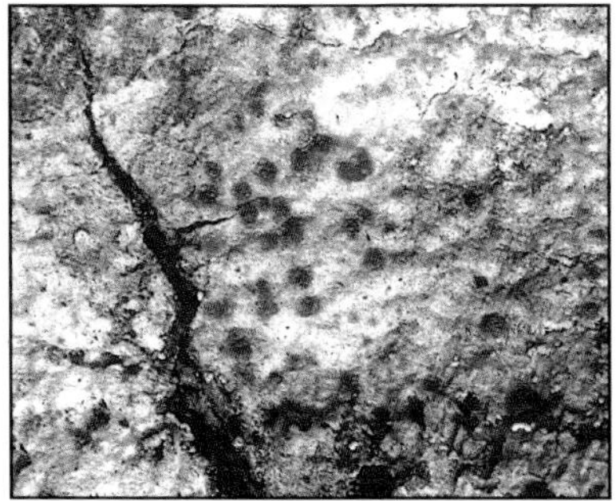

A. vinosa x 5.

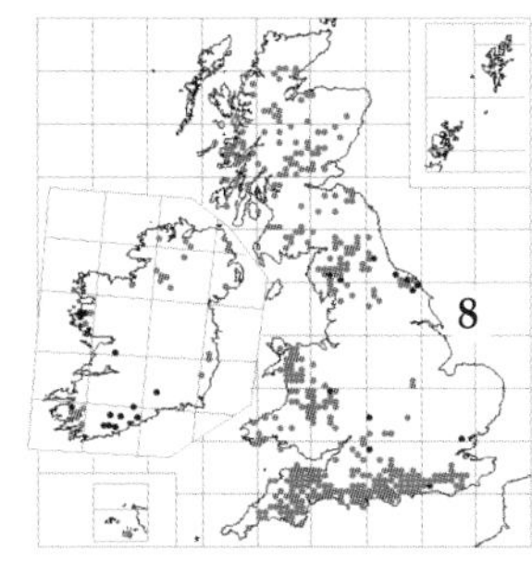

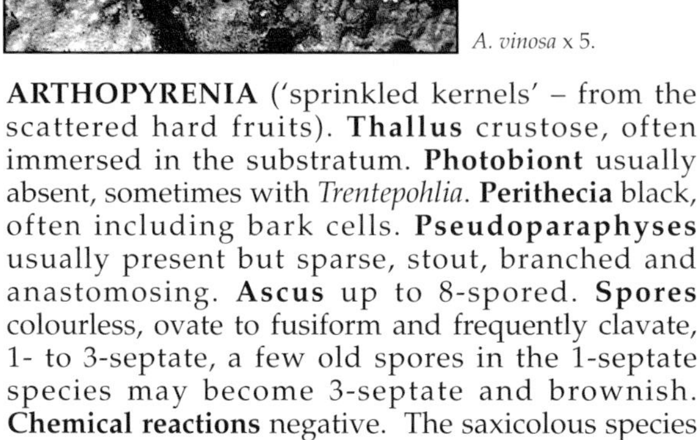

ARTHOPYRENIA ('sprinkled kernels' – from the scattered hard fruits). **Thallus** crustose, often immersed in the substratum. **Photobiont** usually absent, sometimes with *Trentepohlia*. **Perithecia** black, often including bark cells. **Pseudoparaphyses** usually present but sparse, stout, branched and anastomosing. **Ascus** up to 8-spored. **Spores** colourless, ovate to fusiform and frequently clavate, 1- to 3-septate, a few old spores in the 1-septate species may become 3-septate and brownish. **Chemical reactions** negative. The saxicolous species formerly in this genus are now in *Pyrenocollema* and *Acrocordia* and differ in the structure of their perithecia.

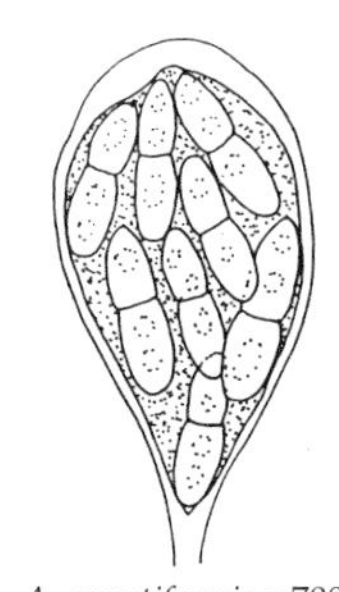

A. punctiformis x 700.

1.	Apothecia over 0.4 mm	**2. A. lapponina**
–	Apothecia up to 0.4 mm	2
2.	Spores over 25 µm long	**1. A. antecellans**
–	Spores less than 25 µm long	3
3.	Spores 16–20 µm long with ± equal cells	**3. A. punctiformis**
–	Spores 13–16 µm with a larger upper cell	**4. A. ranunculospora**

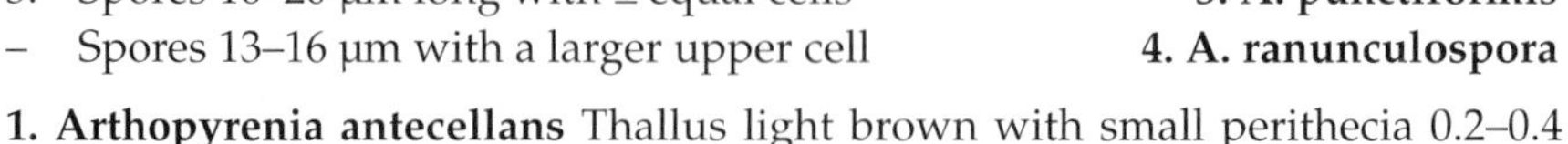

1. Arthopyrenia antecellans Thallus light brown with small perithecia 0.2–0.4 mm. Spores 1-(3-) septate, 27–40 x 7–12 µm. There are usually numerous pycnidia present about 0.1 mm diam. Conidia 4-6 x 1 µm, bacilliform.
Habitat: Smooth bark, particularly beech and hazel in old woodlands.

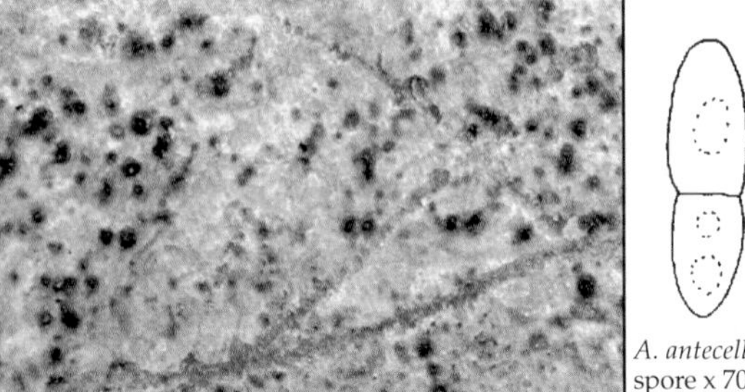

A. antecellans x 6.

A. antecellans spore x 700.

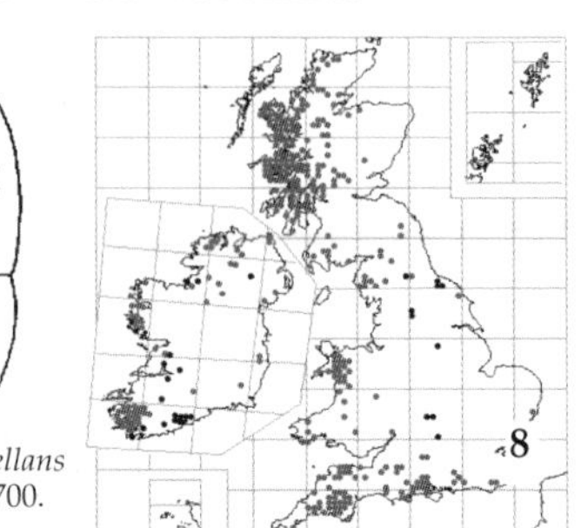

2. A. lapponina (A. fallax) Thallus thin or evanescent, looking as though varnished. Probably not lichenized. Perithecia oval, piercing the epidermis of the host, and surrounded by a dark belt just under the bark surface. It has the largest perithecia of the British species of *Arthopyrenia,* up to about 0.6 mm diam (the rarer **A. cerasi** is similar but has 3-septate spores). Asci cylindrical. Spores 1-septate with a colourless perispore, 15–23 x 5.5–8 µm.
Habitat: Common on twigs and smooth bark in moderate shade.

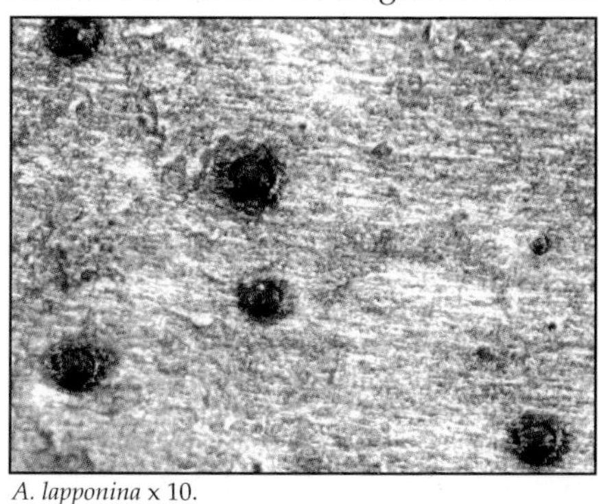

A. lapponina x 10.

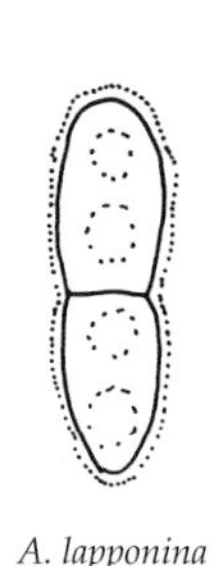

A. lapponina spore x 1200.

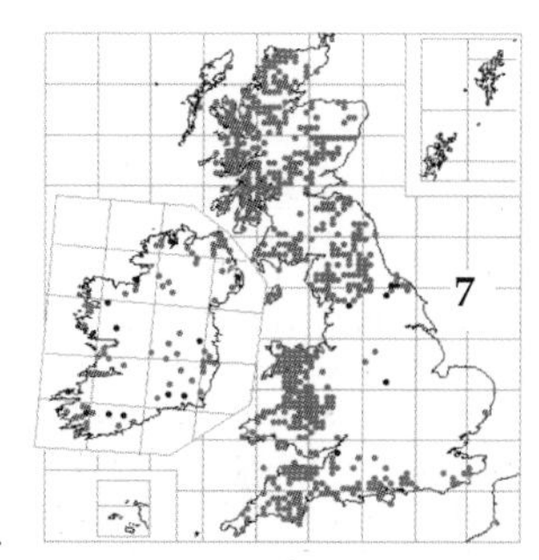

3. A. punctiformis Similar to the last species but with the thallus scarcely apparent to evanescent. The perithecia only about 0.3 mm diam with a circular to oval base. Spores 1-septate with a colourless perispore, 16–20 x 4–5 µm.
Habitat: Common on smooth bark especially on twigs and young trees in moderate shade. This is an aggregate of several closely related species.

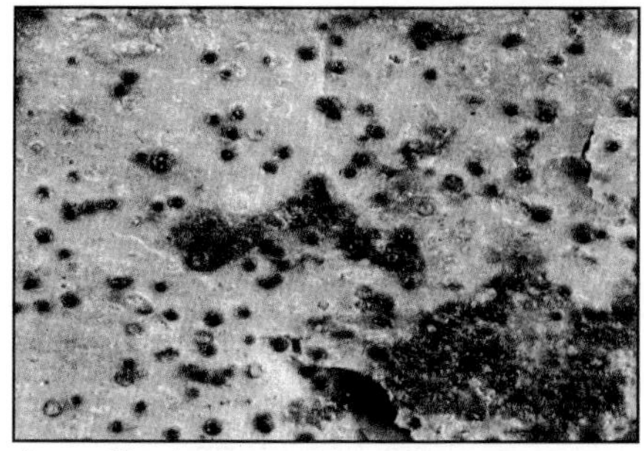

A. punctiformis x 6.

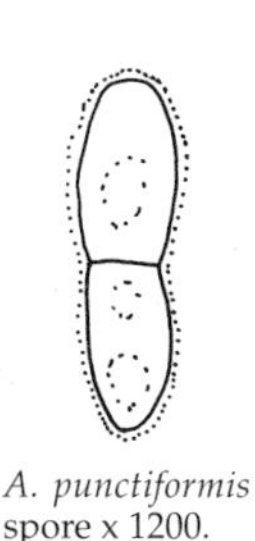

A. punctiformis spore x 1200.

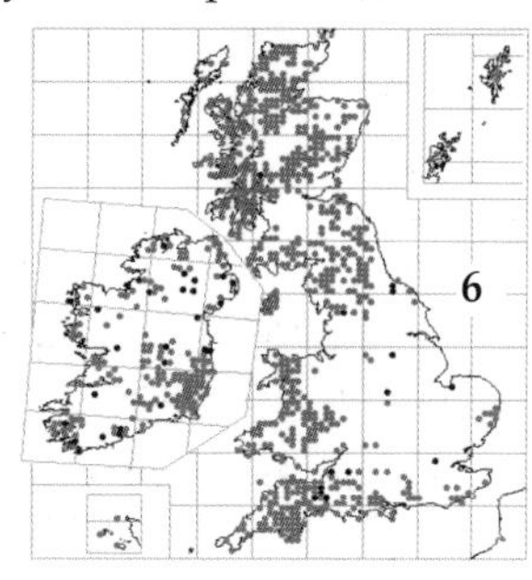

4. A. ranunculospora Thallus immersed in the bark forming light-coloured patches (often looking slightly pink) with a brown margin. Apothecia conical but spreading, up to 0.3 mm diam. Often with the remains of the bark cells on the surface. Spores 1- septate, 13–16 x 4–6 µm, with a broad upper cell, like a head.
Habitat: Frequent in old shaded woodland on smooth bark or flat areas of rough-barked trees, especially oak.

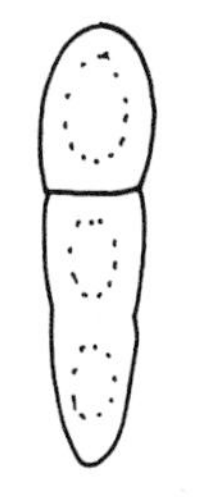

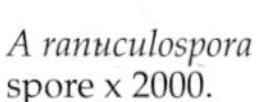

A ranuculospora spore x 2000.

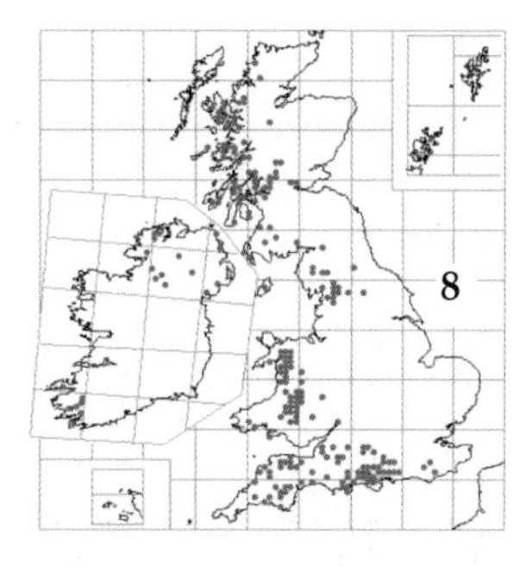

ARTHRORHAPHIS ('jointed needle' – from the shape of the spores). **Thallus** crustose and parasitic, at least in its early stages, when it occurs within the thallus of the host, becoming granular to squamulose and free-living. **Photobiont** chlorococcoid. **Apothecia** black, concave to flat and usually found between the squamules. **Ascus** cylindrical-clavate, 8-spored, K/I–. **Spores** multi-septate, needle-like. **Pycnidia** unknown.

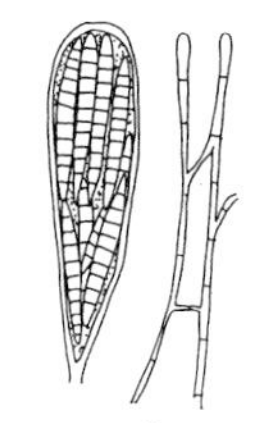

A. citrinella x 250.

Arthrorhaphis citrinella Thallus of lemon-yellow to green-yellow, fragile, clumped granules (up to 0.5 mm across) which become sorediate. It is often associated with *Baeomyces rufus*. Usually sterile but when fertile it has dark green to black apothecia between the granules. Spores 8- to 11-septate, large, 40–80 x 2–5 µm.
Habitat: In upland regions, common only in the Scottish Highlands.

A. citrinella x 9.

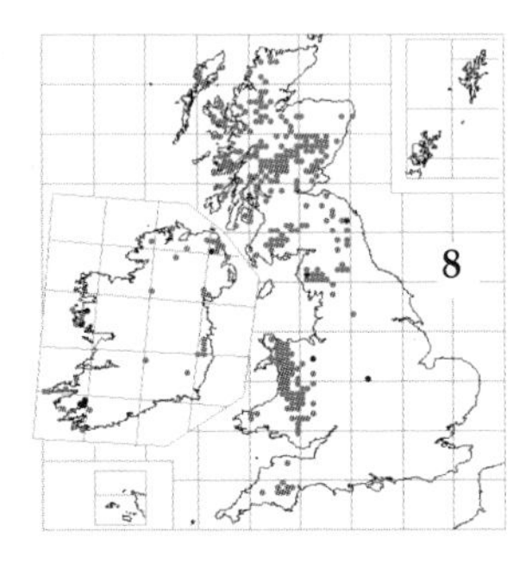

ASPICILIA ('ciliate shield' – from the torn margins found in some old apothecia). **Thallus** crustose, areolate, becoming continuous and rarely lobate at the margins. **Photobiont** trebouxioid. **Apothecia** lecanorine, usually sunken in the thallus with a dark brown to black disc and a thin or indistinct thalline margin. **Ascus** 4- to 8-spored. K/I+ outer wall or K–. **Spores** simple, colourless. All the British species are found on rocks.

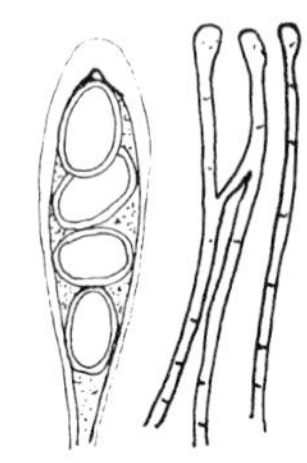

A. contorta x 300.

1.	K+ red, P+ orange	2
–	K– or faint yellow, P–	4
2.	On calcareous rocks. Placodioid at margin	**8. A. subcircinata**
–	On acid rocks. Not placodioid at margin	3
3.	Apothecia sessile, 0.3–0.6 mm diam. Poorly delimited	**5. A. grisea**
–	Apothecia immersed, 0.5–1.2 mm diam. Grey prothallus	**3. A. cinerea**
4.	Thallus dark green-grey, on rocks by streams	**6. A. laevata**
–	Thallus white to light grey, not restricted to water	5
5.	On acid rocks	7
–	On calcareous rocks	6

6. Thallus white, ± continuous **2. A. calcarea**
– Thallus light green-grey, ± separate areoles **4. A. contorta**
7. Thallus of scurfy grey granules. Prothallus grey-green **7. A. leprosescens**
– Thallus cracked-areolate. Prothallus grey **1. A. caesiocinerea**

1. Aspicilia caesiocinerea Thallus bluish to brown-grey, thick and warted, cracked or with areoles having flat to slightly concave tops and sharp edges and a slightly rough surface. Usually surrounded by a dark grey prothallus. It looks like a dark *A. calcarea.* Apothecia up to 1.5 mm diam, immersed, becoming somewhat sessile. Disc black, not pruinose. Margin thin and persistent. Asci usually with 4 (–8) spores. Spores 15–30 x 7–15 µm.
P–, K–.
Habitat: Frequent on nutrient-enriched seepage tracks on acid rocks often near water and especially on the tops of chest-tombs.

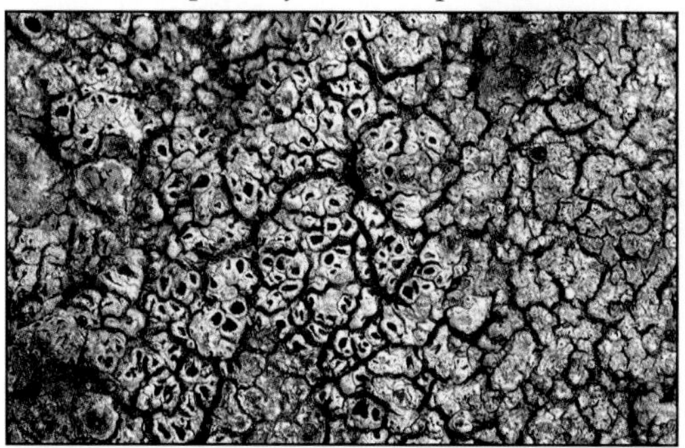

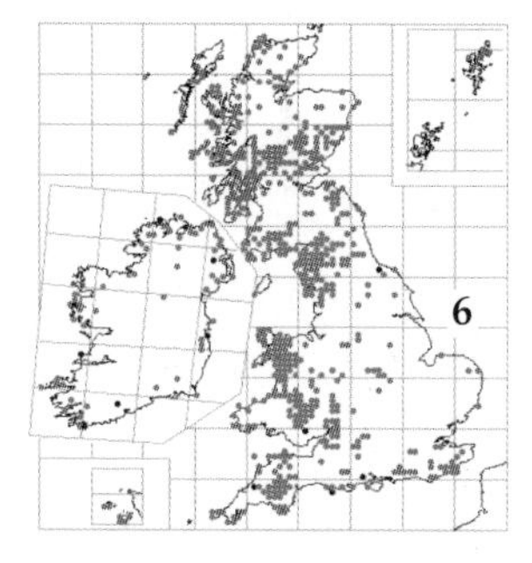

A. caesiocinerea x 3.

2. A. calcarea Thallus white to pale grey, smooth and usually divided into areoles, sometimes becoming almost placodioid and often surrounded by a grey prothallus. Apothecia irregular in shape, one or more in the centre of an areole, disc black often pruinose with a distinct, uneven, overarching margin which often disappears as the apothecium matures. Spores 4 per ascus, 18–30 x 14–27 µm.
K–.
Habitat: Common on hard calcareous rocks, walls and tombstones; large white patches (to 40 cm diam) seen in these habitats usually prove to be this species.

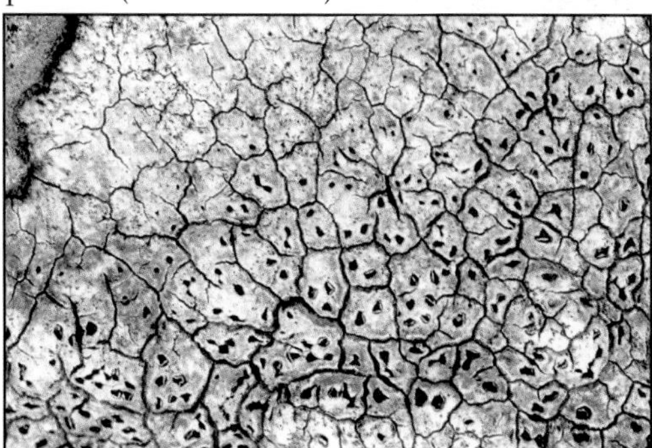

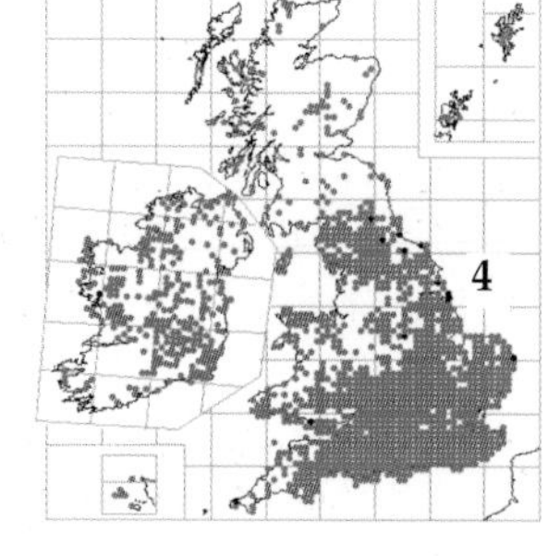

A. calcarea x 3.

3. A. cinerea Thallus cracked to warted, areolate, dark grey, frequently with a grey prothallus. Apothecia up to 1 mm diam, immersed, becoming slightly raised with a persistent thalline margin. Disc black. Spores 8 per ascus, 10–20 x 6–13 µm.
This is probably an aggregate of species which includes **A. epiglypta**, an overlooked species which has a pale fawn thallus of coarse, rounded areoles, a thin, persistent proper margin and a roughened, very dark brown disc.
P+ orange, K+ red.
Habitat: Common on well-lit acid rocks, mainly in the North and West. *A. epiglypta* is found on nutrient-enriched coastal rocks in the West.

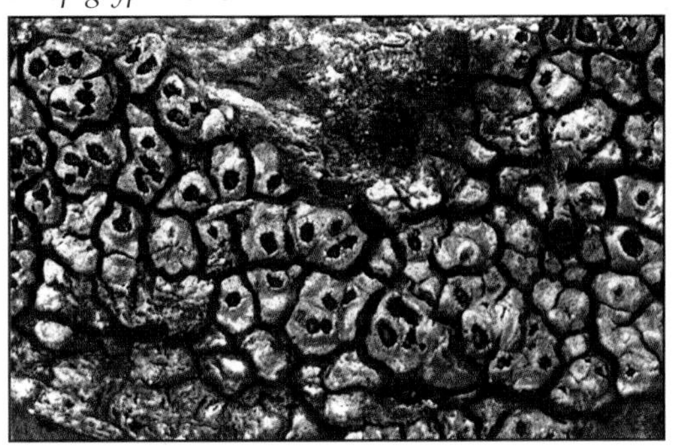

A. epiglypta x 6.

A. cinerea

4. A. contorta Thallus differs from *A. calcarea* in being a greenish glaucous grey, in its younger stages forming separate, more convex areoles, each with an apothecium (sometimes 2 or 3) in the centre which look like small volcanic islands. These may merge and become paler but do not have a placodioid-like margin and prothallus. Specimens where the squamules merge with angled, rather than rounded margins, belong to subsp. **hoffmaniana**. This latter subspecies can also be found on less basic rocks. Apothecia immersed, frequently with a blue-white pruina over the black discs. Spores 8 per ascus, 12–25 x 5–6 µm.
K–.
Habitat: Common on hard calcareous rocks, somewhat rarer on concrete and chest-tombs.

A. contorta x 6.

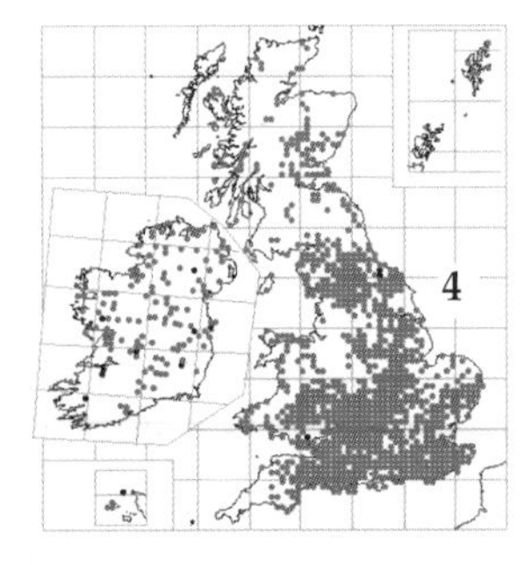

5. A. grisea (A. insolata) Thallus grey, cracked, thin and forming irregular patches. Usually with scattered pale isidia that soon become eroded. Apothecia small (up to 0.5 mm), and less immersed than other species retaining the proper margin when mature. Spores 8 per ascus, 18–22 x 9–12 μm.
K+ red, P+ orange.
Habitat: Frequent on well-lit acid rocks especially nutrient-enriched flat tops of tombs. Most common in the West.

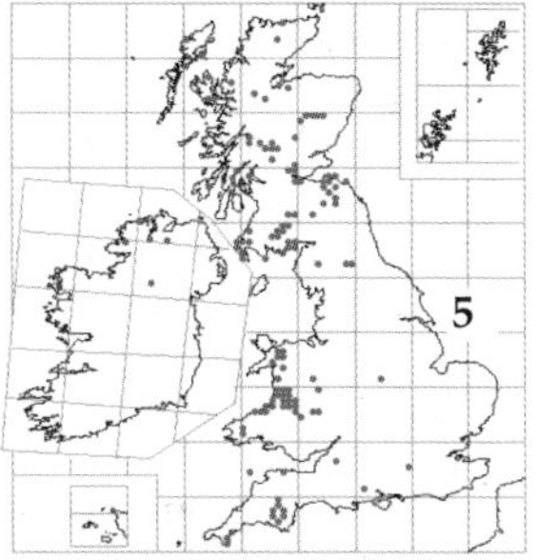

6. A. laevata Thallus olive-green, smooth, thin, limited by a black prothallus. (white in *Bacidia inundata*). Apothecia immersed and usually abundant, up to 0.5 mm, margin prominent, disc flat to concave. Spores 15–24 x 9–16 μm.
P+ orange, K– or faint yellow.
Habitat: Frequent on shaded acid rocks in the splash zone of streams. Mainly found in North and West.

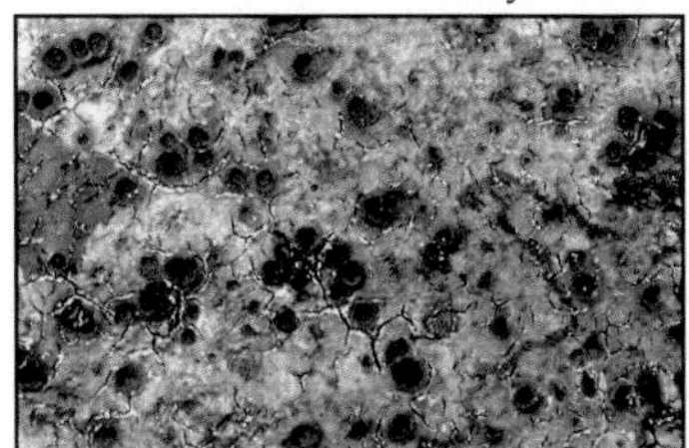
A. laevata x 2.

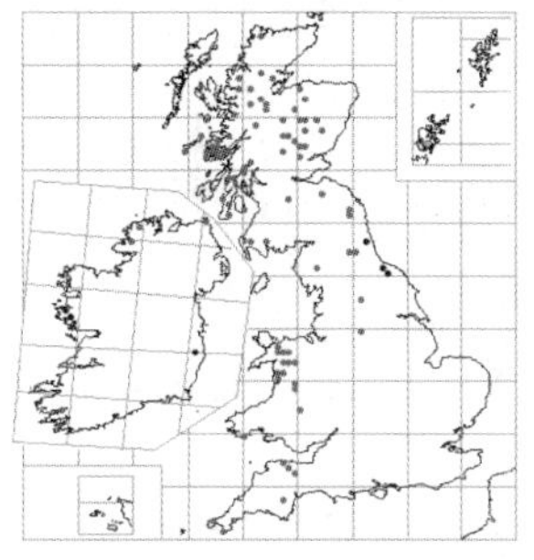

7. A. leprosescens Thallus areolate, pale to dark grey, consisting of loosely attached areoles that become sorediate. Often limited by a greenish grey prothallus. Apothecia are uncommon, up to 1 mm diam, innate becoming somewhat raised. Spores 8 per ascus, 14–30 x 7–16 μm.
P–, K–.
Habitat: Common on coastal, acid, nutrient-enriched rocks. Very rare inland.

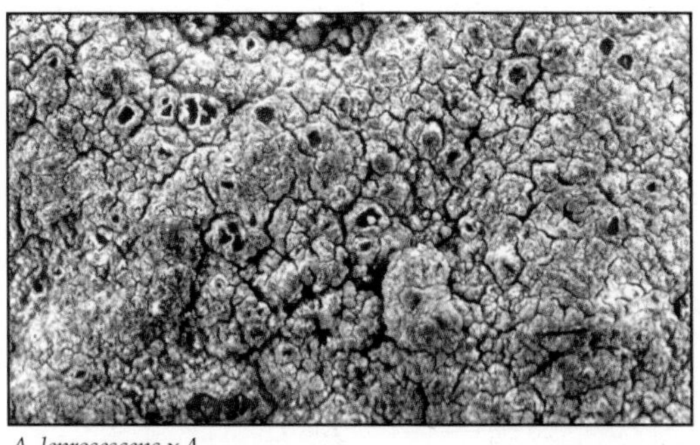
A. leprosescens x 4.

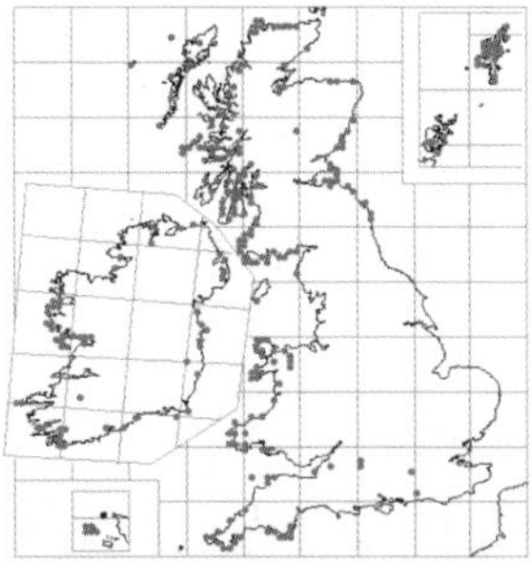

8. A. subcircinata Thallus grey and lobate, radiating, lobes often pruinose at the ends. Apothecia brown-black, up to 1 mm diam, covering the centre of the thallus. The flattish apothecia appear rather like a rubbed-down *Tephromela atra.*
P+ orange, K+ red.
Habitat: Infrequent, on calcareous rocks but mainly on the tops of chest-tombs and wall tops in the South.

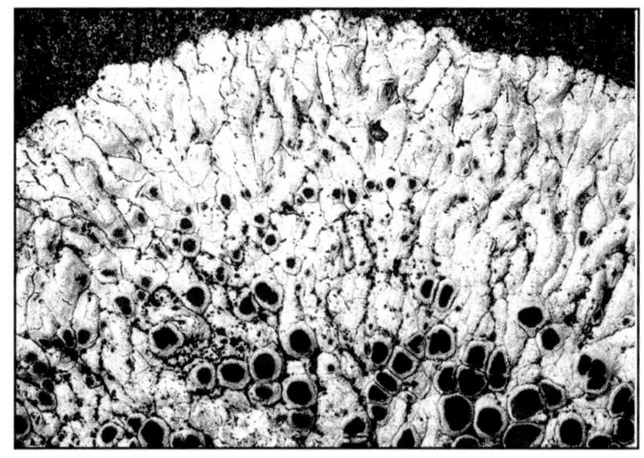

A. subcircinata x 5.

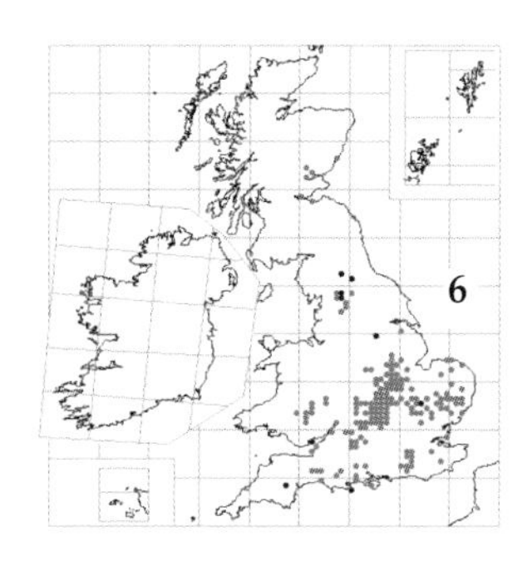

BACIDIA ('rod-shaped' – from the form of many of the ascospores). **Thallus** crustose. **Apothecia** lecideine and usually convex. **Ascus** mainly clavate with a K/I+ blue apical dome and, in some species, a blue outer wall. 8-spored. **Hymenium** I+ blue. **Spores** colourless and only about 3 µm wide, multi-septate but the septa are often indistinct. **Chemical reactions and UV** negative. An apothecium should be sliced in half when examining specimens as the colour of the internal tissues is often important.

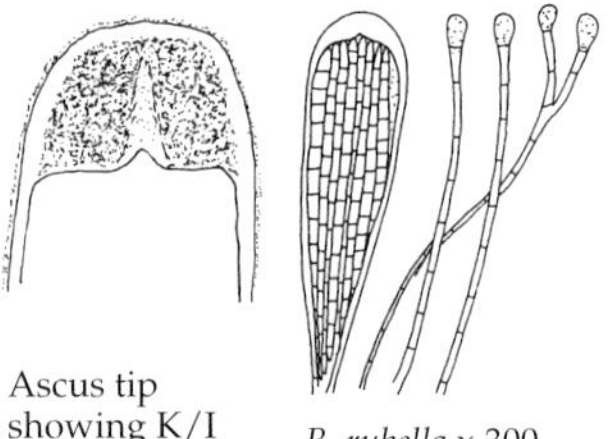

Ascus tip showing K/I reaction.

B. rubella x 300.

1. Fertile — 6
– Sterile (this keys-out the species most commonly found sterile) — 2
2. Greenish buff, on coastal acid rocks and soil — **11. B. scopulicola**
– On trees or basic substratum, not confined to coast — 3
3. Thallus granular isidiate — **9. B. rubella**
– Thallus finely granular — 4
4. Pycnidia numerous, brown, sessile, globose to rod-like — **12. B. vezdae**
– Pycnidia absent or scattered, innate, white — 5
5. Granules 20–40 µm diam, not sorediate — **1. B. arnoldiana**
– Granules 15–35 µm diam, often somewhat sorediate — **3. B. delicata**
6. On bark — 7
– On stone, plants, moss or soil — 13
7. Hymenium up to 65 µm high — 8
– Hymenium over 65 µm high — 12
8. Hymenium pale yellow, K+ faint yellow — **8. B. phacodes**
– Hymenium or hypothecium colourless or brown, K– or K+ green-brown — 9
9. Apothecia brown to grey-brown. Hypothecium brown — **12. B. vezdae**
– Apothecia orange-pink, pale or dark grey to black. Hypothecium colourless — 10
10. Ascospores up to 24 µm long — **7. B. naegellii**

–	Ascospores greater than 24 µm long	11
11.	Hypothecium red-brown	**1. B. arnoldiana**
–	Hypothecium colourless	**3. B. delicata**
12.	Thallus smooth or cracked	**6. B. laurocerasi**
–	Thallus granular or isidiate	**9. B. rubella**
13.	On stone	14
–	On mosses, plants or soil	18
14.	Apothecia up to 1.25 mm diam, on seashore acid rocks	**11. B. scopulicola**
–	Apothecia up to 0.6 mm diam, not only on seashore acid rocks	15
15.	On shaded rocks by freshwater	**5. B. inundata**
_	Not on shaded rocks by fresh water	16
16.	Hymenium up to 70 µm high	**9. B. rubella**
–	Hymenium over 70 µm high	17
17.	Hypothecium red-brown	**1. B. arnoldiana**
–	Hypothecium colourless	**3. B. delicata**
18.	Hymenium 45–60 µm high, spores up to 3 µm wide	19
–	Hymenium 70–110 µm high, spores 5–8 µm wide	**10. B. sabuletorum**
19.	Apothecial disc red-brown. Ascospores 35–60 µm long	**4. B. herbarum**
–	Apothecial disc black. Ascospores 25-45 µm long	**2. B. bagliettoana**

1. Bacidia arnoldiana Thallus green to buff, of minute granules which may cover large areas. Frequently sterile. Apothecia up to 0.75 mm diam, pale grey to brownish grey. Disc flat, with a prominent, paler, often pruinose, proper margin. Hymenium colourless, 40–50 µm high. Hypothecium red-brown in its upper part. Spores 1- to 3-septate, 20–45 x 1–2 µm. Pycnidia innate, white.
Habitat: Common in S.E. England becoming rarer northwards. Found on damp shaded calcareous rocks, monuments and bark (mainly elder).

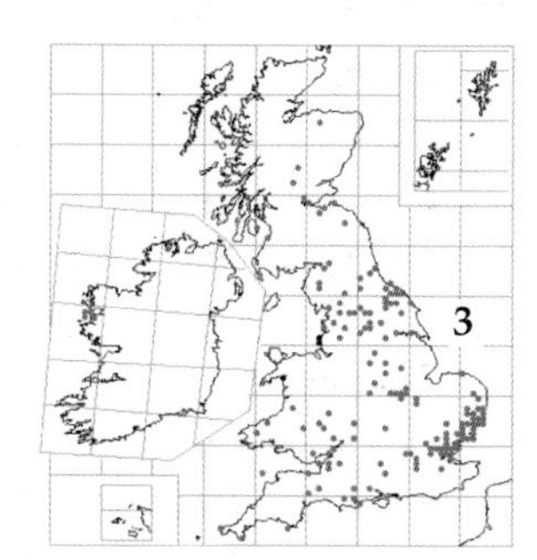

2. B. bagliettoana (B. muscorum) Thallus white to light grey and rather granular. Apothecia up to 1.4 mm diam, black, sessile, with a persistent margin. Disc almost flat even in mature apothecia. Hymenium 40–55 µm high. Hypothecium colourless but brown in upper part. Spores 3- to 7-septate, 25–50 x 3 µm.
Habitat: on mosses or exposed tops of walls or rocks. Often directly on the ground or on rocks in limestone regions, also found on shell-sand dunes. In the field it may resemble *B. sabuletorum* but that species has paler, brown fruits which become globose when mature. It also has wider spores.

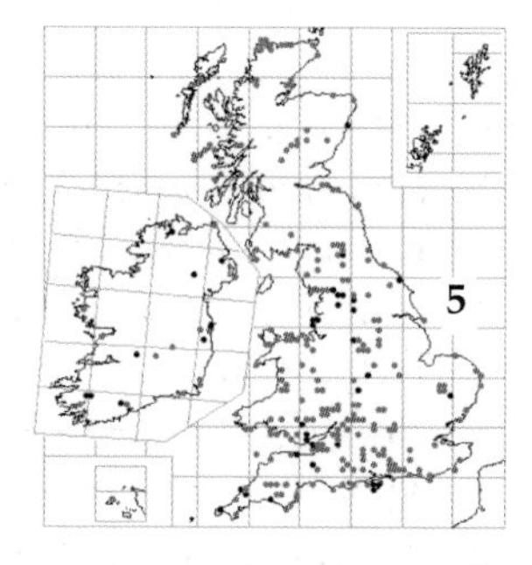

3. B. delicata Thallus bright green to buff, wide-spreading, consisting of very fine granules. Frequently found sterile. Apothecia rare, about 0.5 mm diam, grey to pinkish, sessile with a persistent, paler margin and a flat disc even in mature fruits. Hymenium 35–55 µm high, colourless. Hypothecium colourless. Spores 25–50 x 1–2 µm, 3- to 7-septate.Pycnidia white and innate.
Habitat: Common but overlooked in shaded sites. On calcareous rocks and memorials often overgrowing moss, frequent on urban, basic-barked trees.
Very difficult to separate in the field from *B. arnoldiana* and probably under-recorded. In a section of an apothecium the total lack of pigment is diagnostic.

B. delicata x 2.

4. B. herbarum Thallus white to pale grey, membranous to warted. Apothecia up to 0.7 mm diam. Red-brown to dark brown, usually flat with a persistent proper margin. Hymenium 45–60 µm high, colourless but light orange in upper part. Hypothecium orange, fading to colourless in the lower part. Spores 30–50 x 2–3 µm, 3- to 7-septate. Pycnidia unknown.
Habitat: A rare species of calcareous grassland and hard limestone rocks overgrowing mosses and other small plants.

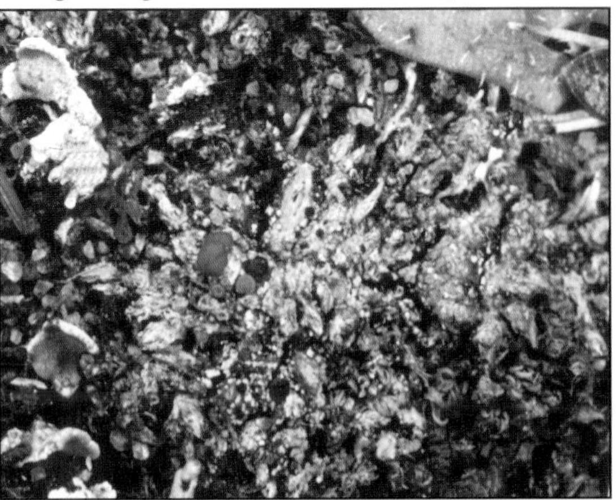

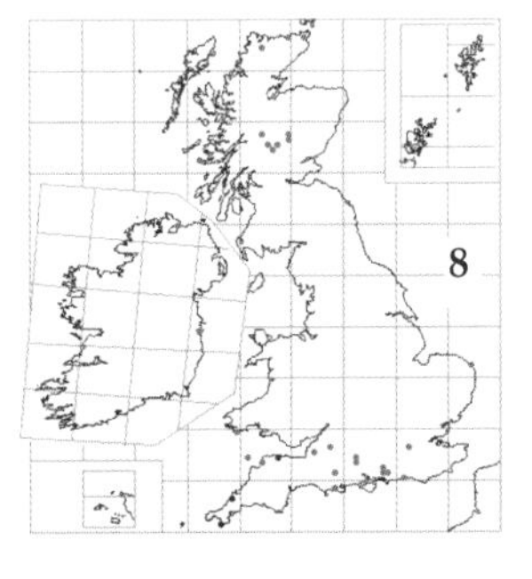

B. herbarum x 5.

5. B. inundata Thallus green-grey which may dry to a straw colour. It has a white prothallus which makes it resemble an aquatic *Verrucaria mucosa*. Thick with clumped granules, areolate or smooth. Apothecia small, up to 0.6 mm, light to dark brown, flat becoming convex and contorted, often with a paler margin. Hymenium 45–55 µm high, colourless becoming pinkish. Hypothecium colourless to fawn. Spores 25–45 x 2–3 µm, usually 3-septate, sometimes up to 8-septate.
Habitat: Fairly common on wet, often shaded, acid rocks by or in non-polluted streams and lakesides, rarely found on trees and wood by water.

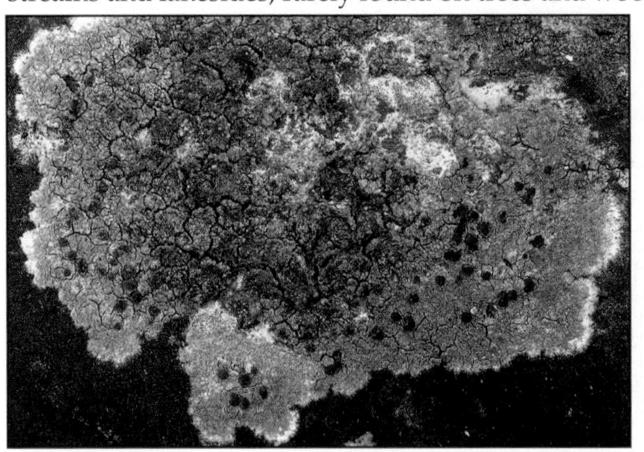

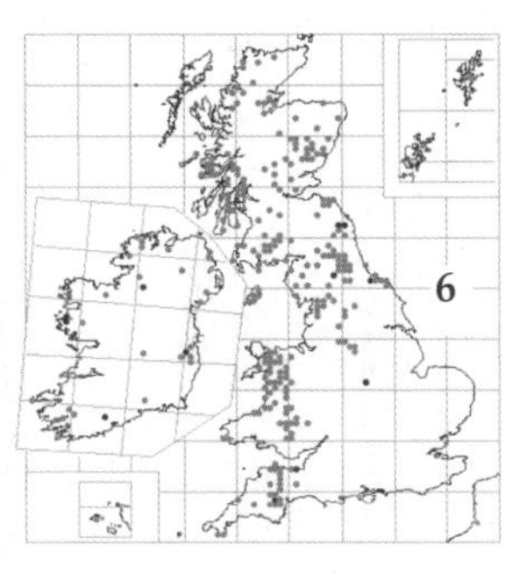

B. inundata x 3.

6. B. laurocerasi (B. endoleuca) Thallus grey to green-grey, smooth to warted. Apothecia frequent, brown-black, up to about 1 mm diam. Hymenium 65–90 µm high, colourless. Hypothecium colourless to pale brown. Epithecium K+ violet or purple. Spores 35–80 x 3–4 µm, 7- to 16-septate.
Habitat: Fairly common on basic, rough-barked, deciduous trees and shrubs in open shade. It becomes rare in the North.

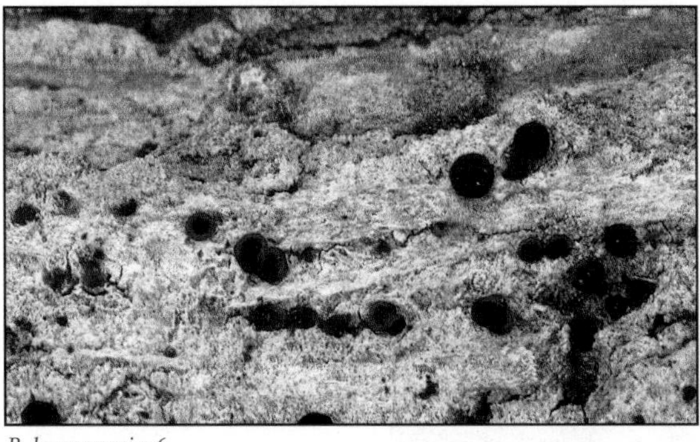

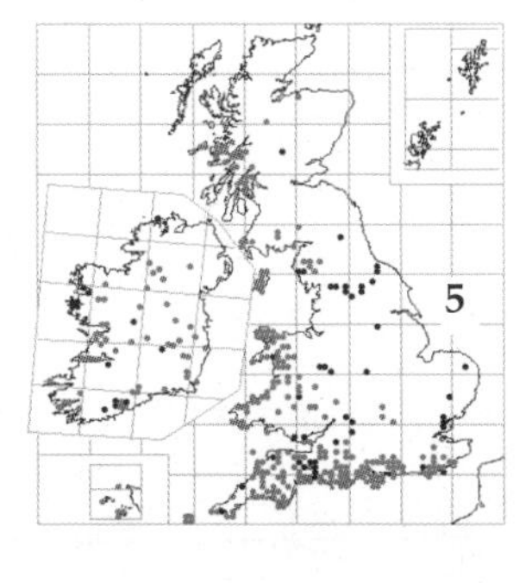

B. laurocerasi x 6.

7. B. naegelii Thallus grey to green-grey, smooth. Often forms small islands amongst other species. Apothecia often in groups, up to 0.7 mm diam, becoming slightly convex. Pale grey to black or piebald, translucent when wet, margin paler. Hymenium 50–65 µm high. Hypothecium colourless. Spores 15–28 x 4–6 µm often bent, 3- to 5-septate.
Habitat: Common throughout British Isles on basic-barked trees.

8. B. phacodes Thallus grey to green-grey, almost granular or areolate, sometimes smooth. Apothecia flesh or pink in colour, up to 0.5 mm diam, slightly convex, often irregular, scattered thickly over the surface. Hymenium 35–50 μm high, colourless to pale yellow, K+ faint yellow. Hypothecium colourless. Spores 30–45 x 2 μm, 3- to 7-septate but the septa are indistinct.
Habitat: Not common. Usually on basic, rough-barked trees in damp and deep shade. Becoming rare in North.

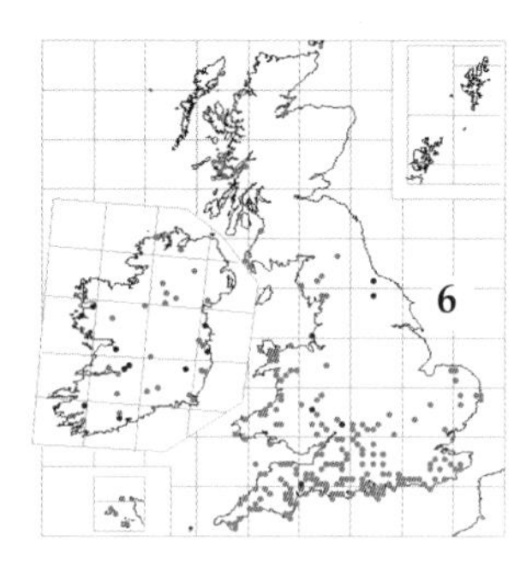

B. phacodes x 8.

9. B. rubella Thallus yellow-green to grey, granular, or especially where sterile, granules isidia-like. Apothecia sessile, orange-brown, not very convex, up to or just over 1 mm diam. Margins usually persistent, rarely white-pruinose. Hymenium 70–100 μm high, colourless. Hypothecium colourless, pale brown in upper part, K+ yellow. Spores 40–70 x 3 μm, 4- to 16-septate.
Habitat: Frequent, once mainly on elms but also plane, ash and other trees with basic bark. It has also been found on the east side of the calcareous 'Horton Stone' gravestones in the South Midlands.

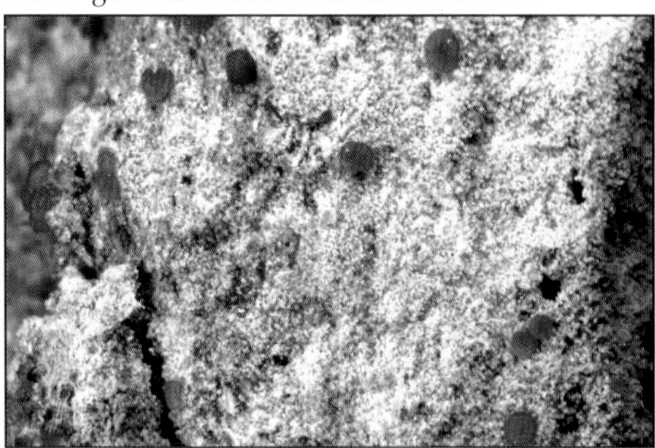

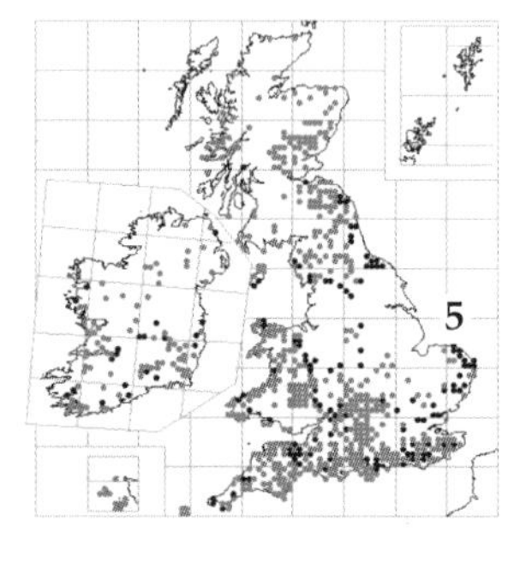

B. rubella x 5.

10. B. sabuletorum Thallus light grey, more or less coarsely granulose. Apothecia numerous, dark brown, pinkish brown when wet, immarginate when mature but with a pronounced margin when young, very convex and

almost globose, up to about 0.75 mm diam. Hymenium 70–110 µm high, colourless becoming brown to blue-green in upper part. Hypothecium brown, sometimes K+ red to purple in upper part. Spores 18–45 x 5–8 µm, 3- to 9-septate, rarely with a cross septum in one cell.
Habitat: Common on mosses on basic-barked trees or ledges on the north side of churches, more rarely on mossy calcareous rocks and soil.

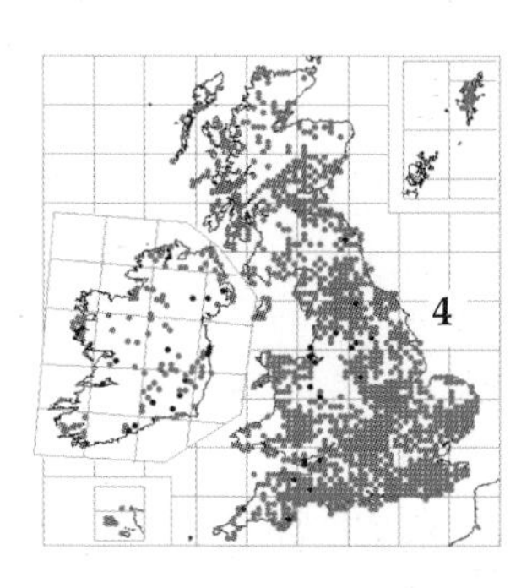

B. sabuletorum x 5.

11. B. scopulicola Thallus fawn-brown to dark yellow-green, granular, often with isidia covering the whole surface; this is a very variable species. Apothecia rare, large, up to 1.25 mm diam, dark brown with a darker margin, often contorted. Hymenium 45–60 µm high, colourless, sometimes orange in the lower part. Hypothecium colourless to pale orange. Spores 30–45 x 2 µm, 3- to 7-septate. Pycnidia brown, innate.
Habitat: In moist overhangs or in cracks on acid rocks on the upper seashore.

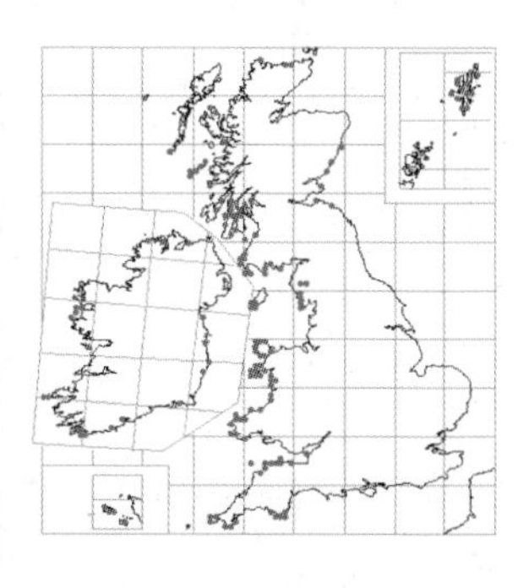

B. scopulicola x 5.

12. B. vezdae Thallus grey to green-grey, thin. Apothecia up to 0.5 mm diam, light brown to grey-brown, top-shaped to convex. Proper margin persistent. Hymenium 40–50 µm high, colourless. Hypothecium brown, K–. Spores 30–40 x 3–5 µm, 3- to 7-septate. There are usually conspicuous groups of brownish, sessile, cylindrical pycnidia present, about 0.2 mm diam.
Habitat: Found throughout on trees in shade and also over moss.

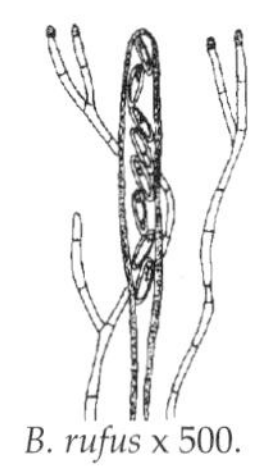
B. rufus x 500.

BAEOMYCES ('small mushroom'). **Thallus** crustose or squamulose. **Photobiont** *Cystocococcus* or *Elliptochloris*. **Apothecia** stalked, stalks rather translucent or short and mostly ecorticate, apices swollen, convex, immarginate, the hymenium sometimes I+ blue. **Ascus** 8-spored, K/I– or with a thin K/I+ blue cap. **Spores** colourless, simple or becoming up to 3-septate. The spores and some cells of the thallus contain oil globules. **Pycnidia** immersed in warts.

1. Thallus grey, rather granular. Podetia up to 6 mm high. Apothecia flesh-pink — **2. B. roseus**
– Thallus green-grey, finely granular or conspicuously lobate. Podetia up to 3 mm high. Apothecia reddish brown — 2
2. Thallus finely granular to small squamules — **3. B. rufus**
– Thallus with marginal lobes up to 5 mm wide — **1. B. placophyllus**

1. Baeomyces placophyllus Thallus light grey-green to fawn, green when wet, squamulose to lobate with upturned margins (lobes up to 5 mm wide) and becoming schizidiate, forming rosettes up to 5 cm across. Apothecia rare, to 2 mm diam on short, corticate furrowed stalks, to 3 mm high. Hymenium red-brown. Spores 8–14 x 2–4 µm.
Thallus: P+ orange, K+ yellow, KC+ orange, C–, UV+ orange. Apothecia: K–.
Habitat: Scarce, mainly in the West and NorthWest. On peat and gravel (especially river gravels). It is often associated with mine-spoil heaps.

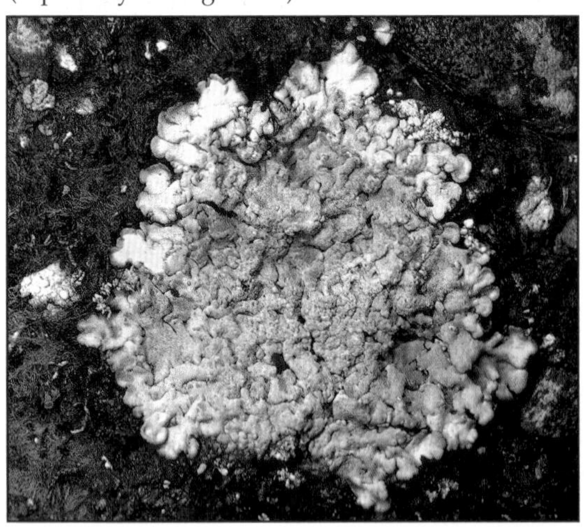
B. placophyllus x 2.

2. B. roseus (Dibaeis baeomyces) Thallus crustose, consisting of light grey, rarely greenish, granules of various sizes bearing very pale pink, shiny, rounded schizidia up to 1 mm diam. Frequently sterile and sometimes with farinose soredia. Stalked apothecia up to 6 mm high bear a globular pale pink hymenium, I+ blue. Spores 10–25 x 2–3 µm, 1-septate but may appear simple. P+ orange, K+ yellow turning orange, KC+ orange, C–. UV+ orange.

Habitat: Common on peaty soil where it is an early recolonizer after disturbance of the peat, usually in damp heathland. Mainly found in the North and West. Frequently sterile in lowland areas and mine-spoil heaps.

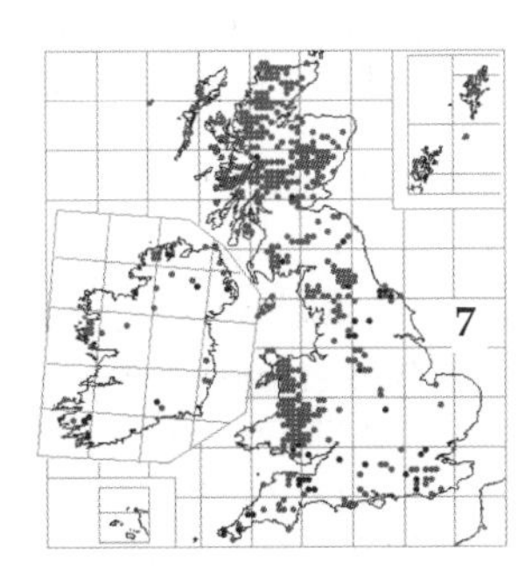

B. roseus x 5.

3. B. rufus Thallus greenish grey, granulose, often becoming sorediate, or of minute squamules (particularly at the margins). The apothecia differ from the last species. The stalks are somewhat darker in colour, furrowed, shorter, sessile or up to 6 mm high. Hymenium flatter and reddish brown in colour, K/I–. Spores simple to indistinctly 1-septate.
Thallus: P+ orange, K+ yellow, KC+ yellow, UV–.
Habitat: As the previous species, but usually in more shaded, damp situations and frequently encountered on damp, shaded siliceous rocks. Common and very often sterile.

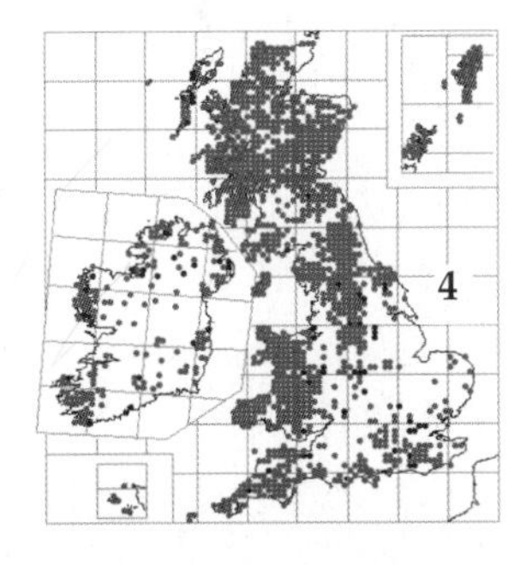

B. rufus x 8.

BELONIA ('arrow' – from the shape of the spores). **Thallus** crustose, lacking a cortex and often thin. **Photobiont** *Trentepohlia*. **Apothecia** in thalline warts and resembling perithecia that open out as they mature. **Ascus** 6- to 8-spored, thin walled. **Hymenium** I+ blue, with yellow oil droplets. **Spores** long and pointed, septate to muriform. **Pycnidia** unknown. **Chemical reactions** negative.

Belonia nidarosiensis (Clathroporina calcarea) Thallus a powdery crust, orange to red, flecked with white, fading and becoming ± invisible in the herbarium. Apothecia are rare, orange to red, usually widely spaced in thalline warts with a dot-like brown hymenium showing in the centre. Spores are muriform, up to 15-septate when young, colourless, 40–60 x 10–15 µm, tapering to a thin 'tail'. The spores often vary in size in each ascus. It is frequently found infertile when the more orange forms resemble *Opegrapha gyrocarpa,* but that species is C+ red and occurs on siliceous substrata.
Hymenium I+ blue becoming reddish brown.
Habitat: Not uncommon but often overlooked, on vertical shaded dry limestone and mortar, especially on the north and east walls of churches.

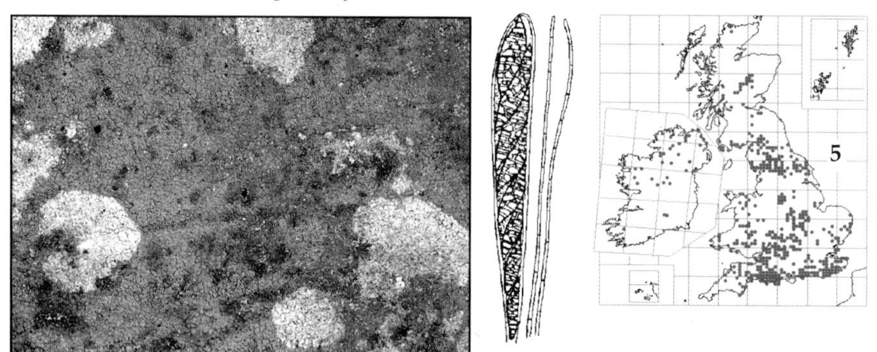

Belonia nidarosiensis x 3.

Ascus x 250.

BIATORA ('little goblet' – from the shape of the apothecia of the type species). **Thallus** crustose, granular. **Photobiont** chlorococcoid. **Apothecia** lecideine (biatorine). **Ascus** cylindrical-clavate, K/I+ blue apical dome, darker towards centre, 8-spored. **Spores** colourless, simple to 3-septate. **Pycnidia** not known.

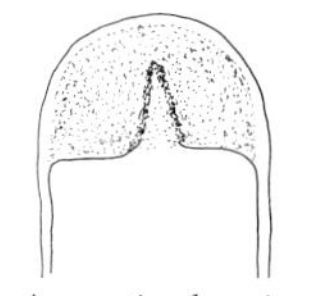

Ascus tip showing K/I reaction.

Biatora sphaeroides (Catillaria sphaeroides) Thallus green to green-grey, finely granular. Apothecia buff to pinkish orange, about 0.6 mm diam. Soon becoming globose and often clustered. Spores 1-septate (with a few old spores 3-septate).
Habitat: Mature deciduous trees in shaded, often humid valley bottoms. Frequently on or near the base of these trees. Sometimes on mossy rocks.

B. sphaeroides x 8.

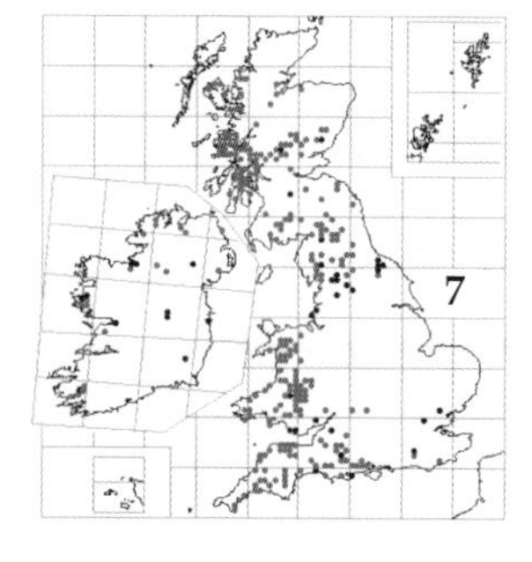

BLARNEYA ('Blarney' – based on kissing the Blarney Stone from its unexpected partnership). **Thallus** crustose, like compressed cotton wool, becoming rather crusty with C+ red crystals. **Photobiont** *Trentepohlia*. **Apothecia** not present. **Conidia** simple to 1-septate, in sporodochia with the spore mass on the tips of conidiophores and intermingled with numerous crystals. A hyphomycete on epiphytic lichens.

Blarneya hibernica Thallus pale pink or white (in the herbarium) with a loose, dark fimbriate margin. Sporodochia usually present, often over the fruiting bodies of the host. Conidia 8–13 x 3–5 µm.
KC+ red or –, C+ red.
Habitat: Found growing on *Enterographa* and *Lecanactis* species towards the base of sheltered trees (mainly holly) in ancient woodland. It is at first parasitic, taking over the algae of the host. After the death of the host it continues with an independent existence.

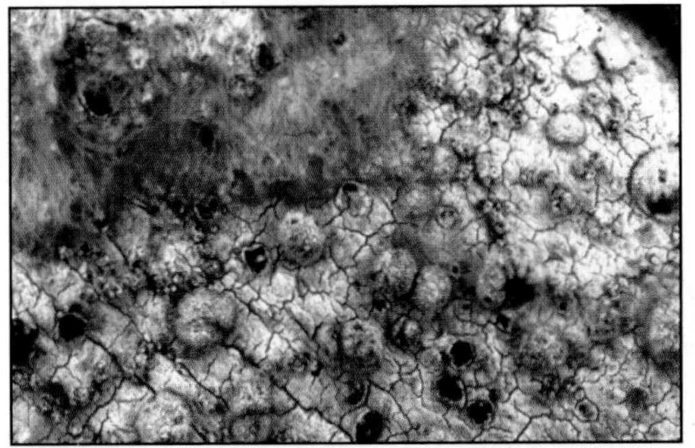

B. hibernica on *Lecanactis abietina* x 6.

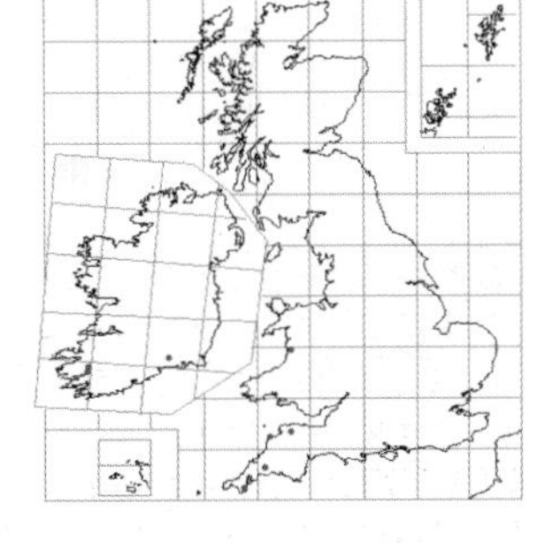

BRYORIA ({Bry}opogon, Alect{oria} – from older names of the group). **Thallus** fruticose, often sorediate but not isidiate. It can be separated in the field from *Alectoria* by the lack of any *conspicuous* pseudocyphellae. **Photobiont** trebouxioid. **Apothecia** lecanorine, very rare in Britain. **Ascus** thick-walled, K/I+ blue apical dome. **Spores** simple, colourless, oval. The corticolous species form an important food for reindeer and caribou in sub-arctic and boreal areas when the ground is snow-covered, and are also eaten by man. A table giving the characteristics of *Bryoria*, *Pseudephebe* and *Alectoria* species is given under *Alectoria* (page 53). If a P test is thought to be negative, it should be repeated on other parts of the thallus, especially at the apices which usually contain more of the active substances.

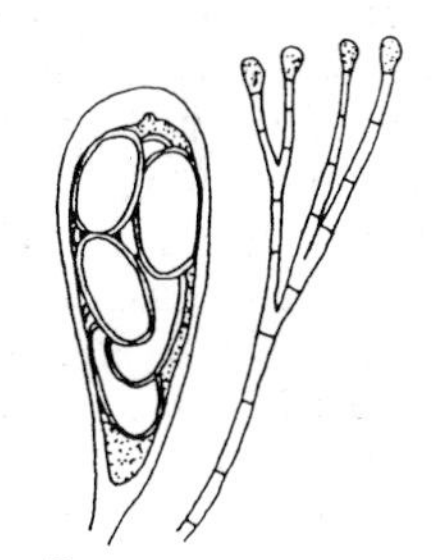

B. fuscescens x 600.

1. Bryoria bicolor Erect, forming dense tufts, usually 2–4 cm tall. Branches round, 0.2–0.7 mm diam, glossy. Green-grey at apices, brown-black at base. Numerous spiky spinules with constricted bases arise at right angles to the main stem. Soralia absent.
Cortex: K–, KC–, C–, P–. Medulla: P+ red at least in parts.
Habitat: Frequent in the West and North on mosses on boulders and trees but apparently declining.

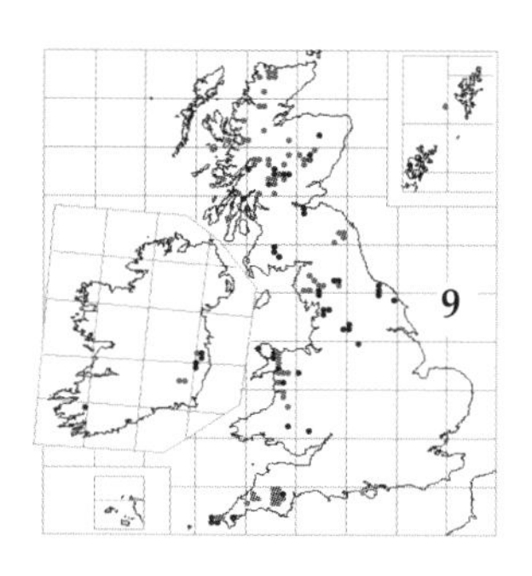

B. bicolor x 3.

2. B. capillaris Thallus usually pendent, black, mixed with mid- or pale grey areas. The base of the thallus frequently decays away. Soralia often abundant but may be absent. Separated from *B. fuscescens* by the P+ orange, K+ bright yellow, KC+ red, C± red reactions.
Habitat: Chiefly confined to the old conifer forests of the Scottish Highlands.

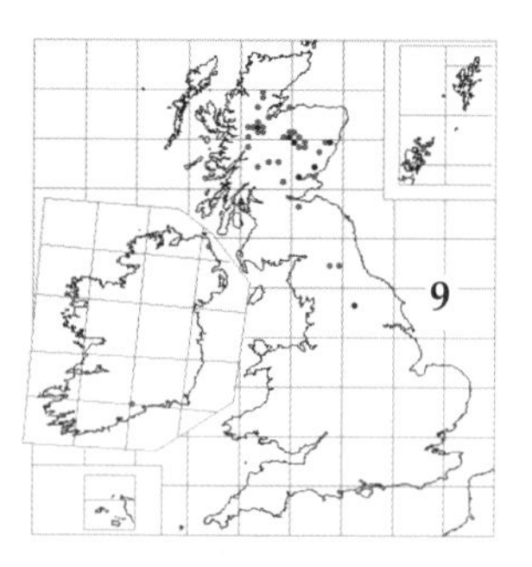

B. capillaris x 3.

3. B. chalybeiformis Thallus forms entwined prostrate mats up to 10 cm. across. May be distinguished from *B. fuscescens* by the dark grey to black glossy thallus, the sparse branching towards the base with wider, contorted main branches of 0.5–2 mm diam. Soralia sparse and tuberculate. Pseudocyphellae absent.
Thallus: K–, C–, P–. Soralia: P+ red.
Habitat: A rare species of upland areas. Found on mossy acid rocks, soil, or rarely on the horizontal branches of trees.

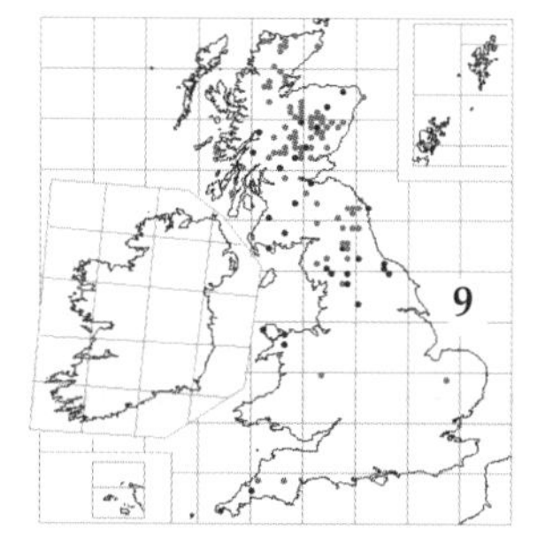

4. **B. fuscescens** The commonest and most widespread species in Britain. Thallus prostrate or pendent, 5–15 (–65) cm long, branching mainly at acute angles. Branches terete, somewhat flattened at the axils of the main branches which are up to 0.5 mm diam (sometimes closer to the base in var. *positiva*). Matt or with a very slight sheen, smoky green-brown or very dark brown, usually paler at the base. Very rarely fertile. Apothecia up to 2 mm diam. Soralia are frequently abundant. Pseudocyphellae absent.
Thallus: K–, C–, KC–, P+ red or P–. Soralia: P+ red.
Habitat: Common on trees (especially birch and conifers), fence posts and siliceous rocks.

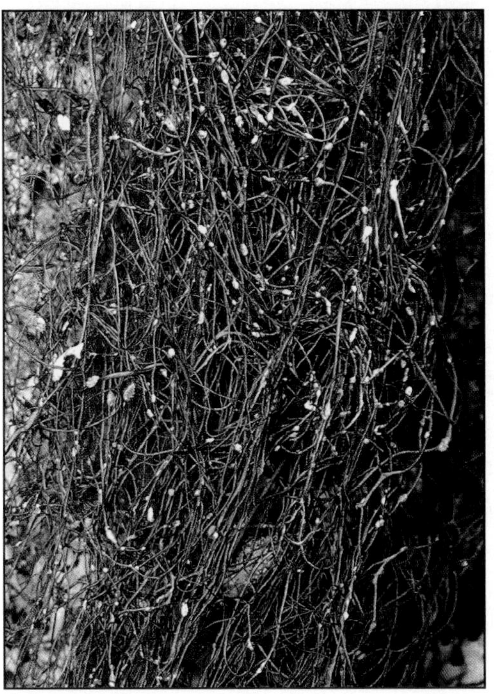

B. fuscescens x 2.

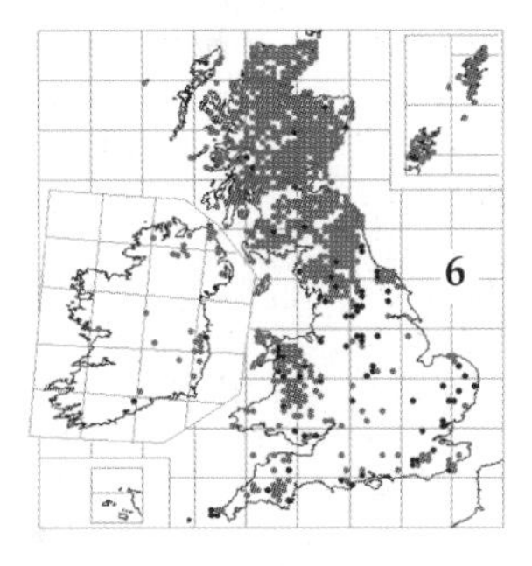

5. **B. subcana** Pendent, branching frequently from the base at obtuse angles. Pale grey-green, often smoky brown towards the base. Soralia always tuberculate.
Thallus: K–, KC–, P+ intensely orange-red. The stronger and more rapid P reaction together with the pale thallus colour and much neater branching pattern helps to differentiate this species from *B. fuscescens*.
Habitat: Fairly rare, on both conifers and deciduous trees in upland areas, most common in Scotland.

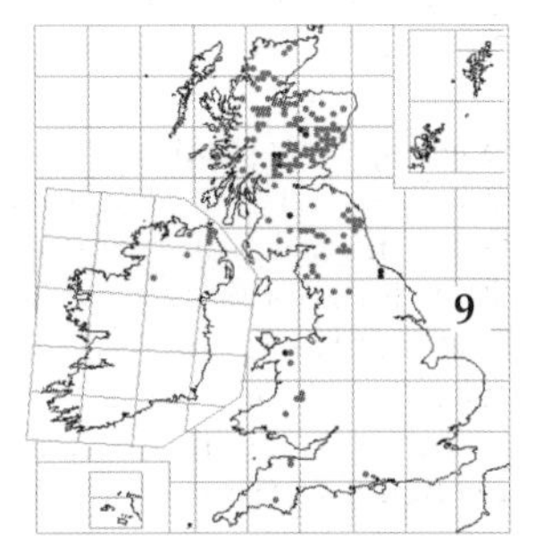

BUELLIA (named by De Notaris after his friend Esuperanza Buelli). **Thallus** crustose, thin or areolate, usually with a black prothallus. **Photobiont** chlorococcoid. **Apothecia** black, lecideine. **Ascus** usually 8-spored, *Lecanora*-type. **Paraphyses** sparsely branched, with dark clavate apices. **Hymenium** colourless or pale green in upper region, I+ blue. **Spores** brown, mainly 1-septate (becoming 3-, or irregularly septate or submuriform in some species). **Pycnidia** immersed, containing simple, colourless conidia.

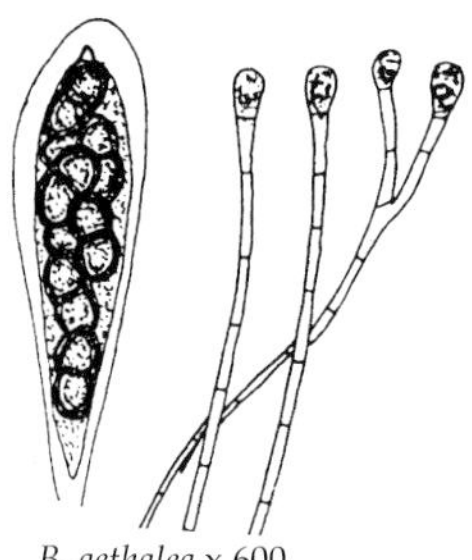
B. aethalea x 600.

1.	On trees	2
–	On rocks	4
2.	With grey-green soralia, K+yellow turning red	**3. B. griseovirens**
–	Not with soralia	3
3.	Thallus pale grey, thin, ± continuous, K+ yellow	**2. B. disciformis**
–	Thallus dull grey-green, thick, warted or areolate, K–	**Amandinea punctata**
4.	Apothecia to 1.5 mm diam, sessile	**7. B. subdisciformis**
–	Apothecia less than 1 mm diam	5
5.	C+ orange or red	6
–	C–	7
6.	K+ yellow, apothecia sessile	**5. B. saxorum**
–	K–, apothecia innate	**4. B. ocellata**
7.	K+ yellow or K–	8
–	K+ yellow turning red	**1. B. aethalea**
8.	Thallus K– or rarely faint yellow, P–. Apothecia ± sessile	**Amandinea punctata**
–	Thallus K+ yellow, P+ yellow. Apothecia innate	**6. B. stellulata**

1. Buellia aethalea Thallus grey to brown-grey, areolate in the centre, less so near the darker margin. It often forms mosaics with related species. The black prothallus is also visible between the areolae. Medulla I± blue. Apothecia innate, small (to 0.4 mm) with a black disc and found more towards the centre of the thallus than in *B. stellulata.* The proper margin is usually inconspicuous (if pronounced, check for the muriform spores of *Rhizocarpon reductum*). Spores 1-septate, 10–20 x 5–9 µm. P+ yellow, K+ yellow turning red, rarely negative. Habitat: Frequent on well-lit siliceous rocks.

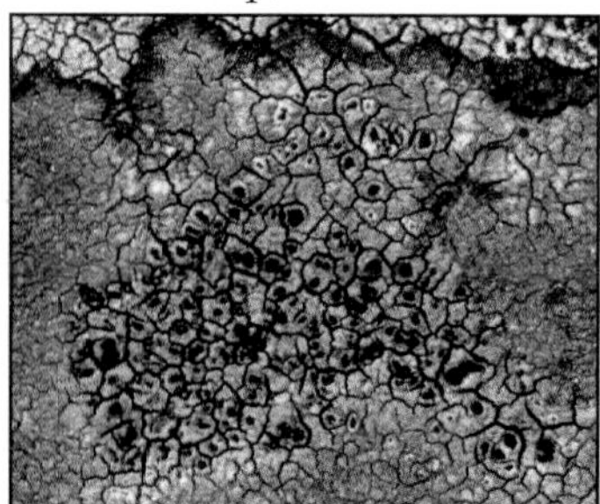
B. aethalea x 5.

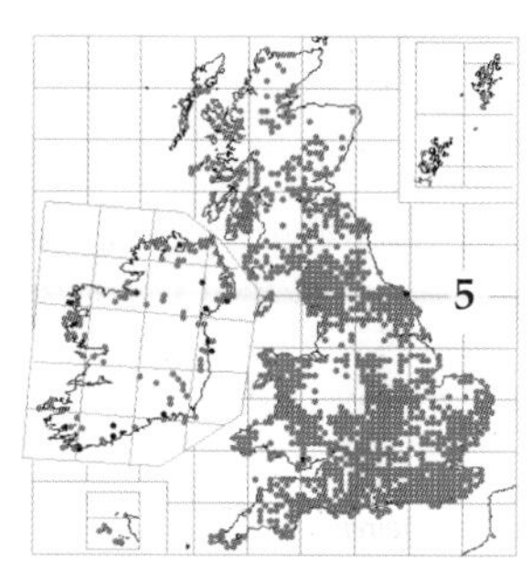

2. B. disciformis Thallus thin, cracked, glossy, whitish to pale yellowish grey, sometimes a black prothallus is visible. Medulla I–. Apothecia sessile, black, up to 1 mm diam, with a thick, rarely pruinose margin, flat but sometimes becoming slightly convex. Spores 1- or rarely 3-septate, 15–25 x 7–10 µm.
P+ yellow, K+ yellow.
Habitat: Frequent, mainly in the North and West on smooth-barked trees.

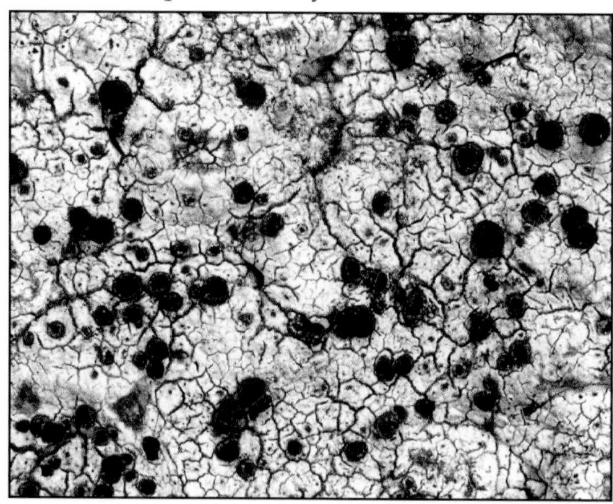

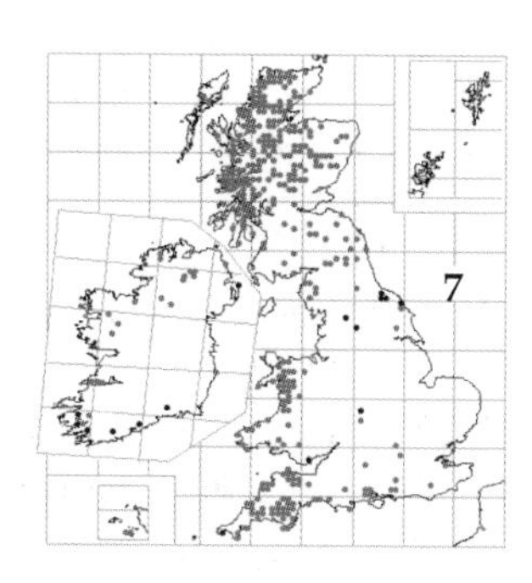

B. disciformis x 4.

3. B. griseovirens Thallus grey, thin or cracked, limited by a black prothallus. Light bluish green-grey soralia which scratch yellowish are scattered over the surface. These may become confluent and almost cover the thallus. The soralia give it the appearance of a corticolous *Lecidella scabra*. Medulla I–. Apothecia are rare, up to 1 mm diam, plane to convex. Spores 15–30 x 7–13 µm, irregularly septate so that they may look almost muriform.
Soralia: K+ yellow turning red, P+ yellow.
Habitat: Common on trees, rarely on brick.

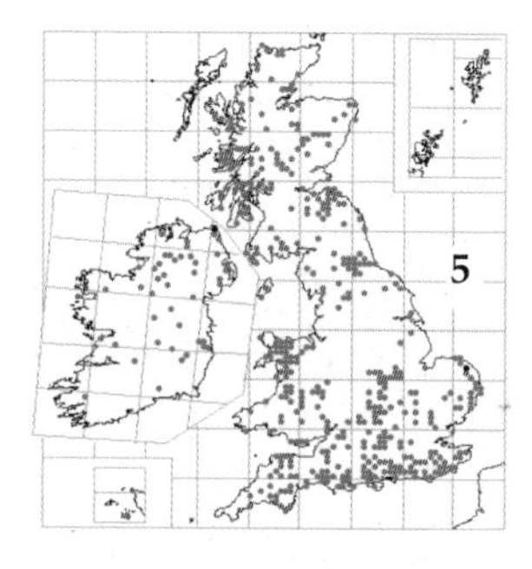

B. griseovirens x 6.

4. B. ocellata (B. verruculosa) Thallus warm greenish grey to yellowish grey, areolate, with a distinct fimbriate, black prothallus. Often forming mosaics, each thallus up to 2 cm across. Medulla I–. Apothecia immersed when young, up to 0.5 mm diam. Discs black sometimes with a thin, crenulate margin, often only one in each areole giving a *Rinodina*-like appearance. Spores 1-septate, 11–20 x 7–10 µm.
C+ orange.
Habitat: Frequent. Found on smooth, well-lit siliceous rocks, gravestones, flints and shingle. Often growing with *B. aethalea* but with a more yellow-green, not grey, thallus. These are pioneer species on walls and memorials.

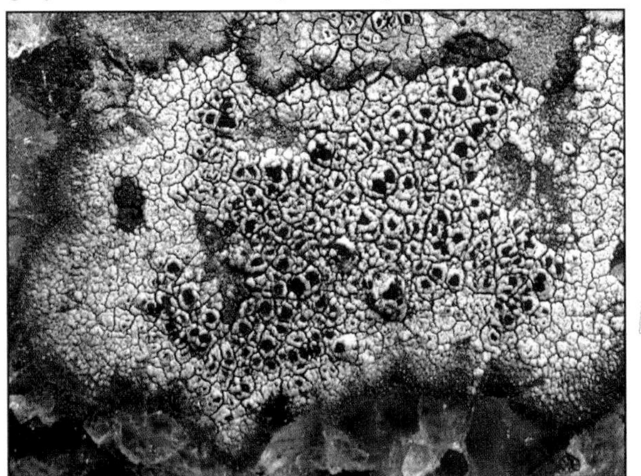

B. ocellata x 6.

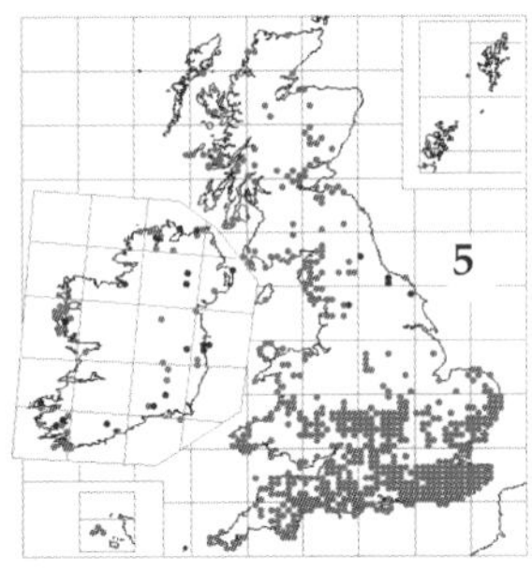

5. B. saxorum Thallus warm grey and cracked which, with its ± sessile apothecia, make it resemble a *Rhizocarpon*. It is limited by a dark grey prothallus. Medulla I+ blue. Apothecia up to 1 mm diam with a flat disc and a distinct proper margin. Spores 1-septate, 10–18 x 5–10 µm.
P+ yellow, K+ yellow, C+ deep orange-red.
Habitat: Uncommon. On hard acid rocks and the flat tops of chest-tombs.

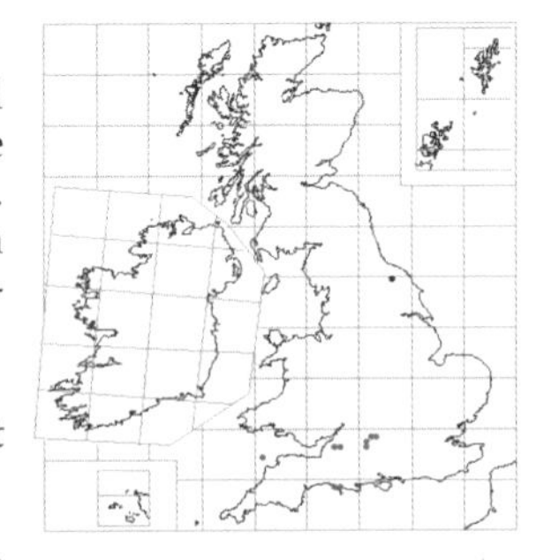

6. B. stellulata Thallus light grey, areolate on a broad radiating dark prothallus. Medulla I–. Apothecia up to 0.4 mm diam, between the areoles, immersed when young but becoming more prominent. Discs black. Spores 1-septate, 8–15 x 5–8 µm, slightly constricted at the septum.
K+y, P+y (*B. aethalea* usually K+ yellow turning red).
Habitat: Common on well-lit siliceous rocks, mainly in maritime areas, often with *B. ocellata*. The map probably shows over-recording due to confusion with *B. aethalea*.

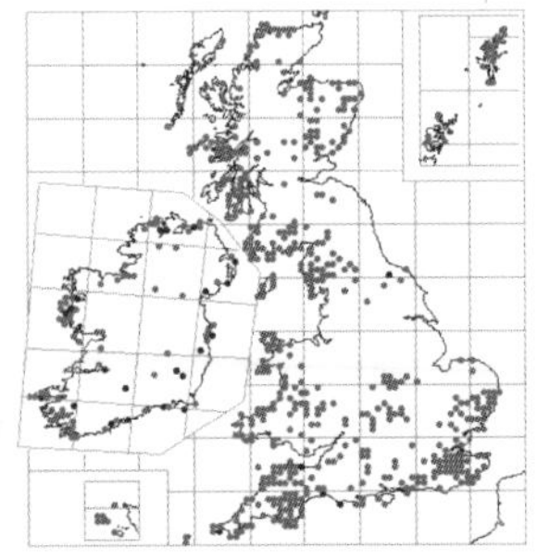

1. B. subdisciformis Thallus white to light grey, usually limited by a black prothallus. Medulla I–. Apothecia sessile, up to 1.5 mm diam, with a distinct, often pruinose and slightly contorted, proper margin. Spores 1-septate, 10–20 x 5–10 µm. Pycnidia numerous. Conidia 6–10 x 1 µm.
K+ yellow turning red, P+ yellow.
Habitat: Locally common in the west on acid maritime rocks.

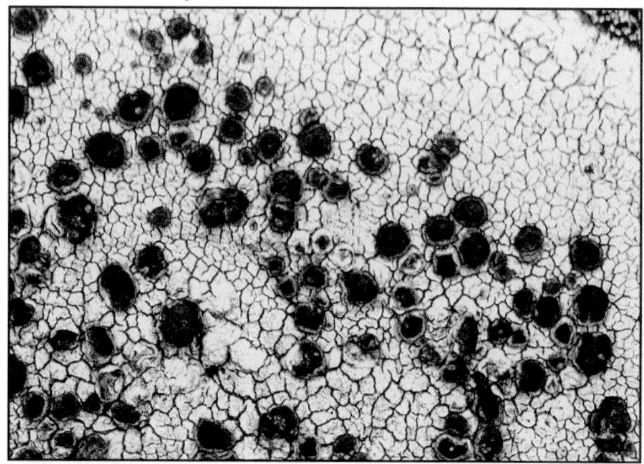

B. subdisciformis x6.

CALICIUM ('wine-cup'). **Thallus** crustose, thin or granular. **Photobiont** *Trebouxia*. **Apothecia** stalked like small pins or, rarely, sessile. **Ascus** disintegrates to leave a powdery black spore mass (a mazaedium). **Spores** 1-septate, brown. **Pycnidia** usually sessile, globose. **Conidia** simple, colourless.

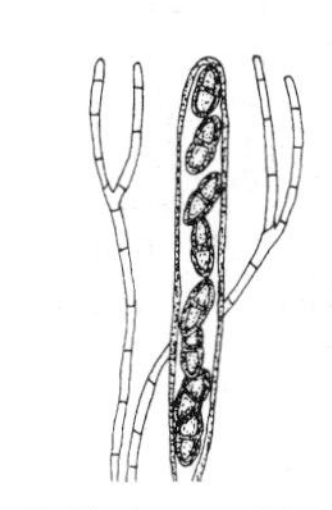

C abietinum x 400.

1.	Thallus thick, green, granular	**4. C. viride**
–	Thallus thin, or almost absent, greyish	2
2.	Capitulum black or pale grey, open	3
–	Capitulum light to dark brown, almost globose	**3. C. salicinum**
3.	Spore mass usually slightly pruinose, exciple white	**2. C. glaucellum**
–	Spore mass not pruinose, exciple not white	**1. C. abietinum**

C. abietinum

C. glaucellum

C. salicinum

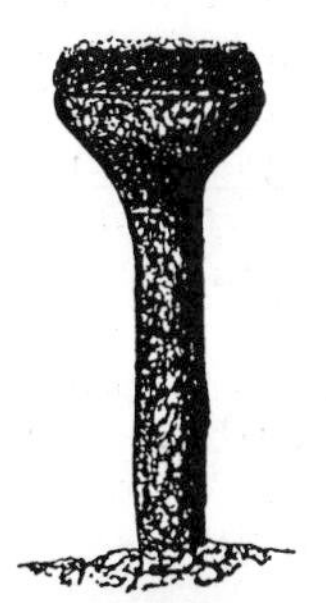

C. viride

1. Calicium abietinum Thallus thin, light grey, often immersed and sometimes scarcely apparent. Apothecia are often crowded over the thallus and are borne on dark brown to black stalks up to 1 mm high and 0.1 mm wide. Apothecia are black, not pruinose, about 0.2–0.3 mm wide. Spores warted, 12–15 x 5–7 µm.
Spot reactions: negative.
Habitat: Common on decorticated wood and old trees, particularly conifers. Often old tree stumps. The commonest species with a greyish thallus in lowland Britain (the map only shows confirmed records).

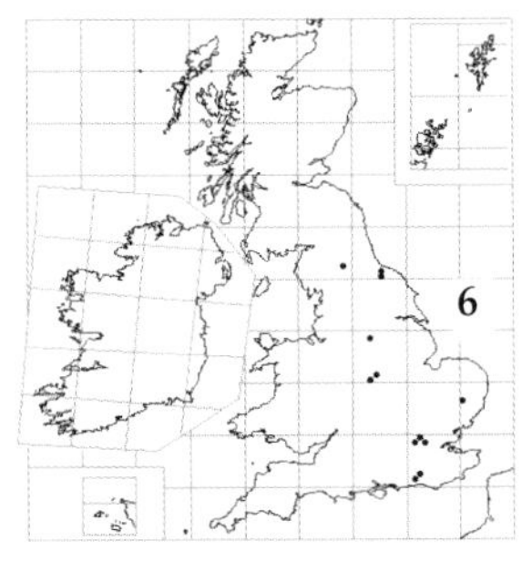

2. C. glaucellum Very similar in appearance to the previous species but the apothecia are black, rather stouter and have a white pruinose margin, often faintly pruinose on the lower side of the head. Spores white-ridged, 9–13 x 5–7 µm. Gobose pycnidia are common.
K± yellow.
Habitat: Uncommon. Found in similar habitats to *C. abietinum* and probably over-recorded in error for that species (beware the maps for these two species).

C. glaucellum x 12.

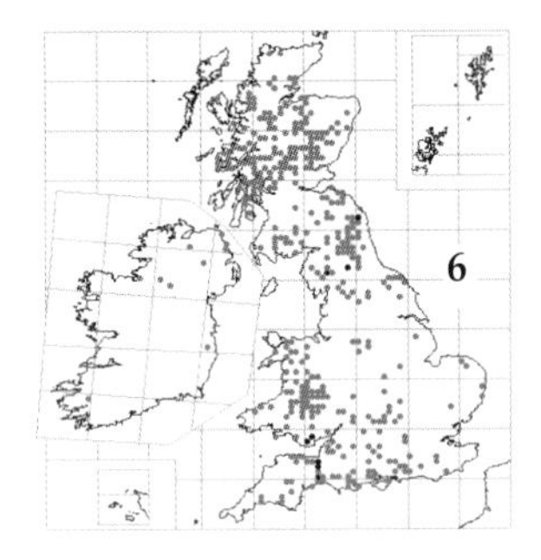

3. C. salicinum Thallus pale grey, sometimes scarcely apparent. Apothecia 0.2–0.5 mm wide, brown-pruinose (K+ purple) on lower suface and with a black spore mass. Stalk 0.4–1.2 mm high. Spores spirally ridged, 8–11 x 4–5 µm.
Spot reactions: negative or K+ orange, P+ orange.
Habitat: Frequent on dry, decorticated wood and old bark.

C. salicinum x 12.

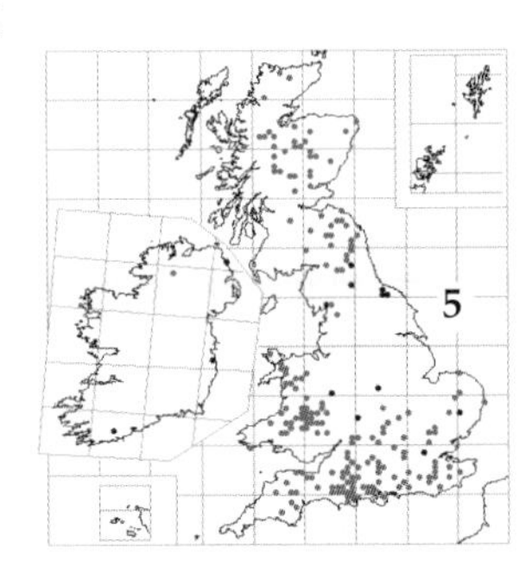

4. C. viride Thallus bright emerald green to sulphurous yellow-green, becoming browner when dry, granular. Frequently sterile. Apothecia 0.2–0.6 mm wide, black, not pruinose, stalks 1–2 mm high. Cups often with a reddish brown pruina. Spore surface cracked, 11–14 x 4–5 µm. The thallus is usually thicker, and it has clavate asci, rather than the cylindrical asci of *C. salicinum.*
Spot reactions: negative, UV+ bright orange.
Habitat: Common on the dry bark of trees, particularly oak and conifers, tolerant of moderate pollution.

C. *viride* x 12.

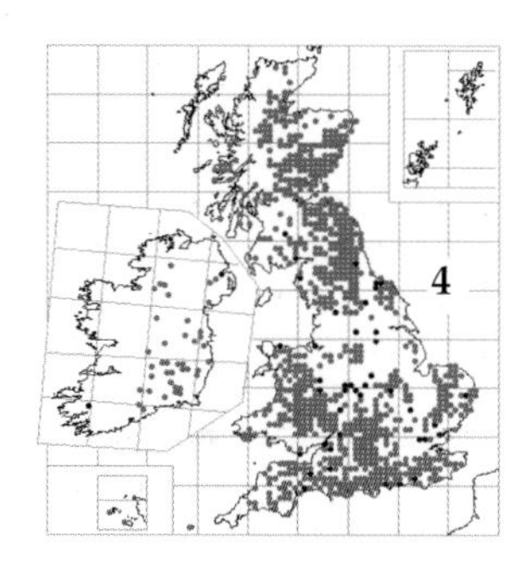

CALOPLACA ('beautiful patches'). A member of the family *Teloschistaceae* and like the other genera (which include *Leproplaca, Xanthoria* and *Teloschistes*) most are K+ crimson, at least in part. **Thallus** more or less placodioid (called sect. *Gasparrinia*) or crustose. **Photobiont** trebouxioid. **Soredia** and **isidia** are present in some species. **Apothecia** lecanorine or lecideine. **Ascus** 8-spored in the species described, *Teloschistes*-type with a K/I blue outer layer to the ascus tip. **Spores** colourless, polarilocular. Spore shape is useful for identification. Many species have a yellow or orange thallus, or at least the apothecia are orange or red, these contain physcion (parietin) which produces the K+ crimson reaction. These species are often found on nutrient-rich sites and it has been suggested the orange colour acts as a filter to protect the algae from excessive light as the species are mainly found in exposed and sunny situations.

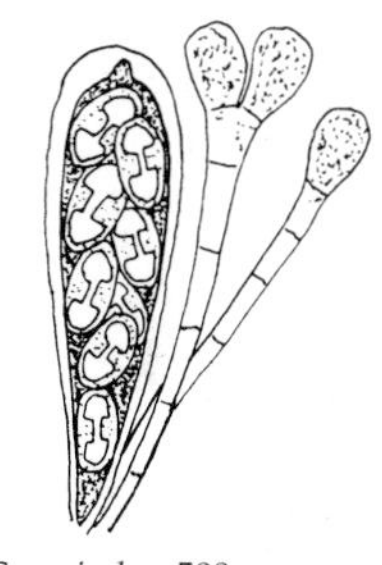

C. saxicola x 500.

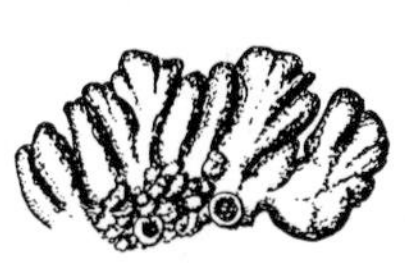

C. saxicola
Yellow to yellow-brown
Lobes convex, short, palmate
pruinose

C. aurantia
Golden creamy yellow
Lobes flat, palmate
not pruinose

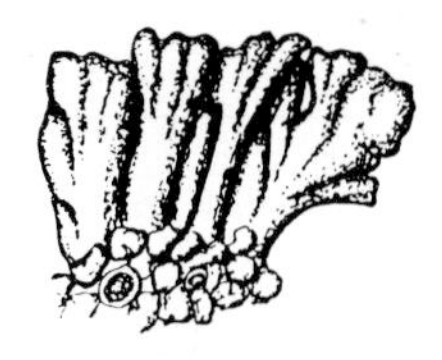

C. flavescens
Bright orange
Lobes narrowly convex, long
slightly palmate, may be pruinose

Caloplaca spore shapes. Note that there is often a variation of spore shape within a species

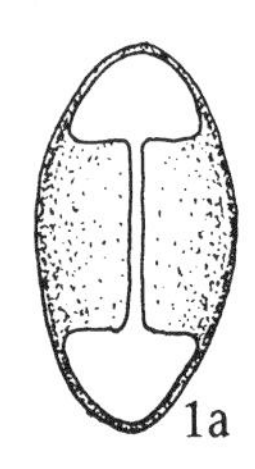

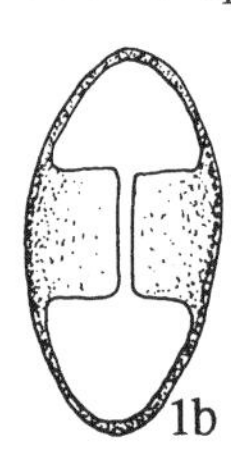

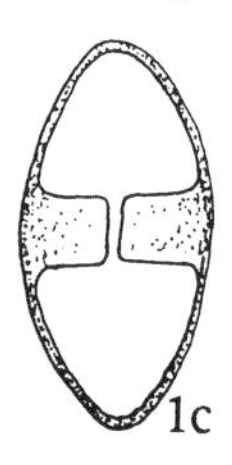

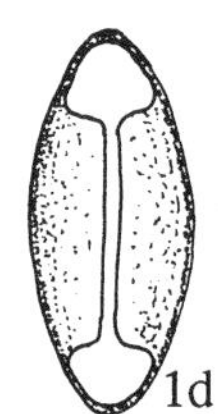

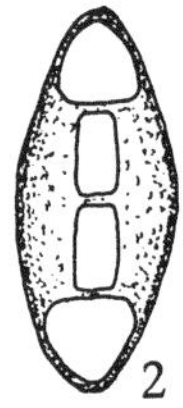

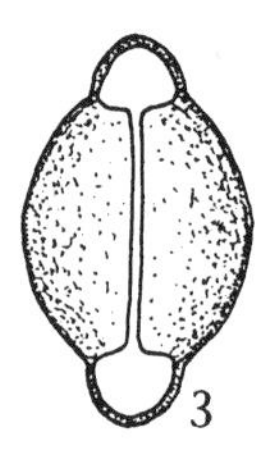

1.	Thallus grey or white. K– (apothecia may be K+ crimson)	2
–	Thallus yellow or orange, K+ crimson	12
2.	Discs rust-red	3
–	Discs yellow to deep orange or black	4
3.	Apothecia becoming translucent and greener when wet	**3. C. ceracea**
–	Apothecia unchanged on wetting	**10. C. crenularia**
4.	On bark or wood (see also 15. *C. holocarpa*)	5
–	On rock	6
5.	Apothecia up to 0.3 mm, often crowded, yellow with pale to yellow margins	**5. C. cerinella**
–	Apothecia up to 2 mm, usually scattered, orange-yellow with a grey margin	**4. C. cerina**
6.	Disc of apothecia black, often pruinose	7
–	Disc of apothecia yellow or orange to orange-red	9
7.	Thallus innate or a thin grey scurfy film. Apothecia in pits	**1. C. alociza**
–	Thallus thick, smooth to areolate. Apothecia not in pits	8
8.	Apothecia up to 0.5 mm, immersed to plane	**6. C. chalybaea**
–	Apothecia over 0.5 mm, sessile	**25. C. variabilis**
9.	Apothecia bright orange-yellow, not soridiate or isidiate	**16. C. lactea**
–	Apothecia deep orange to orange-brown and/or sorediate or isidiate	10
10.	Thallus usually thick, sorediate or isidiate	11
–	Thallus innate, thin, grey to black, not isidiate or sorediate	**15. C. holocarpa**

11. Thallus sorediate, slightly placodioid **23. C. teicholyta**
– Thallus finely isidiate, not placodioid **7. C. chlorina**

12. Thallus not lobate 13
– Thallus lobate, at least at the margin 19

13a Prothallus pale grey; apothecia convex; large isolated thalli **14. C. flavovirescens**
13b Prothallus pale or absent, apothecia flat, isolated thalli **10a. C. crenulatella**
13c Prothallus absent or dark and/or apothecia flat, may be mosaic-forming 14

14. On maritime rocks; not isidiate; yellow to light orange 15
– Not exclusively on maritime rocks; isidiate and/or deep orange 16

15. With coralloid isidia, apothecia orange-yellow **17. C. littorea**
– Lacking isidia, apothecia orange-red **18. C. marina**

16. Thallus yellow to golden, thin, or yellow-orange and granular 17
– Thallus lime-yellow to greenish-yellow, granular, sorediate **9. C. citrina**

17. Thallus thick, granular-areolate, apothecia over 0.5 mm 18
– Thallus very thin, apothecia less than 0.5 mm **20. C. ochracea**

18. Thallus finely rimose-areolate; black prothallus **11. C. dalmatica**
– Thallus of coarse, convex areoles; no black prothallus **21. C. ruderum**

19. Thallus with isidia or soralia, rarely fertile 20
– Thallus lacking isidia or soralia, usually fertile 23

20. Thallus isidiate 21
– Thallus sorediate 22

21. Isidia dense and coralloid, a crust with only poorly defined lobes **17. C. littorea**
– Isidia scattered and coarse, neatly lobate **26. C. verruculifera**

22. Lobes short and close. Soralia concolorous: open habitats **12. C. decipiens**
– Lobes long, narrow; soralia paler yellow; on shaded rocks **8. C. cirrochroa**

23. Thallus of squamules up to 2 mm **19. C. microthallina**
– Thallus larger 24

24. Thallus yellow to creamy orange, lobes very flattened **2. C. aurantia**
– Thallus yellow to deep orange, lobes obscure and/or convex 25

25. Lobes obscure. Thallus of irregular swollen areoles; mainly yellow. Found mainly on south-facing church walls in the east. **21. C. ruderum**
– Thallus lobate and/or orange, not of swollen areoles 26

26. Thallus yellow to yellow-brown, often pruinose **22. C. saxicola**
– Thallus orange 27

27. Thallus with long narrow lobes, often pruinose **13. C. flavescens**
– Strictly maritime at high water mark (HWM) or orange zone not pruinose 28

28. Forming a regular rosette, lobes long and well defined **24. C. thallincola**
– Forming diffuse patches, lobes irregular or scattered lobules, at or above HWM **18. C. marina**

1. Caloplaca alociza Thallus immersed or a thin, grey, scurfy film. Prothallus usually present, black. Apothecia about 0.5 mm, in shallow pits, the disc level with substratum surface or slightly sessile. Disc black, often bluish pruinose with a paler thalline margin which becomes excluded. Spores type 1c, 15–18 x 7–8 µm.
Thallus and apothecia: K–. Epithecium: K+ violet.
Habitat: An overlooked species (mistaken for *Sarcogyne regularis*) on hard, exposed limestone; mainly near the coast.

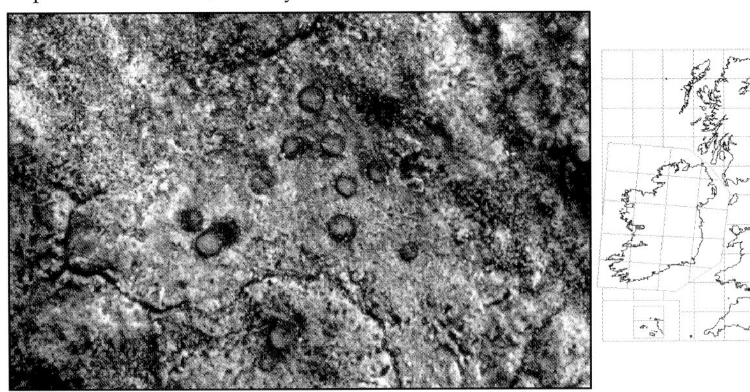

C. alociza x 8.

2. C. aurantia Thallus pale egg- to golden yellow, sometimes darker in the centre. Lobes adpressed, long, distinctly flat, palmate and usually matt. The orange colour looks creamy as if mixed with white and is more coloured towards the lobe tips. The centre of the thallus is rimose-areolate and darker. Apothecia often numerous, large (up to 1.5 mm diam), flat to slightly convex, disc orange-brown with a slightly lighter margin. Spores lemon-shaped, type 3, 10–13 x 8–10 µm.
Thallus and apothecia: K+ crimson.
Habitat: Common on nutrient-enriched, very well-lit, hard, calcareous rocks, especially erratics, also frequent on tombstones. More common in the South.

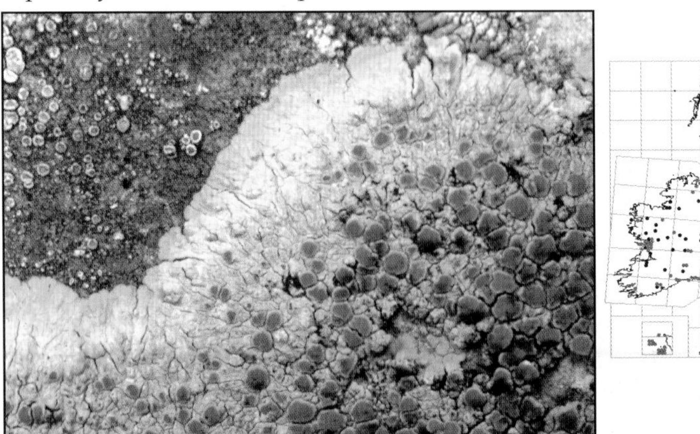

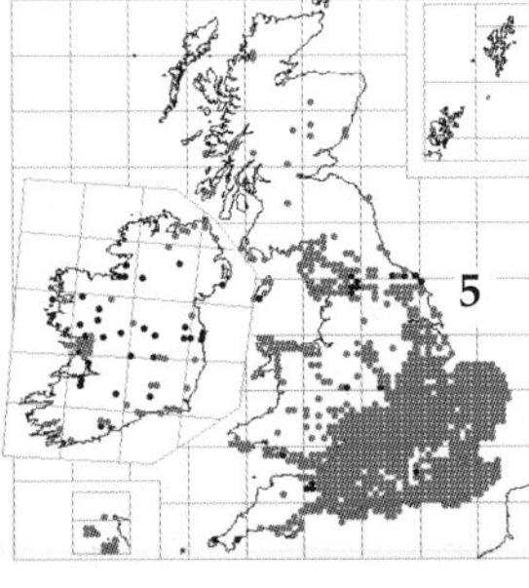

C. aurantia x 3.

3. C. ceracea (C. caesiorufa) Thallus grey with pale areas, granular or areolate. Apothecia chestnut to rust-brown when dry, with a paler, matt orange margin which is often almost white on the under-surface. Disc plane, becoming convex, the disc and margin often pruinose. Spores type 1b, 13–15 x 7–9 µm. Differs from *C. crenularia* as *C. ceracea* has apothecia that are brighter orange and which become greener on wetting (due to algal layer under the hypothecium) and also by the paler, matt margins.
Disc: K+ crimson.
Habitat: Common on siliceous maritime rocks, very rare inland.

4. C. cerina Thallus light grey, very thin to almost areolate. Apothecia large (up to 2 mm diam), sessile, crowded, with a bright orange-yellow roughened disc and a thick grey, often flexuose, thalline margin. Spores type 1b, 12–15 x 8–10 µm.
Disc: K+ crimson.
Habitat: Common on basic bark of deciduous trees of unpolluted areas, becoming rarer.

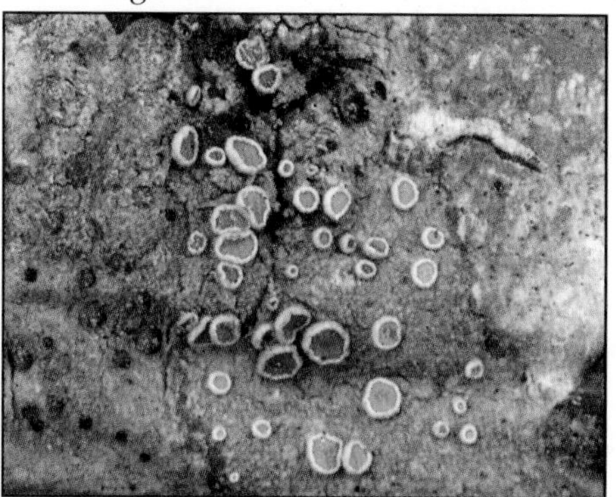

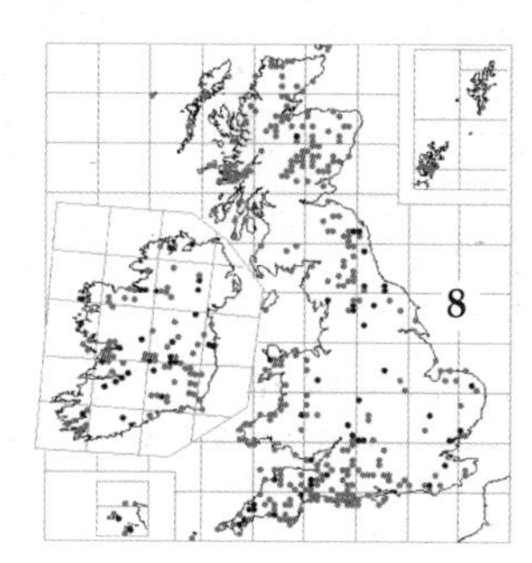

C. cerina x 4.

5. C. cerinella Thallus grey to white but frequently immersed. Apothecia only about 0.3 mm wide, usually in densely packed clusters. Disc yellow to orange with a paler margin. Ascus 12- to 16-spored. Spores type 1b or 1c, 10–13 x 6–7 µm.
Apothecia: K+ crimson.
Habitat: Fairly common on twigs and bark especially elder.

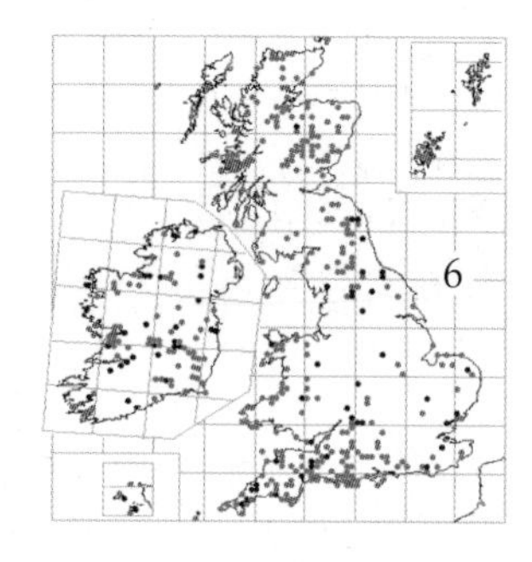

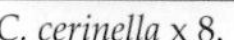
C. cerinella x 8.

6. C. chalybaea Thallus brown-grey to blue-grey, rimose to areolate with wide cracking and a black prothallus. Apothecia up to 0.5 mm, immersed, concave becoming plane, one or more per areole. Disc black and usually pale bluish pruinose. Spores type 1b, 10–15 x 6–8 µm. Differs from *Aspicilia calcarea* which has simple spores. It also resembles *C. variabilis* which is darker grey with sessile, not immersed, apothecia and a less well developed thallus.
Thallus: K– rarely K+ pale violet. Epithecium: K+ violet.
Habitat: On nutrient-enriched, hard calcareous rocks and especially on the flat tops of tombstones.

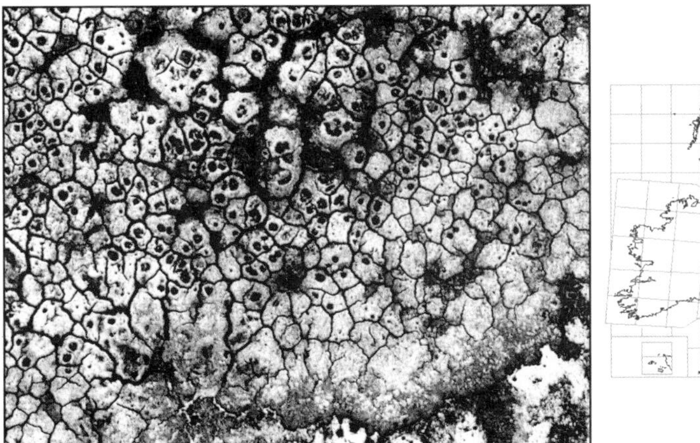

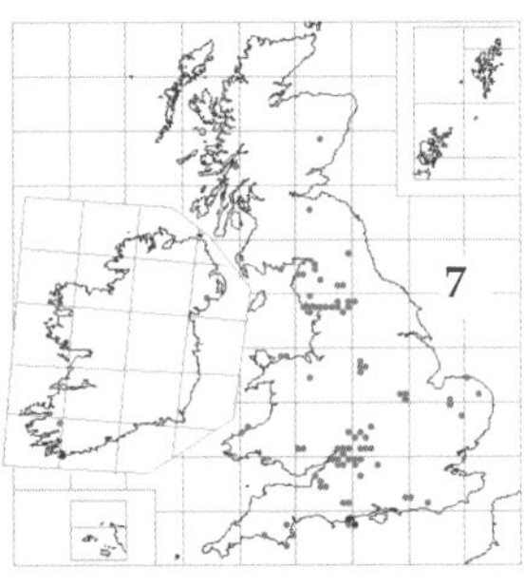

C. chalybaea x 5.

7. C. chlorina (C. isidiigera). Thallus dark bluish grey, cracked to areolate, often densely covered in small, irregular, granular isidia. These gives the surface a rough appearance. Apothecia are rare, immersed amongst the granules, about 1 mm diam. The disc is yellow to orange with a thick irregular and often granular thalline margin. Spores type 1c, 10–15 x 5–7 µm.
Thallus and isidia: K+ pale violet or K–. Disc: K+ crimson.
Habitat: Common on flat tops of limestone memorials and shaded rocks, frequently near water or close to the ground. Rarely on basic bark.

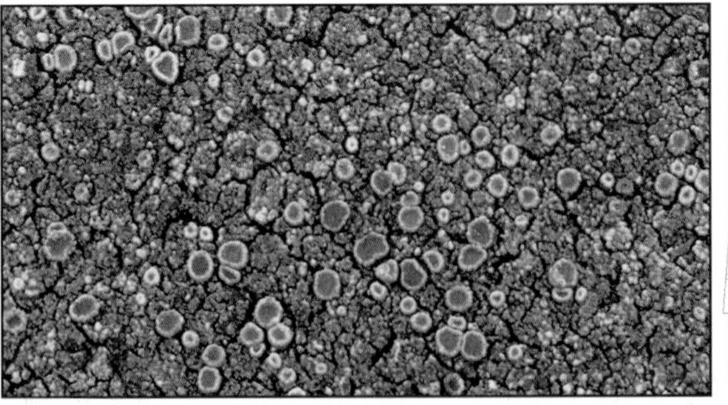

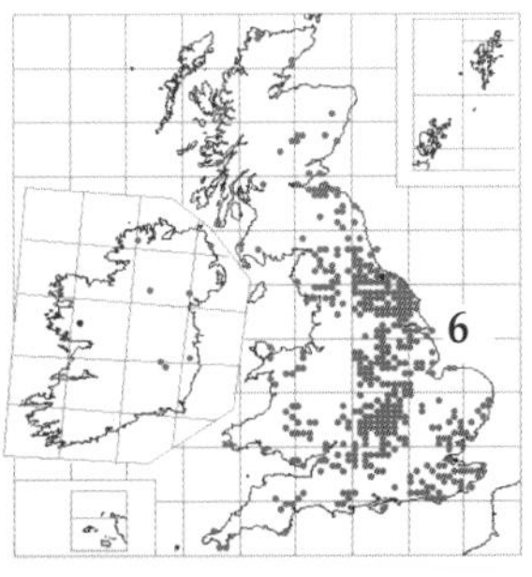

C. chlorina x 8.

8. C. cirrochroa Thallus bright yellow-orange or a dull orange, with long narrow (up to 0.5 mm wide), radiating, separated, convex lobes. Lobe tips sometimes pruinose. The centre of the thallus consists of contorted areolae but this is often missing in mature specimens. Very distinctive when the bright

lemon-yellow, convex soralia are present on the lobes. Seldom fertile but apothecia are small (up to 0.5 mm diam), orange-yellow. Spores type 1c, 10-16 x 4–6 µm.
Thallus: K+crimson.
Habitat: A rather local species of dry, shaded, especially vertical, hard, highly calcareous rock.

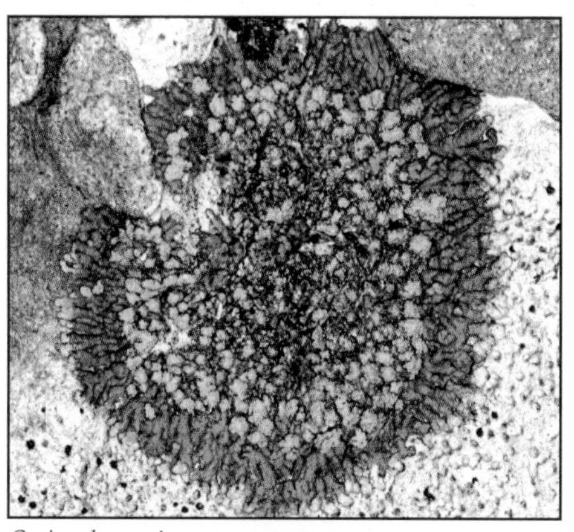

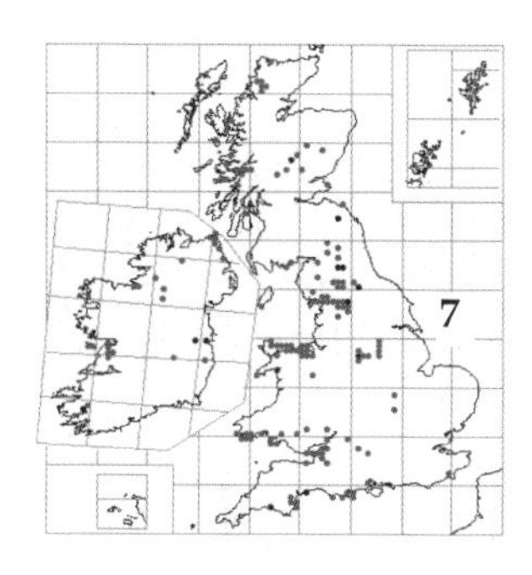

C. cirrochroa x 4.

9. C. citrina Thallus lime-yellow to greenish yellow or sometimes bright orange. Consisting of minute granules that become sorediate. Frequently sterile. Apothecia up to 1 mm diam, yellow-orange often having yellow granules and a thick paler margin. Spores type 1b, 10–15 x 5–6 µm.
K+ crimson.
Habitat: Very common on calcareous substrates, concrete and walls, occasionally on basic bark. It may be separated from *Candelariella* sp. by the K+ crimson reaction and from *Leproplaca* by its granular, not leprose, thallus.

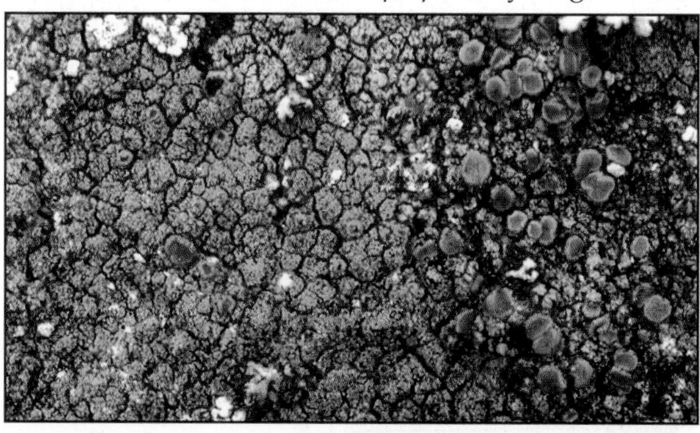

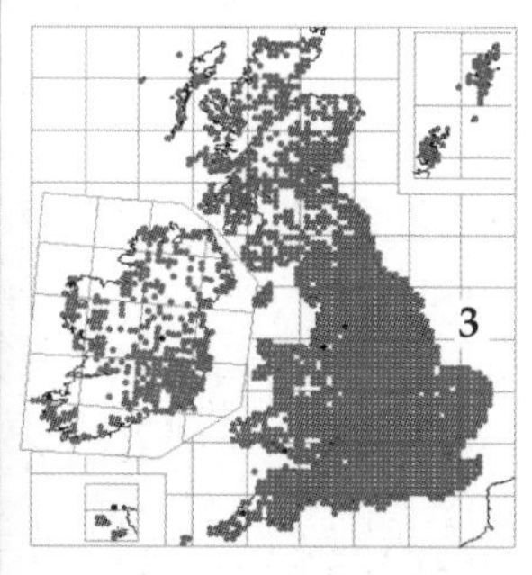

C. citrina x 6.

10. C. crenularia (C. ferruginea, C. festiva) Similar to *C. ceracea* being grey, cracked to areolate but thallus may be evanescent. Apothecia to 1 mm diam, rust-red. Often present only as red pimples in polluted sites. Disc roughened, plane, becoming convex. Colour does not become greener with wetting (see *C. ceracea*, there is no algal layer under the hypothecium). The margins are glossy even when dry and only slightly paler. Spores type 1b, 12–14 x 6–8 µm.
Apothecia: K+ crimson.

Habitat: Common on siliceous rocks, in both shaded and damp, or well-lit sites in inland as well as maritime situations. Mainly in the West and North. A similar looking species on trees is the much rarer **C. ferruginea.**

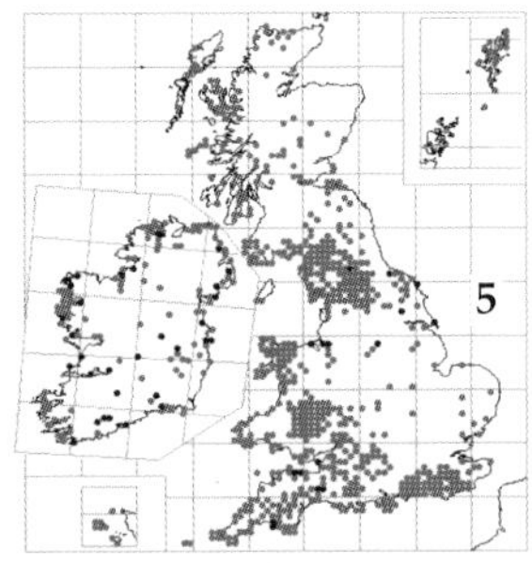

C. crenularia x 5.

10a. C. crenulatella Thallus greenish buff, deeply cracked, with the appearance at a distance of *Protoblastinia rupestris.* Apothecia common up to 0.8 mm diam and formed almost to the edge of the thallus. The thick yellow margin and disc darken with age. Disc flat to slightly convex. Spores 14–19 x 6–10 µm with a narrow septum 2–3.5 µm.
Apothecia: K+ crimson.
Habitat: Recently reported from many sites on old concrete and mortar, mainly near the ground.

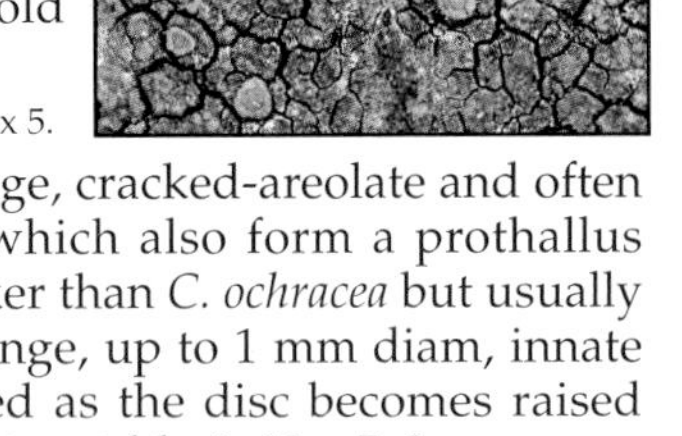

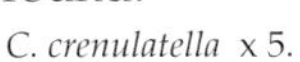

C. crenulatella x 5.

11. C. dalmatica Thallus pale yellow to dirty orange, cracked-areolate and often pruinose, intersected by thin, dark grey lines which also form a prothallus (rarely pale) and often forming mosaics. It is thicker than *C. ochracea* but usually thinner than *C. ruderum.* Apothecia yellow to orange, up to 1 mm diam, innate when young but with the margin being excluded as the disc becomes raised and convex. Spores type 1c but the septum varies in width, 9–13 x 5–9 µm.
K+ crimson.
Habitat: Frequent in the South and SouthWest on hard calcareous rocks and walls or on more acid substrata in the washout below mortar. Often found on the south walls of churches, usually on stonework over 300 years old.

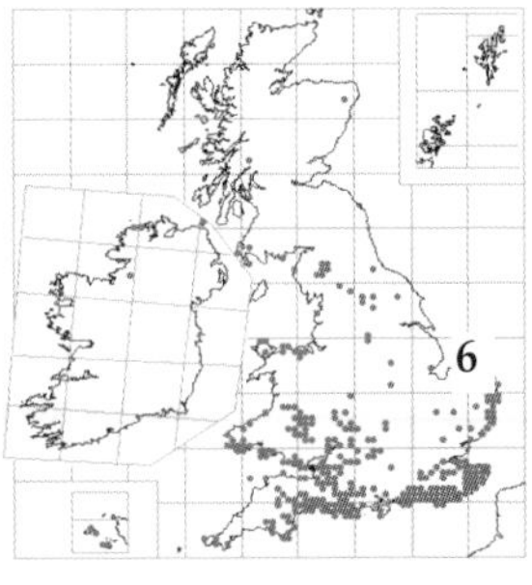

C. dalmatica x 4.

12. C. decipiens Thallus placodioid, small (up to about 3 cm across), light yellow to tawny orange, darker in the centre. Lobes often indistinct, irregular, long, convex, pruinose with palmate, crenulate tips. Yellow, granular soredia are found on the tips of the inner lobes and may cover the centre of the thallus. Seldom fertile, apothecia up to 1 mm diam. Spores type 1c, 10–15 x 5–9 µm.
K+ crimson.
Habitat. Frequent on mortar, tombstones and asbestos-cement, more rarely on nutrient-enriched hard limestone, mainly in the East.

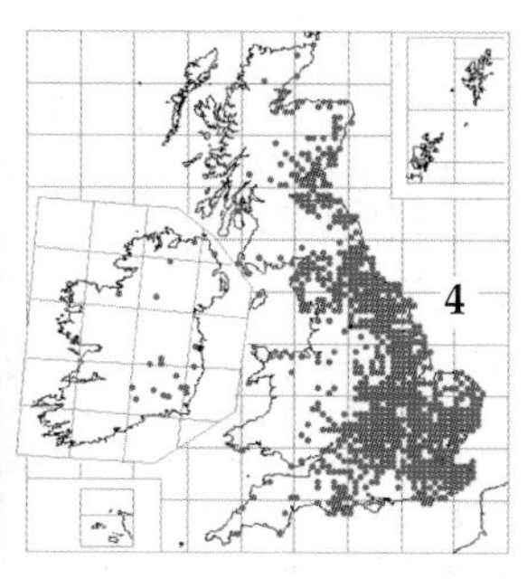

C. decipiens x 3.

13. C. flavescens (C. heppiana) Thallus placodioid, orange, often with a whitish zone behind the apices. Lobes long, narrow, smooth, convex, wider at the apices, very rarely slightly pruinose, crenulate. The centre of the thallus may be almost areolate but it often falls out leaving the thallus in the form of an arc. Apothecia usually more than 4 mm from margin of thallus, up to 1.5 mm diam, numerous, orange with paler margins, flat or only slightly convex. Spores lemon-shaped, type 3, 12–15 x 8–10 µm.
K+ crimson.
Habitat: Very common on hard calcareous rocks, asbestos-cement and tombstones, more rarely on brick. It is probably the commonest lobate *Caloplaca* in south-east England.

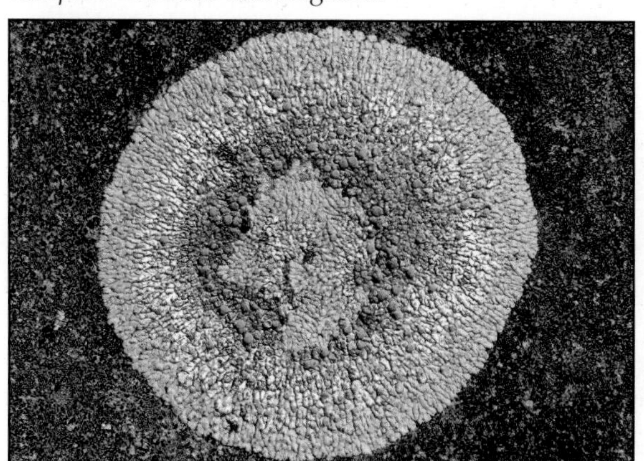

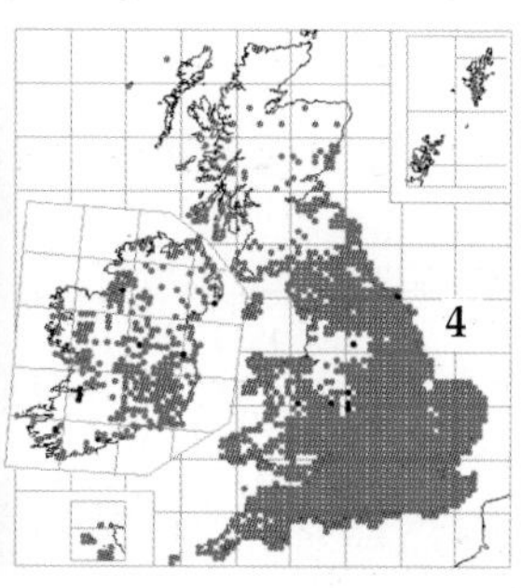

C. flavescens x 3.

14. C. flavovirescens Thallus large (to 15 cm wide), of angular areoles, greenish orange with lighter patches, surrounded by a pale prothallus. Apothecia frequent, up to 1 mm diam, brownish orange with convex discs and a paler margin. Spores type 1b, 15–20 x 5–10 µm.
K+ crimson.
Habitat: Frequent on rather calcareous rocks and on more acid rocks where affected by basic downwash. Mainly an upland and coastal species. Often occurring as isolated specimens. A very similar rare species, **C. flavorubescens**, is found on isolated trees especially ash in the NorthWest.

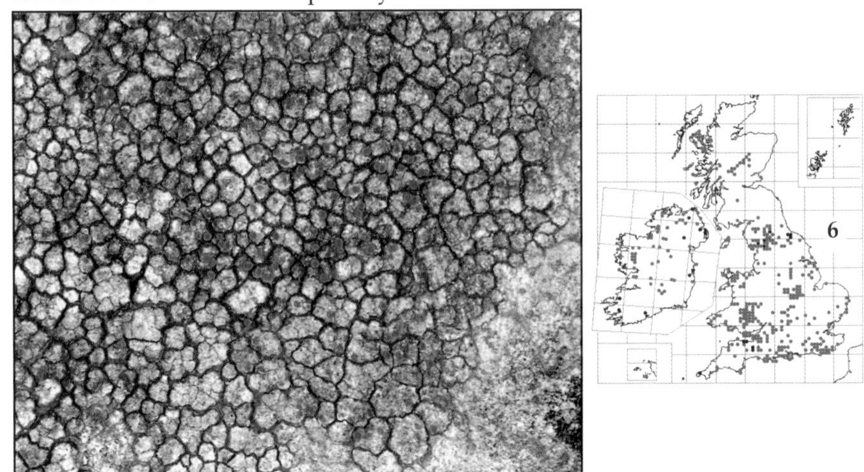

C. flavovirescens x 5.

15. C. holocarpa Thallus thin grey to black (especially in urban situations), often not visible. Apothecia up to 0.4 mm wide, abundant and often crowded, orange with a slightly paler and glossy margin which becomes excluded, and convex disc. Spores type 1c, 10–15 x 5–10 µm. In the field it resembles *Protoblastenia rupestris* (for differences see that species).
Apothecia: K+ crimson.
Habitat: Common on nutrient-enriched, well-lit, calcareous stone and cement, occasionally found on many other substrata, especially on wood in the North.

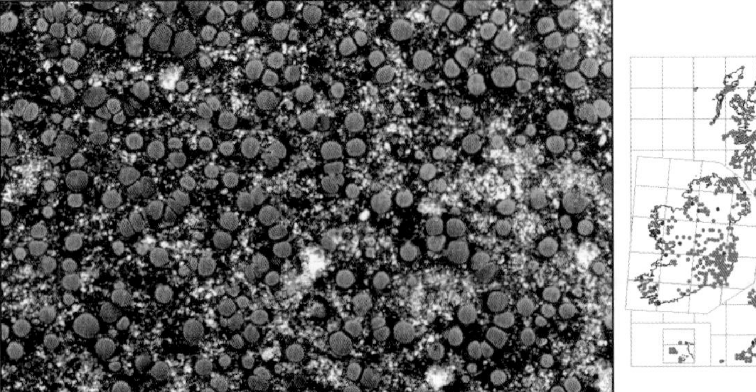

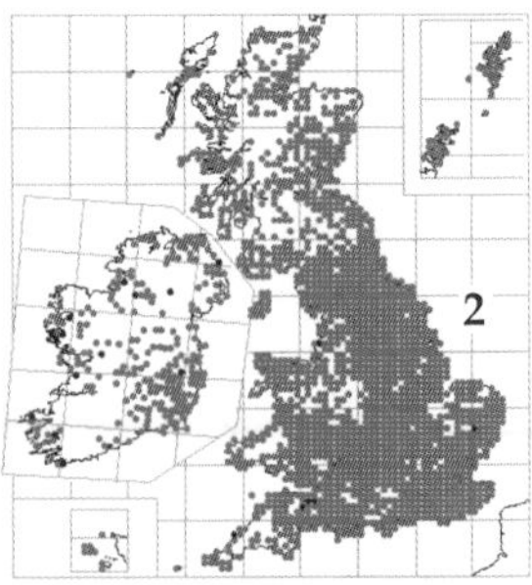

C. holocarpa x 7.

16. C. lactea Thallus white, thin or immersed. Apothecia to 0.5 mm diam, plane or concave when young, sometimes forming shallow pits in the substratum. Disc bright orange-yellow with a swollen margin which may become obscured as the apothecium matures. The apothecia are paler and look translucent when wet with deeply sunken discs which never become as convex as in *C. holocarpa*. Spores type 1c with a very thin septum.
Apothecia: K+ crimson.
Habitat: Uncommon, on hard calcareous rocks, shells and old tomb tops.

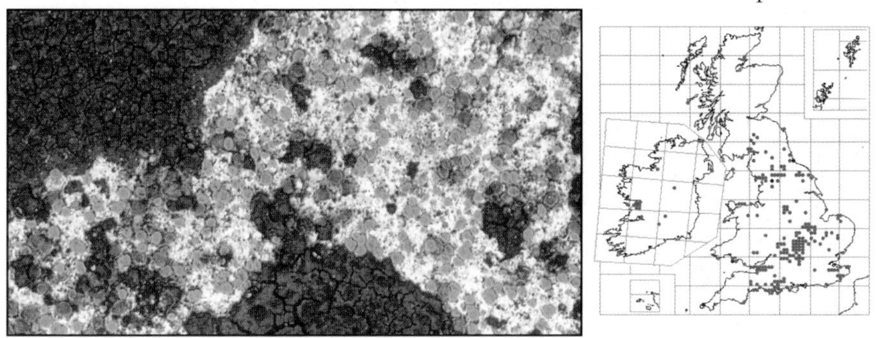

C. lactea x 4.

17. C. littorea Thallus deep orange-yellow. Often bordered with a pale orange prothallus. The thallus is essentially areolate but largely concealed by dense masses of dull orange globular to coralloid isidia which can give it a granular appearance. Often forming large patches on rocks. Apothecia rare, up to 1 mm wide, flat, orange-yellow and pruinose. Spores type 1c, 11–14 x 5–7 µm.
K+ crimson.
Habitat. A local south-western 'Mediterranean' species of dry recesses in hard, siliceous, maritime rock, well above high-water mark.

C. littorea x 4.

18. C. marina Thallus yellow orange to bright orange, consisting of small granules or a cracked areolate crust. When well-developed it has small convex irregular areoles often with a pale prothallus. Apothecia convex, deep reddish orange. Spores type 1b, 10–16 x 4–8 µm.
K+ crimson.

Habitat: Common on hard maritime rocks and cement from just above high-water mark. Often with *C. thallincola* (which is more common on sheltered shores), from which it may be separated by the darker colour and less clearly defined marginal lobes. **C. maritima** is similar but is never orange and has more convex, paler, wax-like areoles. It is found in sheltered aspects higher up the shore.

C. marina x 5. *C. maritima* x 8. *C. marina*

19. C. microthallina Thallus consisting of minute, yellow-orange, often scattered squamules up to about 1.5 mm long. Lacks a prothallus. Apothecia up to 1 mm wide, becoming convex and the margins crenulate. Spores type 1c, 12–15 x 6–8 µm. Thallus: K+ crimson.
Habitat: Common, usually on *Verrucaria maura* above high-water mark, especially along cracks and on ridges, more rarely directly on sheltered bare rocks.

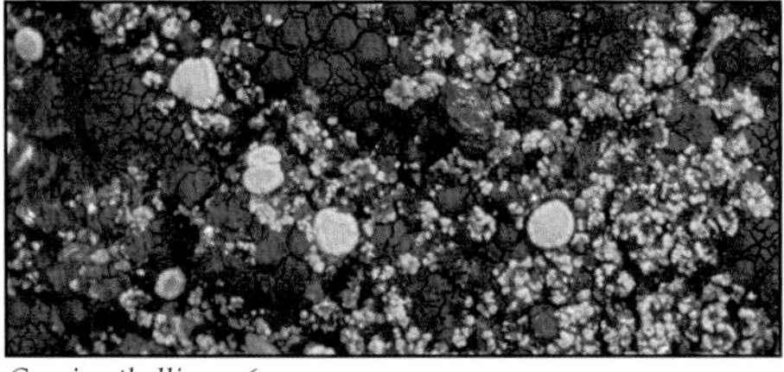

C. microthallina x 6.

20. C. ochracea Thallus matt, patchy light yellow to pale golden yellow with greyish areas, superficial, almost granular, felted, thin, scurfy to continuous, mosaic-forming. Apothecia up to 0.5 mm, dark orange-yellow, never convex as in *C. dalmatica*. Margin thick and slightly paler. Spores differ from other *Caloplaca* species in often becoming 4-loculate, type 2, 12–15 x 5–7 µm.
K+ crimson.
Habitat: Common on maritime and inland, well-lit, hard limestones.

C. ochracea x 6.

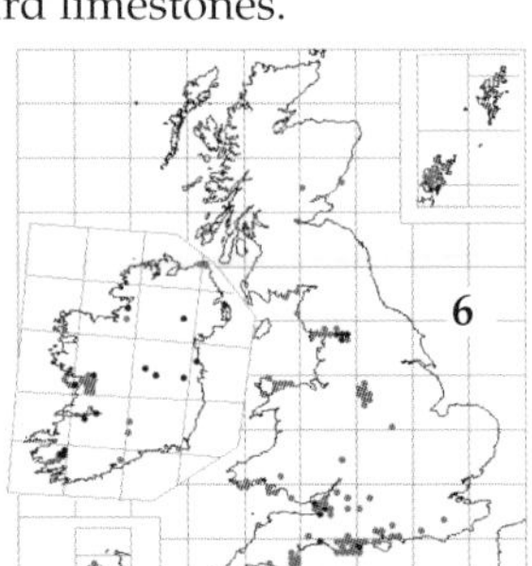

21. C. ruderum Superficially resembles a very well developed *C. citrina* but has a yellow, very pruinose thallus consisting of coarse, convex irregular granules. The apothecia are large (up to 1.5 mm diam), dirty orange with thick, pruinose margins. The disc is never convex. Spores variable but mainly type 1c, 10–15 x 6–8 µm.
K+ crimson.
Habitat: Locally frequent but overlooked. Confined to eastern England on well-lit, soft calcareous substrata especially the south-facing walls of churches.

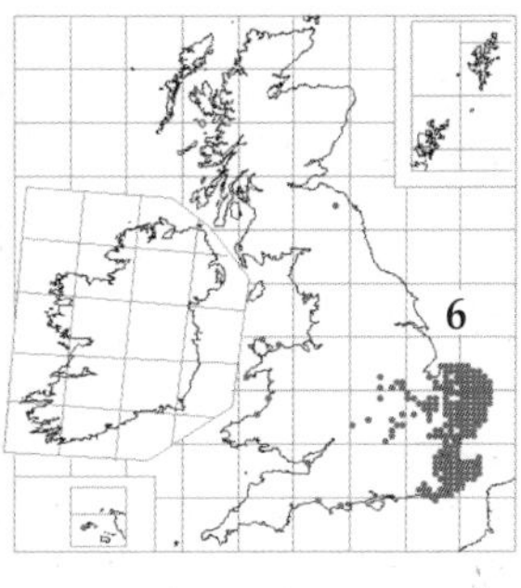

C. ruderum x 5.

22. C. saxicola Thallus placodioid, up to about 2 cm wide, yellow to brownish orange. Lobes palmate, convex, short (under 4 mm in length to the first apothecia), often very pruinose and appearing to turn under at the tips. The centre of the thallus is lobate, granulose, darker than the lobes and with crowded apothecia. Apothecia up to 1 mm diam, brown-orange, soon becoming convex, with paler margins. Spores type 1c, 9–16 x 4.5–7 µm. Thallus sometimes reduced to separate lobules.
K+ crimson.
Habitat: Common on hard calcareous rocks, walls and tombstones, rarely on nutrient-enriched siliceous rocks or bark. Often in dry, shaded situations. Particularly common in the West on buildings and walls.

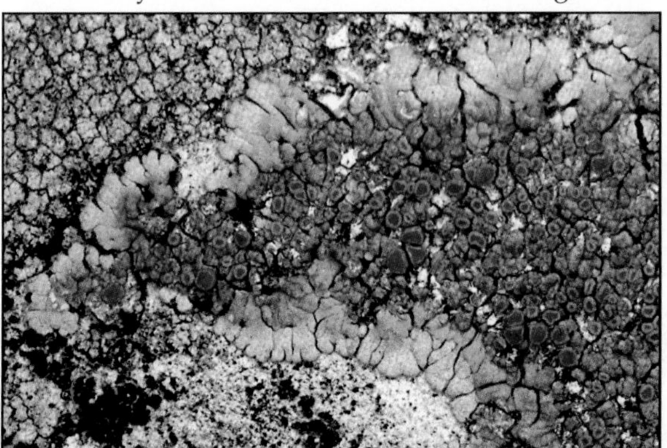

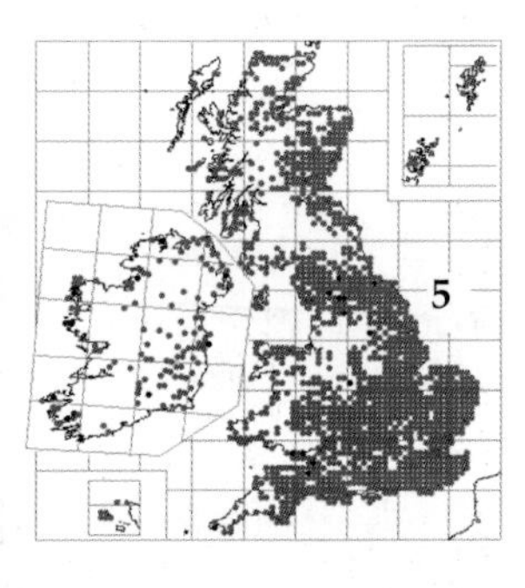

C. saxicola x 5.

23. C. teicholyta Thallus white to bluish grey, scurfy, becoming sorediate in the centre. Usually slightly placodioid with rounded lobe tips. Frequently infertile but when in fruit it has apothecia up to 0.75 mm diam, innate at first. Disc a distinctive orange-brown and sometimes orange-pruinose. Initially concave becoming flat. Spores type 1c, 14–18 x 8–10 µm.
Cortex: K–. Apothecia: K+ crimson.
Habitat: Common in the South East, mainly on calcareous substrates, especially tops of chest-tombs. Rarer in the rest of Britain but found on ironstone and calcareous coastal rocks.

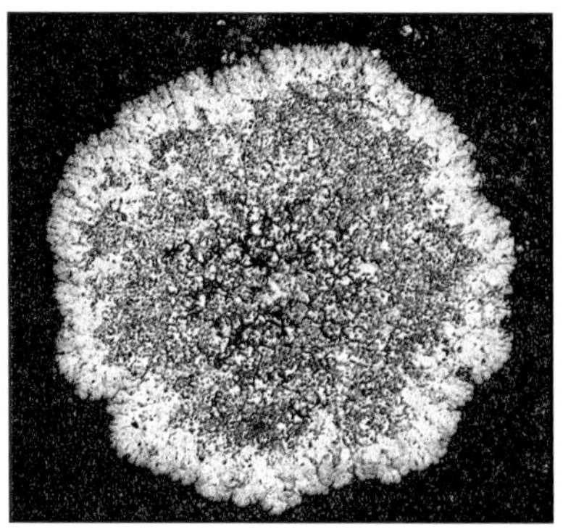

C. teicholyta x 3.

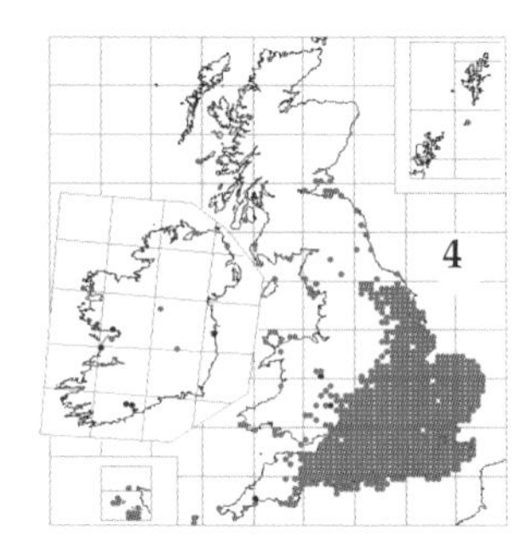

24. C. thallincola Thallus placodioid, usually forming neat rosettes, bright orange. Lobes long, convex but may be flattened towards the tips. Apothecia up to 1 mm diam, in the centre of the thallus, convex, orange with paler margins that often become excluded. Spores becoming lemon-shaped, type 3, 10–15 x 8–12 µm.
K+ crimson.
Habitat: Common on hard rocks above high-water mark, often growing on *Verrucaria maura*. Often with *C. marina* but prefers more sheltered situations. Similar in appearance to *C. flavescens*, but it has a different habitat, a brighter, cleaner colour, is not matt and the lobes extend more towards the centre of the thallus.

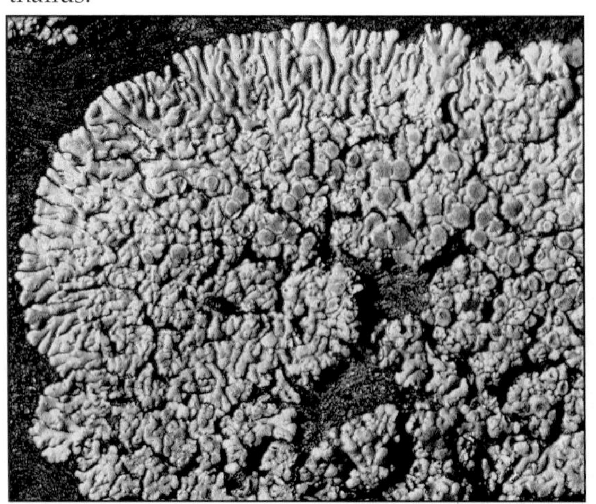

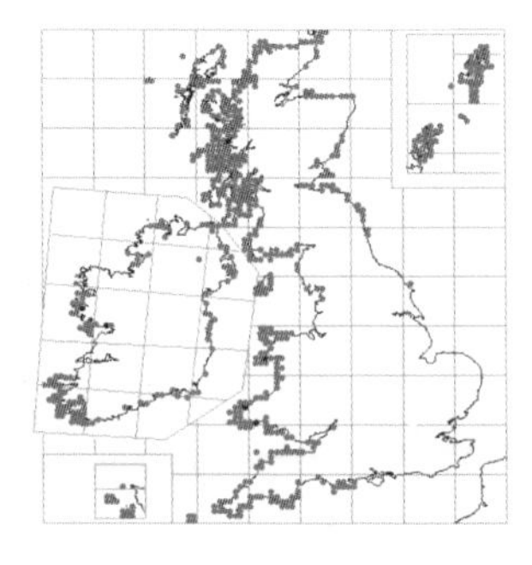

C. thallincola x 4.

25. C. variabilis Thallus thick, dark grey to dark grey-brown, cracked or areolate. The marginal area of the thallus is normally almost white and often surrounded by a dark prothallus. Apothecia usually present, sessile, 1 mm, with a black, bluish-white pruinose disc. The persistent grey-pruinose thalline margin gives it the appearance of a *Rinodina*. Spores type 1c, 14–18 x 7–9 µm.
Thallus and apothecia: sometimes K+ pale violet. Epithecium: K+ violet.
Habitat: Frequent, especially in the Midlands, on nutrient-enriched, hard calcareous rocks and the tops of walls and chest-tombs.

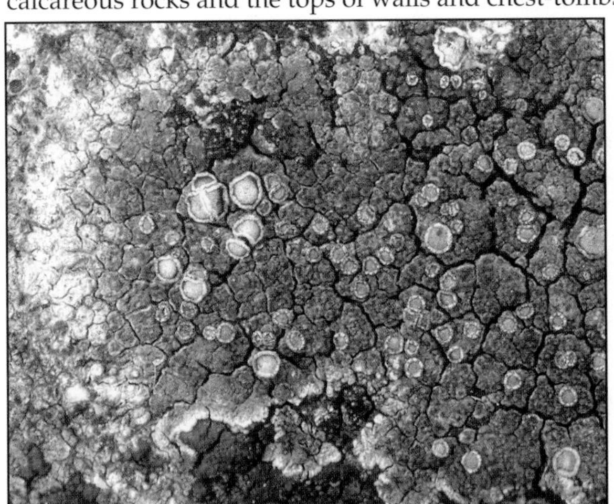

C. *variabilis* x 3.

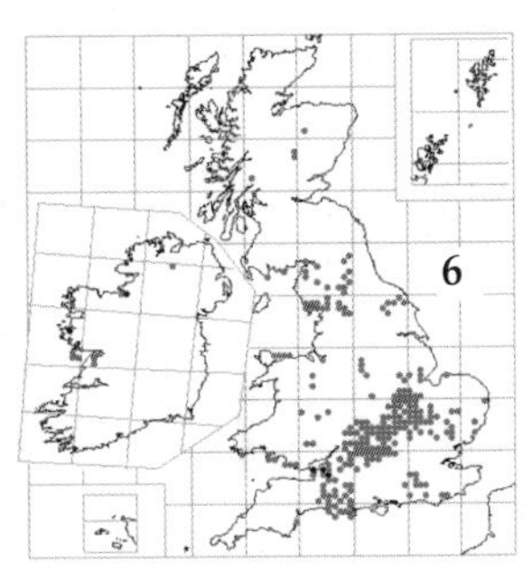

26. C. verruculifera Thallus placodioid, dull lemon-yellow to bright yellow-orange. Lobes long, narrow (up to 1 mm wide), very convex, branched with wider tips. Centre of the thallus areolate with irregular, granular isidia extending to the inner parts of the thallus. Apothecia very rare, flat, yellow-orange. Spores type 1c or with an even narrower septum, 10–15 x 5–6 µm.
Habitat: Not uncommon on hard nutrient-enriched rocks above high-water mark. May be parasitized with *Buellia vezdana* (brown muriform spores). In the South West it is often confused with the rare **C. granulosa** which is smaller (up to 2 cm wide) and is found only on sheltered, inland limestone.

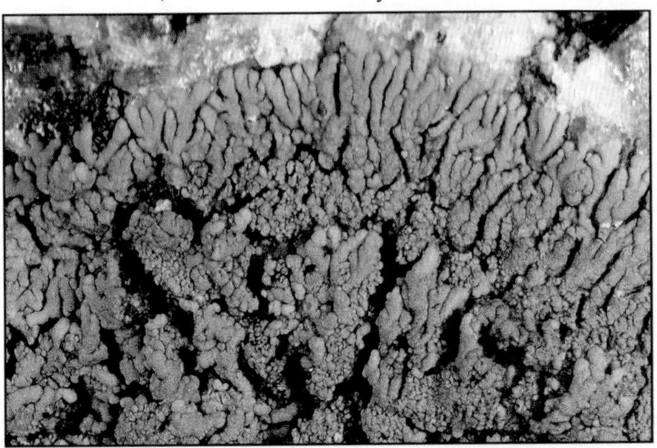

C. *verruculifera* x 6.

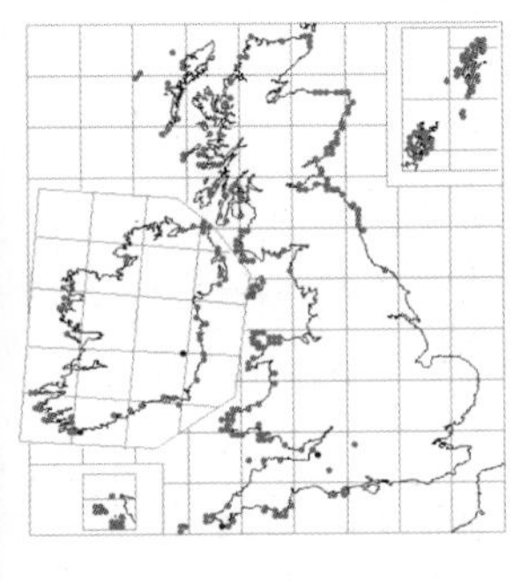

CANDELARIA ('candle' – from the candle-light colour of the thallus). **Thallus** minutely foliose. **Photobiont** chloroccoid. **Apothecia** lecanorine. **Ascus** up to 50-spored. **Hymenium** colourless, I+ blue. **Spores** colourless, simple, but having two oil globules (biguttulate) and appearing 1-septate. **Pycnidia** in warts. **Conidia** simple, colourless, ellipsoid. There is only one British species.

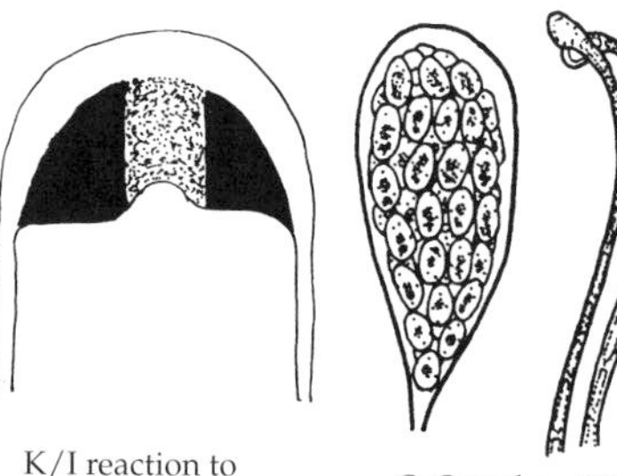
K/I reaction to ascus tip

C. Concolor x 300

Candelaria concolor Thallus greenish yellow to lemon-yellow, consisting of dense tufts of erect minute lobules (to 1 mm long) with neatly incised margins and ends which are sorediate on the margin. Rarely, the soredia may spread to cover the thallus. Under-surface white, with rhizinae. Apothecia fairly rare, up to 1 mm wide, dirty yellow, often with a roughened margin. Spores 6–15 x 4–6 µm. May be distinguished from *Xanthoria candelaria* by its K– reaction (sometimes dirty brown).
Habitat: A local and decreasing species now found only in areas of low pollution. It grows on well-lit to lightly shaded basic-barked trees, also on fences, exceptionally on rocks.

C. concolor x 6.

CANDELARIELLA ('little candle'). **Thallus** crustose or subsquamulose to placodioid. **Photobiont** chlorococcoid. **Apothecia** lecanorine. **Ascus** *Candelaria*-type, normally 8-, but may be up to 32-spored. **Hymenium** colourless, I+ blue. **Spores** simple, colourless, biguttulate (with an oil globule towards each end). **Pycnidia** immersed in thallus. **Conidia** colourless, ellipsoid. Distinguished from *Caloplaca* species by the consistently K– (or brownish) reaction from the yellow pigment calycin and in having simple, not polarilocular, spores.

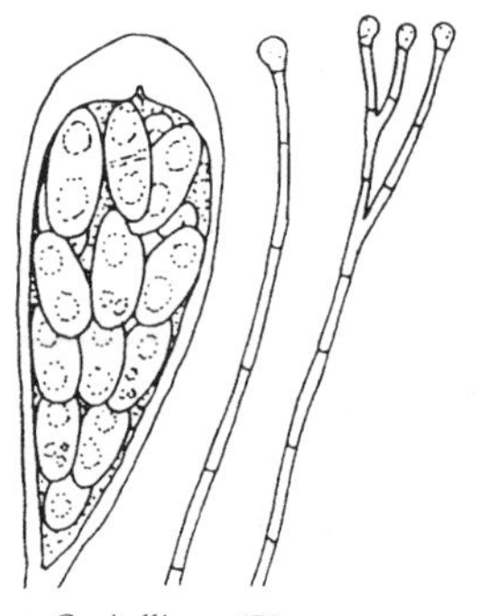
C. vitellina x 650.

1. Thallus placodioid, not sorediate, pruinose **3. C. medians**
– Thallus crustose, granular, or minutely squamulose and/or sorediate 2
2. Thallus minutely squamulose and/or sorediate 3
– Thallus crustose-granular to areolate, not pruinose 4
3. Thallus squamulose with bright yellow soredia **4. C. reflexa**
– Thallus entirely buff-yellow soredia **5. C. xanthostigma**
4. Thallus, scattered granules on a black prothallus. Spores 8 per ascus **1. C. aurella**
– Thallus irregular, conspicuous clumped granules. Spores more than 8 per ascus 5
5. Thallus golden-yellow, thick, deeply cracked rounded granules; on hard acid rocks **2. C. coralliza**
– Thallus orange-yellow, of flat to oval, not rounded, granules forming a cracked crust; on various substrates **6. C. vitellina**

1. Candelariella aurella Thallus mustard-yellow, consisting of thinly scattered granules on a distinctive black prothallus which is most pronounced in urban situations. Apothecia almost always present, up to about 1 mm diam, with a pale to dirty yellow disc. The margins become crenulate. Spores 8 per ascus, 10–18 x 5–6 µm. Specimens with yellow-green fruits and thallus are placed in f. *smaragdula* (*heidelbergensis*).
K–. This reaction separates this and the following species from the superficially similar *Caloplaca citrina* or *Leproplaca* species.
Habitat: Common on nutrient-enriched calcareous rocks, bricks and mortar in towns, much rarer in rural areas. Commonest in the South and East.

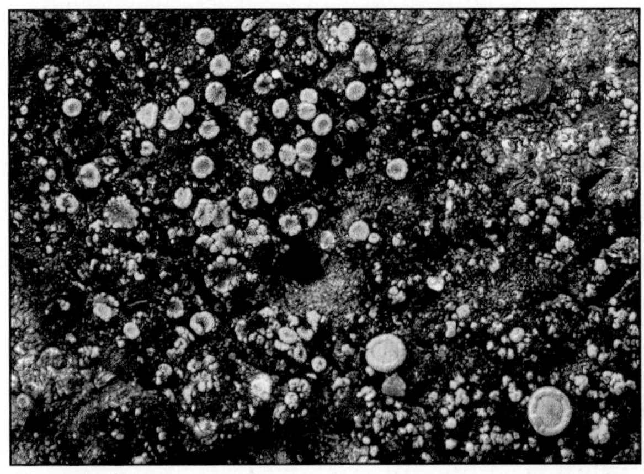

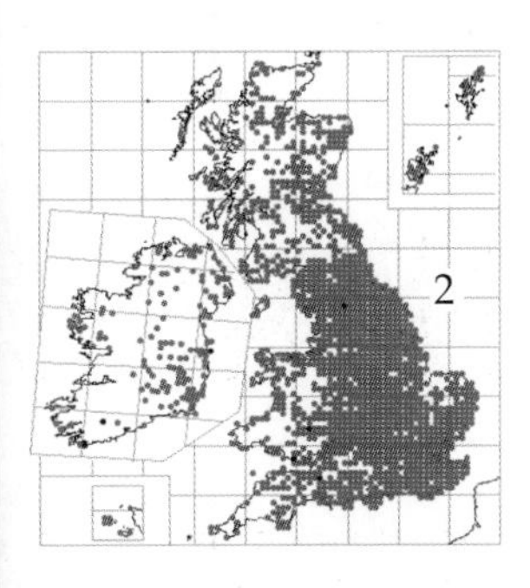

C. aurella x 7.

2. C. coralliza is similar to *C. vitellina* but has a thick areolate thallus with deep cracking and more rounded, even-sized and compacted granules. It is a clear, golden yellow but never orange. Rarely fertile, apothecia and spores resemble *C. vitellina*.
Habitat: Uncommon, on acid rocks that form well-lit, often isolated, bird-perching sites, mainly in rural and coastal areas.

3. C. medians Thallus yellow, placodioid. Lobes flattened and pruinose, the centre often areolate, grey-yellow (especially in shade) and sometimes with very small isidia. Apothecia rare, 0.3–1 mm diam, brown-yellow with a smooth or crenulate margin. Spores 8 per ascus, rarely 1-septate, rarely sole-shaped, 11–17 x 4–6 µm. May be distinguished from *Caloplaca* species, especially *C. decipiens,* by the K– reaction and from *Caloplaca flavescens* by the lighter, more yellow, colour.
Habitat: Formerly, and still, a very rare species of natural hard calcareous rocks but now common in the South East on well-lit, man-made calcareous substrates, e.g. concrete, asbestos-cement, tombstones, etc.

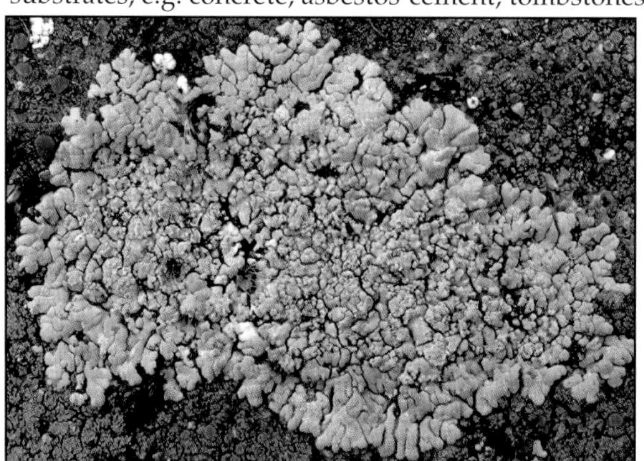

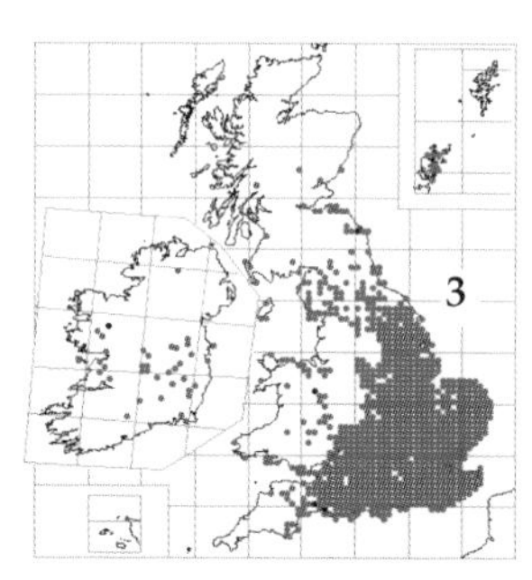

C. medians x 2.

4. C. reflexa Thallus of small (up to 1 mm), scattered to continuous, yellow to yellow-green granules or corticate squamules which quickly become covered in soredia to look like small fluffy balls. Apothecia are very rare, yellow, about 0.5 mm diam. Spores 8 per ascus, 10–15 x 4–6 µm.
Habitat: Common on shaded nutrient-enriched trees, especially willow, and on the bases of trees up to the level that dogs can reach when urinating.

C. reflexa x 6.

Sorediate squamule of *C. reflexa* x 25.

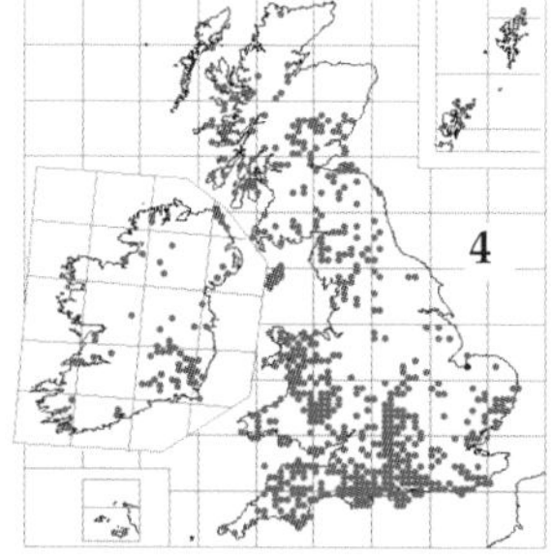

5. C. xanthostigma Similar to the previous species but consisting of numerous small, buff-yellow, sorediate granules (0.2 mm diam) on a dark hypothallus. Apothecia are rare. Spores 12 to 32 per ascus, 9–12 x 5 µm.
Habitat: Found on less shaded, not nutrient-enriched, isolated trees and in open woodland.

6. C. vitellina Thallus mustard-yellow to brownish, consisting of larger, flatter granules than *C. aurella*. The granules are irregular in shape and often clump together to form a thick, areolate crust, several centimetres across, with a distinctive upper surface which looks like the top of a cauliflower. Apothecia common, up to 1.5 mm diam, dirty yellow. Spores 12–32 per ascus, 9–15 x 3–7 µm. Pycnidia frequent, conidia 2–3 x 1–2 µm.
Habitat: Common on nutrient-enriched siliceous rocks, especially those frequented by birds. More rarely on slightly calcareous rocks, bricks and trees. More common than *C. aurella* except in fairly heavily polluted urban areas.

C. vitellina x 8.

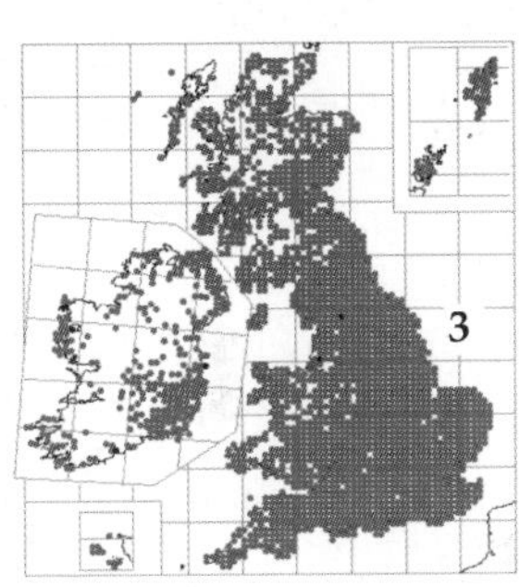

CARBONEA (from the colour and texture of the proper margin). **Thallus** crustose, immersed, or parasitic on other lichens. **Photobiont** chloroccoid. **Apothecia** lecideine with a persistent, opaque, black margin. **Ascus** 8-spored, *Lecanora*-type. **Paraphyses** simple, conglutinated. **Hymenium** pale but bright blue to green in the upper parts. **Spores** colourless, simple. **Pycnidia** immersed in thallus. **Conidia** simple, colourless, thread-like and often curved. **Chemical reactions** negative. The species were formerly in *Lecidea*.

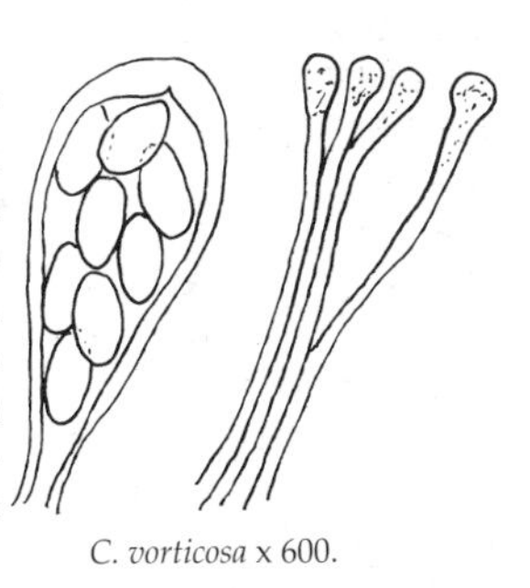

C. vorticosa x 600.

C. vorticosa Thallus small, up to 2 cm across, cracked-areolate, wrinkled, green-grey to black. Usually fertile, apothecia up to 0.5 mm diam, often in groups. Spores 10–12 x 3–5 µm. Pycnidia frequent. Conidia 17–30 x 1 µm.
Habitat: On acid rocks and walls in upland regions, especially where metal-rich. Two other species are found in the British Isles as parasites on the thallus of other lichens: **C. supersparsa** on *Lecanora polytropa* in Scotland and **C. vitellinaria** on *Candelariella vitellina* in the West.

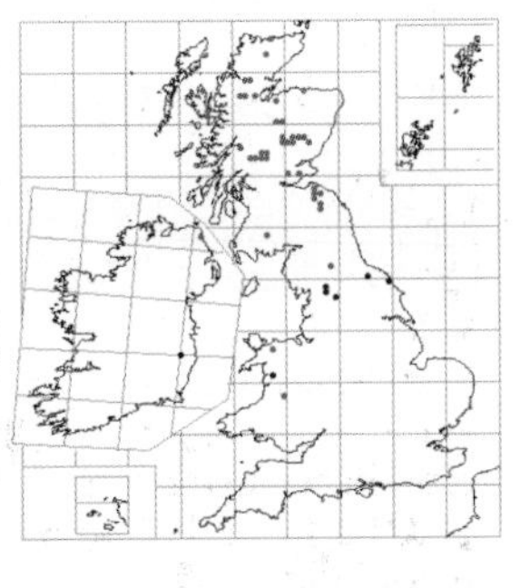

C. vorticosa x 10.

CATAPYRENIUM ('downwards stone' – from the innate perithecia). **Thallus** squamulose with rhizines on the lower surface. **Photobiont** chlorococcoid. **Perithecia** immersed in the thallus. **Spores** colourless, simple, 8 per ascus. **Pycnidia** immersed in the thallus or as marginal projections. **Conidia** colourless, cylindrical or ellipsoid. **Chemical reactions** negative.

C. squamulosum x 300.

1.	Squamules up to 1 cm wide, pycnidia marginal	2
–	Squamules up to 0.5 cm wide, pycnidia laminal	**4. C. squamulosum**
2.	Squamules up to 3.mm wide. Spores in ascus, biseriate	**1. C. cinerum**
–	Squamules up to 1 cm wide. Spores in ascus, uniseriate	3
3.	Spores 6–8 µm wide, pycnidia conspicuous	**2. C. lachneum**
–	Spores 8–10 µm wide, pycnidia inconspicuous	**3. C. rufescens**

1. Catapyrenium cinerum Thallus of small squamules, up to 3 mm across, often closely grouped. Green-brown but usually very white-pruinose with a darker margin and a roughened centre. Lower surface dark on a black, loose hypothallus. Usually very fertile with the ostiole slightly protruding. Ascus cylindrical-clavate, spores biseriately arranged. Spores becoming clavate, 17–23 x 6–9 µm.
Habitat: On soil (especially where calcareous), mosses and plant debris. In upland regions and near the coast.

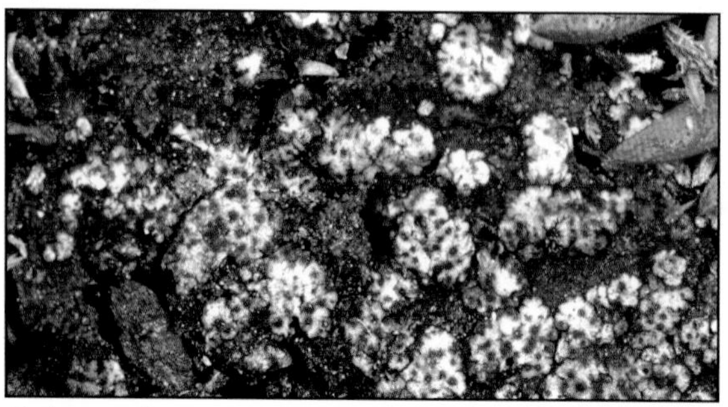

C. cinerum x 4.

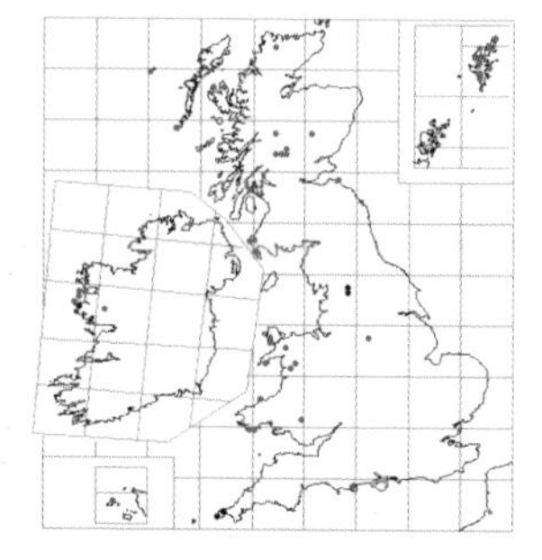

2. C. lachneum Squamules up to 1 cm across, dark reddish brown with a black lower surface. The margins of the squamules have distinctive pycnidia (up to 0.5 mm diam). Perithecia are immersed in the surface of the squamules with only the pale margin and dark ostiole visible. Spores uniseriately arranged in the ascus, 15–18 x 6–8 µm. Conidia 5–7 µm long.
Habitat: Frequent on basic soils in upland Britain.

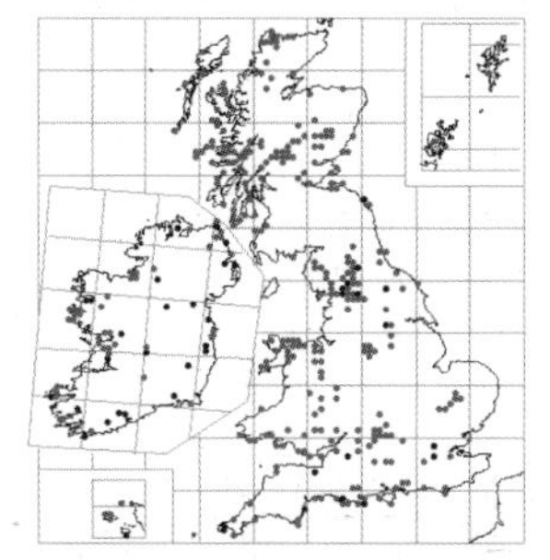

3. C. rufescens is similar to the previous species but has broader spores, 15–20 x 8–10 µm. Conidia 3–5 µm long.
Habitat: Locally common on well-lit calcareous soils in upland Britain.

4. C. squamulosum (Dermatocarpon hepaticum) Thallus buff to reddish brown. Under-surface black and felted. Forms discrete, adpressed squamules up to 5 mm wide. Pycnidia and perithecia immersed laminally in the thallus with a pale margin and dark brown ostiole. Spores uniseriately arranged in the ascus, 12–15 x 5–7 µm. Conidia 3–5 µm long.
Habitat: Locally common on calcareous soils, especially in crevices in hard calcareous rocks, sometimes on walls amongst mosses.

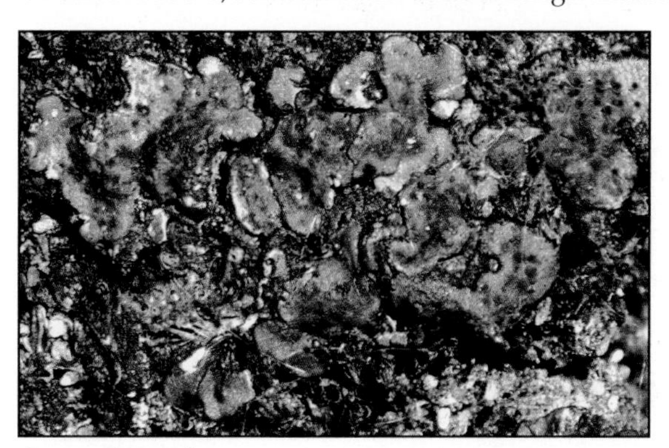

C. squamulosum x 4.

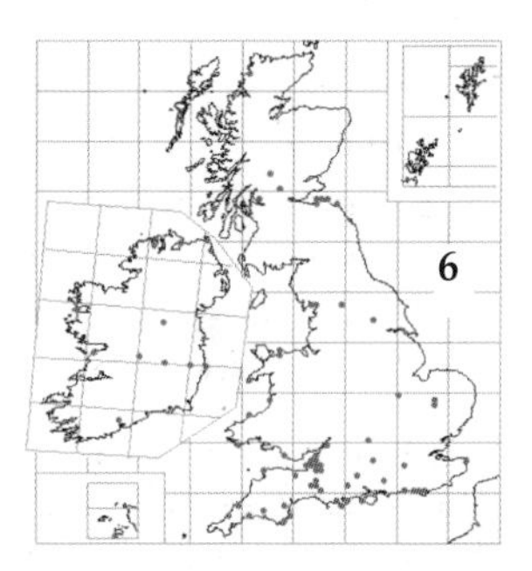

CATILLARIA ('little saucer' - from the shape of the fruit bodies). **Thallus** crustose. **Photobiont** green, various. **Apothecia** lecideine. **Ascus** usually 8-spored, In the species described below, with K/I the whole apical dome is an even blue surrounded by a blue outer layer. **Spores** colourless, 1–(to 3–) -septate. **Pycnidia** immersed. **Conidia** simple, colourless, mainly ellipsoid. **Chemical reactions** negative. This genus is in need of a modern revision.

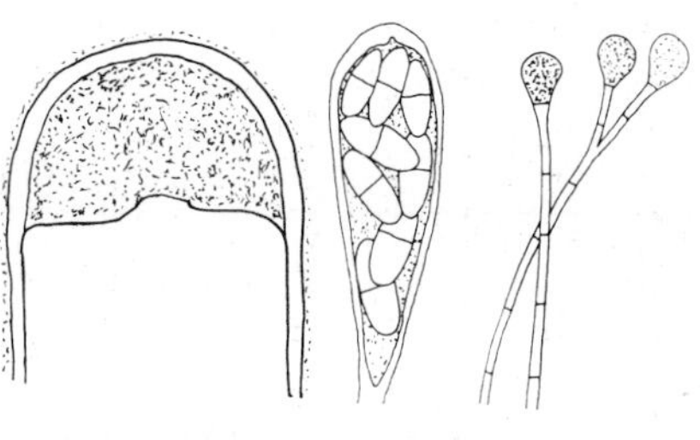

K/I reaction to ascus tip.

C. lenticularis x 700.

1.	Apothecia up to 0.75 mm, on mosses and 'old-forest' trees	**1. C. atropurpurea**
–	Apothecia up to 0.5 mm, on rocks and walls	2
2.	Apothecia 0.5 mm, dark brown to black	**2. C. chalybeia**
–	Apothecia less than 0.4 mm, red-brown	**3. C. lenticularis**

1. Catillaria atropurpurea Thallus thin, grey-brown, evanescent or minutely granular. Apothecia up to 0.75 mm, dark purple-brown when wet, black when dry, with a wide margin which gives it a 'wine gum' like appearance, this margin becomes excluded as the apothecia mature and become convex. Hymenium colourless. Spores 1-septate, 10–15 x 5–8 µm.
Habitat: On rough-barked trees and growing over mosses on 'old-forest' trees.

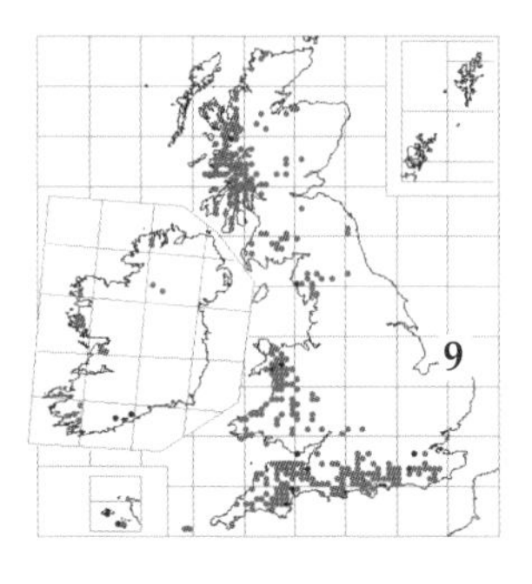

C. atropurpurea x 6.

2. C. chalybeia Thallus grey, greenish grey to black, effuse, sometimes evanescent, or cracked-areolate and often with a black prothallus. Apothecia small, about 0.5 mm, matt black, convex or flat with a thin margin. Paraphyses with very dark brown swollen tips. Hymenium colourless to blue-green. Epithecium very dark brown to black. Spores 1-septate, 8–12 x 3–5 µm.
Habitat: Common on acid rocks and walls especially nutrient-enriched or becoming basic, particularly near the sea, rarely also on trees.

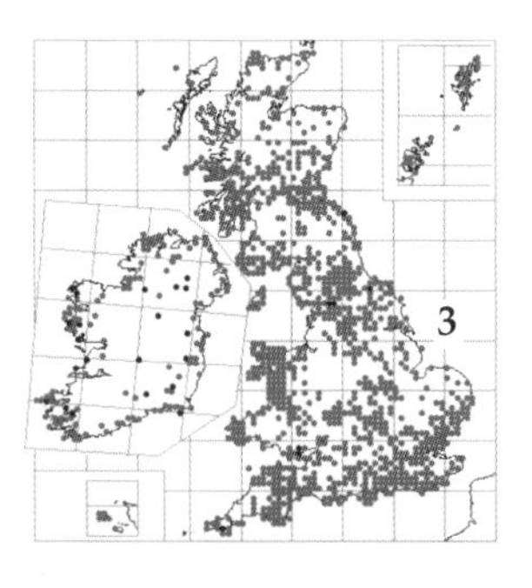

C. chalybeia x 5.

3. C. lenticularis Similar to *C. chalybeia* but the thallus is paler and may be almost entirely endolithic. It it differs in the small (up to 0.35 mm), dark red apothecia with more prominent margins and lighter brown epithecium.
Habitat: Common on basic rocks and mortar but easily overlooked.

CAVERNULARIA ('small cavities' – from the depressions on the lower surface). **Thallus** foliose with many deep depressions on the lower surface which also lacks rhizines. **Photobiont** *Trebouxia*. **Apothecia** lecanorine. **Ascus** 8-spored. **Spores** simple, colourless and rather globose. **Pycnidia** immersed. **Conidia** rather spindle-shaped. There is only one British species.

Cavernularia hultenii Thallus grey, orbicular, up to 2 cm diam. Lobes rarely more than 1 mm wide with pale-coloured soredia on the apices. Resembles a small *Hypogymnia physodes* but the thallus is not completely hollow and the dark brown under surface has numerous distinctive small dark pits. Apothecia not found in Britain, brown on short stalks. Spores very small and globose.
Cortex: K± yellow. Medulla: KC+ red, C–, P–.
Habitat: A rare species of pine, birch and rowan trees and heather stems in old pine forests of central and north-western Scotland.

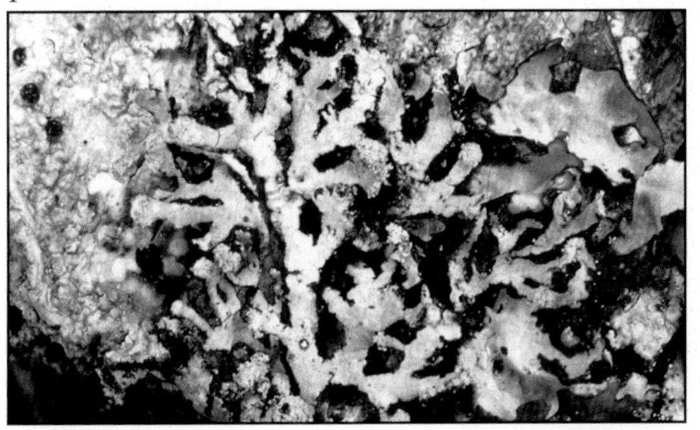

C. hultenii x 3.

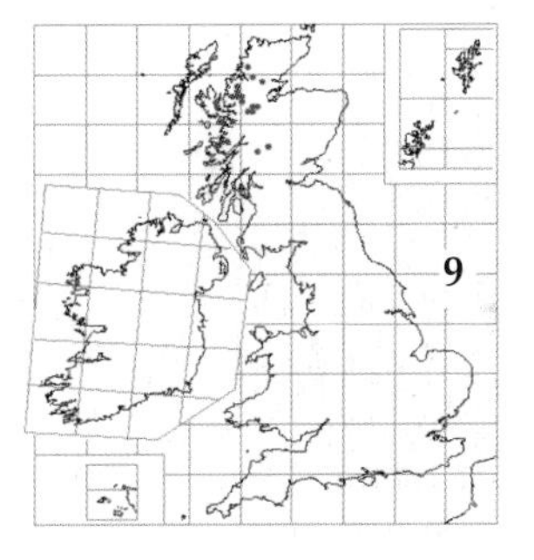

CETRARIA ('shield' – from the shape of the apothecia). **Thallus** foliose to almost fruticose. Rhizines absent or sparse and confined to the central region. **Photobiont** *Trebouxia*. **Apothecia** lecanorine, rare in Britain, usually on the margins. **Ascus** 8-spored, *Lecanora*-type. **Spores** colourless, simple, 5–10 x 3–6 µm. **Pycnidia** stalked, mainly on the margin of the lobes. **Conidia** bacilliform or dumb-bell shaped. A mainly northern genus that is poorly represented in Britain.

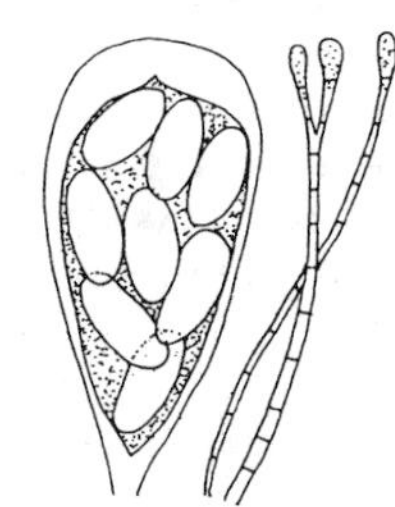

C. islandica x 600.

1.	Lobes over 2 mm wide	2
–	Lobes less than 2 mm wide	6
2.	Grey-green to brown-green	3
–	Creamy yellow, chestnut or dark brown	4
3.	Thallus greenish brown, tufted. K–	**2. C. chlorophylla**
–	Thallus grey-green, fairly erect. K+y	**Platismatia glauca**
4.	Thallus creamy yellow. High altitudes in Scotland. KC+y	**7. C. nivalis**
–	Thallus chestnut or dark brown.	5
5.	Up to 6 cm high. P+ orange to red. Rarely fertile	**5. C. islandica**
–	Up to 1 cm high. P–. Usually abundantly fertile	**8. C. sepincola**

6.	Thallus terate or flattened, fruticose	7
–	Thallus foliose, rosette forming	8
7.	Main branches flattened, to 1 mm wide, loose bush-like	**1. C. aculeata**
–	Main branches terete, to 0.5 mm wide, densely branched	**6. C. muricata**
8.	Lower surface light brown, K–, P–	**3. C. commixta**
–	Lower surface dark brown, K+y, P+y	**4. C. hepatizon**

1. Cetraria aculeata (Coelocaulon aculeatum) Thallus chestnut to dark brown, usually glossy and looking as if varnished, up to 4 cm high. Branches somewhat flattened, up to 1 mm diam, usually with elongated, white pseudocyphellae in depressions, especially near the axils. The branches terminate in short blunt spines which may also be present on the main branches. It may be scattered or form interwoven mats. Apothecia very rare.
Spot reactions: negative.
Habitat: Very common on heaths and acid sand dunes, rarely amongst mosses.

C. *aculeata* x 4.

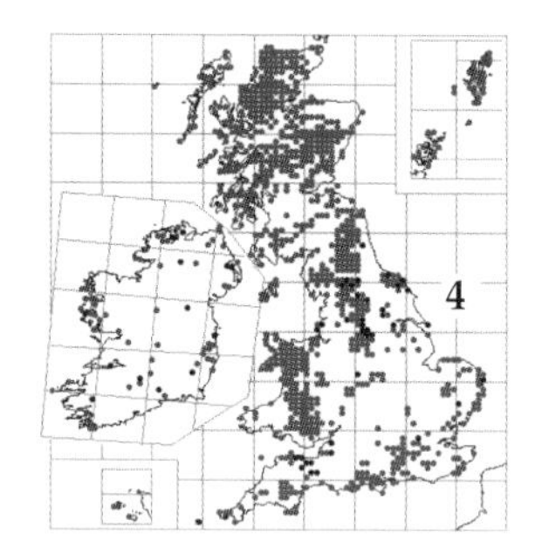

2. C. chlorophylla Thallus dark green to brown (dull green when wet), lobes erect, rarely rising above 1.5 cm from the substrate and forming tufts with upright margins, apices of lobes incised, with soralia on the margin. Undersurface pale coffee-brown, shiny and wrinkled, paler towards the centre where there are a few simple rhizinae. Apothecia rare, usually with sorediate margins. They are located on the margins of the lobes.
It may be separated from the rather similar *Platismatia glauca* (K+ yellow) by the negative reaction, its greenish brown as opposed to grey-green colour (not much greener when wet) of *P. glauca* and its smaller size.
Spot reactions: negative.
Habitat: Common in upland areas particularly on coniferous trees, fence posts, and siliceous rocks. It is often found in the South and Midlands on both coniferous and deciduous trees. Very rare in Ireland.

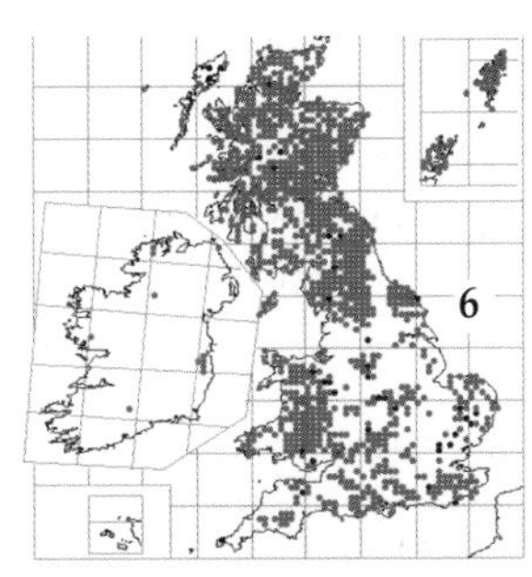

C. *chlorophylla* x 2.

3. C. commixta Thallus up to about 8 cm diam with narrow, overlapping lobes about 2 mm wide. Glossy, very dark brown on the upper surface, the lower surface is light brown, becoming paler towards the edge of the thallus, with a few simple or branched rhizinae. Apothecia fairly common, up to 5 mm wide with crenulate margins. Black globose, pycnidia found along the margins of the lobes. Conidia bacilliform.
Spot reactions: negative (medulla: rarely KC+ pink).
Habitat: Rare, on exposed acid rocks in upland areas.

4. C. hepatizon is similar to *C. commixta* but the lower surface is dark brown, the thallus is rather more adpressed and it has a different chemistry. Conidia dumb-bell shaped.
Medulla: K+ yellow, P+ yellow.

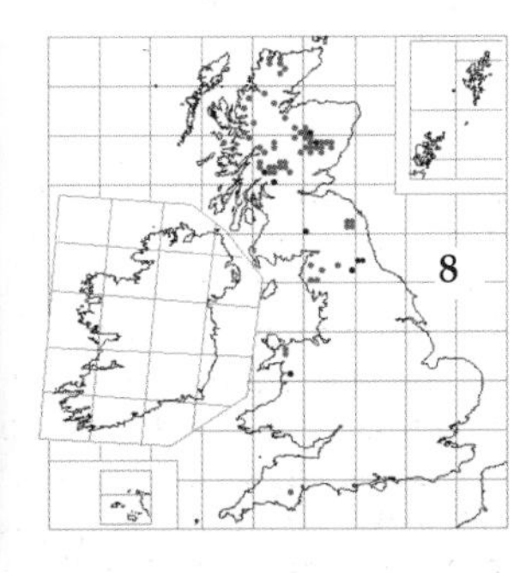

C. *hepatizon* x 3.

5. C. islandica Thallus strap-like, shining, chestnut to dark brown on both sides, frequently more red towards the base, forming dense tufts or straggling entangled mats with lobes up to about 6 cm high and 1 cm wide, loosely attached to the substrate. Lobes long, thin, curled inwards and deeply incised, ciliate on the margins. The lower surface has scattered, white, rather fusiform pseudocyphellae. Apothecia are rare but marginal pycnidia are common.
Medulla: P+ orange to red.

Habitat: Common on ericaceous heaths in the Scottish Highlands becoming much less common in England and Ireland. Still known from single sites on heaths in Derbyshire, Lincolnshire and Norfolk.
This is 'Iceland Moss' which, due to the high isolichenin content, was once soaked for a few days to remove the bitter acids it contains, then boiled and eaten either as a broth or jelly. It also forms an important food for reindeer and caribou in sub-arctic and boreal areas. In Germany it is sold as a tea, as a hangover cure and also in cough-sweets.

C. islandica x 3.

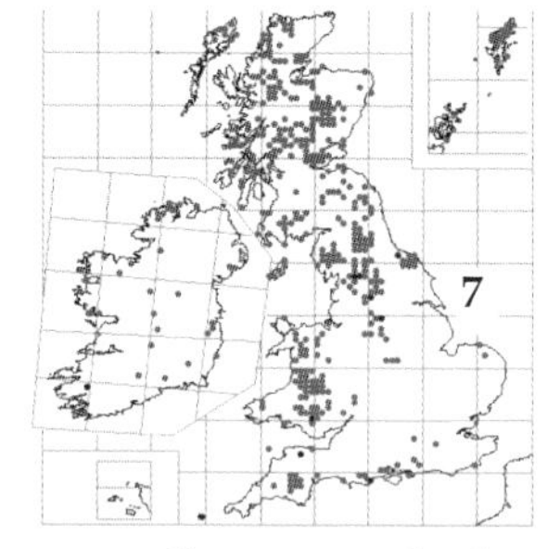

6. C. muricata Similar to *C. aculeata* but is shorter (up to 3 cm high) and more densely branched. It has numerous small spinules with the branching often at a narrower angle. The branches are more or less terete and up to about 0.4 mm diam. The pseudocyphellae are not in depressions. It usually forms very dense, spiky mats.
Habitat: As *C. aculeata* but less common. It is often found on mineral spoil-heaps.

7. C. nivalis Thallus creamy yellow, both surfaces more yellow towards the base. Forming loose tufts up to 5 cm high. The lobes are long and narrow up to 1 cm wide, deeply incised and pitted-undulate, lacking soralia or isidia.
KC+y.
Habitat: Locally abundant in ericaceous heaths at high altitudes in the Scottish Highlands, just below the line of the longest persisting winter snow.

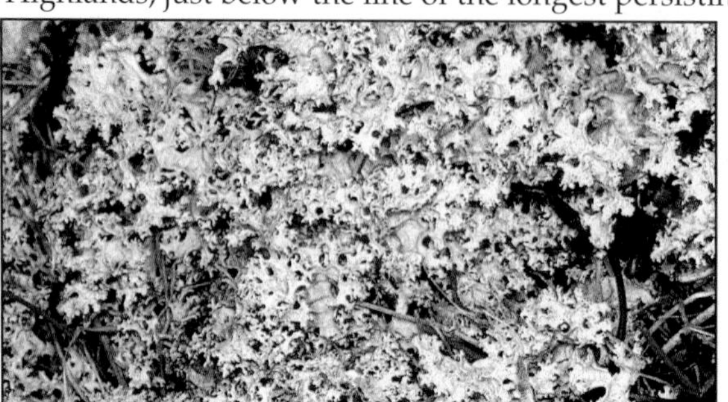

C. nivalis x 2.

8. C. sepincola Thallus foliose, up to about 2 cm diam. It forms neat rosettes of grey-green to chestnut lobes. Lower surface pale. Usually very fertile, the apothecia often obscuring the thallus. The disc up to 4 mm across.
Spot reaction negative.
Habitat: Common in Scottish Highlands, less common towards the north of England. Found mainly on twigs (especially birch and alder) and fence posts.

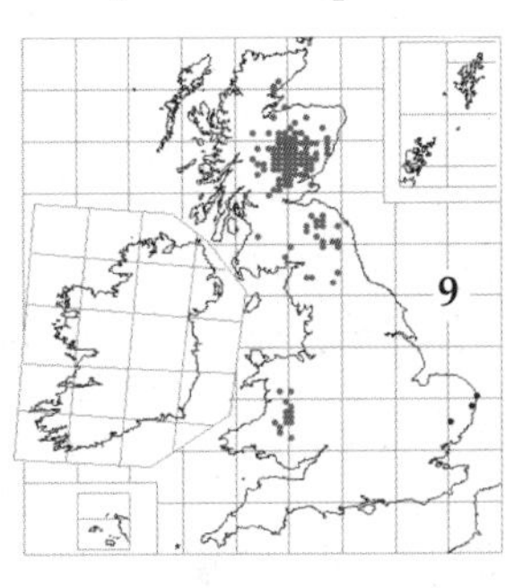

C. sepincola x 3.

CETRELIA. Thallus foliose with pseudocyphellae on the upper surface of the rather large, rounded lobes. **Photobiont** *Trebouxia.* **Apothecia** lecanorine. **Asci** 8-spored, *Parmelia*-type. There is only one British species and that has never been found fertile. There are, however, three chemical races in Britain with differing C and KC reactions.

Cetrelia olivetorum Thallus grey, forming a large thallus up to 10 cm wide. The upper surface has small, scattered, white dot-like pseudocyphellae (use hand-lens) and the mature margins are covered in soralia. The centre of the underside has simple rhizinae and is black, becoming brown or white and smooth towards the lobe tips. It can be separated from *Platismatia glauca* by the larger, more spreading thallus, the presence of pseudocyphellae and the I– reaction of the medulla. The lack of marginal cilia helps to separate it from *Parmelia perlata* and *P. robusta*.
K–, P–, C– or C+ red, KC– or pink or red.
Habitat: Infrequent, on mossy trees and rarely rocks, in damp woodlands.

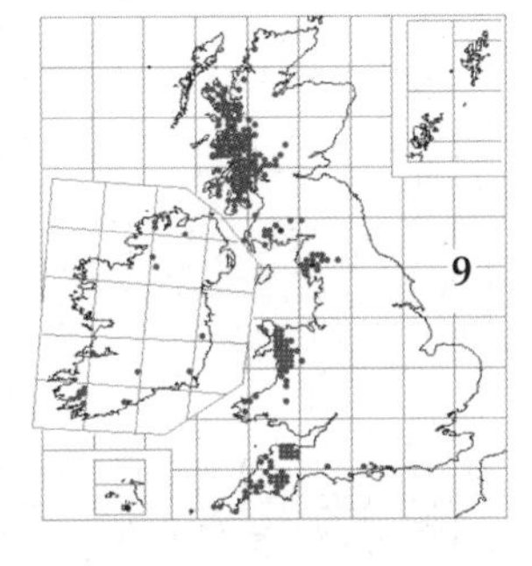

C. olivetorum x 2.

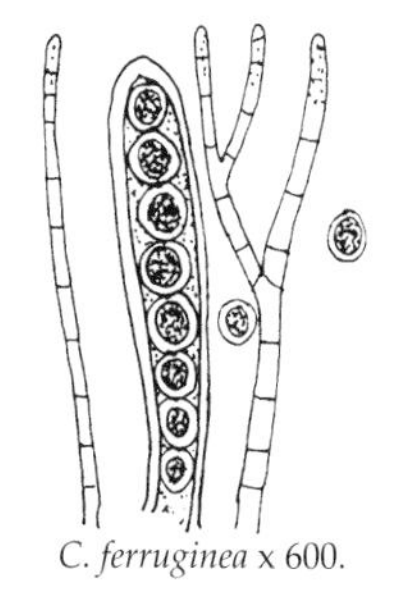
C. ferruginea x 600.

CHAENOTHECA ('split container' – from the often multiple heads on the fruiting bodies). **Thallus** crustose and granular to squamulose. **Photobiont** green, various. **Apothecia** yellow to dark brown, stalked, so as to resemble pins. **Spores** distinguished from other genera with stalked apothecia by the simple (rarely septate), spherical to elliptical, brown spores. **Asci** and paraphyses breaking down to form a brown powdery spore mass at maturity (black in *Calicium*).

1.	Thallus yellow to yellow-green	2
–	Thallus absent or grey to orange	4
2.	Thallus bright yellow or greenish grey. On bark	3
–	Thallus greenish yellow. On or near siliceous soil	**5. C. furfuracea**
3.	Thallus finely granular, bright yellow	**3. C. chrysocephala**
–	Coarsely granular to subsquamulose, greenish grey	**6. C. trichialis**
4.	Thallus with patches of orange which are K+ red	**4. C. ferruginea**
–	Thallus absent or P+ yellow	5
5.	Thallus absent (any vestiges of thallus P–). yellow-green pruina on stalk	6
–	Thallus granular, P+ yellow. No pruina on stalk	**2. C. brunneola**
6.	Spores 3–4 µm, globose. Photobiont *Stichococcus*	**1. C. brachypoda**
–	Spores 6–9 x 2–5 ellipsoid. Photobiont *Trebouxia*	**3. C. chrysocephala**

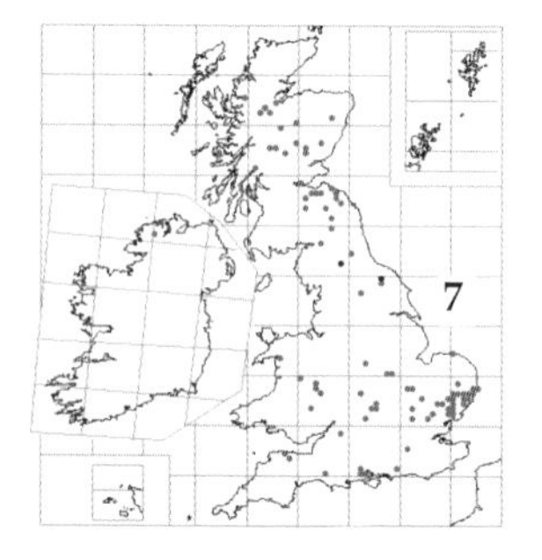

1. Chaenotheca brachypoda Thallus immersed. Both head and stalk of apothecia and also the spore mass covered in greenish yellow pruina. Stalk up to 1.4 mm high. Under the pruina the spore mass is dark brown. Spores 3–4 µm, globose.
Spot reactions: negative.
Habitat: Mainly found in the East in bark crevices and hollow trees.

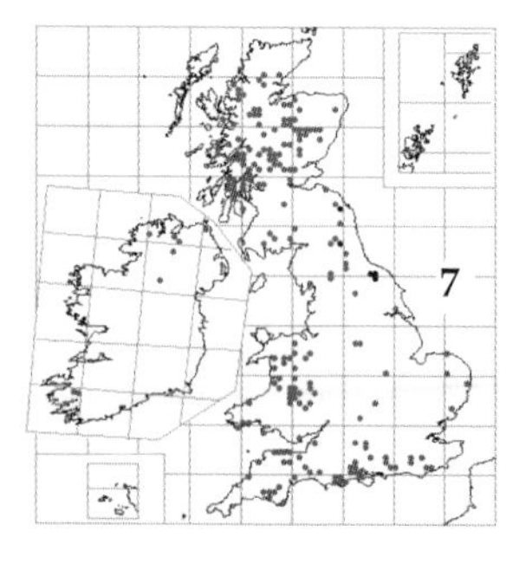

2. C. brunneola Thallus usually immersed in the substrate with only a few granules on the surface. Apothecia with shiny black stalks, up to 2 mm tall, which are sometimes branched with an apothecium, containing a brown spore mass, on each branch. Spores 3–5 µm diam.
K–, P+y.
Habitat: Infrequent on bark and decorticated trees, rarely on old bracket fungi on trees.

C. brunneola x 8.

3. C. chrysocephala Thallus normally of vivid yellow-green granules or sometimes immersed. Apothecia are usually present, up to 1.5 mm tall with the head on the top of a thin stalk. This stalk is pale brown, covered in yellow pruina on the upper part, the pruina spreading onto the lower part of the head. The spores are uniseriately arranged in the ascus, 6–9 x 4– 5 µm.
Spot reactions: negative.
Habitat: Most common in East Scotland. Found on both bark and wood on mature trees (mainly conifers and birch).

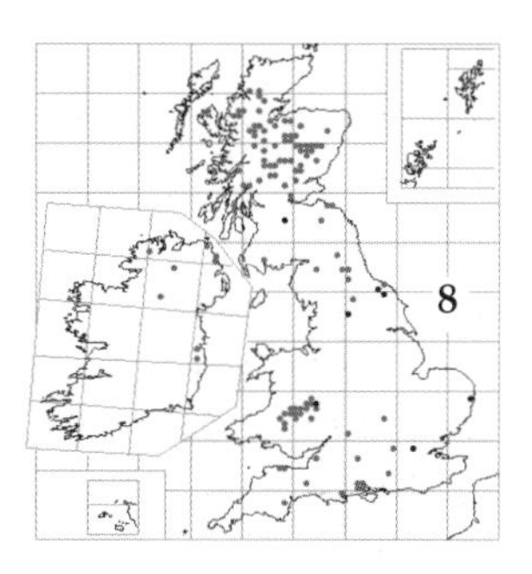

C. chrysocephala x 10.

4. C. ferruginea Thallus blue-grey to orange-grey with orange or mustard-yellow patches, often forming an areolate crust. Often infertile. Apothecia dark brown, convex with a paler yellow-orange or brown spore mass. Apothecial stalks shiny black, about 1–2 mm tall, but may be rudimentary in some specimens. Spores globose, 5–8 µm diam.
Thallus: K–. Orange patches: K+ red.
Habitat: Frequent in dry bark recesses of deciduous trees or old pines (it avoids direct rain or water run-off), particularly in the North and East. Common in areas of moderate air pollution as it prefers acid bark.

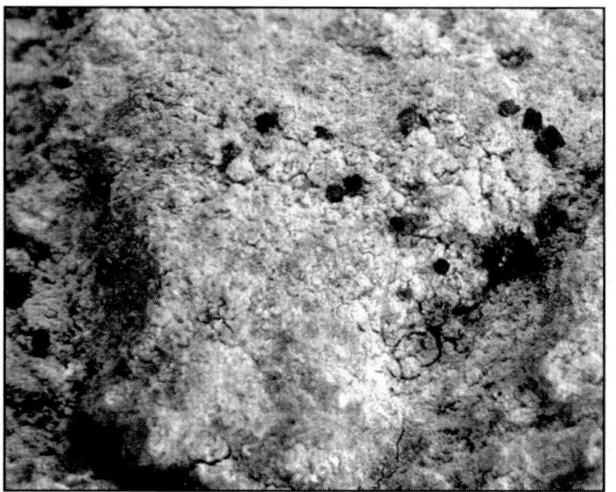

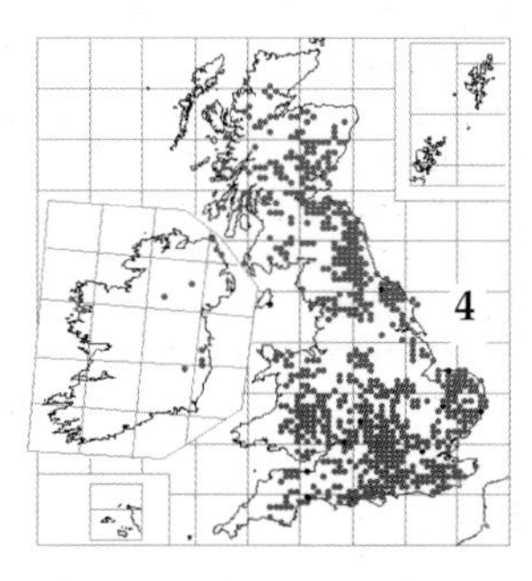

C. ferruginea x 10.

5. C. furfuracea (Coniocybe furfuracea) Thallus sulphur-yellow to yellow-green, granular, almost leprose. The apothecia are yellow-brown, with stalks up to 3 mm high which are concolorous with the thallus but often appear black where rubbed.
Habitat: Rather rare with apothecia. Found in the South and West, mainly in upland regions in siliceous rock crevices or on roots and tree stumps. Often found sterile when it is difficult to separate from sterile *Psilolechia lucida* except by chromatography and the alga.

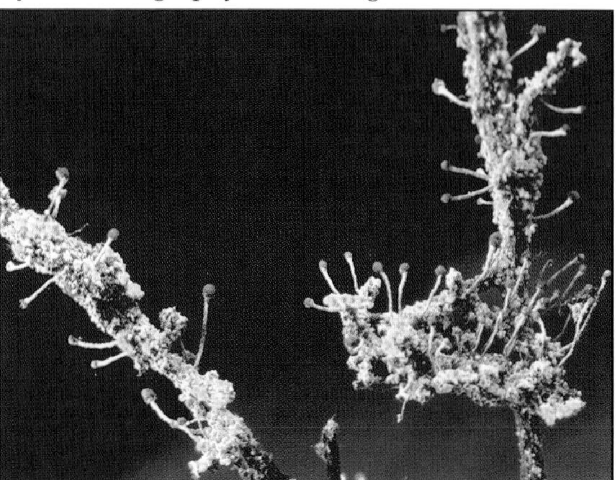

C. furfuracea x 10.

Round-celled alga *Trebouxia* in *Psilolechia*. Elongate-celled alga *Stichococcus* in *Chaenotheca*.

6. C. trichialis Thallus granular to almost squamulose, greenish grey. Apothecia up to 2 mm tall. The margin of the apothecia and sometimes the upper part of the stalk has a thin white pruina. Spores globose, 4–5 µm diam. A very variable species.
Spot reactions: negative.
Habitat: Rare, in dry recesses of acid bark and wood, especially in the East.

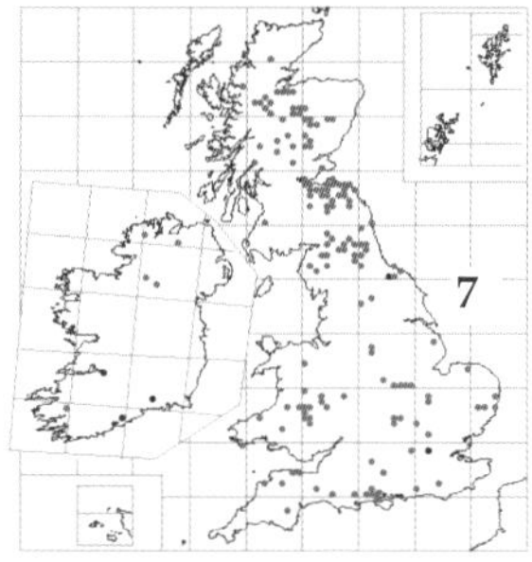

CHRYSOTHRIX ('golden hair' – from the colour and the thallus structure). **Thallus** leprose, often thin, mainly yellow due to the presence of pulvinic acid derivatives which probably help to protect it from being eaten. **Photobiont** chlorococcoid. **Apothecia** rare (most frequent in the very rare *C. chrysophthalma*). Ascus 8-spored. **Spores** usually 3-septate. **Pycnidia** unknown.

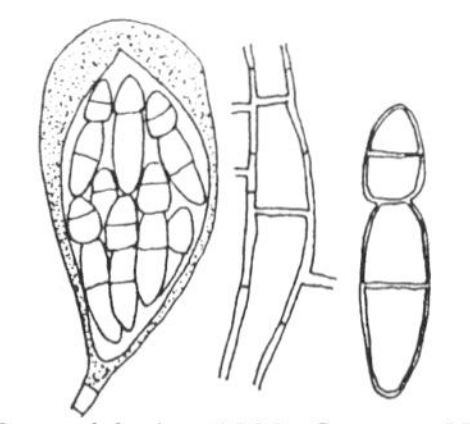

C. candelaris x 1000. Spore x 2500.

1. Thallus immersed, grey but frequently ± yellow-green sorediate — **3. C. flavovirens**
– Thallus entirely leprose — 2
2. Yellow-green — **3. C. flavovirens**
– Vivid or golden yellow — 3

3. Yellow or slightly orange, granules up to 0.1 mm diam **1. C. candelaris**
– Bright yellow, granules 0.1–0.2 mm diam **2. C. chlorina**

1. Chrysothrix candelaris Thallus bright golden yellow to slightly orange or greenish, thin and of powdery granules or forming a matt crust of very small granules up to 0.1 mm diam. Apothecia very rare (probably not found in Britain), about 0.5 mm, pale orange and often with a yellow pruina making them difficult to notice. Spores mainly 3-septate.
P–, rarely P+ orange, K–, rarely K+ orange, C–.
Habitat: Common in dry shaded crevices on rough-barked deciduous trees, especially oak. Often found with *Calicium viride, Lecanactis abietina* and *Chaenotheca ferruginea*, it also occasionally occurs on shaded vertical acid rocks. In France it is reported to colonize old stained glass.

C. *candelaris* x 3.

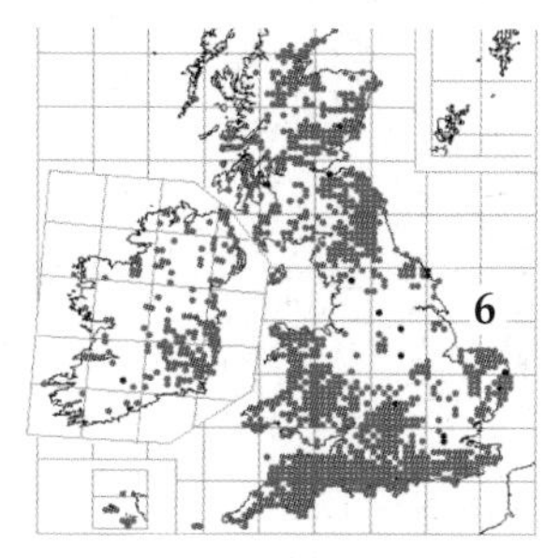

C. *candelaris*

C. *chlorina*

2. C. chlorina Thallus vivid lemon-yellow when fresh, thick and granular. The granules are larger than in the previous species being about 0.1–0.2 mm diam. Apothecia are unknown. It may be separated from *Psilolechia lucida* by its vivid, thicker, granular thallus.
K–, rarely K+ red.
Habitat: A rather rare but distinctive species found in dry crevices of hard, very shaded, acid rocks in the Scottish Highlands, rarely on conifers.

3. C. flavovirens Thallus an inconspicuous, spreading, pale grey stain, more or less covered by scattered, or a thin continuous layer, of yellow-green soredia. Apothecia rare, scattered, convex, concolorous or with a flesh-coloured disc, without a margin, up to 0.9 mm diam. Spores 3-septate.
K–.
Habitat: Frequent and increasing on the dry sides of old trees often in nutrient-poor situations. Richly fertile material without soredia as referred to the rare **C. chrysophthalma** confined to old pine forests in Scotland.

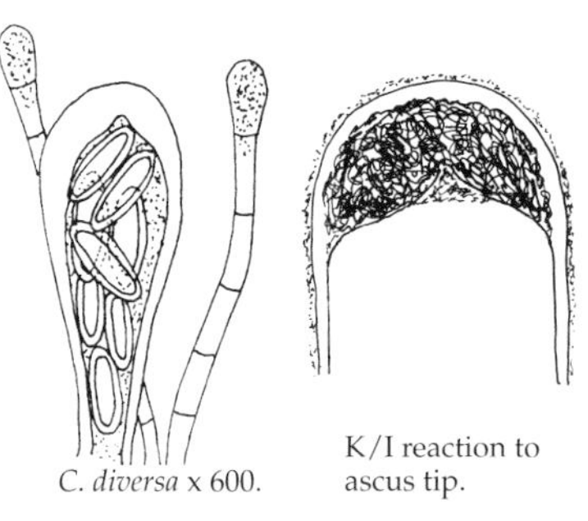
C. diversa x 600. K/I reaction to ascus tip.

CLADONIA ('branch or twig-like'). **Primary thallus** crustose or squamulose, disappearing or persistent. To some extent, many are variable depending on the microclimate in which they grow. **Secondary thallus** fruticose, consisting of hollow, lichenized, stalked apothecia called podetia which bear the hymenium or pycnidia at their tips. **Photobiont** trebouxioid. **Apothecia** lecideine. **Ascus** 8-spored with a thickened tip. **Spores** simple, colourless. **Conidia** 5–15 x 1 µm.

Some species are an important food for reindeer and caribou in sub-arctic and northern boreal areas. It takes from 4 to 30 years for grazing to regenerate for re-cropping. They are used in Scandinavia for producing antibiotics and even alcohol in the former U.S.S.R. The more bush-like species are dyed and used in flower arrangements, as trees in model railways etc. and in frost-resistant wreaths in Germany.

1. Apothecia red, K+ crimson (at least in a squash) — 2
– Apothecia brown, K– or absent — 9

2. Podetia grey to grey-green, K–, apothecia dark red — **4. C. floerkeana**
– Podetia yellow to green, of if grey K+ yellow, apothecia bright red — 3

3. Primary squamules white sorediate or yellowish cottony on under-surface — 4
– Primary squamules not sorediate or yellowish cottony on under-surface — 5

4. K+ deep yellow, P+ orange — **2.C. digitata**
– K–, P– — **25. C. luteoalba**

5. Podetia K+ yellow or K+red, P+ orange or red — 6
– Podetia K–, KC+ yellow, P– — 7

6. Podetia unbranched, without a distinct cup — **5. C. macilenta**
– Podetia often branched, horn-like and usually proliferating from the rim of a deformed cup — **6. C. polydactyla**

7. Podetia with peeling squamules, never sorediate — **1. C. bellidiflora**
– Podetia sometimes squamulose but with soredia or with coarse granules — 8

8a. Podetia stout, squamulose or with coarse granules, cup flared, common on sand and peat — **3. C. diversa**
8b. Podetia sorediate, slender, lacking cup, longitudinal splits — **7. C. sulphurina**
8c. Podetia sorediate, narrow cup, no longitudinal splits — **8. C. deformis**

9. Primary thallus granular. Podetia papillate, tooth-like often in a dense mass — **Pycnothelia papillaria**
– Primary thallus squamulose or ± absent, podetia prominent or not — 10

10. Thallus predominantly of primary squamules — 21
– Thallus of just podetia, or with podetia growing from basal squamules — 11

11. Thallus an interwoven, often much branched mat of tubular podetia — 12
– Thallus with podetia which are not usually interwoven, sparsely or not branched, and which may have a cup at the tip — 28

12. K+ yellow — 13
– K– — 15

13. Thallus light grey with a distinctive brownish mauve tinge; many apical branches all bent in one direction, P+ red — **31. C. rangiferina**
– Apical branches not all bent in one direction, usually more calcareous substrates, P+ red or P– — 14

14. Thallus brown-grey, podetia prostrate, contorted — **37. C. subrangiformis**
– Thallus grey-green, podetia not contorted; forming a more or less erect mat — **31. C. rangiformis**

15. Thallus P– — 16
– Thallus P+ yellow or red — 18

16. Thallus sparsely branched, yellowish or brown-grey to olive-green — 17
– Thallus very richly branched, pale grey — **28. C. portentosa**

17. Thallus yellow to greenish, spiky, little or not branched — **39. C. uncialis**
– Thallus brown-grey to olive-green, no yellow tinge, contorted, ± erect, forming lax tufts — **32. C. rangiformis**

18. Thallus ashy grey to green-grey, richly (dichotomously) branched — **14. C. ciliata**
– Thallus green-grey or brown-grey, side branches more widely spaced (not dichotomously) — 19

19. Branches strongly curved in one direction, tri- or tetrachotomously branched at tips — **9. C. arbuscula**
– Branches not strongly curved in one direction — 20

20a. Branches diverging at a narrow angle, no cups, brown-green, mainly acid substrates. Common and variable — **21. C. furcata**
b. Mainly unbranched, tall (to 6 cm), smooth, often with narrow cups — **23. C. gracilis**
c. Branches diverging at a wide angle, grey-green to pale brown-green, mainly on dunes and ± calcareous substrates — **32. C. rangiformis**

21. Thallus C+ bright green (wet acid heathland) — **35. C. strepsilis**
– Thallus C– — 22

22. Under-surface of squamules yellowish — 23
– Under-surface of squamules white — 25

23. Basal squamules 2 cm long, forming loose bunches — **16. C. convoluta**
– Basal squamules to 1 cm long — 24

24. Squamule tip incised, smooth lower surface — **20. C. foliacea**
– Squamule tip rounded, cottony lower surface — **25. C. luteoalba**

25. Squamules K+ yellow — 26
– Squamules K– — 27

26. Squamules blue-green, densely tufted, up to 5 mm wide, blackened base, mainly acid rocks — **36. C. subcervicornis**
– Squamules grey-green, less than 2 mm wide, not blackened at base, mainly on peat and tree bases — **5. C. macilenta**

27. Squamules waxy blue-green, up to 5 mm high, under surface white tinged with purple **11. C. cervicornis** subsp. **cervicornis**
– Squamules bright green, up to 3 mm high, usually spreading, under surface white **15. C. coniocraea**

28. Some podetia with longitudinal splits 29
– Podetia not split longitudinally 30

29. With fringed cups in tiers from one extension of cup, smooth **18. C. crispata**
– With no cups or only narrow terminal cups, sorediate **22. C. glauca**

30. Podetia not terminating in a wide cup 31
– Podetia terminating in a wide cup 39

31. Podetia delicate, branched with minute brownish grey incised squamules, K+ yellow **27. C. parasitica**
– Podetia robust, branched or not, squamules conspicuous, K+y/o or – 32

32. Podetia with antler-like branching towards the tips **38. C. subulata**
– Podetia simple or rarely branched 33

33. Podetia sessile or on very short stalks that lack algae, squamules form cushions **10. C. caespiticia**
– Podetia not sessile and with algae, squamules various 34

34 P+ red **30. C. ramulosa**
– P+ orange or P– 35

35. Podetia with green squamules, K+ yellow **34. C. squamosa** var. **subsquamosa**
– Podetia K– 36

36. Podetia ± densely green or brown-green, squamulose throughout, not farinose sorediate **33. C. squamosa**
– Podetia ± corticate/squamulose at or towards base, sorediate above 37

37. Podetia pointed, lower half corticate, upper half sorediate **17. C. cornuta**
– Podetia to 4 cm, mostly decorticate with a shallow cup **26. C. ochrochlora**

38. Podetia to 2.5 cm, upper part sorediate rarely with a very narrow cup **15. C. coniocraea**
– Podetia to 4 cm, upper part sorediate with a shallow cup **26. C. ochrochlora**

39. Podetia branched or having secondary podetia growing from them 40
– Podetia simple, regular (apothecia sometimes on short stalks around rim of cup) 41

40. Secondary podetia growing from the centre of primary podetia, P+ red **12. C. cervicornis** subsp. **verticillata**
– Secondary podetia or digitate projections growing from the rim of the primary podetia, P– **33. C. squamosa**

41. Podetia finely sorediate 42
– Podetia coarsely sorediate or squamulose-warted 43

42. Podetia to 15 mm tall, sorediate throughout **19. C. fimbriata**
– Podetia to 5mm tall, corticate for about 2 mm at base **24. C. humilis**

43. Podetia and cup interior coarsely sorediate **13. C. chlorophaea**
– Podetia and cup warted or squamulose, not sorediate **29. C. pyxidata**

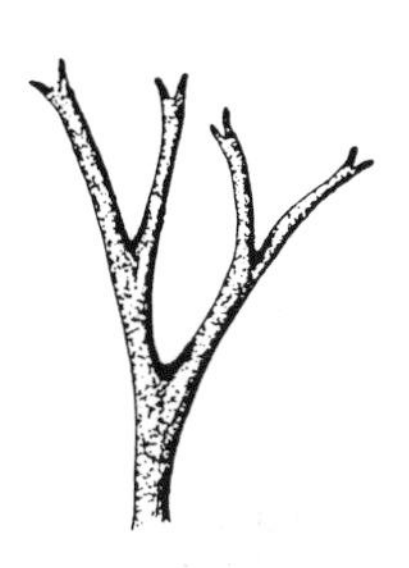
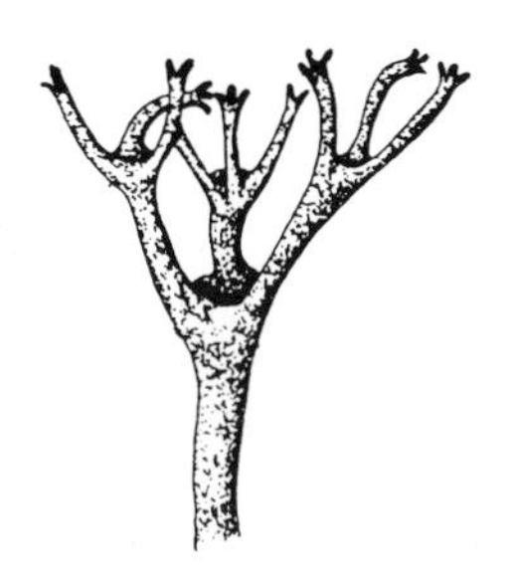
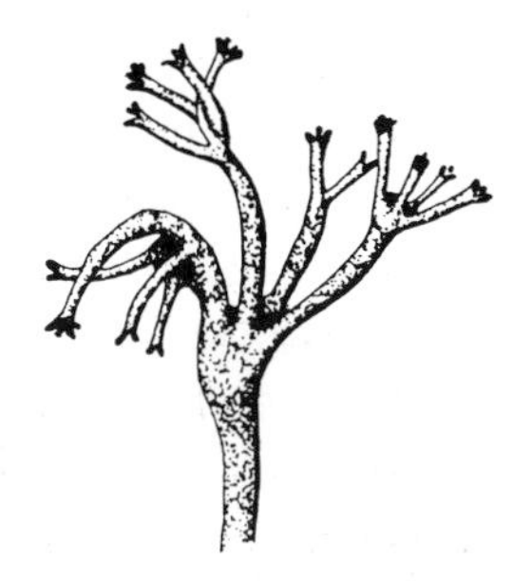

Dichotomous Trichotomous Tetrachotomous

Cladonia branching patterns

APOTHECIA RED

(see also **25. C. luteoalba**)

Many of the red-fruited species are orange to brown at the base of the lower surface of the primary squamules. This coloured area usually reacts K+ red or purple.

1. Cladonia bellidiflora Primary squamules usually disappear early, greyish yellow, much incised and brownish on lower surface towards the base. Podetia to 4 cm tall, with numerous peeling squamules, never sorediate, either without, or with only a narrow cup which is plugged by the bright red apothecium. The cup may rarely have secondary fruiting extensions growing from the rim.
KC+ yellow, UV+ white.
It may be distinguished from *C. squamosa* (which also has peeling squamules on the podetia) by the red apothecia, yellow tinge and the KC+ reaction.
Habitat: Frequent on soil and peat especially in stabilized scree. Mainly found in upland areas of Scotland and northern England.

C. bellidiflora x 6.

8

2. C. digitata Primary squamules large (up to about 1 cm wide), grey-green with rounded lobes. Under-surface white, becoming orange towards the base, entirely covered with farinose soralia which extend right to the upturned margin. Frequently infertile, when it forms a loose mat of squamules. Podetia to 1 cm tall, often curved, pointed or with irregular cups which expand evenly from the base and are covered with farinose soredia. Apothecia bright red.
K+ yellow, P+ orange.
Habitat: Most frequent in the South, on rotting trees, humus and peat.

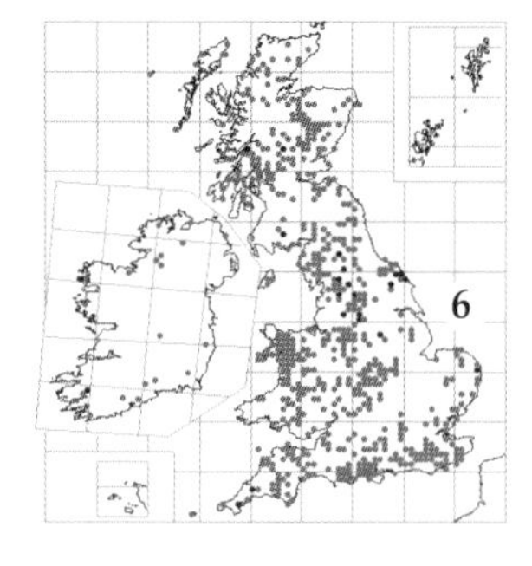

C. digitata x 4.

3. C. diversa (C. coccifera agg.) A very distinctive species in which the apothecia are persistently red. Primary squamules present, yellow-green, rounded to incised with a white under-surface, brownish at the base. Podetia wide, short (to 2 cm tall), stout, yellow-grey or yellow-green, covered in corticate granules and frequently small squamules, and can look like a yellowish *C. pyxidata*. The podetia are often deformed in shape with bright red apothecia or pycnidia around the margin. The apothecia become confluent and may cover the whole of the top of the cup. It contains usnic acid which has antibiotic properties and was formerly applied to cuts to promote healing.
KC+ yellow, P–, UV–.
Habitat: Common on acid soil, rotting trees, heathland, sand dunes and soil pockets on walls in upland regions. **C. pleurota** is entirely sorediate, and rare.

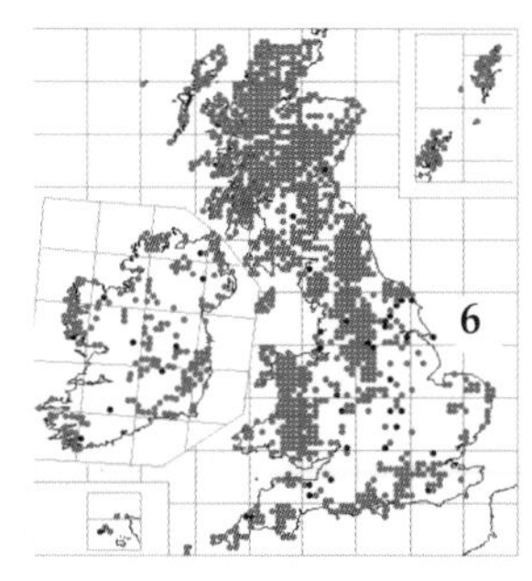

C. diversa x 3.

4. C. floerkeana Primary squamules grey, very small and slightly incised, persistent and forming a thin mat. Podetia grey, simple or branched, sometimes slightly expanding at the apex, covered in grey squamules or granules on the upper part. Apothecia bright to dark red and confluent. This species is known as 'bengal or devil's matchsticks'. A very variable species.
Reactions: usually negative but may be K+y, or P+o, CK+y, UV– or UV+ blue.
Habitat: Very common on rotting wood, humus, peat and sand dunes.

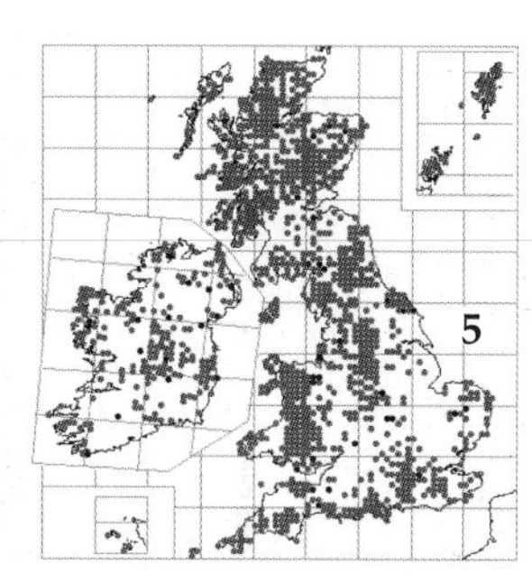

C. floerkeana x 6.

5. C. macilenta Primary squamules small, bluish grey-green, incised and often forming a dense mat which may not persist, often brownish towards the base on the underside. Podetia simple or branched without cups, the lower part sometimes squamulose, the upper part granular or farinose-sorediate. Apothecia bright red. When not fertile may be separated from *C. coniocraea* by its greyer colour, retained when wet, and the K+y reaction; both species are P+ orange. *C. polydactyla* is very difficult to separate when young and before it develops cups. K+ yellow, UV– or UV+ blue.
Habitat: Common on rotting wood, trees, fences and soil.

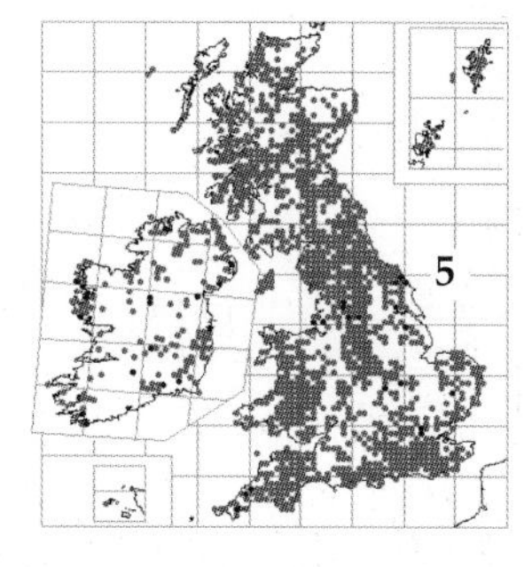

C. macilenta x 5.

6. C. polydactyla Primary squamules bluish grey-green with incised tips, often orange-brown towards the base on the underside. It usually persists as a thin mat. Podetia up to 3 cm tall, branched and lacking cups or, when well-developed, with regular cups which frequently have secondary podetia proliferating from the margins. The lower part of the podetium is squamulose becoming farinose-sorediate above. Apothecia bright red. A variable species.
K+ yellow, P+ orange, UV–.
Habitat: Very common, especially in the West, on wood, humus, soil and peat.

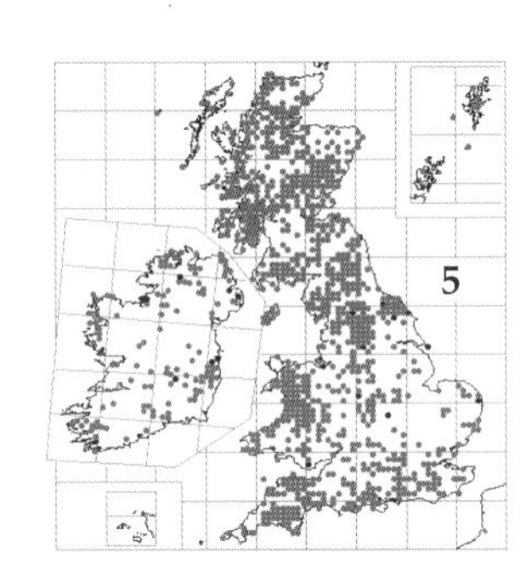

C. polydactyla x 3.

7. C. sulphurina Primary squamules are up to 1 cm long and brown-orange towards the base. Podetia yellowish grey to lemon-yellow, up to 5 cm tall, without a cup. Podetia entirely covered with farinose soralia except at the base, where they are corticate or occasionally squamulose. Longitudinal splits in the upper part are normally present. It is seldom fertile.
KC+ yellow, UV+ white.
Habitat: Very rare in the South but becomes common in upland Scotland. On rotting wood, old thatch, humus and peat.

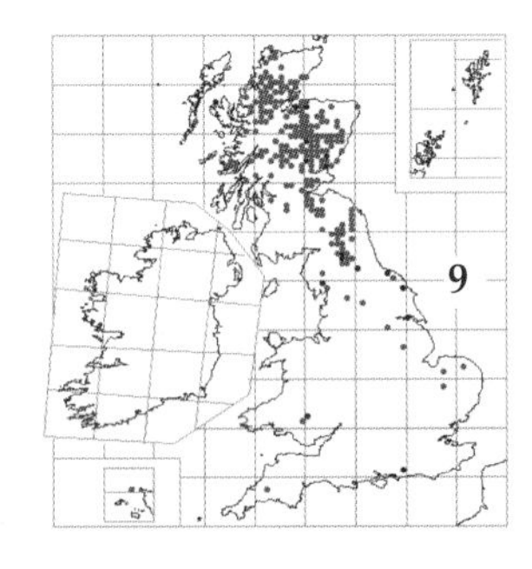

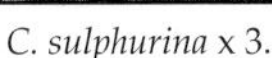
C. sulphurina x 3.

8. C. deformis differs from *C. sulphurina* in the presence of zeorin and the absence of squamatic acid. It has more regular podetia that expand gradually from the base up to distinct cups and which lack the distinctive longitudinal splits of *C. sulphurina*.
KC+ yellow, UV–.
Habitat: Very rare in the Scottish Highlands, on rotting wood and peat.

APOTHECIA BROWN

9. Cladonia arbuscula Primary thallus granular, evanescent. Podetia forming tufted mats up to 8 cm high, green-grey almost always with a yellowish tinge when fresh. Branching tri- or tetrachotomous, the terminal branches being strongly recurved mainly in one direction (in *C. ciliata* only the tips are bent like this). The surface of the podetium is light and spotted with darker patches. The axils are open.
K–, KC+ yellow, P+ red. The very rare **C. mitis** is P– and the branches are less strongly orientated in one direction.
Habitat: Fairly common on acid heathlands, particularly peat moors in upland areas and dunes.

C. arbuscula x 1.

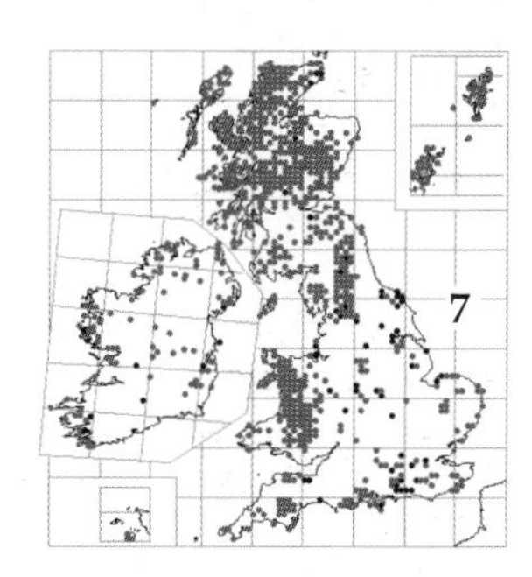

10. C. caespiticia Primary squamules up to 5 mm high and 2 mm wide, incised, ascending and forming compact cushions. The upper surface greyish-green with dark pycnidia and small, light brown apothecia, usually sessile or on very short (up to 4 mm high), pinkish, translucent stalks without algae. Lower surface of squamules white.
K–, P+ red.
Habitat: Frequent, on soil in old woods and sheltered mossy banks. Mainly in the West and South West.

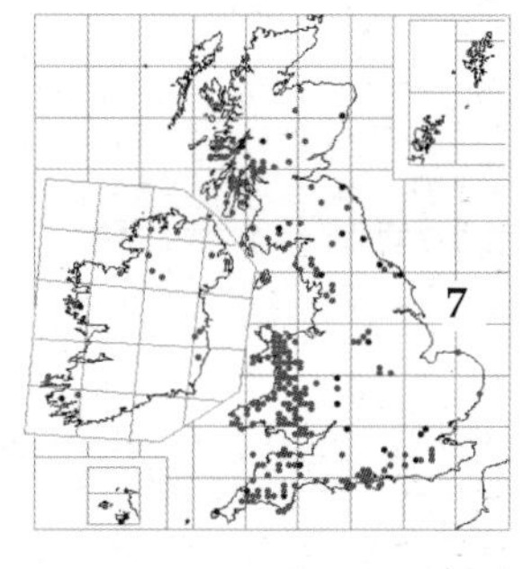

C. caespiticia x 4.

C. caespiticia showing podetium growing on a squamule.

11. C. cervicornis subsp. **cervicornis** Primary thallus up to 4 mm high. Squamules with rounded but often notched tips. Upper surface blue-green to green. Under surface white tinged with mauve, not blackened towards the base (see *C. subcervicornis*). Podetia not very distorted, to 1 cm tall, not proliferating from the centre, slightly squamulose, surface smooth.

12. C. cervicornis subsp. **verticillata** Squamules smaller, often absent. Podetia very distinctive, dark green-brown, often areolate, opening abruptly into wide shallow cups from the centre of which grow further podetia in tiers.
P+ red.
Habitat: Both subspecies frequent on acid soils, peat and sand dunes.

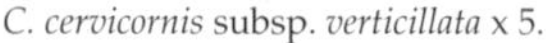

C. cervicornis subsp. *verticillata* x 5.

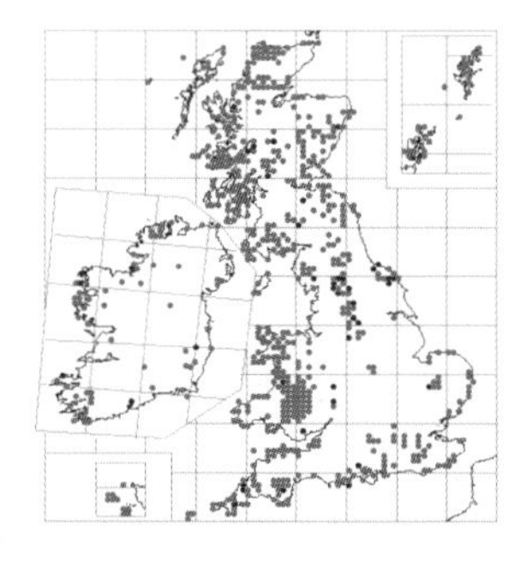

C. cervicornis subsp. *cervicornis* .

13. C. chlorophaea Primary thallus greenish grey, squamules small, broad, erect and incised. Under-surface white and visible where the squamules curl over. Podetia up to 3 cm tall expanding smoothly from the base to the wide cup. The outer surface and the interior of the cup is covered in granular soredia (externally sometimes corticate) and may have digitate proliferations on the margin.

Due to the several chemotypes the reactions are unreliable but it is usually K–, P+ red, UV–.
Habitat: Very common on soil, rotting stumps and peat. The rarer *C. humilis* (24) is K+ yellow and has farinose soredia and is found on sandy, often disturbed soils in lowland Britain.

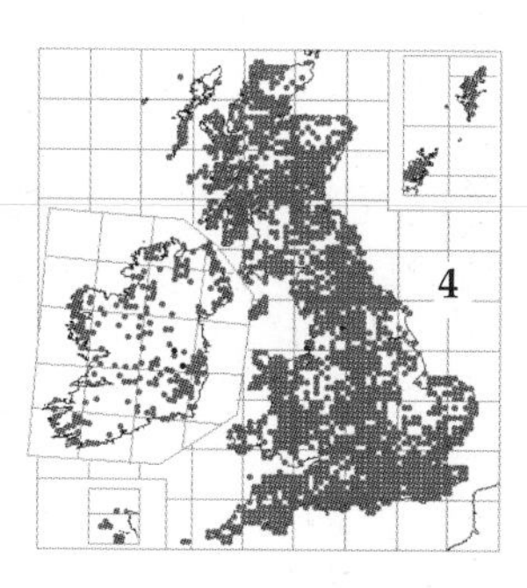

C. chlorophaea x 4.

14. C. ciliata Podetia up to 6 cm long, pale green-grey (var. *tenuis*), often with a purplish tinge towards the tips. Richly branched with short lateral branches. It is a more delicate grey-blue than either *C. arbuscula* or *C. portentosa* with which it is most frequently confused. There are no squamules on the podetia (*C. rangiformis* has squamules on the lower part of the podetia). It is mainly dichotomously branched, only the extreme branch tips curled down and often pointing mainly in one direction. In *C. arbuscula* it is the whole end of the branch that is turned over to one side.
K–, KC–, P+ red (*C. portentosa* is P–), UV–. The rare var. *ciliata* has a light grey thallus without a green tinge.
Habitat: Common (but under-recorded) on dunes, moors, heathland and scree.

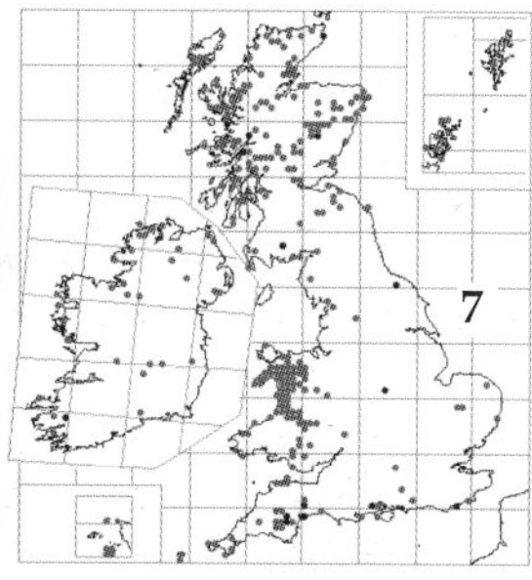

C. ciliata x 3.

15. C. coniocraea Primary thallus green, squamules forming extensive patches, lower surface white, often lightly sorediate. Podetia up to 3 cm tall, corticate, slightly squamulose at the base, becoming sorediate above, pointed or sometimes terminating in a very narrow cup, usually slightly curved.
P+ red, K–.
Habitat: Very common in woods, where it is found on acid-barked trees especially near the base, or on decaying stumps and logs. Rarely on humus-rich acid soils. It is resistant to pollution and, with *C. humulis*, is often the only *Cladonia* species to be found in urban areas. Colour and K– reaction separate infertile material from *C. macilenta* which stays grey, and does not become greener, when wet.

C. coniocraea x 4.

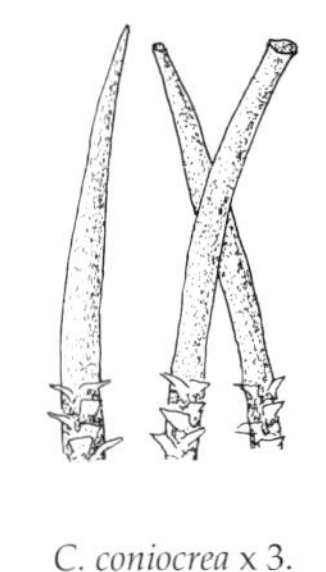

C. coniocrea x 3.

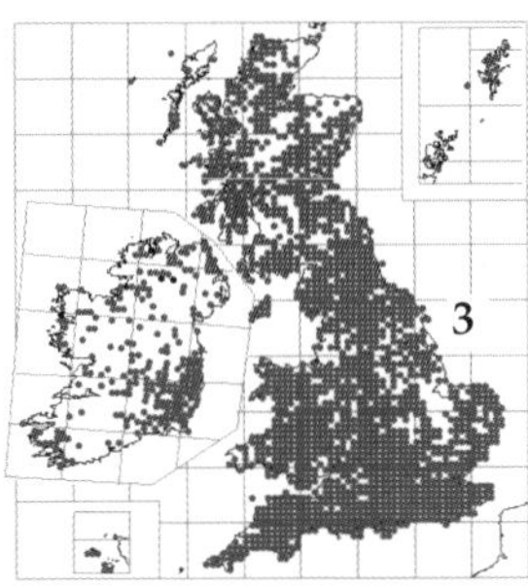

16. C. convoluta Thallus of squamules, yellow-green with a very pale yellow lower surface. Similar to *C. foliacea* but larger (up to 2 cm high), with consistently broader lobes and forming much looser mats or often just one or two thalli. It often has black marginal cilia.
K–, P+ red.
Habitat: A very local species of a few sunny calcareous slopes in south Britain.

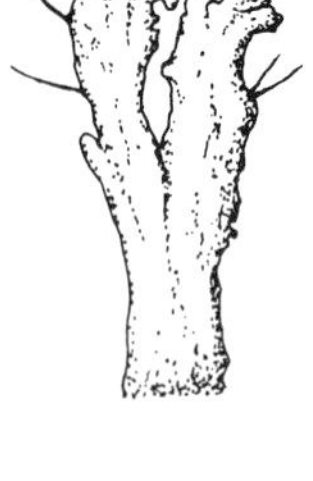

C. convoluta x 3.

17. C. cornuta Primary thallus of small, rather rounded squamules. Podetia to 4 cm tall, green-grey, pointed, farinose-sorediate in upper half, smooth and corticate in the lower half, often with a few squamules present.
P+ red.
Habitat: Rather common in upland Scotland on peat and rotting wood. Rare in other parts of British Isles.

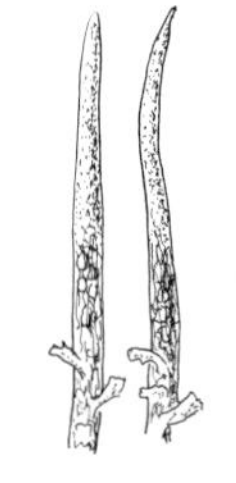

C. cornuta x 3.

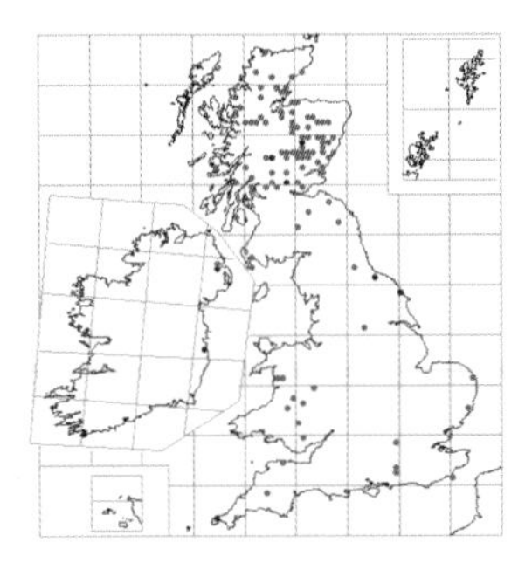

18. C. crispata var. **cetrariformis** Primary thallus of squamules up to 2 mm long, sometimes persisting. Podetia variable, to about 5 cm tall, rather dark brown-grey to olive-green, smoothly corticate and palely reticulated, especially in the paler specimens, axils widely open, podetia squamulose towards the base, usually smooth above. Sometimes bears sharply flaring, narrow cups which are open into the interior of the podetium. Their margins have finger-like outgrowths, one of which usually elongates into another cup, which in its turn may repeat this arrangement.
Spot reactions: negative but UV+ white.
Habitat: Fairly common on acid heathlands and peat bogs, also on decaying trees. Most common in the North and West but a very rich sites is in Norfolk.

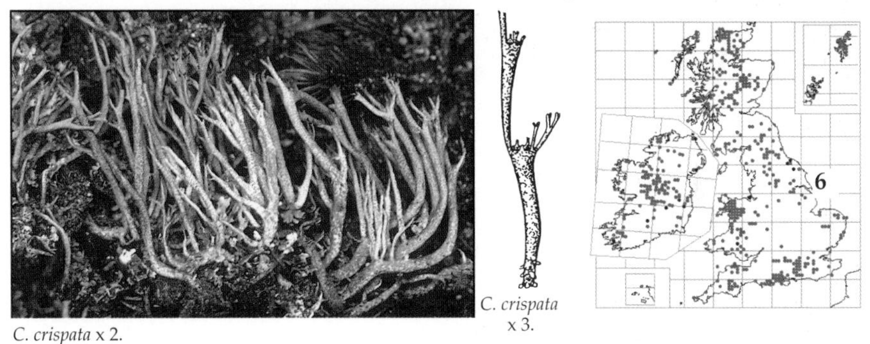

C. crispata x 2.

C. crispata x 3.

19. C. fimbriata Primary thallus of small, incised squamules. Podetia to 1.5 cm tall, distinguished by the slender stems which open abruptly to a very regular cup ('golf-tee' shaped), covered in delicate, greenish farinose soredia without corticate granules or squamules. Not corticate at base (see *C. humulis*).
P+ rust-red, UV–.
Habitat: Very common on rotting wood, earth (especially recently disturbed), humus pockets on walls and dunes, often amongst mosses, even in polluted areas.

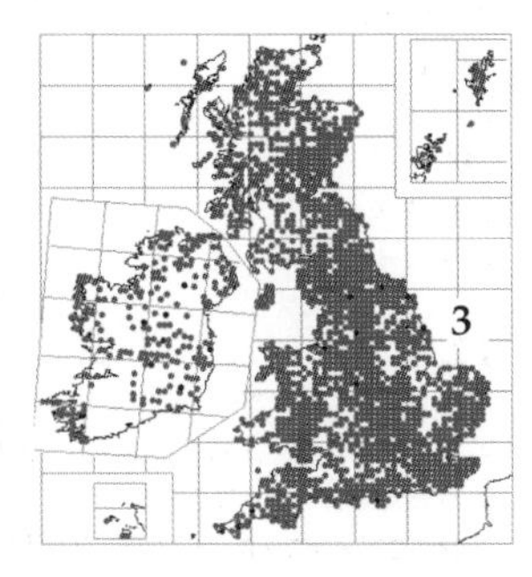

C. fimbriata x 2.

20. C. foliacea Primary thallus yellow-green, tufted, the squamules up to 1 cm tall with deeply incised and recurved tips. Rarely with black cilia on the margin. Under-surface yellowish (this helps separate it from *C. subcervicornis* and *C. cervicornis*). Squamules frequently curled over to show the under-surface. Podetia small, rather rare ,with gradually widening, smooth, irregular cups.
K–, P+ red, KC+ yellow.
Habitat: Widely distributed and often forming extensive patches, particularly

on basic, dry and sunny sandy areas, stabilised shingle and grasslands near the coast; more rarely found inland (e.g. Breckland).

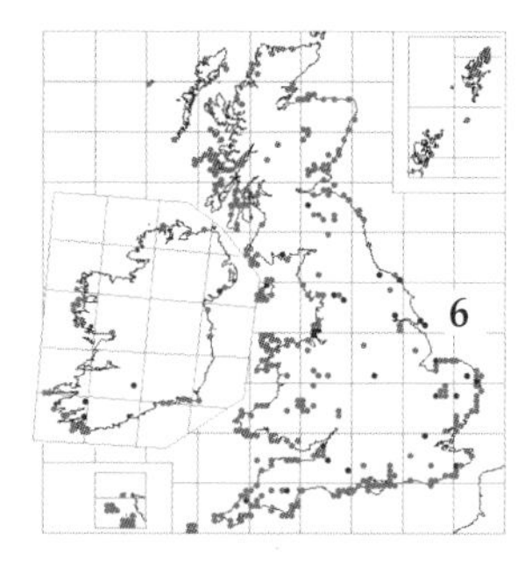

C. foliacea x 2.

21. C. furcata A very variable species. Basal squamules usually disappearing early. The podetia form a loose tufted mat. Brown-grey to olive-green, sometimes with a purplish tinge. Podetia almost smooth except for a mosaic of lighter coloured reticulation (like crazy-paving), often with peeling squamules. It branches dichotomously at a narrow angle with the axils sometimes perforated and ending in pointed tips but never cups. Usually infertile. Apothecia small, brown, globose on the tips of the branches.
Usually K– or K+ yellow, P+ rust-red.
Habitat: Common on acid heathlands and on soil in woods throughout the British Isles.

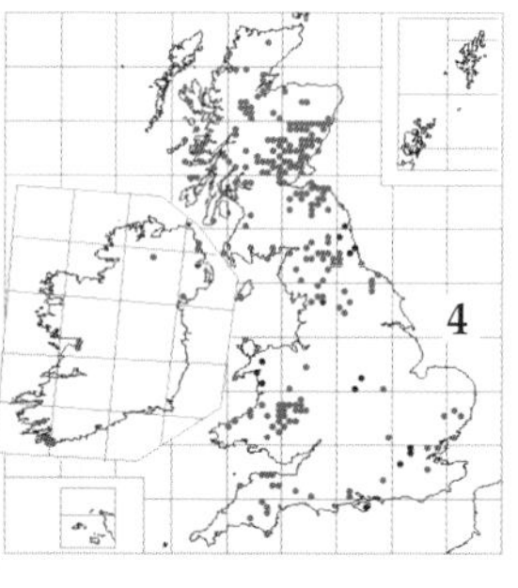

C. furcata (left x 2, right x 3).

22. C. glauca Basal squamules insignificant. Podetia to 5 cm tall, squamulose at the base and densely sorediate above, mostly simple, but sometimes branched. On most podetia a shallow, inrolled longitudinal slit will be found. Cups absent but there is sometimes some digitate branching at the tips of the podetia.
Reactions negative but UV+ ice-blue. (*C. subulata* is P+r, UV–, with antler-like branching.)
Habitat: Frequent in heathland and on rotting tree stumps, mainly in the East.

23. C. gracilis Basal squamules disappearing early. This species resembles a tall *C. furcata* but has smooth and areolate, slender, less branched podetia, up to 6 cm tall. It has closed axils, is brown, becoming darker or greyish green towards the base, usually tipped with a narrow, shallow, non-perforated cup, often with small, finger-like protrusions from the rim. Squamules on the podetia are rare. K–, P+ rust-red.
Habitat: Common on acid soils and in woodlands.

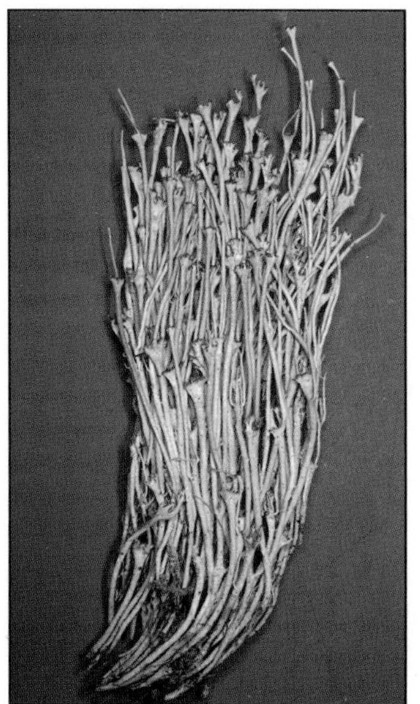

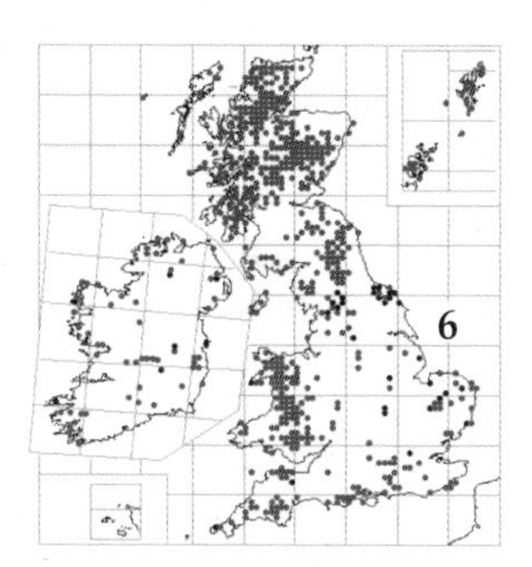

C. gracilis x 2.5.

24. C. humilis (C. conoidea) Basal squamules persistent, up to 5 mm long, rounded or notched tips. Podetia up to 5 mm tall, frequently much shorter. The cup rim is often as wide as it is high, not perforated. Stalk expands from the base or abruptly near the rim. Bottom 2 mm corticate then remainder finely sorediate inside and out. P+r, K+y (the only K+y European species that is brown-fruited and sorediate).
Habitat: Common, especially on sea cliffs, on disturbed soil, often in urban gardens.

C. humilis x 2.

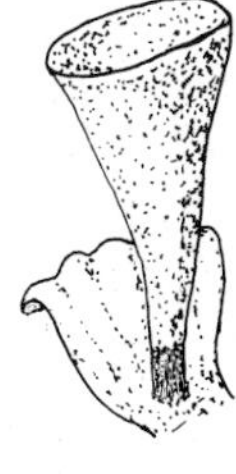

C. humilis x 6.

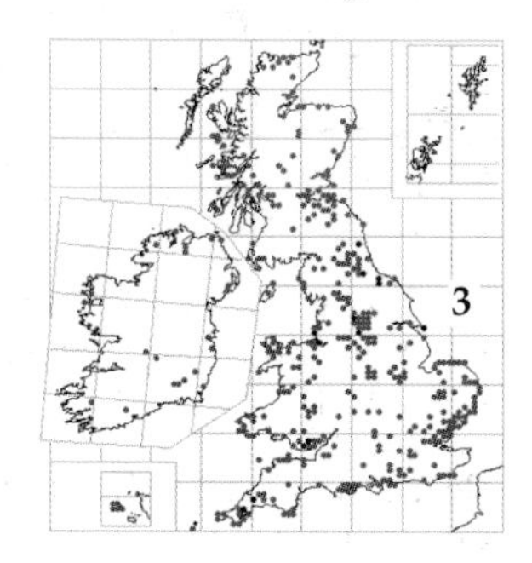

25. C. luteoalba Basal squamules up to 1 cm long, yellowish green, yellowish underneath. Similar to *C. foliacea* but has rounded, only slightly incised lobes with a cotton wool-like lower surface (use x 10 hand-lens). Apothecia are red but are very rare and it is thus put in this section for convenience.
KC+ yellow.
Habitat: Exposed peaty soils and mossy rocks mainly in upland northern England.

C. luteoalba x 3.

26. C. ochrochlora Basal squamules green and often slightly sorediate on the margin. Podetia to 4 cm tall, corticate at the base and mostly sorediate in the upper part. Differs from *C. coniocrea* in the longer podetia which are decorticate in patches and having small, abruptly widening cups.
P+ red, K–, UV–.
Habitat: Fairly common, usually in damper woods than *C. coniocraea*. Found on very rich humus, rotting tree stumps, etc., but also sometimes on heaths.

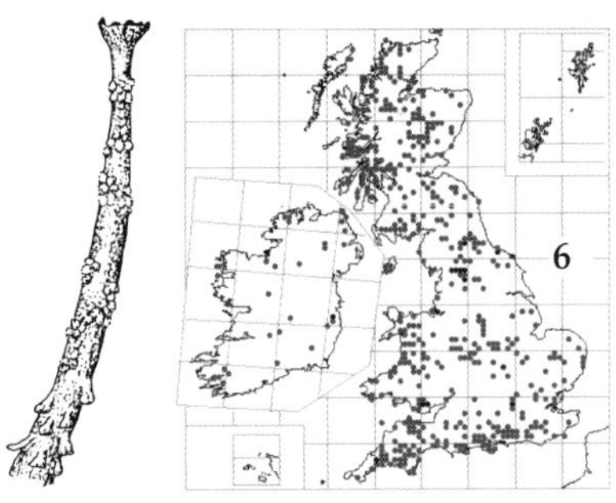

C. ochrochlora x 3.

27. C. parasitica Primary thallus consists of a compact mat of very incised, small, delicate squamules, pale brownish grey with numerous black pycnidia. There are granular soredia on the lower surface. When poorly developed, it often appears to be a granular patch and it needs close inspection to see the very small squamules. Podetia up to 1 cm tall, grey-green, without cups, mostly branched, contorted, furrowed and with soredia or squamules.
K+ yellow, P+ orange.
Habitat: Infrequent, most commonly found in the South East on trees, decorticated tree stumps, logs (especially oak), occasionally on damp humus.

C. parasitica x 4.

28. C. portentosa Thallus light greenish grey or pale cream, very richly branched, branching mainly trichotomous but the final division is sometimes dichotomous. The branchlets spreading out in all directions with the axils often perforate. It forms compact, delicately tufted, interwoven mats up to 6 cm tall.
K–, KC+ yellow, P– (both *C. ciliata* and *C. arbuscula* are P+ rust-red).
Habitat: Very common on heaths, dunes and peat moors. It appears to be declining in many areas.

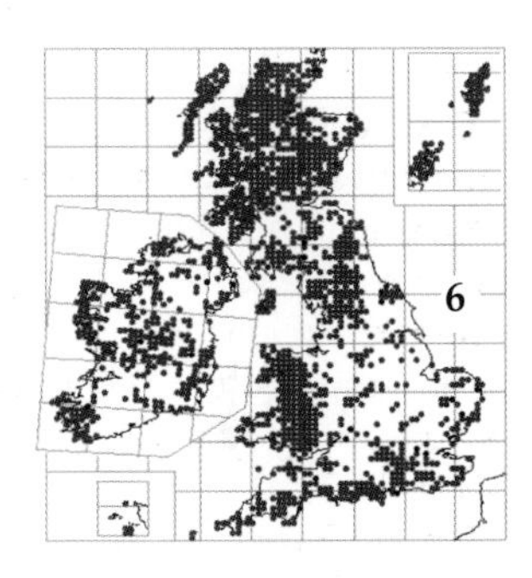

C. portentosa x 4.5.

29. C. pyxidata Basal squamules small and little indented. Podetia to 15 mm tall, green to brown-green, expanding from the base. There is a rough, warted or coarse granular surface on the podetium and also inside the cup where the granules are often smooth, shiny and convex. There are no soredia. It very rarely has proliferations around the margins. This species was used to produce a remedy for whooping cough. **C. pocillum** is similar and probably only an ecotype. It has neatly delimited rosettes of overlapping basal squamules It is found on mossy rocks, mortar and humus in calcareous sites where it is often parasitized by *Diploschistes muscorum*.
P+ red, UV–.
Habitat: Very common, on mossy trees, rocks and walls, often on drier, more sandy soils than *C. chlorophaea*.

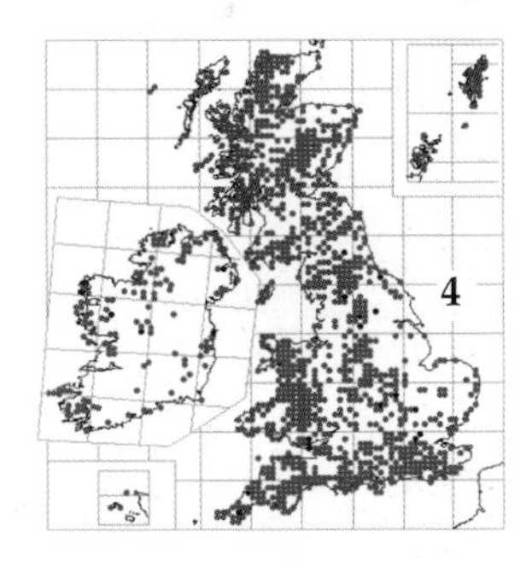

C. pyxidata x 3.

30. C. ramulosa (C. anomaea) Basal squamules small, incised and brittle. Podetia usually present, up to 3 cm tall, sometimes branched, pointed or with very narrow cups which are not perforated in the centre (unlike *C. squamosa*). The apothecia are brown when wet, turgid and translucent. The surfaces of the podetia have coarse squamules which break off easily when dry but often large areas of the podetia are almost decorticate or with scattered granules.
K–, P+ red.
Habitat: Frequent on acid soils, thatch and on rotting tree stumps in woods. It is also a characteristic species of the coast.

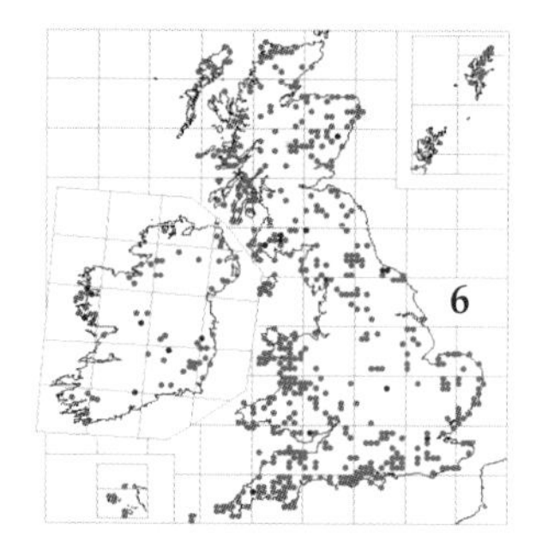

C. ramulosa x 4.

31. C. rangiferina Thallus white to light grey with a purple-brown tinge towards the tips. The surface under a hand-lens appears cottony. Richly branched but at a smaller angle than *C. portentosa*. Branching usually tetrachotomous. Main branches markedly curved in the same direction (similar to *C. arbuscula*). Forms extensive, interwoven mats up to 8 cm tall.
P+ red, K+ yellow, UV–. The K+ yellow reaction, purple tinge, and its usually coarser habit separate it from *C. portentosa* and *C. arbuscula*.
Habitat: Common on Scottish mountains but not essentially an arctic species. It can be found on lowland heaths and by the coast.

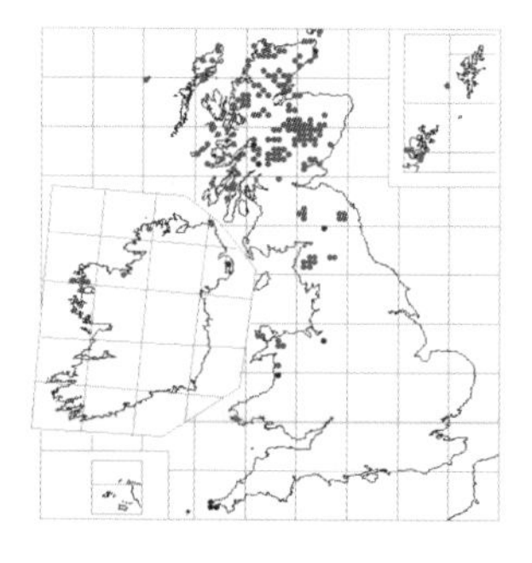

C. rangiferina x 2.

32. C. rangiformis Podetia up to 5 cm tall, much branched, with pointed tips and with usually closed axils. Resembles *C. furcata* but with neat, dispersed islets of green algal cells on a uniform white background. The branching is also at a wider angle.
K+ yellow (*C. furcata* is K–), usually P+ red.
Habitat: Common on similar habitats to *C. furcata* but appears to prefer more basic soils, calcareous grassland and stabilized dunes.

C. rangiformis x 4.

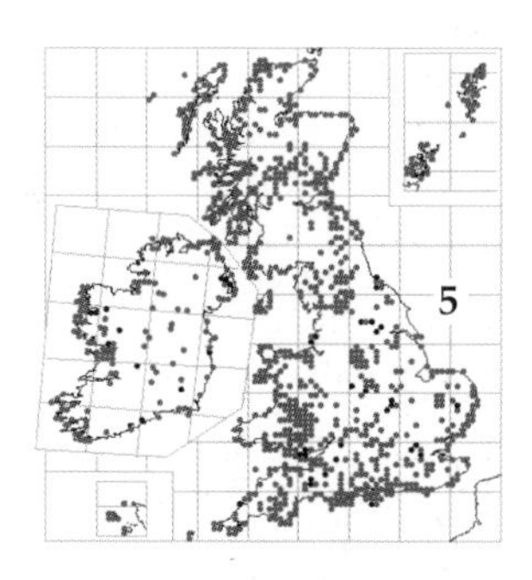

33. C. squamosa Basal squamules incised, forming a dense mat but often disappearing early in development. Podetia to 5 cm tall, very variable, with either pointed tips or poorly developed, narrow cups that may widen out abruptly above the stem, the centre of the podetium becoming open and/or becoming split near the apex. The margin has finger-like extensions, podetia are covered in prominent grey to bright green peeling squamules. It may be distinguished from *C. crispata* by the velvety appearance of the decorticated areas where the squamules have peeled back. There are no soredia.
Spot reactions: negative but UV+ white. A very variable species.
Habitat: Very common on acid soil, peat and rotting wood particularly in sheltered situations.

C. squamosa x 4.

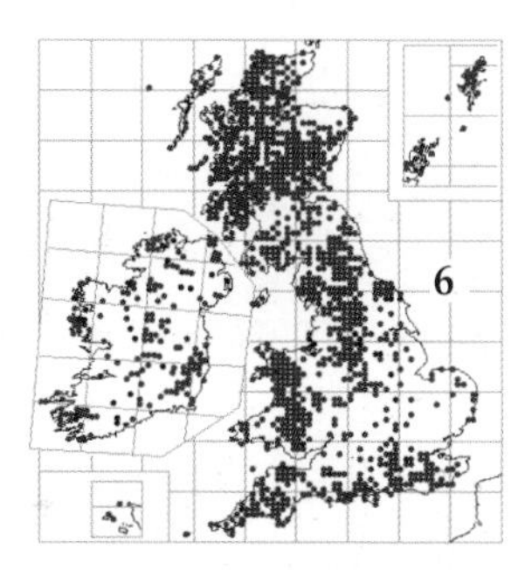

34. C. squamosa var. **subsquamosa** Very similar to the species but tends to be more robust and densely squamulose. It is probably only a chemotype as it differs mainly in its chemical reactions.
K+ yellow, P+ orange, UV–.
Habitat: It is common in similar situations to the species.

35. C. strepsilis Basal squamules bronze to green-brown, up to 5 mm high, shallowly notched at the tips with a shape rather like *C. foliacea*. Very rarely sorediate. Podetia short and irregular but not normally present. Dark brown pycnidia are often found on the squamules.
K–, P+ yellow, C+ bright green. This is the only British lichen to give this C+ reaction (due to strepsilin), UV+ white.
Habitat: Locally abundant, on well-lit open, boggy sites on peat moors and heaths.

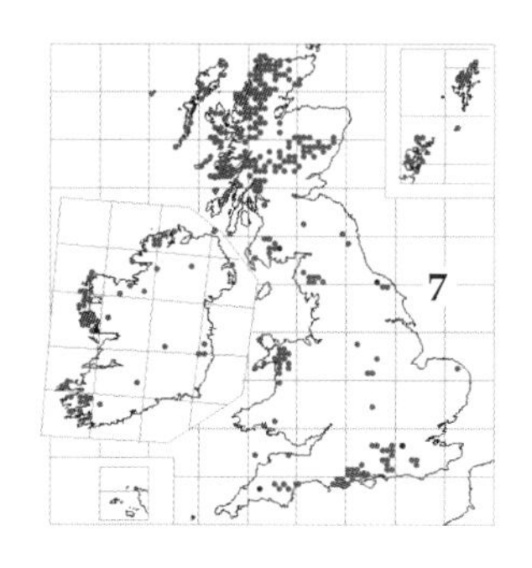

C. strepsilis x 3.

36. C. subcervicornis Basal squamules up to 2 cm long, bluntly incised at the tips. Upper surface pale grey-green to apple-green when wet. Under-surface white, blackened towards the base. Forms compact, dense, cushion-like tufts of ascending squamules. Podetia sometimes present, up to 15 mm tall with an abruptly widening cup with irregular lobules and small brown apothecia.
K+ yellow, P+ red.
Habitat: Very common on acid soil or in small soil pockets and cracks on siliceous rocks in well-lit, rocky, coastal and upland areas.

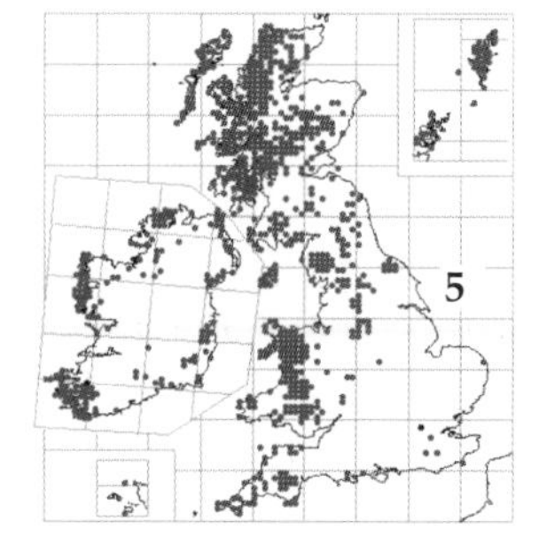

C. subcervicornis x 3.

37. C. subrangiformis (*C. furcata* subsp. *subrangiformis*) is similar to *C. furcata*, (possibly only an ecotype) but usually brown, more coarse and contorted, with short, erect branchlets towards the top, generally in prostrate tufts. Hard, white warts are found near the base of the podetia.
K+ yellow.
Habitat: On closely grazed, open calcareous grassland.

38. C. subulata Primary thallus insignificant. Podetia to 5 cm tall, yellow-green to grey-green, entirely farinose sorediate, occasionally corticate and squamulose towards the base, cups few, irregular with antler-like proliferations rarely tipped with narrow cups.
P+ rust-red, UV– (*C. glauca* is P–, UV+ bluish and has longitudinal slits on the podetia).
Habitat: Frequent on dry sandy heaths and sometimes on soil on the tops of walls.

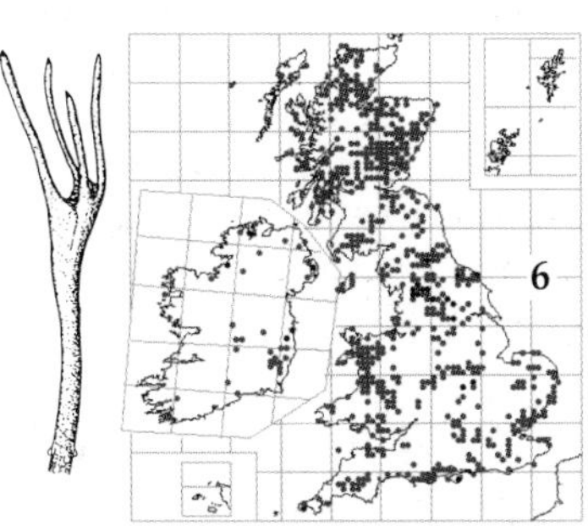

39. C. uncialis subsp. **biuncialis** Basal squamules absent. Podetia about 5 cm long and up to about 3 mm diam, almost white to pale yellowish green, sparsely and strictly dichotomously branched and widening at the open axils. Forming loose mats or more scattered over the substratum. When dry it is very brittle and easily breaks up into small tubes looking like pieces of macaroni.
KC+ yellowish, P–, UV+ white (subsp. **uncialis** is rare, found on sand dunes in the North East. It is not dicotomously branched).
Habitat: Common on open, acid heathlands especially peat bogs even in waterlogged areas.

C. uncialis x 2.

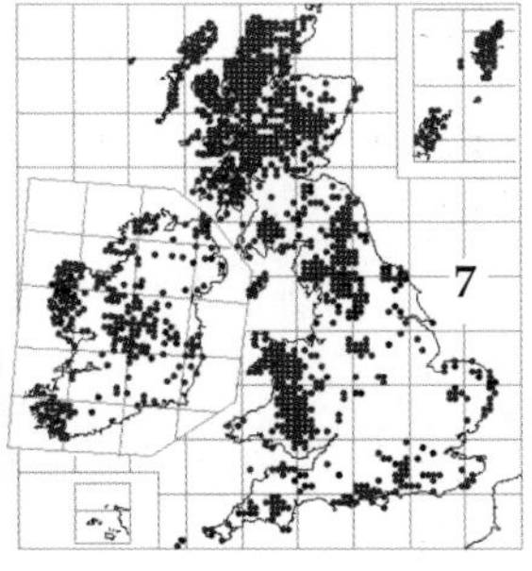

CLAUZADEA (after the French lichenologist Georges Clauzade, born 1914). **Thallus** crustose and usually endolithic. **Photobiont** *Trebouxia*. **Apothecia** lecideine and usually dark brown to black. **Hymenium** I+ pale blue. **Ascus** 8-spored, *Porpidia*-type. **Spores** simple, colourless. **Pycnidia** immersed. **Chemical reactions** negative.

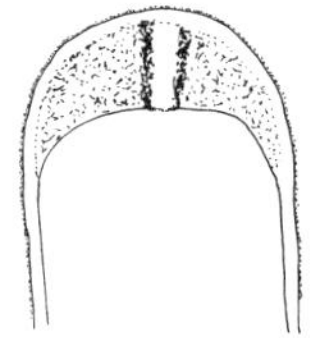
K/I reaction to ascus tip.

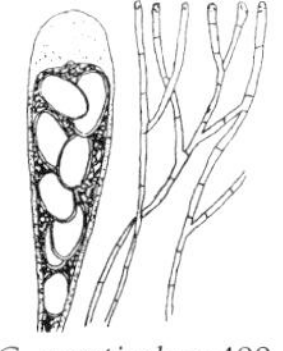
C. monticola x 400.

1. Apothecia sessile, not in pits, not pruinose — **3. C. monticola**
– Apothecia ± immersed in pits, pruinose or not — 2
2. Not pruinose. Spores 12–20 x 6–10 µm, thick-walled — **2. C. metzleri**
– Often pruinose. Spores 6–12 x 4–8 µm, thin-walled — **1. C. immersa**

1. Clauzadea immersa (Lecidea immersa) Thallus white to pale grey, sometimes with a black prothallus. Apothecia regularly arranged, up to 0.5 mm red-brown and becoming translucent when wet, black when dry. Usually covered in a pale grey pruina. It then looks like a *Verrucaria* species, but if closely examined it will be seen that it has apothecia and not perithecia. Apothecia deeply immersed in the substratum and leave pits when they fall out. Hypothecium pale to dark orange-brown. Spores 12–20 x 6–10 µm, thin-walled.
Habitat: Locally frequent, confined to well-lit, hard limestone.

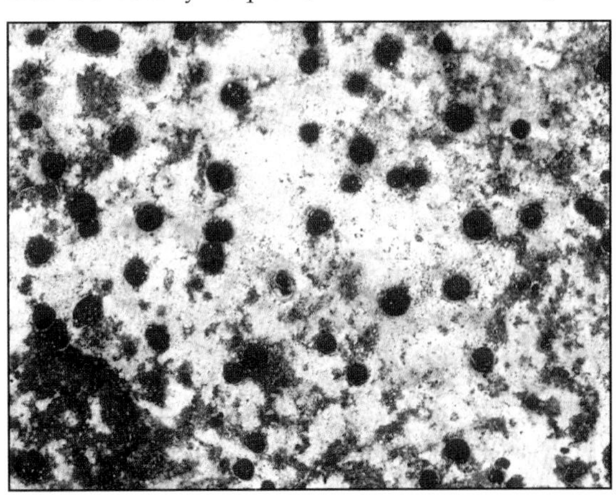
C. immersa x 6.

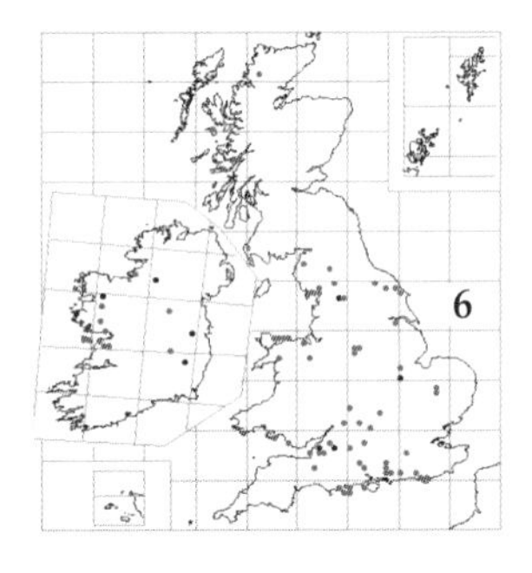

2. C. metzleri (L. metzleri) Similar to the previous species but usually lacking a prothallus. The apothecia are larger (up to 1 mm), not pruinose, often with a brown disc, somewhat more sessile but in shallow pits and in groups or lines. Hypothecium pale to dark reddish brown. Spores 15–25 x 8–10 µm with thick walls.
Habitat: Infrequent, on more shaded, moister sites (e.g. in cracks) than *C. immersa*. It is found on soft as well as hard limestone including chalk pebbles.

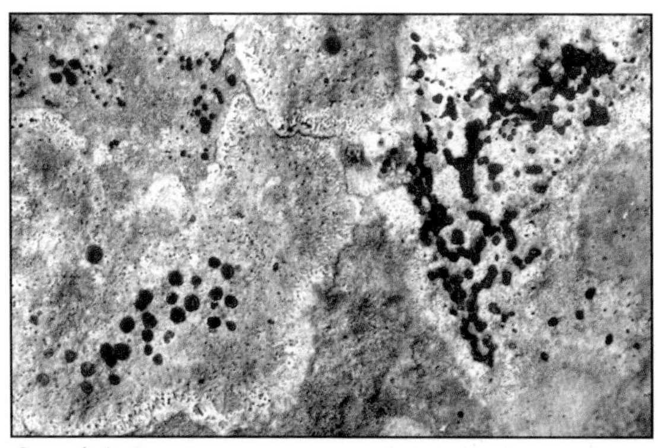

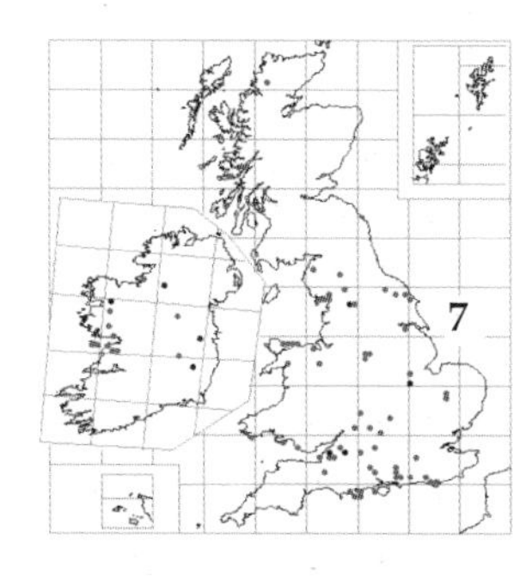

C. metzleri x 2.

3. C. monticola (L. monticola) Thallus darker grey than the previous species and not so frequently endolithic, sometimes grey-brown, it lacks a dark prothallus. Apothecia black (dark red-black when wet), without pruina and becoming convex, sessile and not in pits. Hypothecium reddish brown. The spores are smaller than in the other species, 6–12 x 4–8 µm, thin-walled. The dark red-black apothecia resemble those of *Sarcogyne* but only have 8 spores per ascus instead of the very large number of small spores found in in that genus. *Lecidella stigmatea* has a colourless to pale yellow-brown hypothecium.
Habitat: Frequent on many calcareous substrata, including mortared church walls.

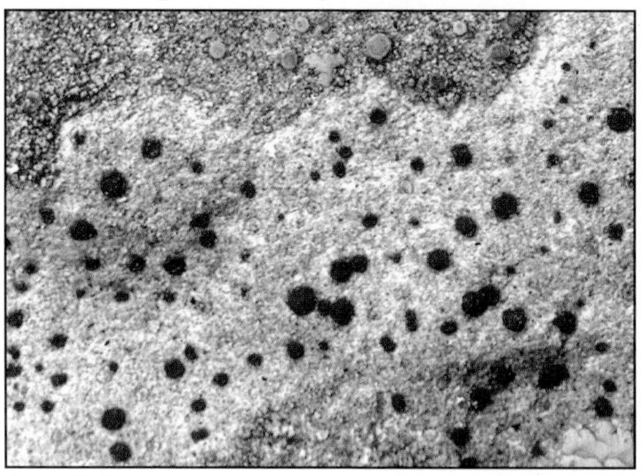

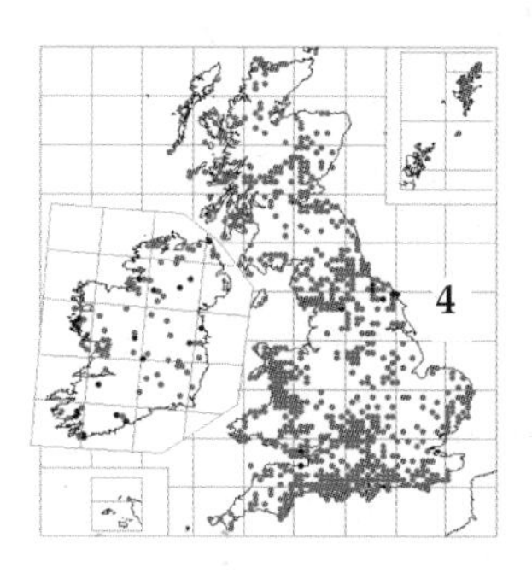

C. monticola x 6.

CLIOSTOMUM ('closed mouth' – from the shape of the pycnidia). **Thallus** crustose. **Photobiont** *Trebouxia.* **Apothecia** lecideine, black. **Ascus** 8-spored, *Biotora*-type. **Spores** colourless, 1- (rarely more) septate, 8 per ascus. **Pycnidia** frequent and conspicuous.

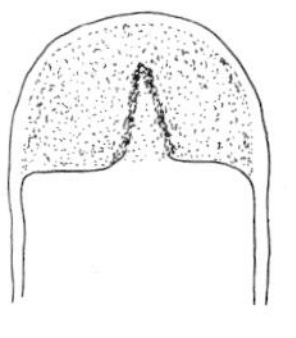

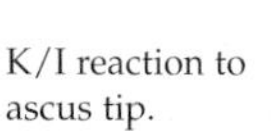

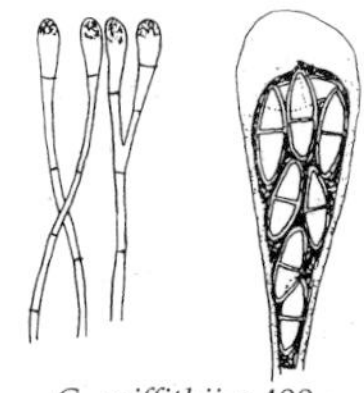

K/I reaction to ascus tip.

C. griffithii x 400.

Cliostomum griffithii (Catillaria griffithii) Thallus white to light grey, shining or warted. Mainly without apothecia but then easily recognized by the numerous, small, black, dust-like pycnidia about 0.2 mm diam. Apothecia much less common, flesh-coloured to light brown, often piebald, with a slightly lighter thin margin, becoming darker with age, frequently pruinose, often convex and distorted. Spores 1-septate, 8–15 x 2–4 µm.
K+ yellow. Walls of pycnidia K+ purple in a squash.
Habitat: One of the more common corticolous species on the drier sides of trees even in moderately polluted areas. Found on all but very acid bark or wood, more rarely on vertical shaded rock.

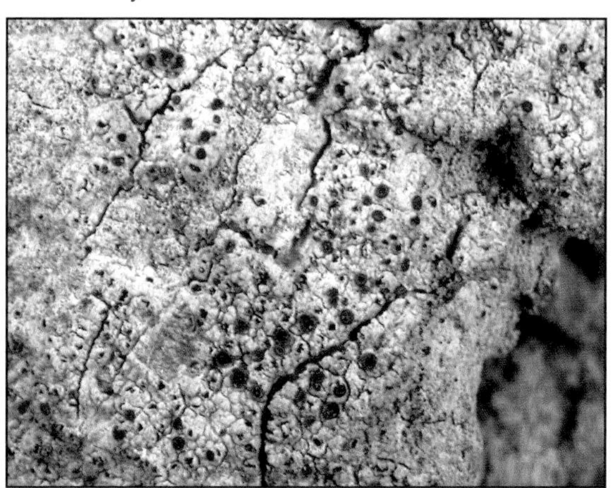

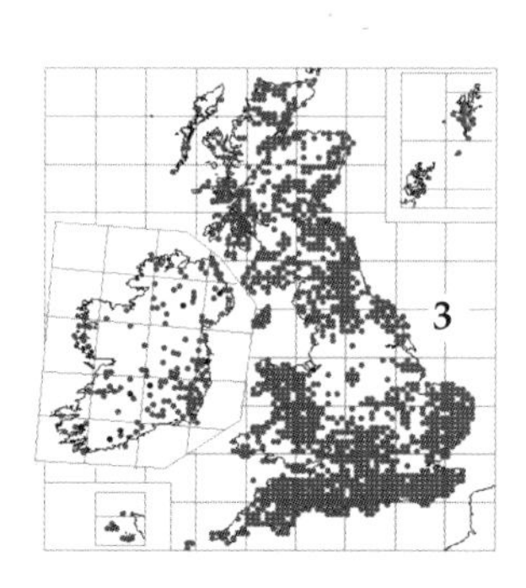

C. griffithii x 5.

COLLEMA ('gelatinous'). **Thallus** foliose to almost crustose, homoiomerous and gelatinous, swollen when wet, becoming thinner when dry. Unlike *Leptogium* it lacks any form of cortex. **Photobiont** *Nostoc*. **Apothecia** lecanorine, the discs appearing reddish when dry. **Ascus** 2- to 8-spored with a thick apex, K/I+ blue apical dome. **Spores** variously shaped, septate or becoming muriform. **Pycnidia** innate, usually with a pale ostiole. **Chemical reactions** all negative.

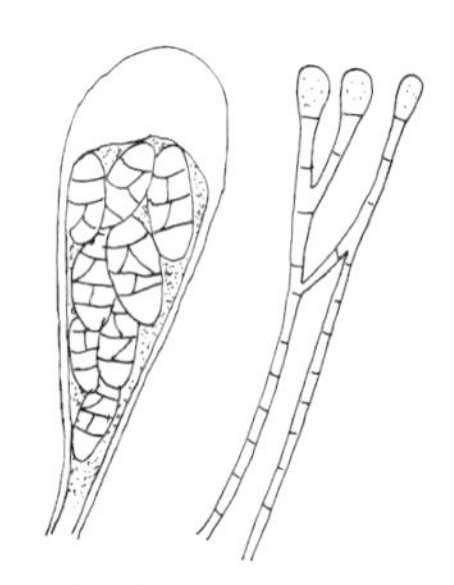

C. crispum x 250.

1. Without isidia, with abundant apothecia, on basic substrata — **9. C. tenax**
– Thallus with isidia or incised lobate margins — 2

2. Isidia globose — 3
– Isidia flattened or coralloid, or with lobate margins — 6

3. Lobes smooth, with minute striations when dry. Very swollen when wet. Apothecia rare — **1. C. auriforme**
– Thallus ridged or smooth, little swollen when wet — 4

4.	On exposed hard calcareous rock	**6. C. fuscovirens**
–	On damp trees and mosses	5
5.	Thallus ridged, rather adpressed. Apothecia numerous	**7. C. nigrescens**
–	Thallus smooth, fairly erect. Apothecia rare	**8. C. subflaccidum**
6.	Longitudinally ridged with coralloid isidia	**5. C. furfuraceum**
–	Lobes not longitudinally ridged, isidia flattened or globular	7
7.	Lobes paper-like and rounded. On mosses or damp, usually acid rock	**4. C. flaccidum**
–	Lobes thicker. On calcareous rock, mortar or soil	8
8.	Lobes with flattened isidia, mainly in the centre	**2. C. crispum**
–	Lobes with incised, rather lobate margins	**3. C. cristatum**

1. Collema auriforme (C. auriculatum) Thallus dark green-brown. Lobes up to 1 cm wide, very swollen when wet, erect and covered with coarse, globular isidia (bead-like when wet) that arise in discrete patches and sometimes cover the thallus (a few isidia are sometimes found on the lower surface). The lobes are smooth and undulating except for minute striations. Apothecia are rare with an isidiate margin. Spores 26–36 x 8–13, submuriform.
Habitat: Common on tombstones, hard calcareous rocks amongst damp mosses in shaded sites, sometimes on the ground in chalk or limestone grasslands.

C. auriforme x 3.

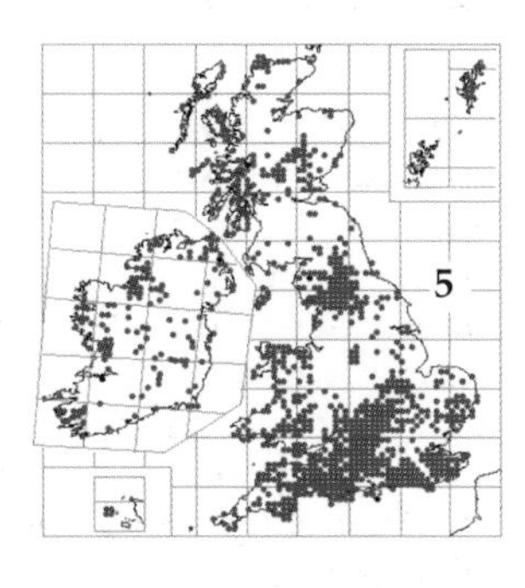

2. C. crispum Thallus green-black to almost-black, lobes under 6 mm across, thin, not greatly swelling when wet, overlapping, margins smooth or slightly incised, pale rhizines on underside. Isidia swollen soon becoming flattened and scale-like, often developing into secondary lobes, mainly confined to the centre of the thallus. Apothecia rather rare, about 2 mm diam, often irregular in shape with a thin margin. Spores becoming muriform, 25–35 x 12–15 µm.
Habitat: Common on damp, calcareous rocks, walls, mortar. Rarely on basic soils.

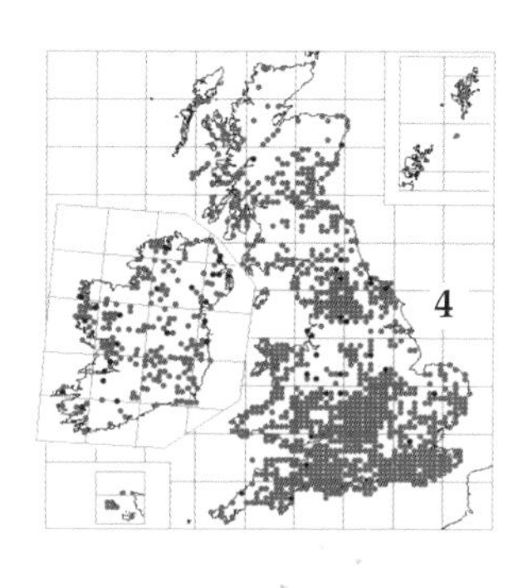

C. crispum x 5.

3. C. cristatum Thallus green-black to black, lobes to 1 cm wide. Often in arcs or rosettes. Lobes rather thin, concave, with deeply incised margins that may appear lobulate, lower surface with clusters of pale rhizines. A few wart-like isidia are sometimes found towards the centre of the lobes, more adpressed than the previous species. The centre of the thallus often dying away. Apothecia are frequent, up to about 5 mm diam. Spores muriform, 18–30 x 8–12 µm.
Habitat: Fairly common on hard limestone, more rarely on mortar, soil or calcareous dunes.

C. cristatum x 3.

4. C. flaccidum Thallus dark green-brown to black and leaflike, not greatly swelling when wet. Lobes up to 3 mm long, ragged, incised, crumpled, raised towards the margins. Isidia become flattened and lobate as they mature. Rarely fertile. Apothecia to 2.5 mm, with smooth margins. Spores 24–36 x 6–7 µm, 3- to 5-septate.
Habitat: Frequent on mosses on damp, mainly acid rocks. Often by waterfalls.

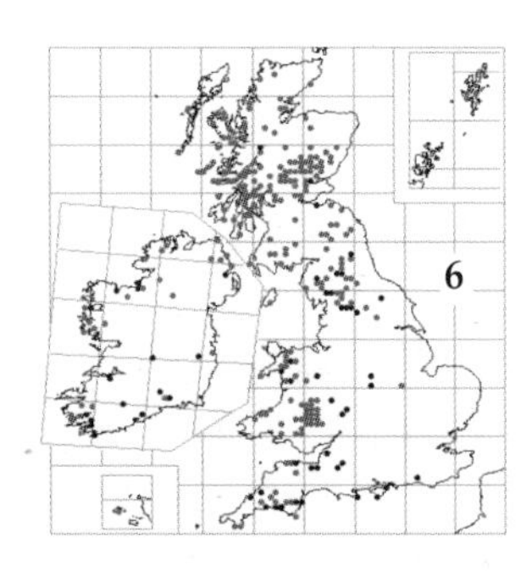

C. flaccidum x 6.

5. C. furfuraceum Thallus very dark green-brown to black, not greatly swollen when wet. A large species with lobes up to 1.5 cm wide and forming extensive colonies. The margins and tips of the lobes often curl upwards, the upper surface has conspicuous radiating, longitudinal ridges. Along these ridges are dense masses of simple or branched, coralloid isidia which may cover the whole upper surface of mature lobes. Apothecia very rare, with isidiate margins. Spores 40–80 x 3–7 µm, 4- to 5-septate.
Habitat: Frequent, mainly in the West, on damp deciduous trees (often on large horizontal branches) or on mosses on trees and, more rarely, rocks.

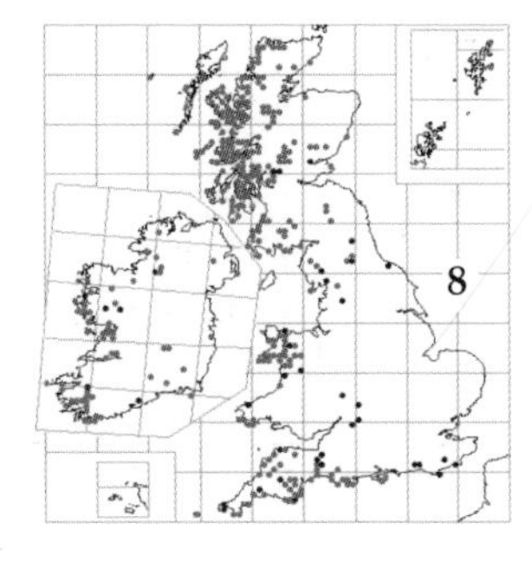

C. furfuraceum x 4.

6. C. fuscovirens (C. tuniforme) Similar in appearance to *C. auriforme* but more adpressed with smaller isidia and thinner lobes that swell little on wetting but become translucent. Lobes to 5 cm wide, few in number and contorted. Lower surface paler. More commonly fertile and, like *C. auriforme*, the margins of the apothecia may be isidiate. Spores becoming muriform, 15–25 x 6–12 µm.
Habitat: Frequent on hard, calcareous rock in full sun.

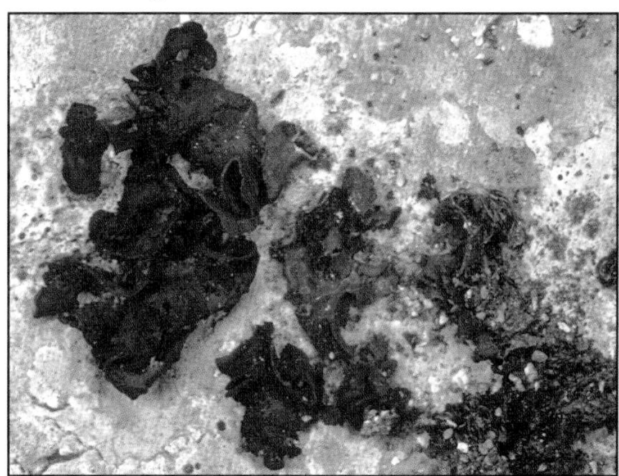

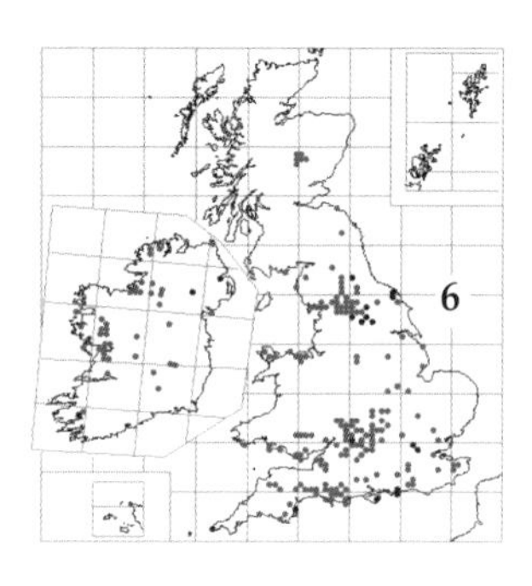

C. fuscovirens x 6.

7. C. nigrescens Thallus dark brown to green-black, lobes to 1 cm wide, longitudinally ridged and bullate. It is adpressed, with small globular isidia and usually with numerous apothecia that may cover the thallus. Spores fusiform, 5- to 12-septate, 50–90 x 3–5 µm. The similar **C. subnigrescens** lacks isidia and has spores 40–75 x 6–7 µm, 4- to 5-septate.
Habitat: Local in the West but declining. Found in similar situations to *C. furfuraceum*.

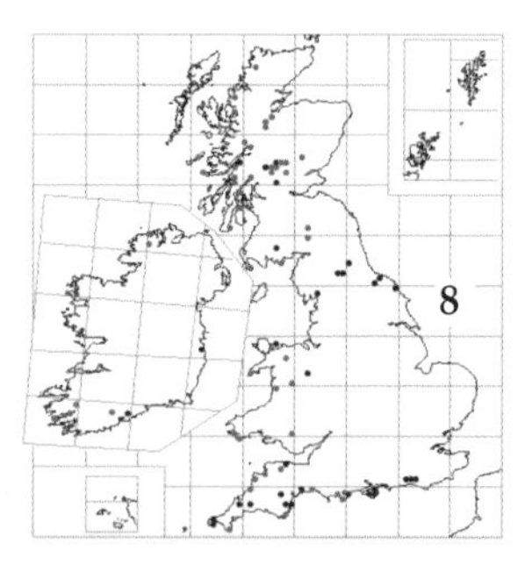

C. nigrescens x 6.

8. C. subflaccidum (C. subfurvum) Thallus paper-like, dark green-brown to black, slightly lighter on the undersurface and at the tips of the lobes. Lobes up to 1.5 cm long, never ridged. More erect than *C. flaccidum* with minute globular instead of foliose isidia, these frequently covering the thallus. Apothecia are very rare. Spores 40–55 x 5–7 µm, 5- to 7-septate.
Habitat: Frequent on damp, shaded deciduous trees and tree stumps.

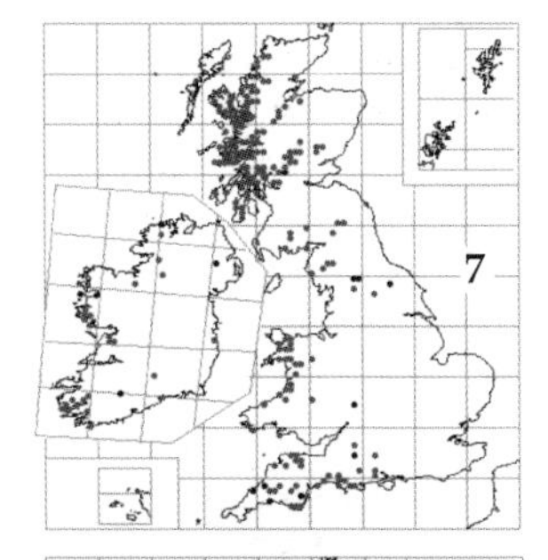

9. C. tenax Thallus dark greenish black, rosette-forming, very variable. Greatly swollen when wet. Lobes up to 1 cm wide, erect, crowded or often obscured by very numerous apothecia. Usually lacking isidia, but where present, globose, becoming flatter. Apothecia about 3 mm diam. Spores mainly 8 per ascus, 3-septate to muriform, 15–25 x 6–10 µm. Pycnidia are common.
Habitat: Common on basic earth, sand and on mortar in walls.

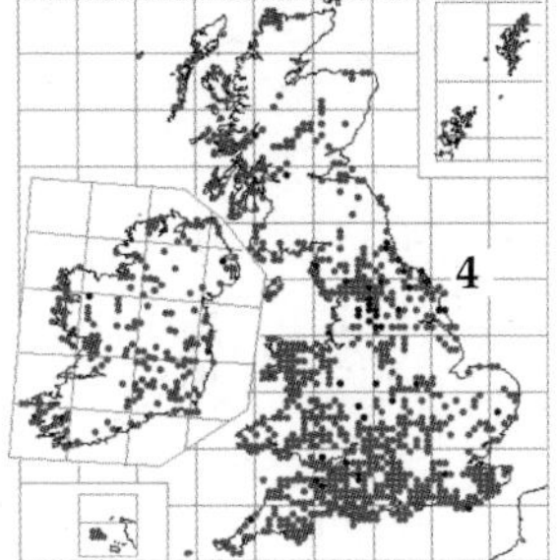

C. tenax x 4.

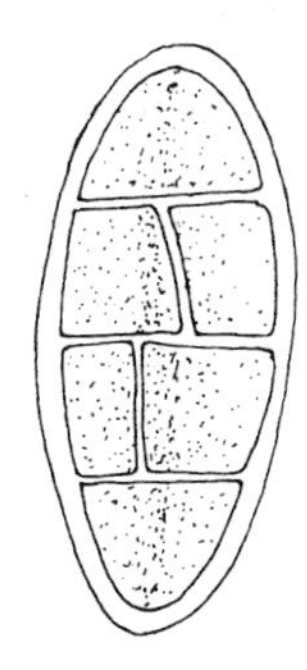

C. tenax spore x 2000.

CORNICULARIA ('little horn'). **Thallus** fruticose, hard and spiny when dry. **Photobiont** *Trebouxia*. **Apothecia** lecanorine. **Ascus** 8-spored, *Lecanora*-type. **Spores** colourless, almost globose, 8 per ascus. **Pycnidia** globose, partially immersed on tips of branches. **Chemical reactions** negative. There is only one British species.

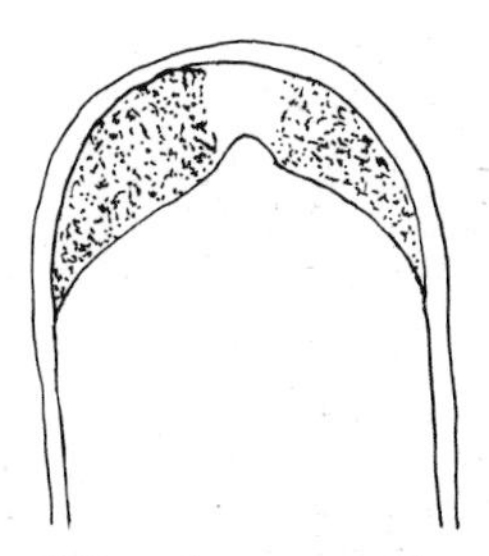

K/I reaction on ascus tip.

Cornicularia normoerica Thallus brown-black, erect and up to 2 cm high and 1 mm wide, slightly dichotomously branched, the branches flattened without pseudocyphellae. Apothecia very common, terminal or sub-terminal, up to 6 mm wide with a shiny, black disc, often with a spiny margin. Spores 5–6 x 3–4 µm.
Habitat: Locally common in upland areas, on coarse-grained siliceous rocks.

C. normoerica x 4.

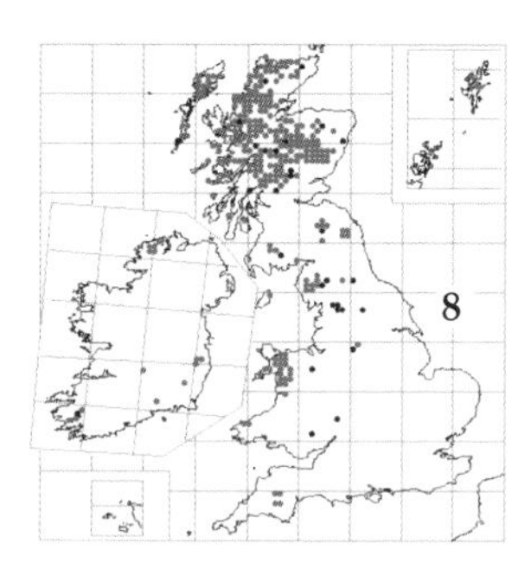

CRYPTOLECHIA ('hidden scales' – from the scurfy appearance of the thallus). **Thallus** crustose. **Photobiont** *Trentepohlia*. **Apothecia** lecideine. **Ascus** 8- to 16-spored. Wall K/I blue. **Spores** persistently septate, never muriform. **Chemical reactions** all negative. There is only one species in Britain.

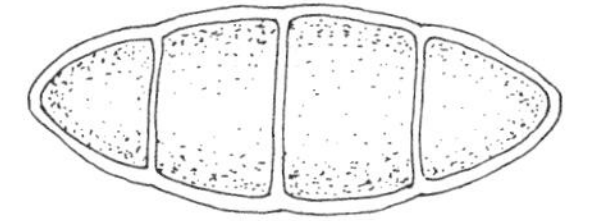

C. carneolutea x 2500.

Cryptolechia carneolutea (Gyalectina carneolutea) Thallus white, thin, matt. Apothecia up to 1 mm diam, immersed at first but becoming more sessile. Disc a translucent pinkish orange with a paler pseudothalline margin that is dentate and may become excluded. Spores 3-septate, 10–20 x 3–5 µm.
Habitat: Rare, confined to the extreme South and SouthWest, previously north to the Isle of Man and Silverdale. Found on lightly shaded ivy stems, ash and elm. It is very rare on limestone, the superficially similar *Petractis clausa* which is always on limestone and has light grey thallus and different apothecia.

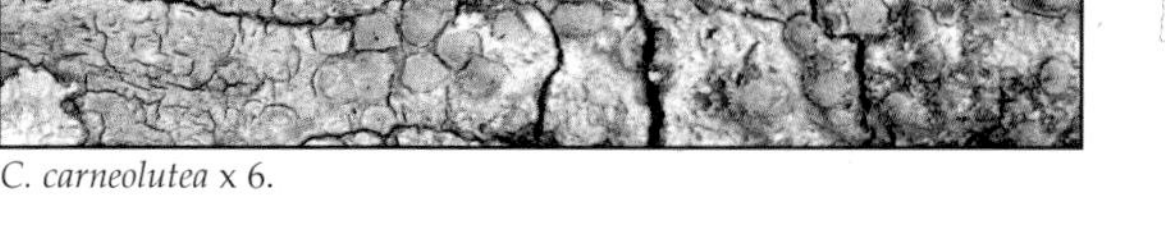

C. carneolutea x 6.

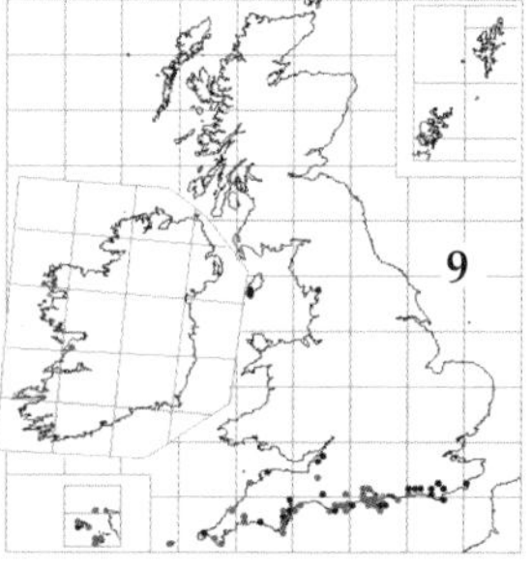

CYPHELIUM ('hump' – from the appearance of the surface of the thallus). **Thallus** crustose. **Photobiont** *Trebouxia*. **Apothecia** lecideine but when mature the cylindrical asci break down to form a loose, powdery mass of spores (a mazaedium) which rubs off on the finger. **Spores** uniseriately arranged in the ascus, brown, 1-septate and much constricted at the septum.

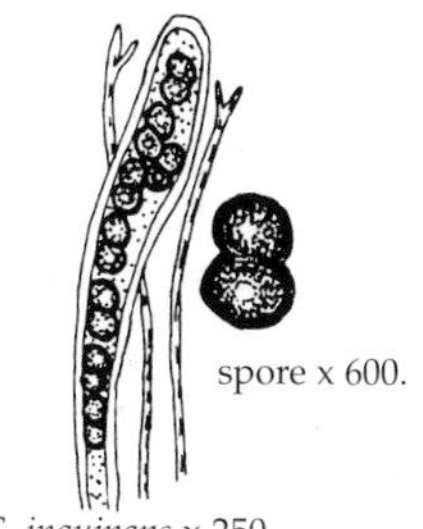

C. inquinans x 250.

Cyphelium inquinans Thallus pale grey, more rarely dark grey, thick and warted. Apothecia usually present, up to 2 mm diam, innate or sessile, irregular in shape, often with a white-pruinose margin. Spores 14–20 x 8–11 µm. May be distinguished from *Lecidea* species by the soot-like mark left on the finger from rubbing a mature apothecium and by the brown, 1-septate spores.
K+ yellow turning orange, P– or P+ pale yellow, UV–.
Habitat: Common on exposed old fence posts, railings and more rarely on old oaks in south-east Britain. It is rare in the Scottish Highlands on decorticate pines.

C. inquinans x 4.

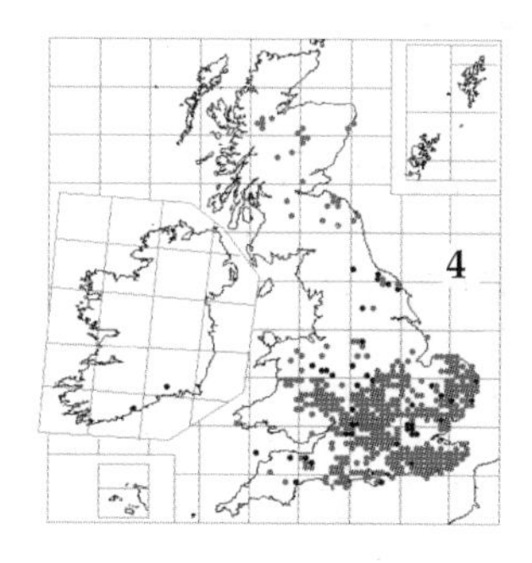

CYSTOCOLEUS ('sheathed tube' – from the form of the thallus). **Thallus** filamentous. **Photobiont** *Trentepohlia* filaments which are enveloped by the fungal hyphae. This is best examined as a squash preparation under a microscope. There is only one species and it is only found sterile. **Chemical reactions** negative.

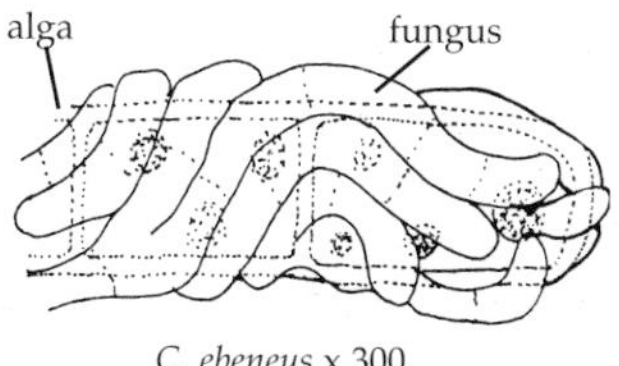

C. ebeneus x 300.

Cystocoleus ebeneus (C. niger) Thallus a dense black felted mass of filaments, often with *Racodium rupestre*. The surrounding, clasping fungal hyphae are contorted and wavy unlike *R. rupestre* where they are straight and parallel.
Habitat: Common in upland areas on damp, shaded, vertical, siliceous rocks but avoiding direct wetting.

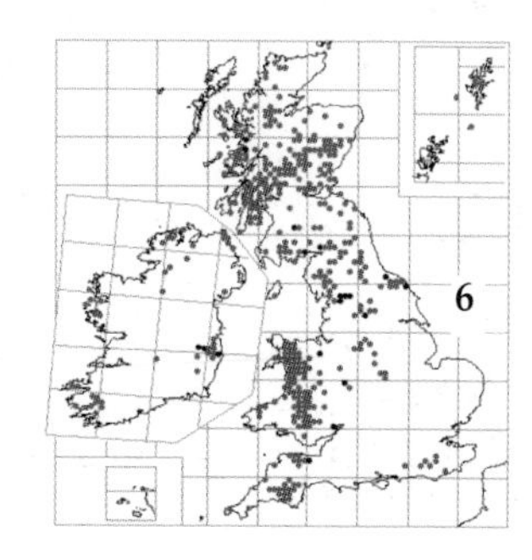

DEGELIA (PARMELIELLA p.p.) (after the lichenologist Gunner Bror Fritjof Degelius, 1903–1994). **Thallus** foliose to squamulose, imbricate. The lower surface covered with a thick, felt-like, tomentose, blue-black layer. **Photobiont** *Nostoc*. **Apothecia** lecideine (the similar genus *Pannaria* is lecanorine). **Hymenium** yellow, I+ intense blue. **Ascus** 8-spored with a K/I+ blue apical plug. **Spores** colourless, simple. **Pycnidia** immersed, wart-like. **Chemical reactions** negative.

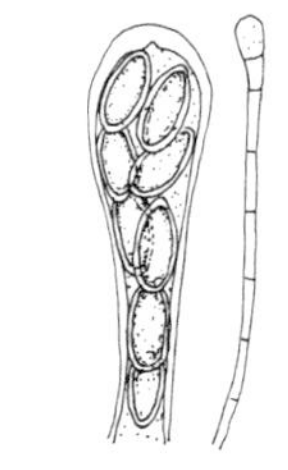
D. plumbea x 250.

1.	Thallus with grey, coralloid or flattened isidia	2
–	Thallus lacking isidia	**3. D. plumbea**
2.	Globose to coralloid isidia	**1. D. atlantica**
–	Flattened to spoon-shaped isidia (schizidia)	**2. D. ligulata**

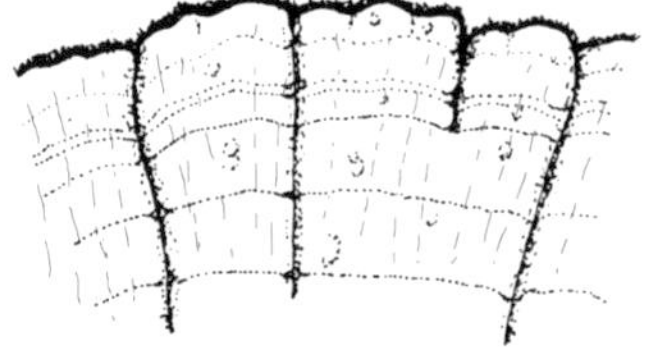
D. plumbea

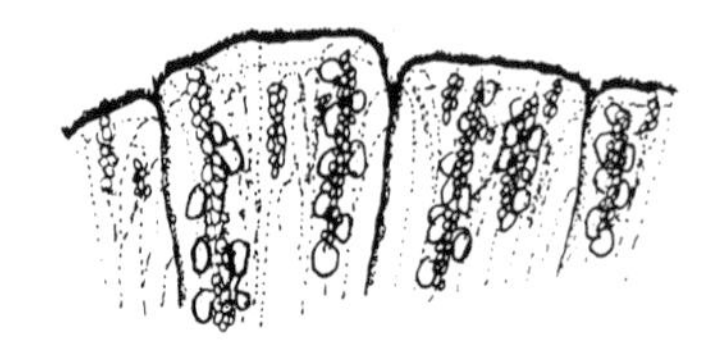
D. atlantica

Usual shape of the thalline ridges towards the margins

1. Degelia atlantica (P. atlantica) Thallus up to 10 cm wide, thick and plate-like, bluish grey, sometimes with a brownish tinge. The ridges are fan-shaped and the lobes have rather large, grey, nodulose isidia that become confluent and may cover the whole surface of the thallus, the inner part of the thallus becoming areolate. Lower surface with a prominant blue-black, fibrous hypothallus that often extends beyond the margin. Apothecia rare.
Habitat: Frequent in western Scotland, rare elsewhere, on shaded damp trees in old woodland, rarely on mossy rocks.

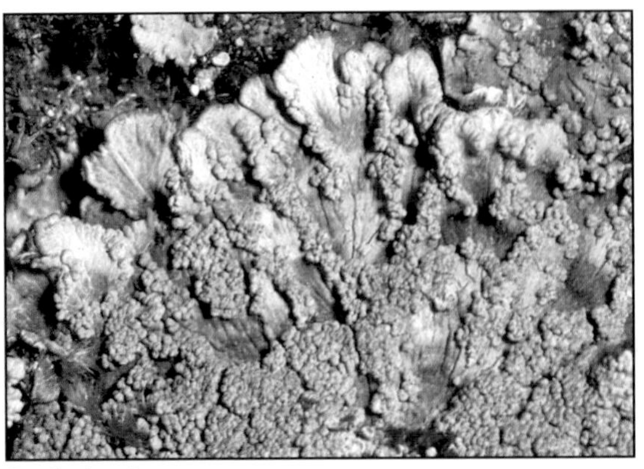
D. atlantica x 2.

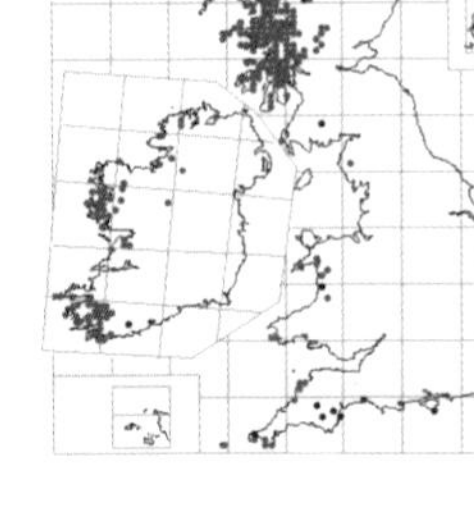

2. D. ligulata Thallus very similar to *D. atlantica* but differs in the isidia which are more elongate, flattened or concave (schizidia) with dark tips. Rarely fertile. Habitat: A rare species of extreme western, coastal, rock crevices, soil, sometimes found near the bases of trees and shrubs in similar situations.

3. D. plumbea (P. plumbea) Thallus light grey when dry, dark grey when wet, sometimes with a brownish tinge. It forms large plate-like patches (up to 10 cm wide) when fully developed. Towards the margin there are pronounced oyster-like concentric ridges. No isidia but sometimes a few coarse lobules. The hypothallus extends to form a blue-black margin to the thallus. The centre of the thallus is thick and imbricate. Usually abundantly fertile. Apothecia up to 1 mm diam, orange-brown to red-brown, the thin proper margin is soon excluded. Spores 16–30 x 7–11 µm. It may be separated from the similar *Pannaria rubiginosa* by the larger size, no pale margins to the lobes and absence of a thalline margin. Habitat: Common on moss-covered trees and rocks in the west of Scotland and western Ireland, rare elsewhere.

D. plumbea x 3.

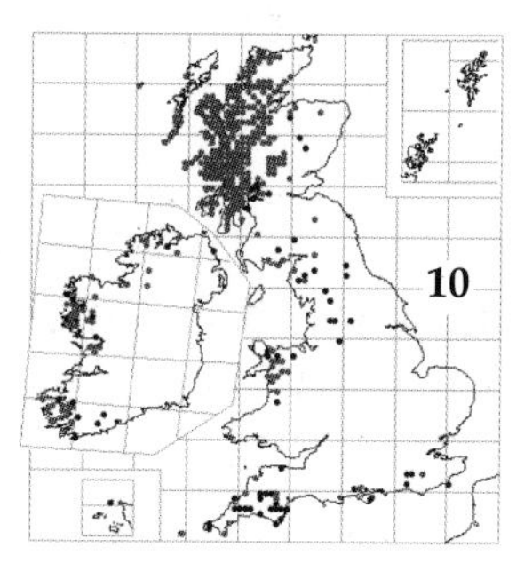

DERMATOCARPON ('fruit skin' – from the innate fruits that open through the cortex). **Thallus** foliose, attached by one or more holdfasts. Lower surface without rhizines. **Photobiont** chlorococcoid. **Perithecia** immersed in the thallus with the ostiole usually clearly visible. No involucrellum. **Paraphyses** numerous but disappearing when mature. Hymenial gel I+ red or blue. **Ascus** 8- to 16-spored. K/I–. **Spores** simple, colourless. **Chemical reactions** negative. Some species have been gathered and used as food in Asia and for making beer in Russia.

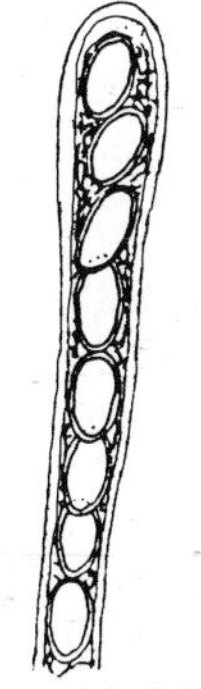

D. miniatum x 400.

1. Thallus green to fawn forming a compact mat of thick lobes. Acid rock, stream, river or lake margins **1. D. luridum**

– Thallus pale grey to grey-brown, not overlapping, attached by central holdfast. On calcareous rocks **2. D. miniatum**

1. Dermatocarpon luridum (D. weberi) Thallus green when wet, fawn when dry, thick, consisting of a compact mat of erect, contorted lobes up to 1 cm wide. The upper surface pitted with the dark brown ostioles of the perithecia. Under-surface light brown, darker towards the centre. Medulla I+ reddish brown. Perithecia about 0.3 diam. Spores 10–20 x 5–8 µm in a clavate ascus.
Habitat: Frequent on siliceous rocks and boulders on the margins of nutrient-deficient streams and lakes in upland areas, where it is frequently submerged.

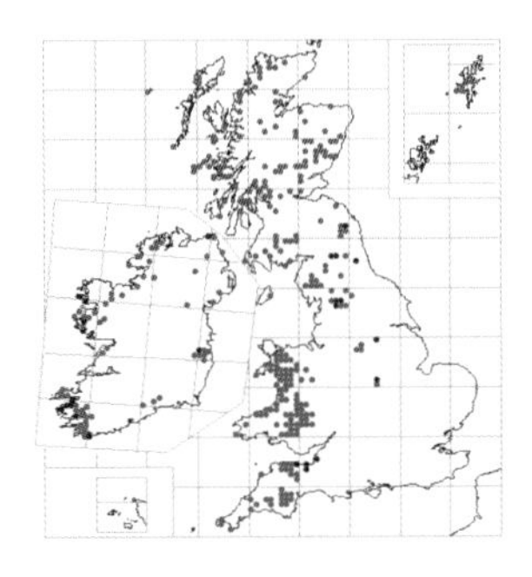

D. luridum x 3.

2. D. miniatum Thallus pale grey to light brown, matt, grey-pruinose, *Umbilicaria*-like and frequently single-lobed, up to 5 cm wide. The margins of the lobes are sometimes deeply incised and contorted. Under-surface tan, slightly pustulate with a tough central holdfast. The small, dark brown ostioles of the perithecia on the upper surface distinguish it from superficially similar *Umbilicaria* species. Perithecia about 0.3 mm diam. Spores 10–14 x 5–6 µm.
Habitat: Locally frequent on damp, often shaded, calcareous (rarely acid) rocks often in vertical nutrient tracks, especially on hard inland limestone, or on coastal rocks. Rarely found on flat limestone tombs or at higher altitudes.

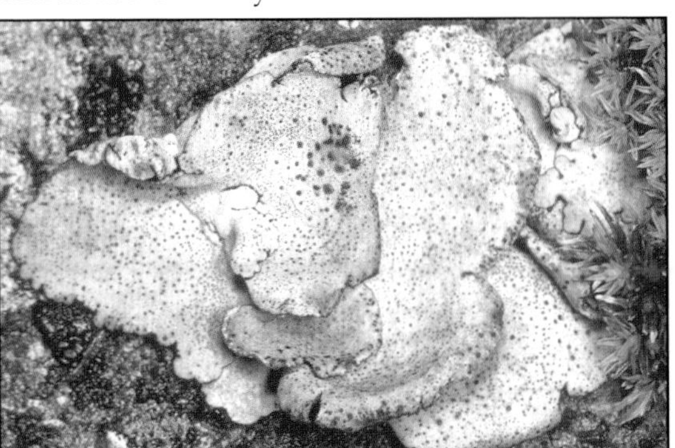

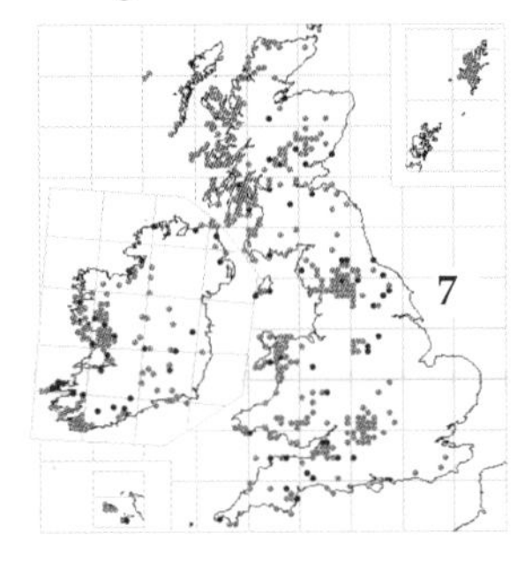

D. miniatum x 4.

DIMERELLA ('two small things together' – from the two-celled spores). **Thallus** crustose, often inconspicuous. **Photobiont** *Trentepohlia*. **Apothecia** lecideine with a pale proper margin. **Ascus** 8-spored, wall K/I pale blue. **Hymenium** K+ blue. **Spores** colourless, 1-septate. **Pycnidia** half-immersed. There are only two British species both of which have negative chemical reactions. The K– reaction of the apothecia prevents confusion with *Caloplaca* species.

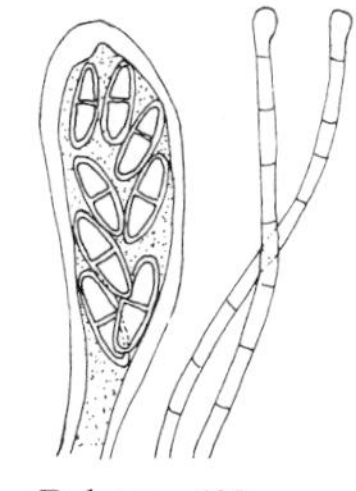

D. lutea x 600

1. Apothecia up to 2 mm, yellow to yellow-orange, mainly on moss, western **1. D. lutea**
– Apothecia up to 0.4 mm, pale pinkish, on bark, widespread **2. D. pineti**

1. Dimerella lutea Thallus light grey to dark greenish-grey, often scarcely visible. Apothecia usually abundant, up to 2 mm diam, bright orange with a paler translucent margin, looking like tinned apricots when wet and a poached egg when dry; this combination is a very distinctive feature. Spores 9–15 x 2–4 μm. Habitat: Frequent on bark and moss on deciduous trees in damp, fairly shaded areas of old woodland, particularly in the West, where it is sometimes also found on mosses growing on the ground or on acid rocks.

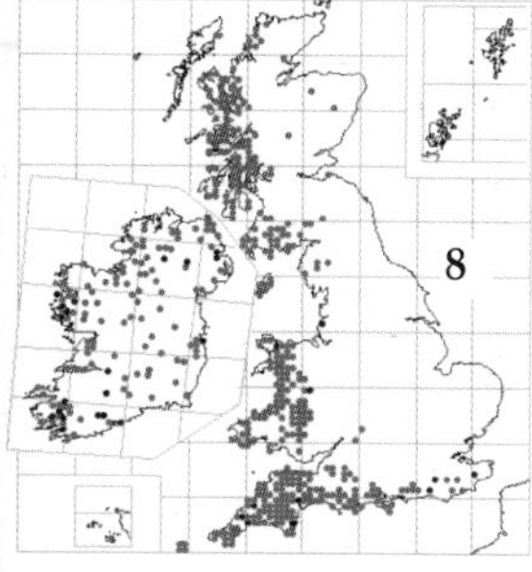

D. lutea x 10.

2. D. pineti (D. diluta) Similar to the previous species but with smaller (up to about 0.4 mm) white or flesh-coloured apothecia. Often with white pycnidia. Habitat: A common species, on conifers in Scotland but also on willows and other trees in lowland areas. Very rarely found on mosses, it prefers acid bark and is usually found in sheltered cracks and towards the bases of boles of trees in more polluted sites, where it is frequently infertile but often with abundant pycnidia.

D. pineti x 5.

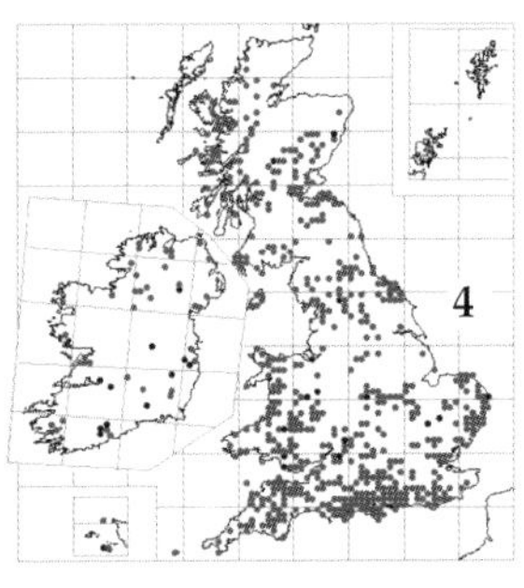

DIPLOICIA ('double' – from the two-celled spores). **Thallus** crustose, strongly placodioid. **Photobiont** green. **Apothecia** lecideine with a black disc. **Ascus** 8-spored, *Lecanora*-type. **Spores** 1-septate, brown. **Pycnidia** immersed, with a dark ostiole. There is only one British species.

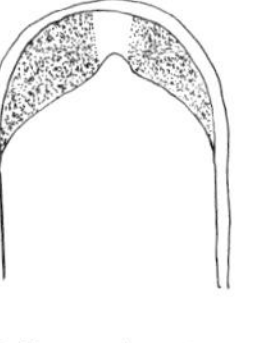

K/I reaction to ascus tip.

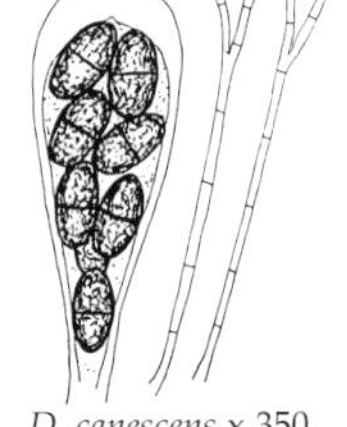

D. canescens x 350.

Diploicia canescens Thallus white to very pale grey, forming rosettes up to 5 cm across with clearly defined marginal lobes. The lobes are convex, up to 1 mm wide, becoming wider towards the apices and very white-pruinose. The centre of the thallus is inclined to be darker and becomes covered in patches of farinose soralia. Due to the nutrient-enriched sites which it prefers, it is often found overgrown by alien green algae. Apothecia rare except in the South. Spores 10–15 x 5–8 µm. Can be confused with *Solenopsora candicans* but that species is usually fertile, K–, and not sorediate.
K+ yellow, UV– or UV+ orange.
Habitat: Very common on basic and very nutrient-enriched trees, rocks and walls, such as farmyard buildings. It becomes rare in Scotland.

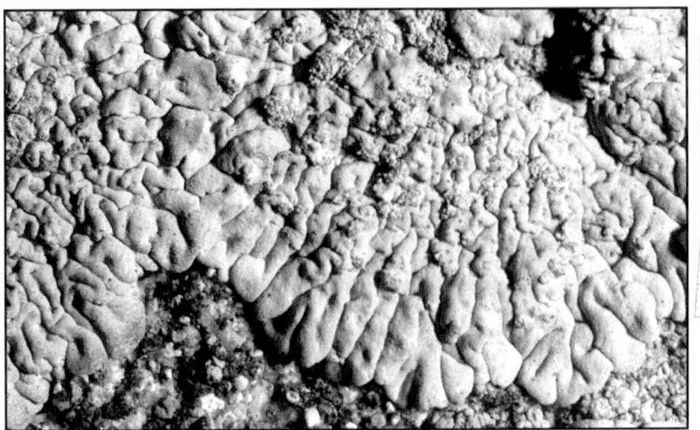

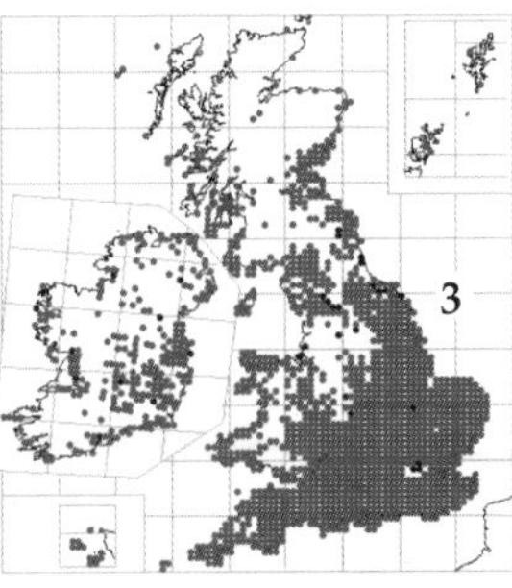

D. canescens x 3.

DIPLOSCHISTES ('double split' – from the fissure between the margin and the hymenium of the apothecia). **Thallus** crustose. **Photobiont** *Trebouxia.* **Apothecia** urceolate, lecanorine. **Ascus** 4- to 8-spored, K/I–. **Spores** becoming dark, muriform when mature. Similar to *Thelotrema* but the inner, proper margin is far less prominent. The C+ red reaction helps to separate *Diploschistes* species from those of *Aspicilia* (*Cyphelium inquinans* only on wood). Many species in this genus commence as parasites on other lichens. If a spore lands on a suitable lichen and germinates, it can then take over the algae from the host.

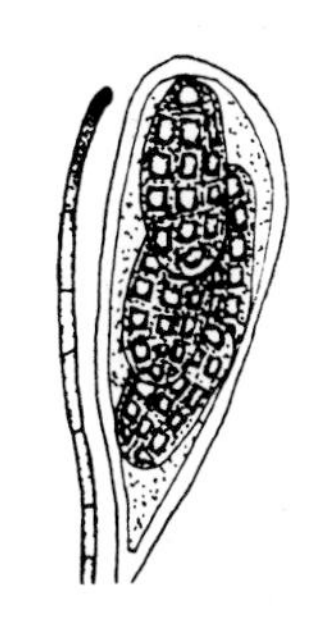

D. scruposus x 350

1.	On hard, shaded, damp limestone	**2. D. gypsaceus**
–	On acid rocks, walls, soil or mosses	2
2.	Thallus smooth, lead-coloured, regularly cracked areolate, maritime. Apothecia immersed, less than 0.4 mm diam	**1. D. caesioplumbeus**
–	Thallus warted. Apothecia urceolate, more than 0.4 mm diam	3
3.	On acid rocks and walls	**4. D. scruposus**
–	On *Cladonia* species, spreading to mosses	**3. D. muscorum**

1. Diploschistes caesioplumbeus Thallus mid- to dark leaden-grey, cracked areolate, smooth, slightly shiny, often with a grey prothallus. Apothecia immersed, looking like the ostioles of perithecia, several often found in each areole. Mature apothecia mainly pruinose and under 0.3 mm diam. Spores becoming dark, muriform, 30–50 x 10–25 µm. This species parasitizes *Lecanora gangaleoides* taking over the algae and specimens with both species intermingled are frequently found.
K–, C+ red, UV–.
Habitat: Frequent on well-lit siliceous rocks in the supralittoral zone in the SouthWest and West.

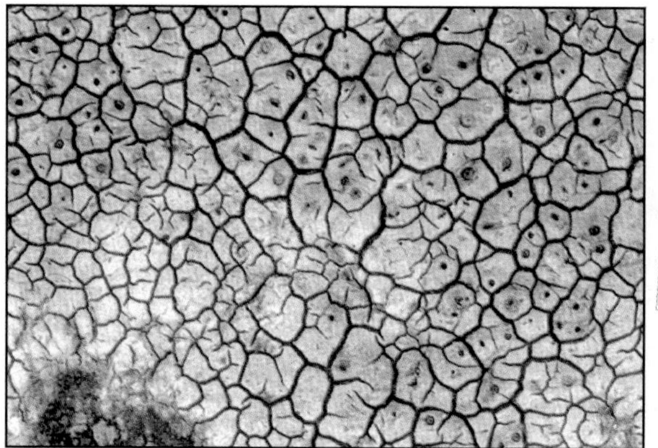

D. caesioplumbeus x 5.

2. D. gypsaceus Thallus thick, pale grey but looking white as it is usually very pruinose. Apothecia are normally present with large discs, up to 4 mm diam. The disc is black but covered in a white pruina. Spores 4 per ascus, 25–40 x 10–15 µm.
K–, C+ red, UV–.
Habitat: Infrequent on shaded, hard limestone.

3. D. muscorum Thallus pale to mid-grey, uneven and rather warted but not pruinose. Apothecia urceolate, up to 2 mm diam with pruinose discs. Spores 4 per ascus, 25–35 x 10–15 µm. In its early stages it parasitizes *Cladonia* species, especially *C. pocillum* where the original shape of the host thallus may persist even when it is completely taken over by *D. muscorum*. The apothecia are less open than in *D. scruposus*.
K+ yellow (often weak), C+ red, UV–.
Habitat: Common on *Cladonia* species on well-lit wall tops, heaths, dunes, etc., spreading onto mosses.

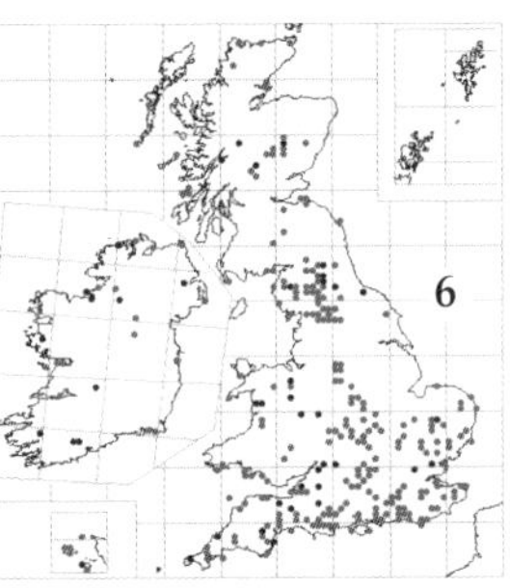

4. D. scruposus Thallus leaden grey but often with a noticeable yellowish tinge, thick, warted, not pruinose. Apothecia urceolate, usually numerous, to 3 mm diam, discs black, deeply immersed at first, sometimes with a noticeable proper margin, becoming more open as they develop, often grey- or white-pruinose. Spores 20–40 x 10–20 µm, colourless at first and appearing 5- to 7-septate, becoming muriform and sometimes very dark purple-brown.
K+ yellow, C+ red.
Habitat: Frequent on acid rocks and walls especially where nutrient-enriched.

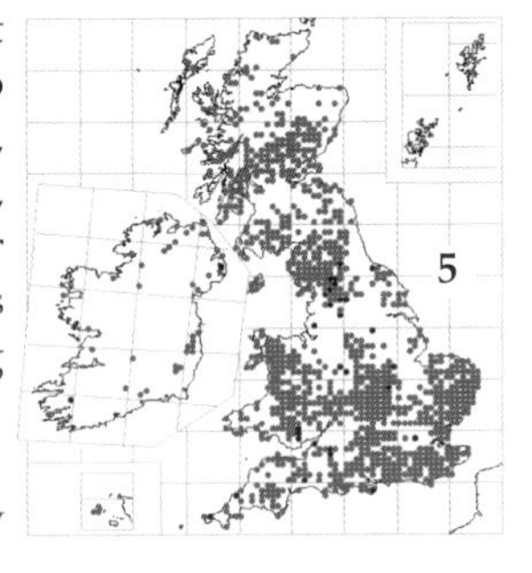

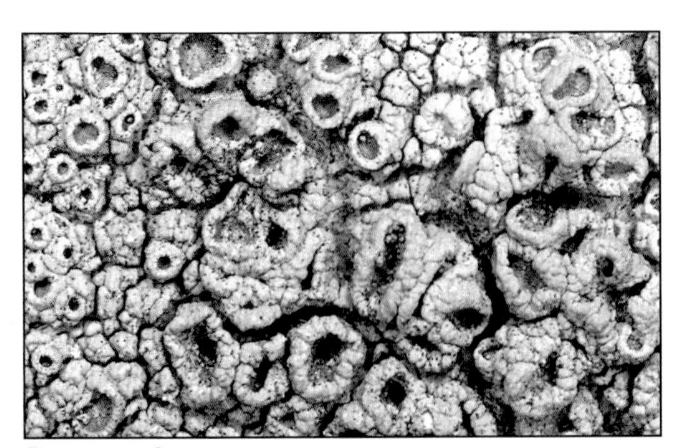

D. scruposus x 8.

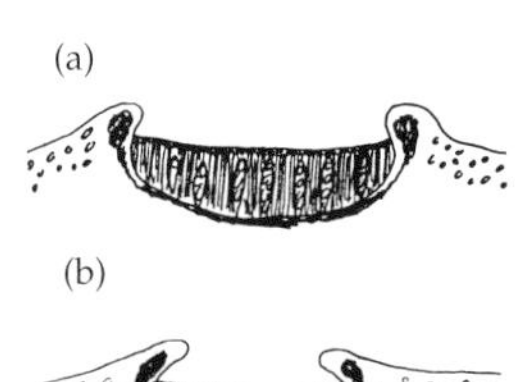

Section through an apothecium of :
(a) *D. scruposus*
(b) *D. muscorum*

DIPLOTOMMA ('double eye' – from the appearance of the margin of the apothecia). **Thallus** crustose. **Photobiont** green. **Apothecia** lecideine but may appear lecanorine in early stages, initially immersed, disc black. **Ascus** 8-spored, *Lecanora*-type. **Spores** septate to submuriform, brown. **Pycnidia** immersed light to dark brown at the ostiole.

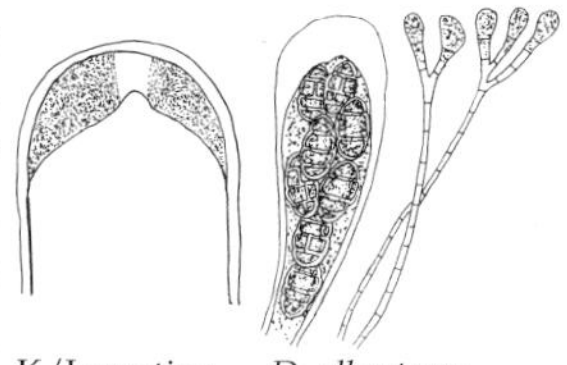

K/I reaction to ascus tip. *D. alboatrum x 300.*

1. Thallus K– , P–. Not confined to coast **1. D. alboatrum**
– Thallus K+ red, P+ orange. Confined to coast **2. D. chlorophaeum**

1. Diplotomma alboatrum Thallus white to pale grey, smooth and cracked or rough. Apothecia 0.3–1.0 mm with a thin, grey, crenulate margin. Disc very white-pruinose often making it look pale. Spores 15–20 x 8–12 µm, up to 3-septate, becoming submuriform. Sometimes initially parasitic on *Caloplaca* species.
Spot reactions: negative.
Habitat: Frequent on basic bark and nutrient-enriched trees. It is then often separated as **D. epipolium** when it is found on mortar or calcareous rocks with the spores remaining strictly 3-septate and not becoming submuriform.

D. alboatrum x 5.

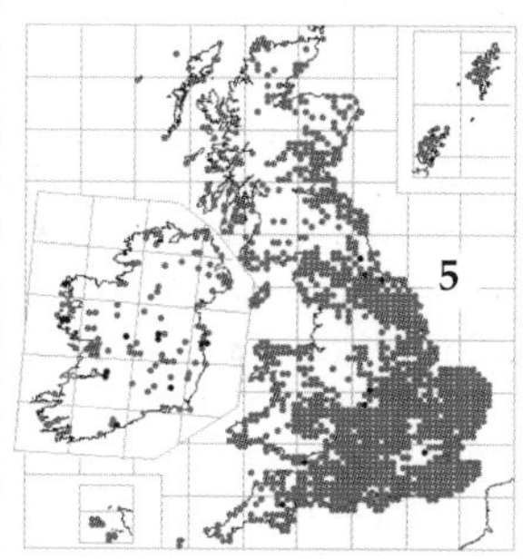

2. D. chlorophaeum Thallus white to cream, warted and areolate. Apothecia up to 0.5 mm across, not pruinose. Spores 16–22 x 8–11 µm, 3-septate becoming submuriform.
Thallus: K+ yellow, very slowly turning red.
Medulla: P+ orange, sometimes I+ blue.
Habitat: Frequent on the coast, mainly in the West, often in slightly sheltered situations. Most frequent on ± acid rock and walls, associated with mortar.

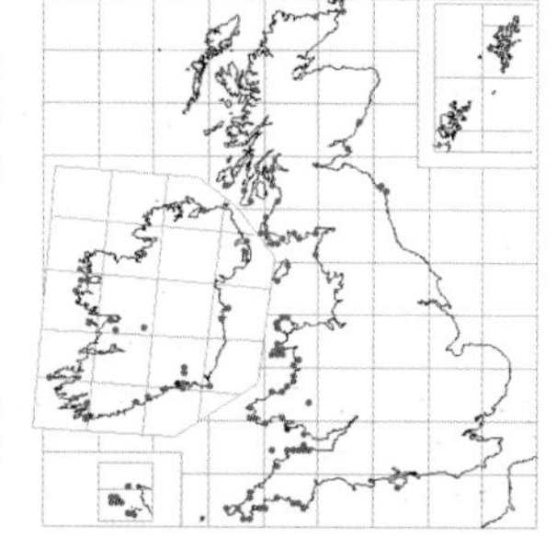

DIRINA (derivation doubtful, possibly di- from the double margin and -rina as a word filler). **Thallus** crustose. **Photobiont** *Trentepohlia.* **Apothecia** lecanorine. Ascus 8-spored, *Opegrapha*-type, with minute K/I blue apical ring. **Spores** colourless, 3- to 8-septate, 8 per ascus. This is a mainly tropical and sub-tropical genus that just extends in range to Britain. The C+ rose-red reaction and the orange colouration on scratched surfaces of fresh material help to identify this genus. There is only one British species.

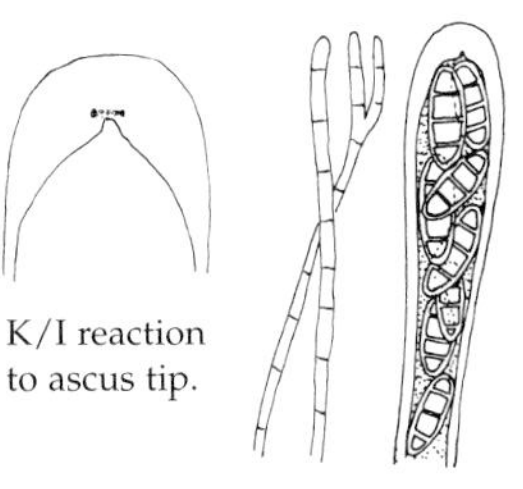

D. massiliensis x 500.

Dirina massiliensis f. **sorediata** Thallus almost white to brownish grey with a lilac tinge, thick, areolate, determinate at the margins with a light brown prothallus. Small (about 0.5 mm), globose, mounds of paler, farinose soredia are scattered over the thallus, these may coalesce to form a complete crust. Not fertile. The rare fertile form of the species (f. **massiliensis**) lacks soredia, has apothecia up to 2 mm diam and is confined to underhangs and vertical, shaded, hard coastal limestone.

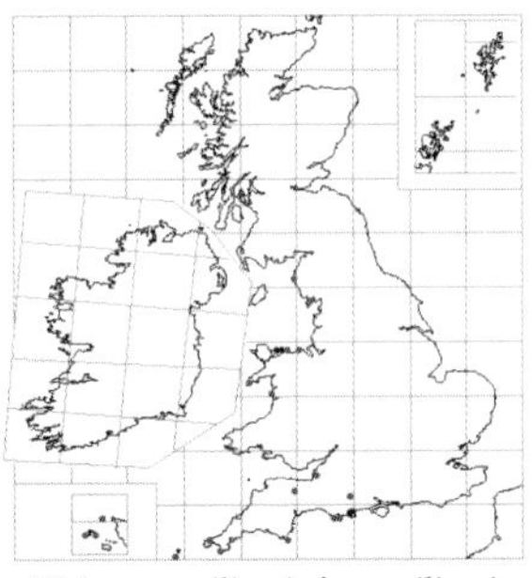
Dirina massiliensis f. *massiliensis*.

Both K–, C+ rose. Medulla: UV+ yellow or blue-white.
Habitat: Locally abundant in the SouthWest on vertical calcareous rocks, not restricted to the coast. Often on mortar on E. and N. walls of churches in the South.

Dirina massiliensis f. *massiliensis* (left), f. *sorediata* (right) x 5.

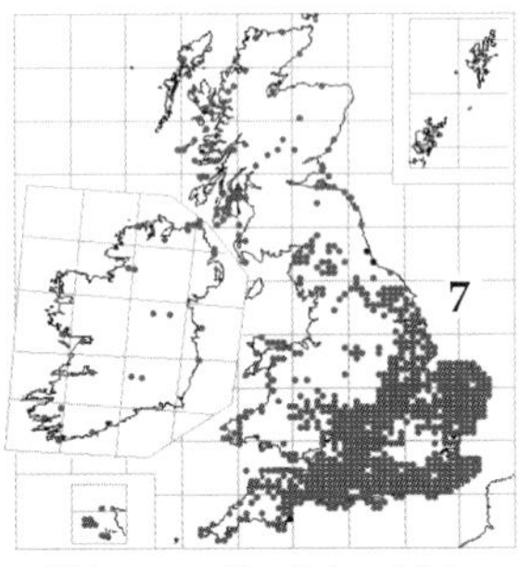

Dirina massiliensis f. *soridiata*.

ENTEROGRAPHA ('internal writing' – from the thead-like, innate fruiting bodies). **Thallus** crustose, black prothallus. **Photobiont** *Trentepohlia*. **Apothecia** usually immersed and forming lines. **Ascus** 8-spored, Apical dome and inner wall K/I+ blue with a minute dark blue ring. **Spores** colourless, multi-septate.

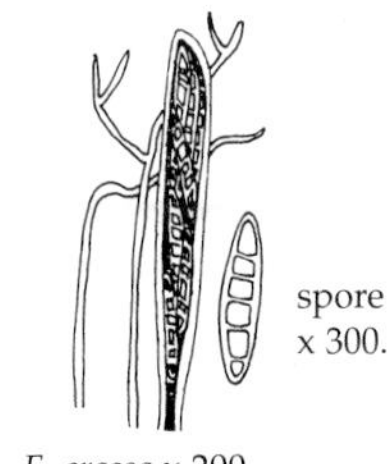

E. crassa x 200.

1. Dark brown to lilac soredia. Apothecia rare, sessile **3. E. zonata**
– No soredia. Usually fertile, apothecia innate, dot or thread-like 2

2. Apothecia 0.1–0.3 mm long. Normally on trees **1. E. crassa**
– Apothecia 0.3–1 mm long. Normally on rocks **2. E. hutchinsiae**

1. Enterographa crassa Thallus very variable, usually grey, brown or dull olive-green, thick, smooth, frequently forming neat mosaics divided by the black prothallus. Apothecia dark brown, in the form of small, thread-like lines or dots, 0.1–0.3 x 0.1 mm, often more crowded towards the edge of the thallus. Spores 20–40 x 4–7 µm, 5- to 7-septate.
Habitat: A very common species in the South on shaded trees, often forming very extensive colonies. Exceptionally it occurs on damp, shaded, acid rocks.

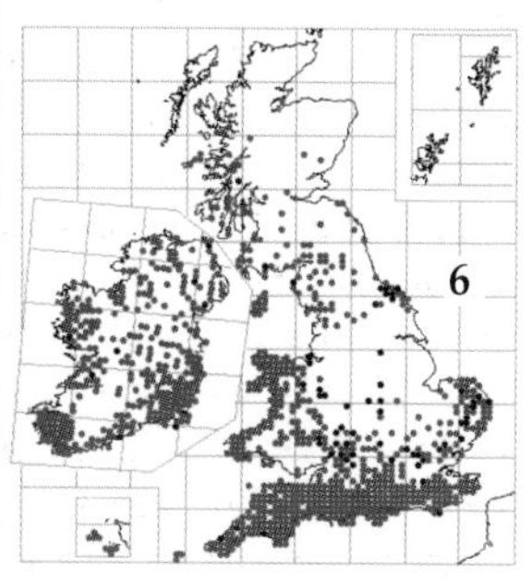

E. crassa x 8.

2. E. hutchinsiae Thallus and general appearance similar to *E. crassa*. Normally very fertile. The apothecia are shorter and usually crescent-shaped to ellipsoid. The discs are more open, have a pale margin and are slightly raised when wet. Spores 24–28 x 4–5 µm, 5- to 8-septate.
Habitat: Found mainly in the West on shaded, wet, acid, often vertical, rocks. Frequently by streams, rarely on tree roots.

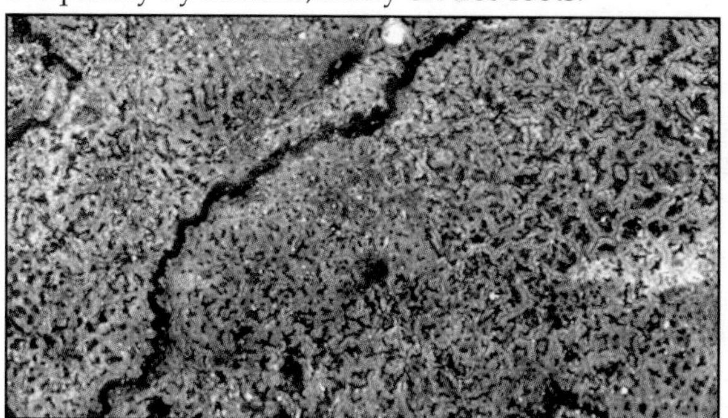

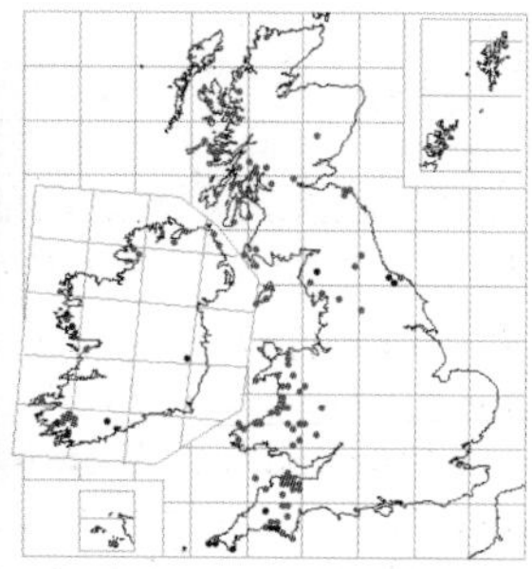

E. hutchinsiae x 8.

3. E. zonata (Opegrapha zonata). Thallus thin to thick, chocolate-brown, often with a violet tinge. Smooth or cracked, often forming large mosaics, each thallus separated by a dark prothallus. The surface has numerous punctiform, large (to 1 mm diam) soralia containing dark brown, mauve-tinged soredia which abrade to leave pale areas. Apothecia rare, elevated and unbranched. Spores 0.2–0.4 x 0.1–0.3 µm, 5- to 7-septate. Habitat: Mainly in the West on damp, very shaded, acid rock, rarely on damp bark.

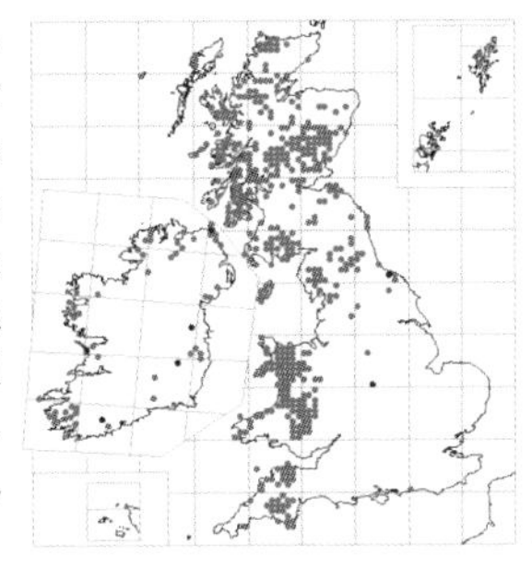

EPHEBE ('covered in youthful hairs' – this is a possible derivation of the name). **Thallus** filamentous. **Photobiont** *Stigonema.* **Apothecia** immersed and formed as globose enlargements of the thallus, either as illustrated or in slight swellings. **Ascus** 8- or 16-spored, thin-walled with a K/I+ blue outer layer. **Spores** colourless, simple to 2-septate. **Chemical reactions** negative.

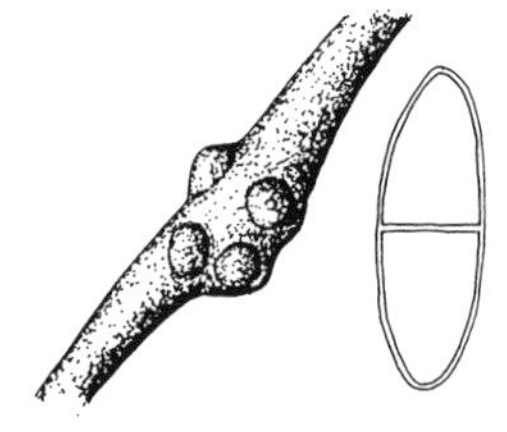

Apothecia of *E. lanata* x 15 and 1-septate form of spore x 1000.

1. Thallus with very numerous branchlets on main stems **2. E. hispidula**
– Thallus with no or very few branchlets **1. E. lanata**

1. Ephebe lanata Thallus dark green to black, soft and filamentous, forming small mats up to 3 cm wide. Filaments much divided (often dichotomously), tapering to fine points. The thallus has a few lateral branchlets and is somewhat incised in places and some of the branchlets may form holdfasts that adhere to the substratum. Apothecia rare in Britain, very small, often in groups in swellings formed on the branches. Spores simple, becoming 1-septate or very rarely 2-septate, 10–20 x 4–6 µm.
Distinguished from *Pseudephebe pubescens* by its softer texture, the presence of blue-green photobiont and the different habitat.
Habitat: Frequent in upland regions in seepage tracks on damp rocks, often near acidic streams and in the splash zone of waterfalls.

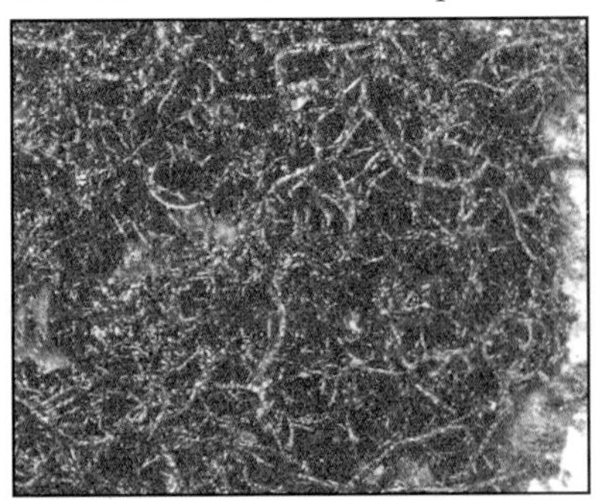

E. lanata x 4.

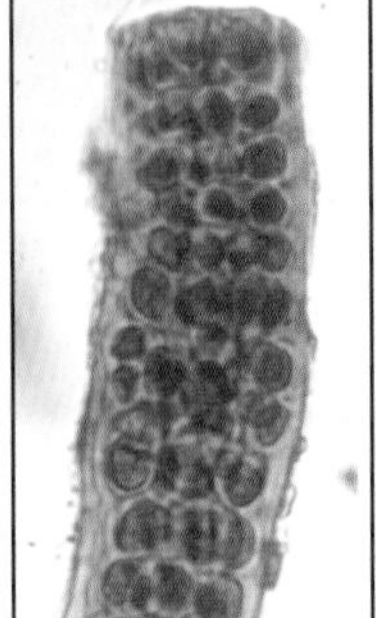

E. lanata x 25.

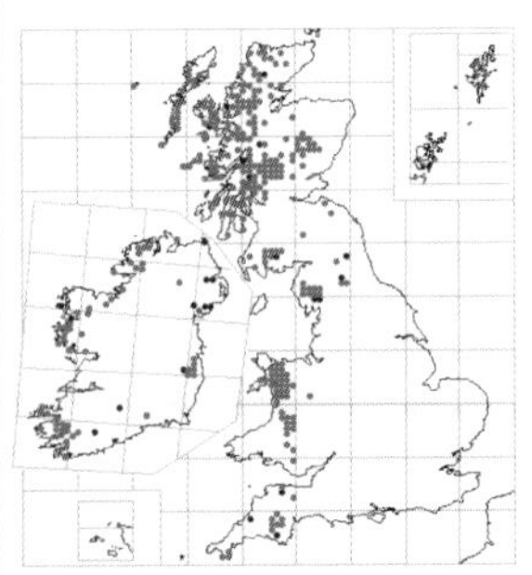

2. E. hispidula is similar to the last species. It forms smaller clumps up to about 1 cm wide and has very many small branchlets. Apothecia are rare and have a more open disc than *E. lanata*. Spores 7–10 x 4–5 µm.
Habitat: Rare on damp acid rocks, mainly in upland regions.

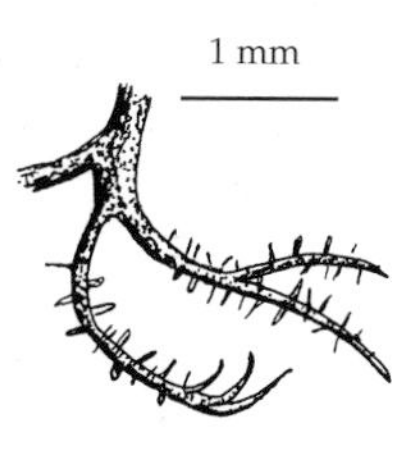

EVERNIA ('branched' – from the often much-branched thallus). **Thallus** flattened and attached at one point so that it appears to be fruticose. As the algal layer is only found under the upper cortex it is anatomically foliose. **Apothecia** lecanorine. **Photobiont** chlorococcoid. **Ascus** 8-spored, *Lecanora*-type. **Spores** simple, colourless. Pycnidia immersed, black at the tip. There is only one British species.

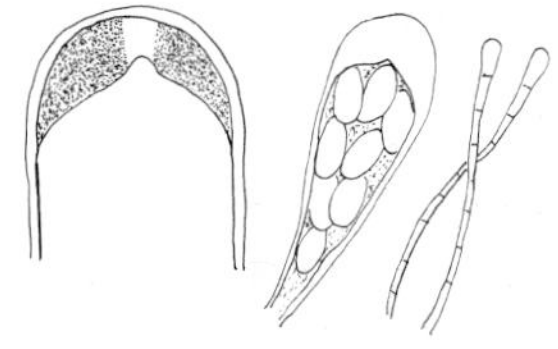
K/I reaction to ascus tip. *E. prunastri* x 400.

Evernia prunastri Thallus strap-shaped, pendent, yellow to green-grey above, white underneath. This pale under-surface separates it from *Ramalina* species which are approximately the same colour all round. It usually feels fairly soft (unlike *Pseudevernia furfuracea* which is stiff, has isidia and a white or black lower surface), lobes strongly flattened, upper surface with net-like ridges that become sorediate in larger specimens (about 3 cm long). Very rarely fertile, apothecia on short stalks, discs dark red-brown, concave to plane. Spores 7–11 x 4–6 µm.
K+ yellow.

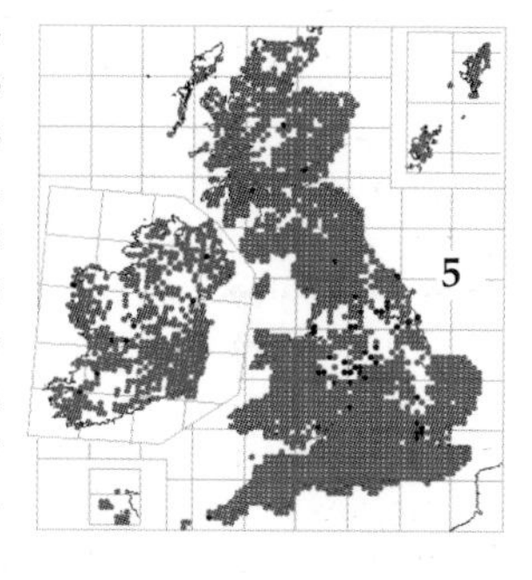

Habitat: Very common on deciduous trees, rarely on rocks, fence posts and stabilized sand dunes. It is more tolerant of pollution than *Ramalina* species and may be found in a very stunted form in regions of moderate pollution. It becomes much rarer in Scotland. It has been used extensively by man for many purposes, including as 'oak moss', a fixative for perfume and as a dyeing agent. It was ground up with rose petals to make a hair powder which whitened wigs, covered up some of the smell of unwashed bodies and killed off head lice. This species was often added as a flavouring to bread in the Middle East. It was also used as wadding in shotguns. The usnic acid it contains can be used to produce an antibiotic but it has also been known to produce an allergy in woodcutters. Long-tailed tits greatly favour this species for their nests where it forms an effective camouflage.

E. prunastri x 2.

FELLHANERA (after the Austrian lichenologist, Josef Hafellner, born 1951). **Thallus** crustose. **Photobiont** chlorococcoid. **Apothecia** lecideine, sessile with a pale yellowish to pink disc. **Ascus** 8-spored, K/I blue apical dome, fuzzy coat and a central darker tube. **Spores** 1- to 3-septate. **Chemical reactions** negative. This is the only British genus consistently found growing on leaves on trees and heather stems in old heathlands.

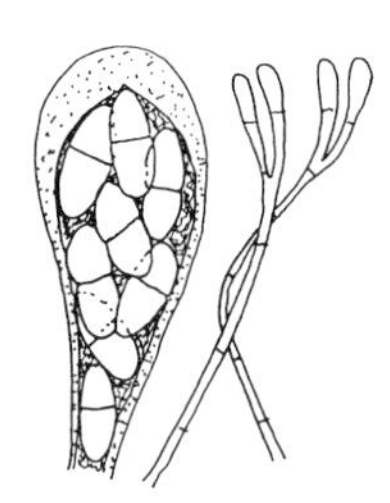

F. bouteillei x 500.

Fellhanera bouteillei Thallus thin and granular, becoming continuous. Apothecia up to 0.3 mm diam. Spores 1-septate, slightly constricted in the middle, 10–15 x 3–5 μm.
Habitat: Infrequent on leaves and small twigs of evergreen trees, mainly box. It is found in sheltered but well-lit situations and it has become much rarer due to pollution. An overlooked species on heather and bilberry stems which appears to be on the increase. If the spores are 3-septate it is probably **F. subtilis**.

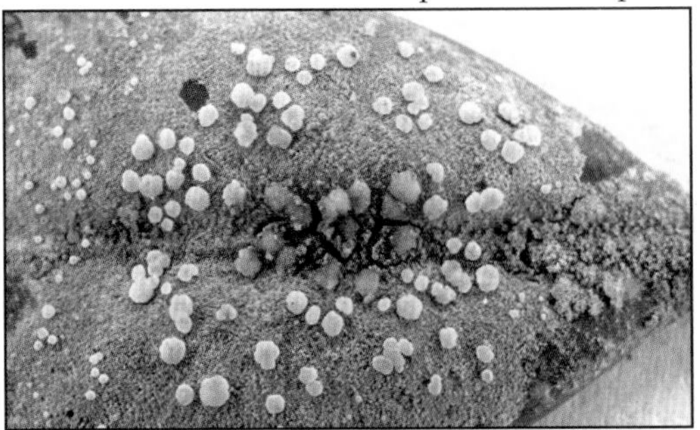

F. bouteillei x 9.

FULGENSIA ('shining' – from the bright colour of the thallus). **Thallus** squamulose to crustose, sometimes placodioid, in various shades of yellow. **Photobiont** *Trebouxia*. **Apothecia** lecanorine. **Ascus** 8-spored, *Teloschistes*-type. **Spores** colourless, simple (may appear 1-septate due to the more dense contents gathering at either end). This genus was transferred from *Caloplaca* due to the simple spores, but the species are K+ purple (physcion).

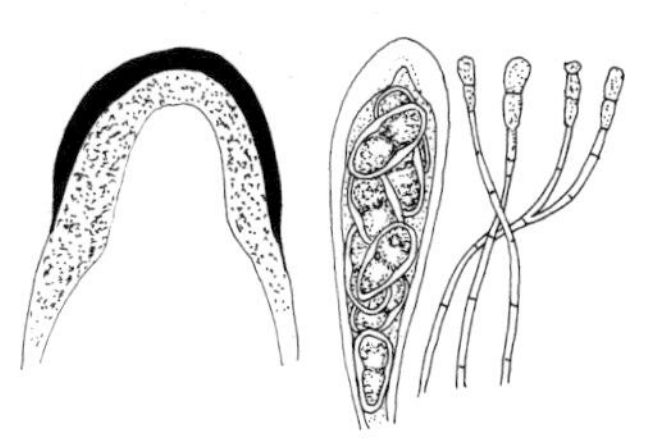

K/I reaction to the ascus tip. *F. fulgens* x 600.

Fulgensia fulgens Thallus egg-yellow, pruinose, consisting of rosettes of small (about 1–2 mm), adpressed, very convex, imbricate, incised squamules. The thallus is lobate around the margins and up to 3 cm diam. The centre of the thallus has flattened lobules (schizidia) that may break off to expose the white medulla. Apothecia fairly small (up to about 1.5 mm), orange, the thin thalline margin being excluded early. Spores simple, but may appear 1-septate, 9–12 x 3–5 µm.
K+ purple. Its pale yellow and white egg-like appearance (it is called the scrambled egg lichen), its habitat and simple spores all help to separate it from *Caloplaca*.
Habitat: Rare in the SouthWest on mosses and soil on well-lit calcareous dunes. It also occurs in a few sites on the calcareous soils of East Anglia, e.g. Breckland. A rare species **F. bracteata**, consisting of dispersed, convex areoles, is found on 'sugar limestone' at altitude in northern Scotland.

F. fulgens x 5.

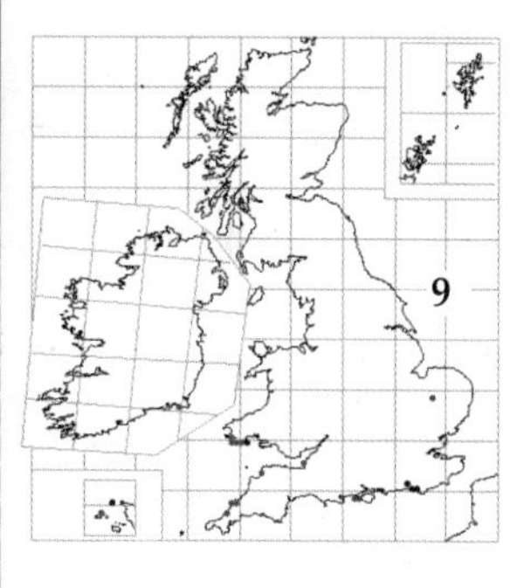

FUSCIDEA ('fuscous' – as the spores often become brownish when old). **Thallus** crustose. **Photobiont** trebouxioid. **Apothecia** lecideine, disc very dark brown (paler brown when wet). **Paraphyses** slightly conglutinate. **Hymenium** I+ blue at least in part. **Ascus** 8-spored, K/I blue inner and outer cap. **Spores** simple, colourless (brownish when very mature), ellipsoid. Pycnidia in warts, towards the thallus margin.

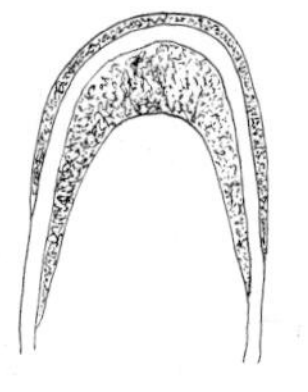

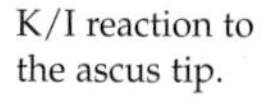

K/I reaction to the ascus tip.

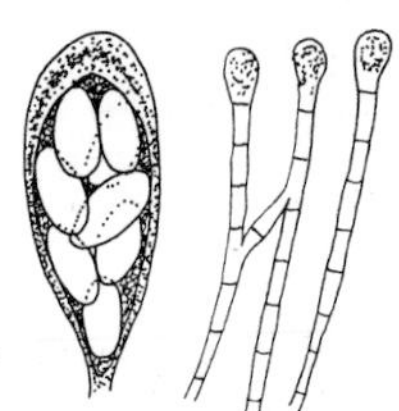

F. kochiana x 700.

1.	On rocks, often in mosaics	2
–	On trees, in neat ± circular patches	**3. F. lightfootii**
2.	Spores bean-shaped, medulla P+ red	**1. F. cyathoides**
–	Spores almost globose, medulla P–	3
3.	Thallus purple-tinged. Apothecia sessile, 0.2–0.6 mm diam	**4. F. lygaea**
–	Thallus grey, tinged brown. Apothecia innate, 0.5–3 mm diam	**2. F. kochiana**

1. Fuscidea cyathoides Thallus colour variable from light grey to a warm mousey brown, areolate, smooth or rough, limited by a black prothallus that is often visible between the areoles. Apothecia sessile, up to 1 mm diam, dark brown or black. The disc becomes convex and the thin, paler proper margin is often excluded. Spores bean-shaped, 9–12 x 4–6 µm. Var. **sorediata** has fawn to greenish punctiform soralia.
Medulla: P+ red, K+ dirty yellow, UV–.
Habitat: Very common on hard, coarse-grained acid rock and rarely on walls, in upland areas. It may form extensive mosaics, sometimes with *F. kochiana*.

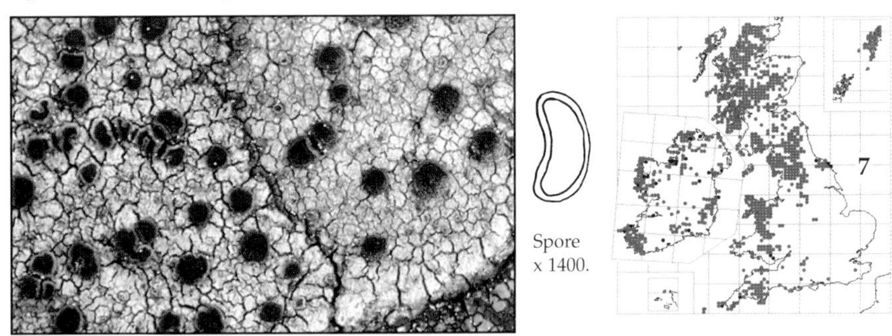

F. cyathoides x 4.

2. F. kochiana Thallus grey, sometimes tinged brown, areoles to 2.5 mm wide. Prothallus dark brown to black. Apothecia to 3 mm wide, innate, irregular-shaped and immarginate. Spores not bean-shaped, almost round, becoming brown, 8–11 x 6–8 µm.
Medulla: P–, K–, UV+ blue-white.
Habitat: Similar to the previous species, less common at lower altitudes.

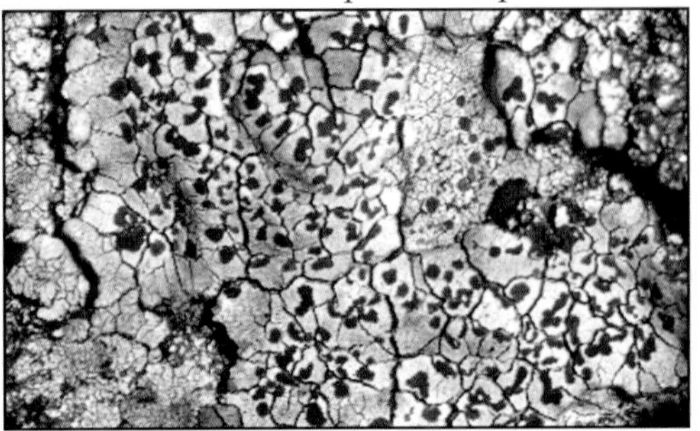

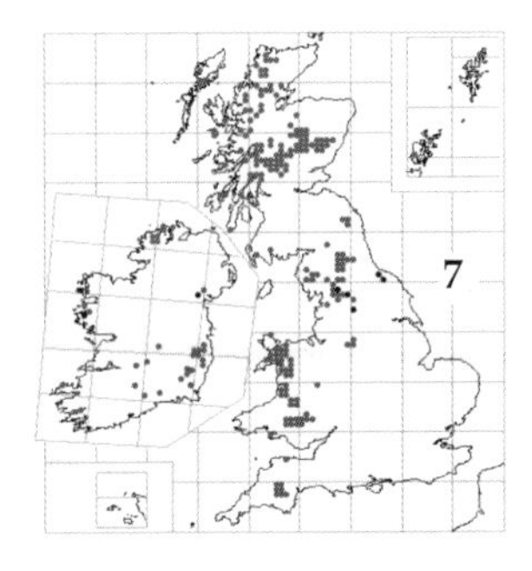

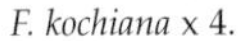
F. kochiana x 4.

3. F. lightfootii Thallus bright grey-green, sometimes olive-brown, warted or often distinctly granulose, usually sorediate, thick, sharply defined, and in neat circular patches up to about 2 cm wide. Frequently with a pale prothallus. Often infertile. Apothecia up to 1 mm diam, very dark grey-brown to almost black, flat to slightly convex, margin slightly paler, thin. Spores 1-septate, constricted in the centre, with obtuse ends, 8–11 x 3–5 µm.
P–, K–, C–, UV+ white.
May be confused with *Lecidella elaeochroma*, but it is C– (*L. elaeochroma* may be C– in polluted areas), has 1-septate (sometimes indistinct), constricted spores and a more granular thallus. A very variable species.
Habitat: Frequent on smooth bark, particularly on twigs. In damp or boggy areas in the South and West.

F. lightfootii x 4.

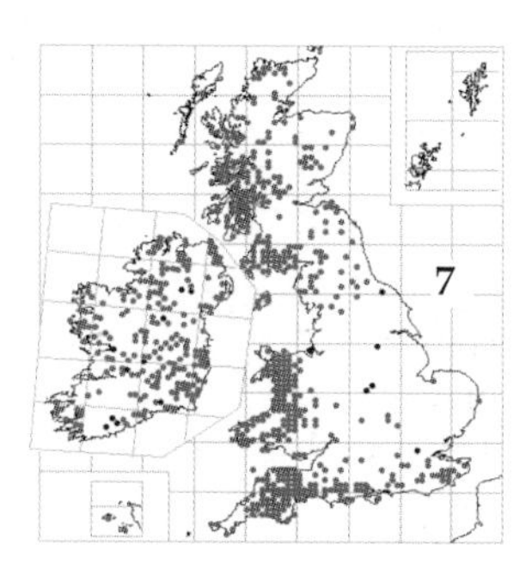

4. F. lygaea Thallus grey or brown, usually with a purplish tinge as if stained with weak blackcurrant juice. Smooth or cracked, surrounded by a very dark brown prothallus. Apothecia to 0.6 mm, sessile, black. The thin margin is soon excluded as the disc becomes convex. Spores almost globose, 5–10 x 5–7 µm.
Spot reactions: negative.
Habitat: Fairly common in upland areas on hard acid rock.

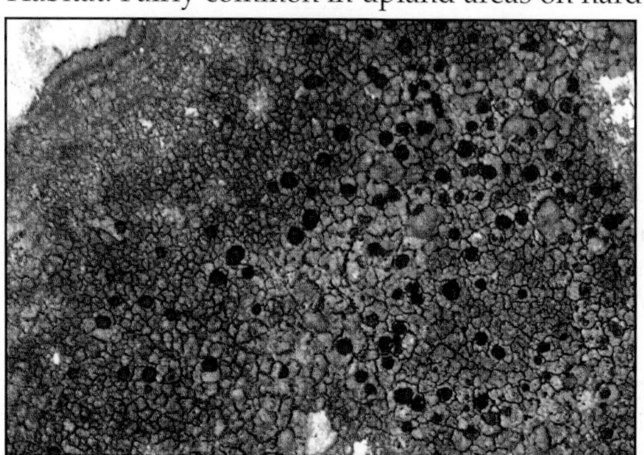

F. lygaea x 4.

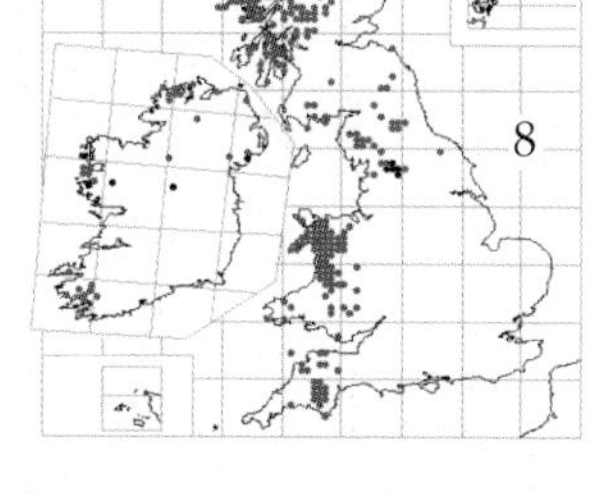

GRAPHINA ('writing' – from the appearance of the apothecia). **Thallus** crustose, sometimes nearly immersed. **Photobiont** *Trentepohlia.* **Apothecia** lirellate with carbonaceous margins. **Ascus** 8-spored, cylindrical to somewhat clavate, K/I–. **Spores** colourless, muriform, I+ violet. **Chemical reactions** negative but sometimes UV+ orange. *Graphis* and *Phaeographis* have septate, not muriform, spores. This is the only British lichen genus with lirellae and colourless muriform spores, but beware of the frequently found British non-lichenized fungal genus *Gloniopsis* which has these features in common too but the spores are I–.

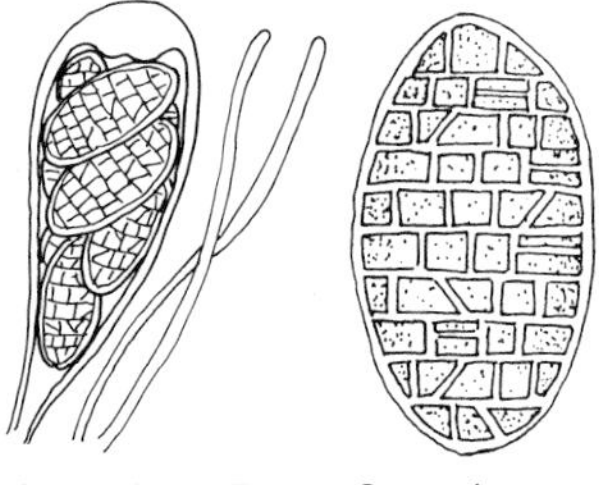

G. anguina x 250. *G. anguina* spore x 750.

Due to their resemblance to writing the *Graphidacae* are historically amongst the earliest listed records that can, with certainty, be interpreted as lichens.

1.	Lirellae innate, much branched and serpentine	**1. G. anguina**
–	Lirellae elevated, rarely branched and ± straight	**2. G. ruiziana**

1. Graphina anguina Thallus grey, usually wrinkled and cracked, slightly shiny, sometimes leprose. Apothecia immersed, the thalline margin often slightly elevated, the carbonaceous margin flat, often pruinose with a narrow slit-like disc. Lirellae are short, serpentine and usually stellate. Spores with more than 30 cells, 30–50 x 14–18 µm.
Habitat: Infrequent, but more common in the South and West, on somewhat shaded, smooth-barked trees, especially in coppice and secondary woodland.

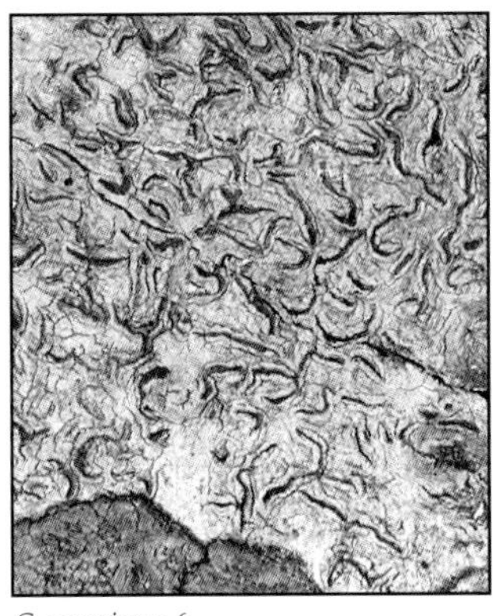

G. anguina x 6.

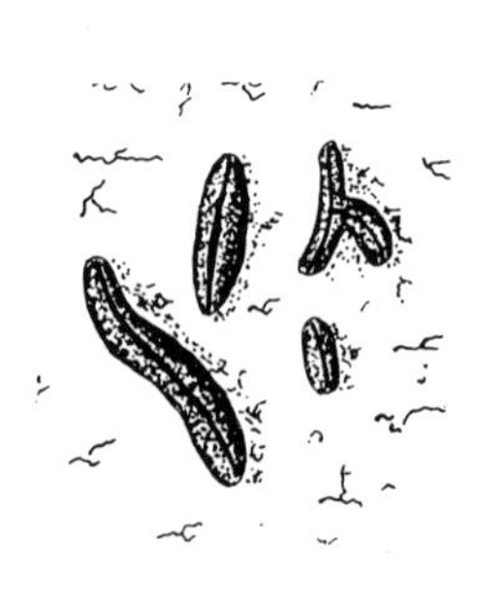

G. ruizina x 20.

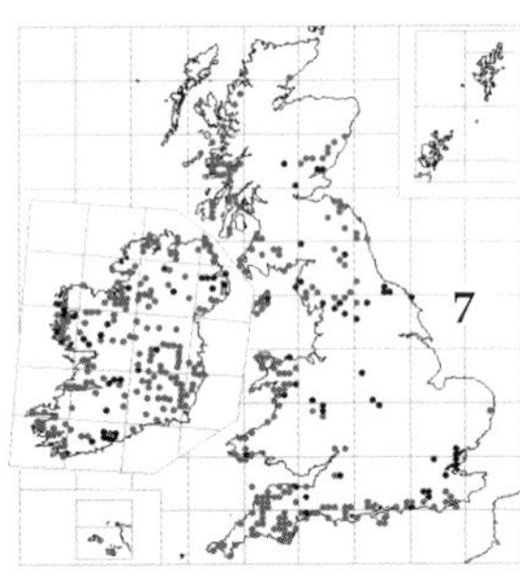

G. anguina

2. G. ruiziana Thallus greenish grey or whitish, sometimes scarcely developed. It differs from the previous species in its markedly elevated, not innate, lirellae which are straight, unbranched (rarely once-branched). The thalline margins of the lirellae are usually excluded, and the disc is often reduced to a slit. Spores with more than 30 cells, 28–45 x 12–18 µm.
Habitat: Similar to the previous species, but much rarer and confined to very high rainfall areas in the extreme West.

GRAPHIS ('writing' – from the appearance of the apothecia). **Thallus** crustose. **Photobiont** *Trentepohlia*. **Apothecia**, lirellate, up to several mm long with pronounced emergent carbonaceous margins . Ascus 8-spored, K/I–. **Spores** colourless (occasionally some old spores become brown), multi-septate. **Chemical reactions** as below but spores are I+ purple. Thallus usually much larger than in *Opegrapha* but small specimens may be separated by the longer, I+ purple spores with lens-shaped cells and the simple paraphyses.

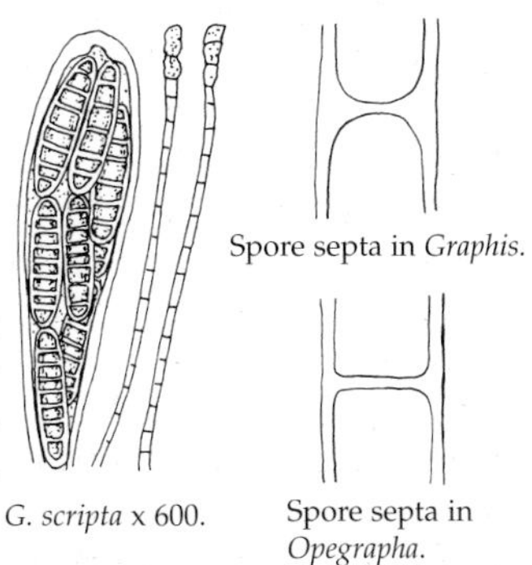

G. scripta x 600.

Spore septa in *Graphis*.

Spore septa in *Opegrapha*.

1. Margins of lirellae with several furrows. Thallus K+y turning red **1. G. elegans**
– Margins of lirellae unfurrowed. Thallus K– **2. G. scripta**

1. Graphis elegans Thallus grey, smooth and slightly shiny or wrinkled. Apothecia very varied in shape and size but always with the carbonaceous margins raised above the thallus and almost meeting in the centre. Rarely with orange pruina. Each margin has 2–7 longitudinal furrows like a ploughed field (these may be difficult to see in some lirellae). Spores colourless, 7- to 12-septate, 30–50 x 6–12 µm.
P+ orange, K+ yellow, slowly turning blood-red.
Habitat: Widespread on smooth-barked trees and twigs, mainly in shade.

G. elegans x 6.

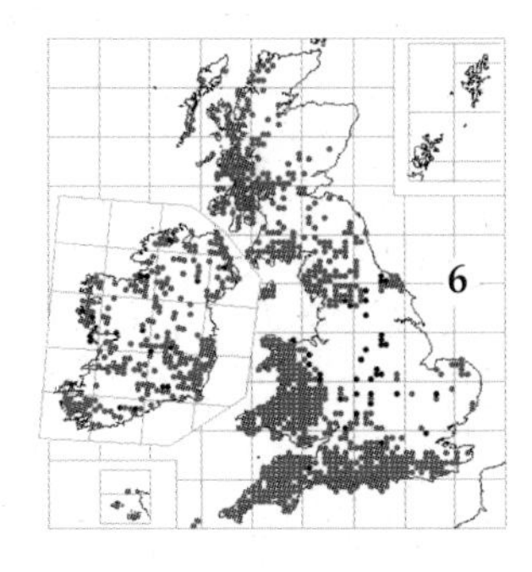

2. G. scripta Thallus white to grey, smooth or wrinkled. Apothecia very variable curved or stellate with raised, unfurrowed, carbonaceous margins. The centres of the lirellae are often more open than in *G. elegans* and are then ± white-pruinose. Spores colourless, 7- to 15-septate, 25–70 x 6–10 µm. Many varieties have been named but are of little significance and in most cases are only due to the nature of the growth of the host substratum.
P–, K–.
Habitat. Very common on smooth-barked trees, heather stems and twigs.

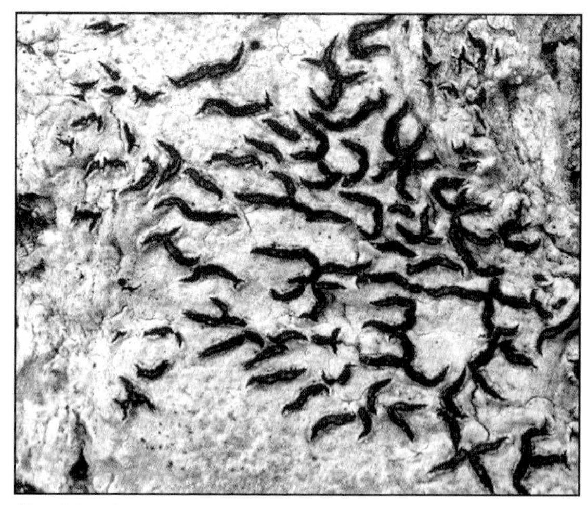

G. scripta x 6.

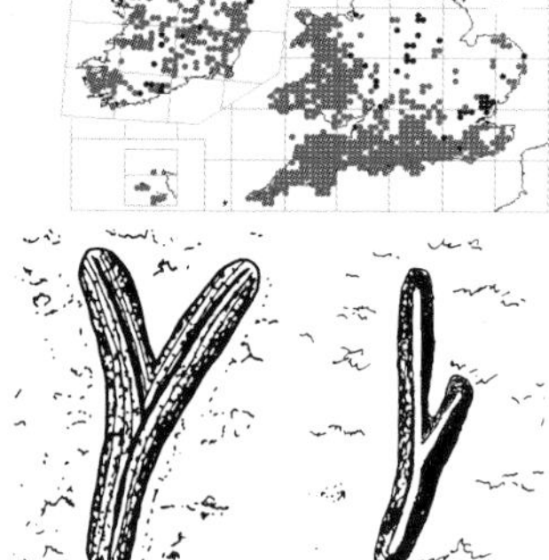

G. elegans *G. scripta*

GYALECTA ('hollow container' – from the concave centre to the apothecia). **Thallus** crustose or nearly absent. **Photobiont** *Trentepohlia*. **Apothecia** lecideine, not immersed, with a prominent orange or yellow pseudothalline margin, disc concave. **Ascus** 8-spored, whole ascus and contents usually K/I blue. **Spores** colourless, septate or muriform. **Pycnidia** innate, colourless to brown. **Chemical reactions** negative.

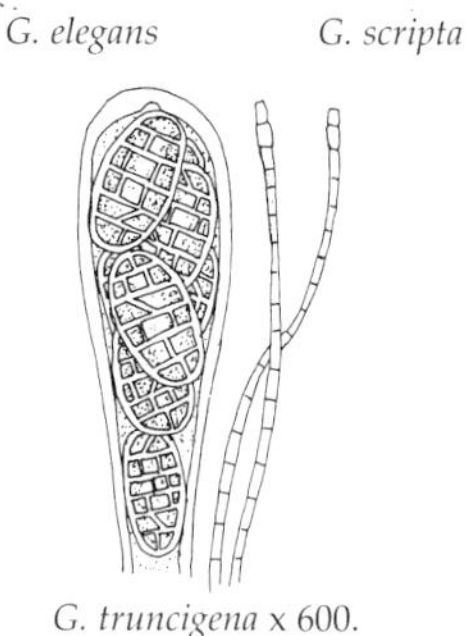

G. truncigena x 600.

1.	Disc chestnut, pruinose, especially when young	**5. G. ulmi**
–	Disc pale orange or pink, not pruinose	2
2.	Apothecia cream to pale orange, on deciduous trees	3
–	Apothecia pink, on hard limestone, spores 3-septate	**4. G. jenensis**
3.	Spores fusiform, 11- to 13- septate, only 1 or 2 cross septa	**2. G derivata**
–	Spores spherical to ellipsoid, submuriform to muriform	4
4.	Spores 15–28 x 5–10 µm	**1. G. truncigena**
–	Spores 9–14 x 6–9 µm	**3. G. flotowii**

1. Gyalecta truncigena Thallus grey, thin and slightly powdery. Apothecia very small (up to 0.5 mm), orange or flesh-coloured, with a thick, smooth, paler margin. Spores 5- to 7-septate, usually with one or two parallel longitudinal septa, 15–30 x 5–10 µm.
Habitat: Not rare but easily overlooked. Found on nutrient-rich rain-tracks on rough-barked deciduous trees (especially elm). Mainly in the South and West.

The following species are also found on deciduous trees and differ as follows:

2. G. derivata has fusiform, 11- to 13-septate spores, with only an occasional cross septum, 20–30 x 4–6 µm. It is a rare species that is found mainly in the West.

3. G. flotowii has smaller, almost spherical to elliptical spores, 9–14 x 6–9 µm with erratically angled septa. It is uncommon but is found throughout the British Isles, especially in nutrient tracks on *Fraxinus*.

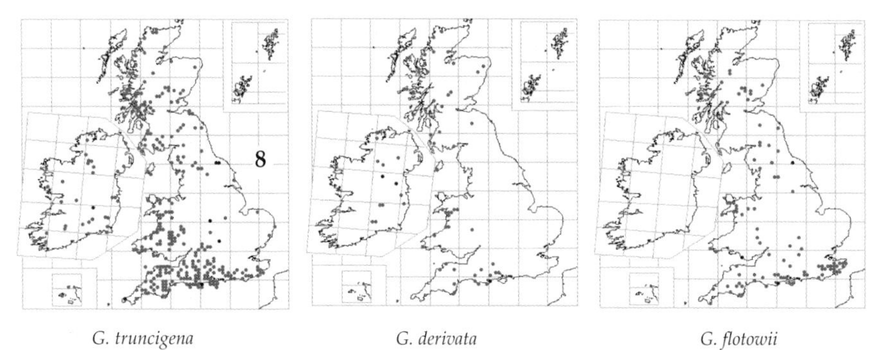

G. truncigena *G. derivata* *G. flotowii*

4. G. jenensis Thallus light grey often with a pinkish tinge, thin, matt. Apothecia up to 1 mm, spherical when young but opening to show a pale orange disc with a thick margin that becomes slightly dentate so that it looks like the edge of a pie crust. Spores 12–25 x 6–10 µm (var. **macrospora** has spores 30–40 x 10–16 µm, and occurs on granite associated with mortar), 3-septate, soon becoming muriform (the spores of the superficially similar *Petractis clausa* are persistently 3-septate and the apothecia more conical and dentate).
Habitat: Infrequent but locally abundant on damp, shaded, hard limestone. It may spread onto adjacent mosses. It is also found on basic rocks near the sea.

G. jenensis var. *macrospora* x 6.

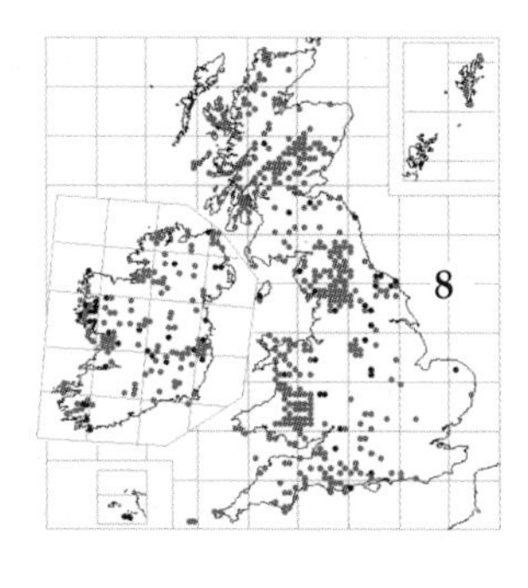

5. G. ulmi Thallus white to pale grey and evanescent. Apothecia numerous, up to 1.5 mm diam with a white, almost stellate, very pruinose, crenulate margin, chestnut to red disc that is often white-pruinose. Spores 3-septate, 10–20 x 5–8 µm.
Habitat: Rare on mosses and calcareous soils, rarely on the damp shaded bases of elm trees. Much declined since Dutch elm disease killed many elms.

GYALIDEOPSIS ('similar to *Gyalidea*'). **Thallus** crustose, thin and filmy. **Photobiont** trebouxioid. **Apothecia** lecideine, dark red-brown, becoming swollen when wet. The margin and hymenium consists of anastomosing hyphae in a gelatinous matrix. **Ascus** 2- to 8-spored, the contents I+ red. **Spores** septate to muriform. **Pycnidia** are absent but hyphophores are present and serve a similar purpose. **Chemical reactions** negative.

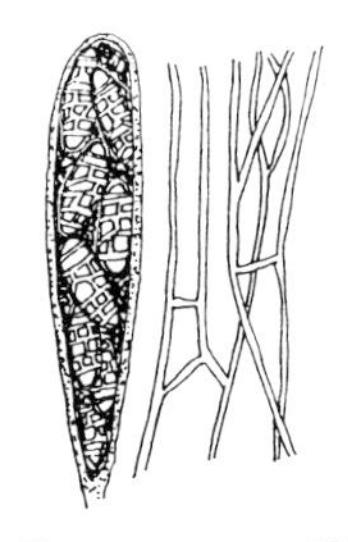

G. anastomosans x 250.

Gyalideopsis anastomosans Thallus grey to pale green, limited by a pale, filmy prothallus forming patches up to about 1 cm across. The surface usually has numerous, minute (0.1 mm long), needle-like hyphophores (special structures for asexual reproduction) with semi-translucent tips. Apothecia red-brown to almost black with an uneven margin, 0.2–0.4 mm diam. Spores muriform, 20–30 x 6–13 µm.
Habitat: Infrequent, in shaded boggy sites on smooth-barked trees especially on the upper surface of inclined trees, also on rotten trunks and wood.

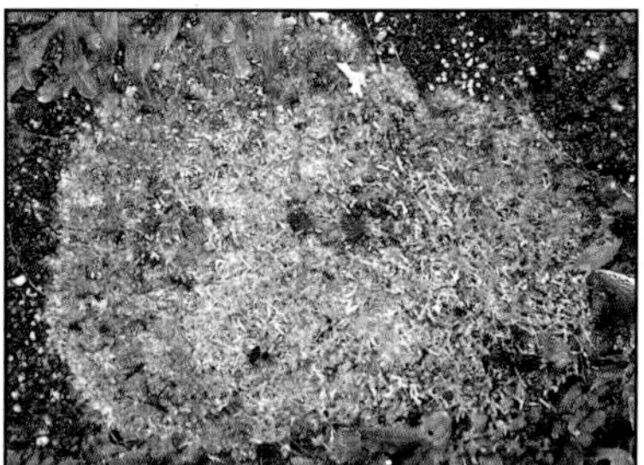

G. anastomosans x 6.

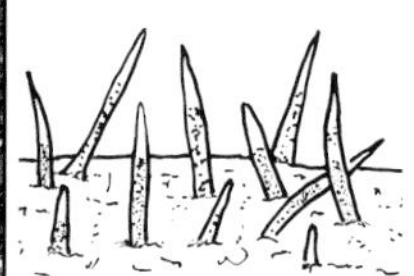

Hyphophores x 100.

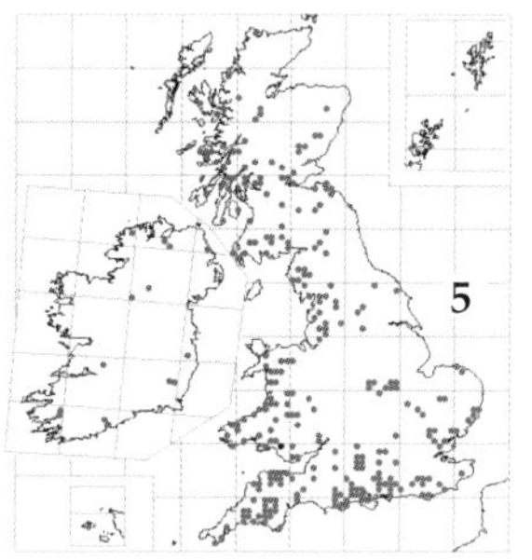

HAEMATOMMA ('bloody eye' – from the colour of the apothecia). **Thallus** crustose, often completely sorediate. **Photobiont** trebouxioid. **Apothecia** lecanorine. **Ascus** 8-spored, *Lecanora*-type but often only giving a weak K/I reaction. **Paraphyses** anastomosing, not thickened at the tips. **Hymenium** I+ blue. **Spores** colourless, multi-septate, straight or curved. **Pycnidia** immersed. **Conidia** simple, colourless.

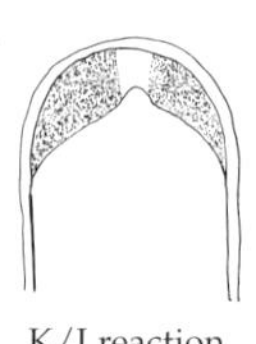

K/I reaction to the ascus tip. (often only weakly reacting).

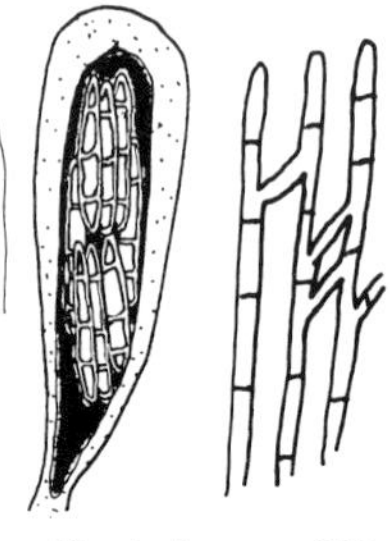

H. ochroleucum x 250.

Haematomma ochroleucum var. **ochroleucum** Thallus yellowish grey, leprose, with a distinct white, fimbriate prothallus. Apothecia with a bright red disc and sorediate margin. Immature apothecia are more common than mature ones. Spores 3- to 7-septate, 30–60 x 5–7 µm. Pycnidia are about 0.2 mm diam with bright red tips and contain curved conidia, 12–20 x 0.5 µm.
Thallus: K+ yellow, P+ yellow. Apothecia: K+ purple.
Habitat: Common throughout the British Isles on dry siliceous rocks and under

overhangs. It is frequently found on monuments and sheltered church walls, exceptionally on weakly nutrient-enriched trees.

The var. **porphyrium** has a white to light grey thallus as it lacks usnic acid. It is common in both lowland and upland Britain on trees, siliceous and calcareous tombstones, rocks and walls.

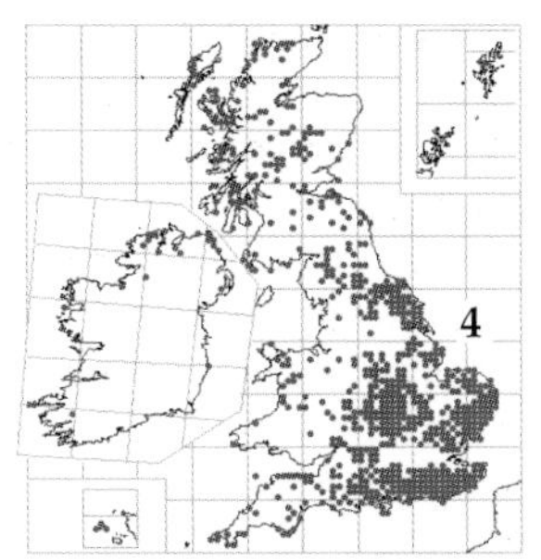

H. ochroleucum var. *porphyrium*

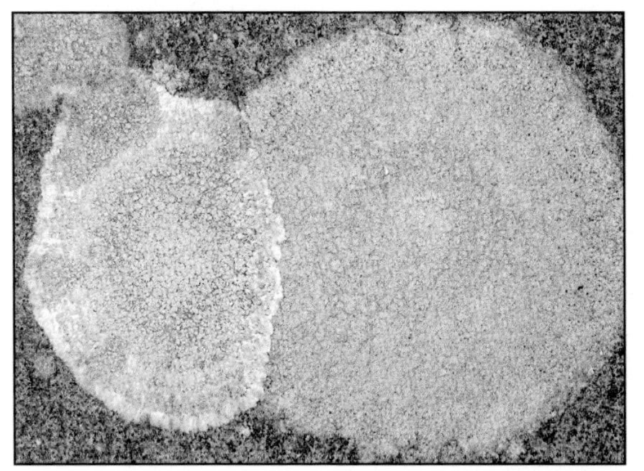

H. ochroleucum var. *porphyrium* (left) var. *ochroleucum* (right) x 3.

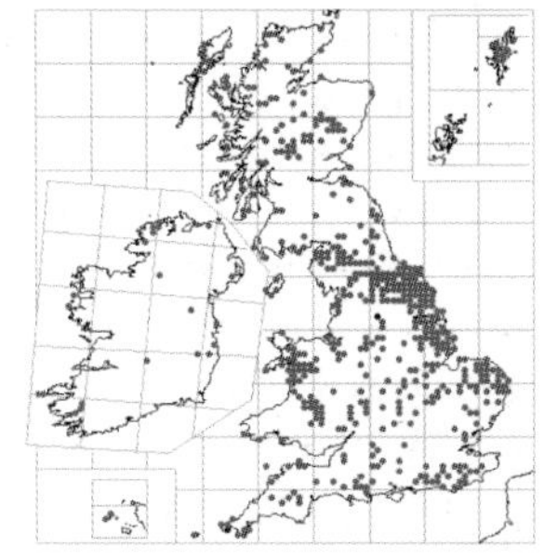

H. ochroleucum var. *ochroleucum*

HERTELIANA (after the German lichenologist Hannes Hertel, born 1939). **Thallus** crustose. **Photobiont** chlorococcoid. **Apothecia** lecideine. **Hymenium** colourless or pale orange I+ blue. **Ascus** 8-spored, K/I blue tholus, darker blue around the ocular chamber. **Spores** simple, colourless with somewhat pointed ends. **Pycnidia** immersed, black. There is only one species in the genus.

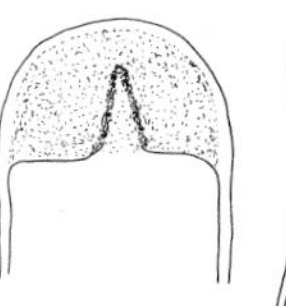

K/I reaction to ascus tip.

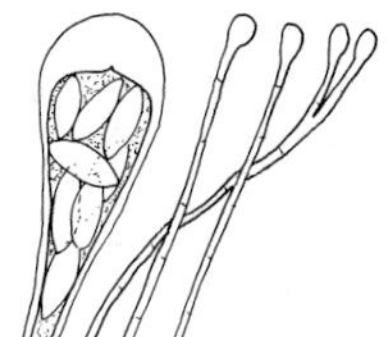

H. taylorii x 250.

Herteliana taylorii Thallus up to 30 cm wide, cream to duck-egg blue when in shade, thick, smooth, becoming cracked in the centre, surrounded by a black prothallus. Apothecia to about 0.7 mm diam, sessile when mature, disc chestnut-brown, very convex. It is often found without mature apothecia but with numerous very young apothecia and pycnidia. Spores 18–22 x 8–10 µm.

K+ yellow, KC+ yellow, UV–.

Habitat: Frequent, mainly in the West, on damp acid rocks, often in old woodland. In The Lizard (W. Cornwall) a form has been found with granular soredia.

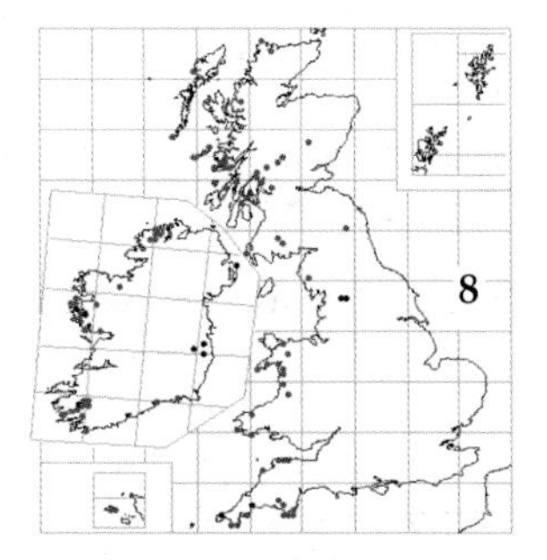

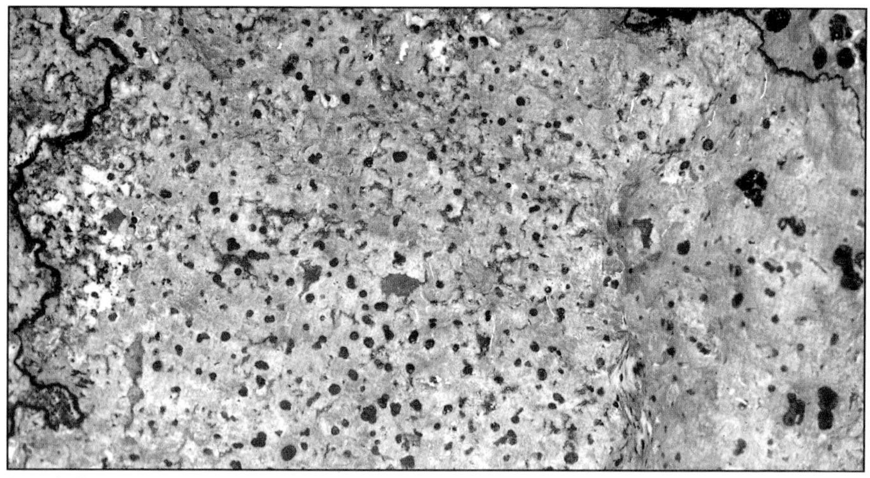

H. taylorii x 6.

HETERODERMIA ('different skin' – from the different form of the upper and lower cortex). **Thallus** foliose, loosely attached and not adpressed. Lower cortex sometimes absent, when it is present there are usually also rhizines and, frequently, marginal cilia. **Photobiont** *Trebouxia*. **Apothecia** lecanorine but very rare in Britain. **Ascus** 8-spored, *Lecanora*-type. **Spores** brown, 1-septate and thick-walled (the thick wall is the main characteristic that separates this genus from *Anaptychia*). All are rare in Britain and are at the northern edge of their range.

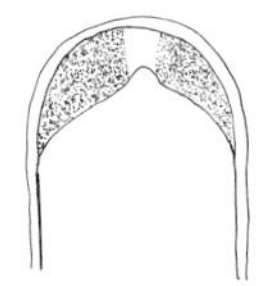

K/I reaction to the ascus tip.

1. Fairly erect and without soralia **1. H. leucomelos**
– More or less prostrate and with apical soralia **2. H. obscurata**

1. Heterodermia leucomelos Thallus white, up to 15 cm wide with ascending lobe tips. Lobes up to 3 mm wide with long black marginal cilia. The lower surface is white and channelled with a cobweb-like to powdery centre. It has only been found sterile in Britain.
Medulla: K+ orange, P+ yellow. Lower surface: K–.
Habitat: Very local on well-lit, sunny, mossy cliffs, on the coast in the SouthWest.

H. leucomelos x 4.

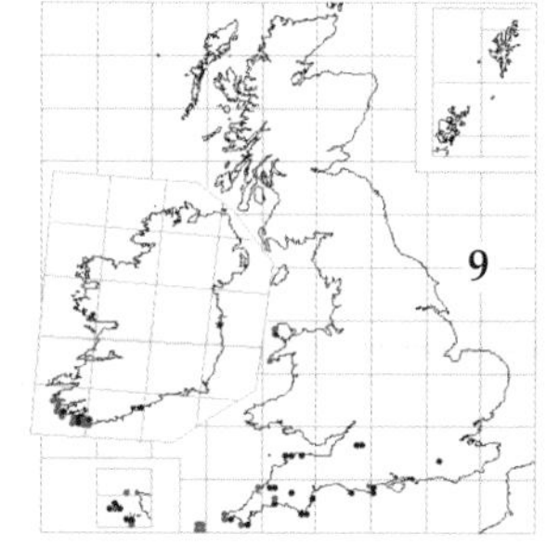

2. H. obscurata Thallus up to 10 cm wide, very pale grey, forming horizontal, spreading rosettes. Lobes up to 2 mm wide with short, black marginal cilia and soralia on the recurved tips. Lower surface white but with brownish hyphae on the surface. Apothecia very rare, with a dark brown disc and irregular margin. K+ yellow, P–. Lower surface K+ purple.
Habitat: Local in old woodlands and short, coastal grass in the West.

H. obscurata x 5.

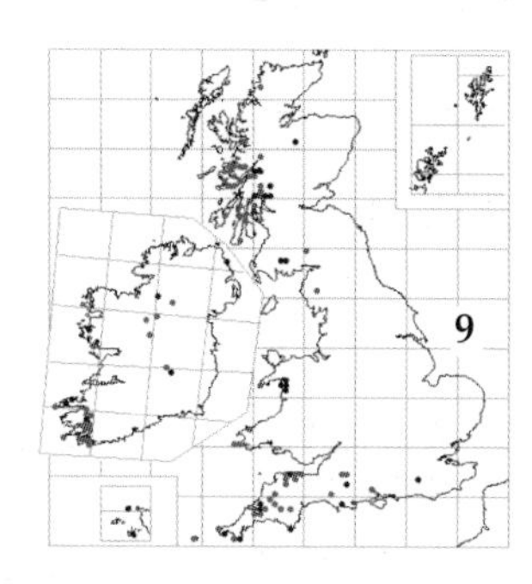

HYMENELIA ('membrane' – from the often thin thallus). **Thallus** crustose. **Photobiont** green. **Apothecia** lecanorine, innate. **Paraphyses** simple and coherent near the base, becoming separate but anastomosing and septate towards the tips. **Ascus** 8-spored, with an I+ blue outer coat, K/I–. **Spores** colourless, simple, ellipsoid. **Chemical reactions** negative.

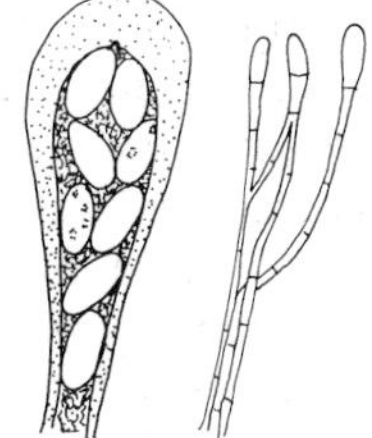

H. lacustris x 250.

1. On damp, acid rocks — **1. H. lacustris**
– On dry, hard limestone — **2. H. prevostii**

1. Hymenelia lacustris A distinctive species with a cream to orange thallus which is smooth and slightly cracked. Usually very fertile, deep orange (translucent pink and convex when wet) apothecia, up to 0.4 mm diam (if larger it is probably *Rhizocarpon lavatum* which has septate to muriform spores). Discs concave, becoming plane. Spores 12–20 x 6–10 μm.
Habitat: Common on inundated, siliceous, upland rocks by streams and lakes.

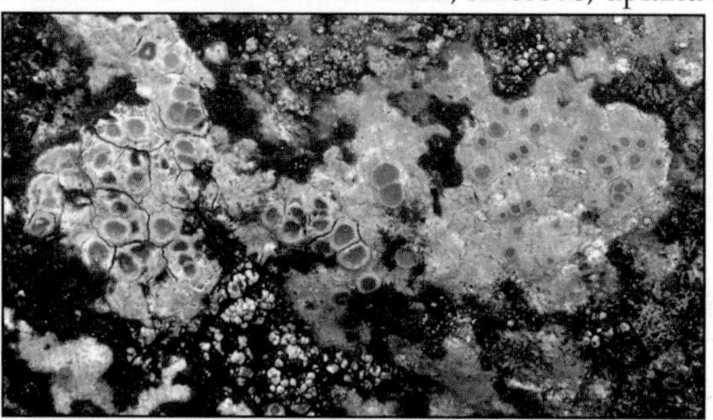

H. lacustris x 5.

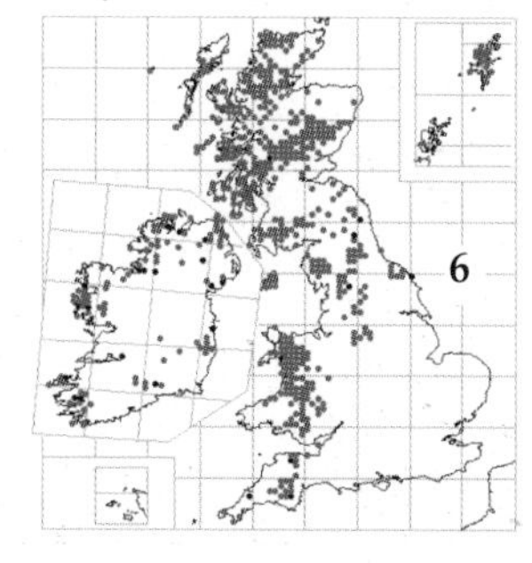

2. H. prevostii Thallus immersed or very thin, cream to pale brown. Apothecia usually present, up to 0.5 mm diam, in pits, separated from the thallus by a surrounding fissure when dry. Disc pink, translucent when wet. Spores 10–25 x 7–18 µm. A species with a similar appearance is *Ionaspis epulotica* which has orange *Trentepohlia* as its photobiont.
Habitat: On hard limestone, especially the tops of shaded chest-tombs.

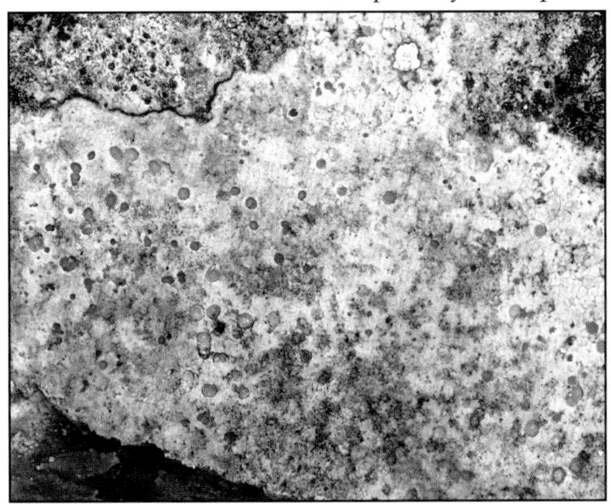

H. prevostii x 3.

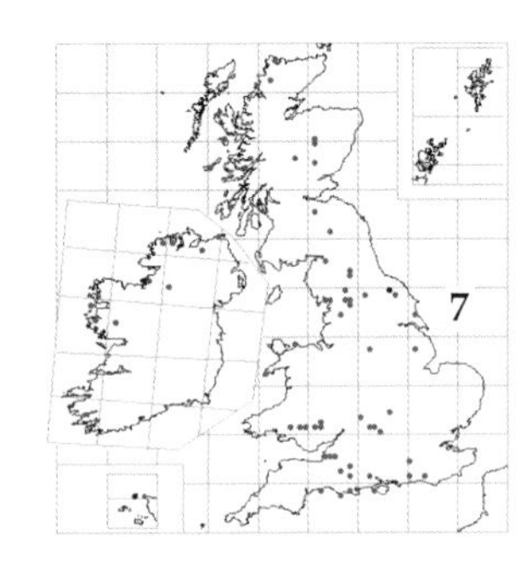

HYPERPHYSCIA ('large *Physcia*'). **Thallus** foliose, rosette-forming. **Photobiont** *Trebouxia*. **Apothecia** lecanorine, sessile with thick margins and dark brown discs, not pruinose. **Ascus** 8-spored, *Lecanora*-type. **Spores** brown, 1-septate. **Chemical reactions** negative. As the name suggests this genus resembles *Physcia*. There is only one British species.

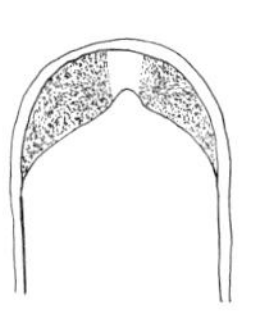

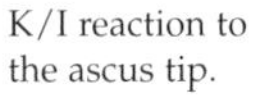

K/I reaction to the ascus tip.

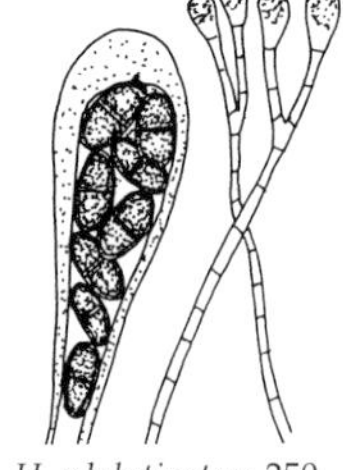

H. adglutinata x 250.

Hyperphyscia adglutinata (Physciopsis adglutinata). Thallus greenish brown, small (only about 1.5 cm), adpressed. Individual thalli coalesce to cover large areas. Lobes long, less than 0.5 mm wide, often overlapping, palmate at the tips. The upper surface splits and greenish soredia fill the crater-shaped soralia. These may become confluent at the centre. Lower surface white with a few minute, simple rhizinae. Apothecia are uncommon, sessile with a brown disc and a smooth, swollen thalline margin. The apothecia often only contain immature asci, when present, the spores are 10–20 x 7–9 µm.
Habitat: Not uncommon, mainly in lowland regions particularly in the South and West, on rather shaded nutrient-enriched trees (especially elder), frequently near the base, rarely also on nutrient-enriched vertical rocks. Most common in sites subject to some enrichment from dust.

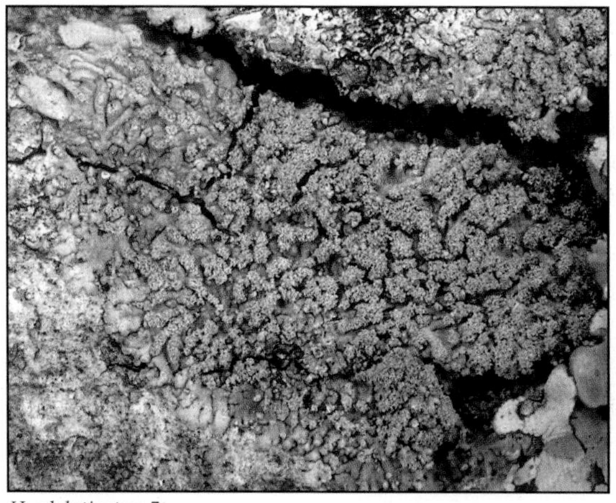

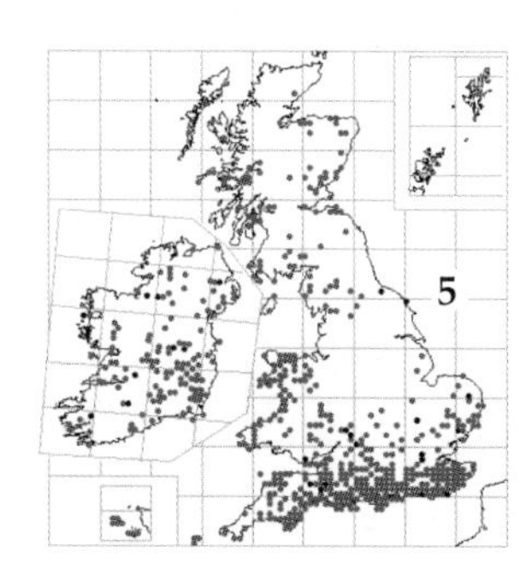

H. adglutinata x 5.

HYPOCENOMYCE ('below worthless fungi' – 'Cenomyce' is an old name for *Cladonia*, from the resemblance to small *Cladonia* squamules). **Thallus** squamulose. **Photobiont** green. **Apothecia** lecideine, sessile, dark brown-black. **Ascus** 8-spored, K/I blue apical dome. **Spores** simple (rarely 1- to 3-septate), colourless, ellipsoid. **Pycnidia** sessile, globose, black. It was separated from *Lecidea* by the squamulose form, slightly conglutinate paraphyses and several other apothecial anatomic features.

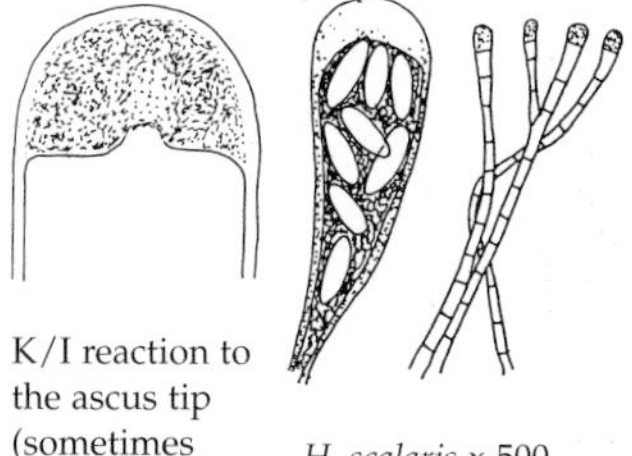

K/I reaction to the ascus tip (sometimes weak).

H. scalaris x 500.

1. Squamules mainly prostrate, lacking sorediate tips. C– **1. H. friesii**
– Squamules with ascending and sorediate tips. C+ red **2. H. scalaris**

1. Hypocenomyce friesii Thallus squamulose, fawn-brown to rarely grey-green, squamules up to 1 mm long, adpressed with rounded or crenulate, but not sorediate, at the tips. Usually fertile with gyrose discs up to 1 mm diam. Spores 5–7 x 2–4 µm. Dark pycnidia are frequently present on the squamules.
Spot reactions: negative but medulla: UV+ white.
Habitat: On bark and decorticated pines especially those which have been burned. It is rarer and more northern than *H. scalaris*.

H. friesii x 6.

2. H. scalaris Thallus light grey-brown when dry, becoming green-brown when wet, consisting of small convex, almost fluted squamules to about 1.5 mm long and overlapping, the free end is turned upwards and covered with very fine soredia. Apothecia are rare, up to 2 mm diam, black with grey-pruinose discs.
Thallus: C+ red. Medulla and soredia: UV+ white.
Habitat: Common on fences and burnt wood, more rarely on acid-barked trees, brick walls and sheltered rocks in old woodland.

H. scalaris x 6.

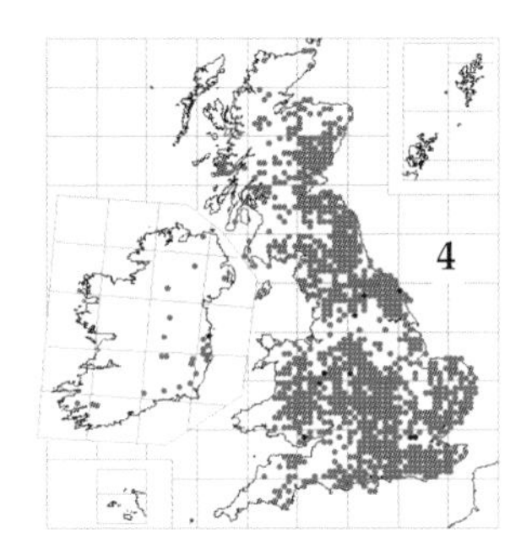

HYPOGYMNIA ('naked below' – from the lack of rhizinae). **Thallus** foliose, hollow (cut a section through the lobe to see this). It does not possess rhizines and is attached directly to the substrate by patches of fungal hyphae. Upper cortex unperforated (if perforated see *Menegazzia*). It is closely related to the genus *Parmelia*. **Apothecia** lecanorine, stalked or sessile. **Ascus** 8-spored. **Spores** simple, colourless, 8 per ascus. **Pycnidia** black, immersed.

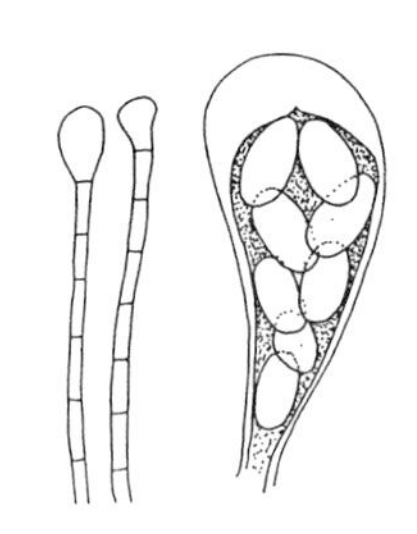

H. physodes x 300.

1. Soredia on lower surface of reflexed lobe tip. Medulla P+ red **1. H. physodes**
– Soredia on tip of raised, terete lobes. Medulla P– **2. H. tubulosa**

1. Hypogymnia physodes Thallus grey to green-grey, often orbicular, very varied, with either wide, or long, narrow, radiating lobes, frequently with black dot-like pycnidia towards the tips of the lobes. Under-surface light brown at the margin, dark brown to black in the centre where it is wrinkled and attached to the substratum. Lobe ends often turn up and split with farinose soredia on the underside extending to the fan-like margin. It is only found fertile in the most unpolluted sites. Apothecia are elevated on short stalks and have red-brown discs and a thin margin.

Cortex: K+ yellow, UV+ purplish. Medulla and soralia: KC+ red, P+ orange-red, UV+ ice-blue.
Habitat: Very common on trees, rocks, moss, heather stems, etc. This species is one of the foliose species most resistant to sulphur dioxide pollution and prefers acidic substrata (to pH 4.5). It is, however, more sensitive to fluoride pollution than some other foliose species.

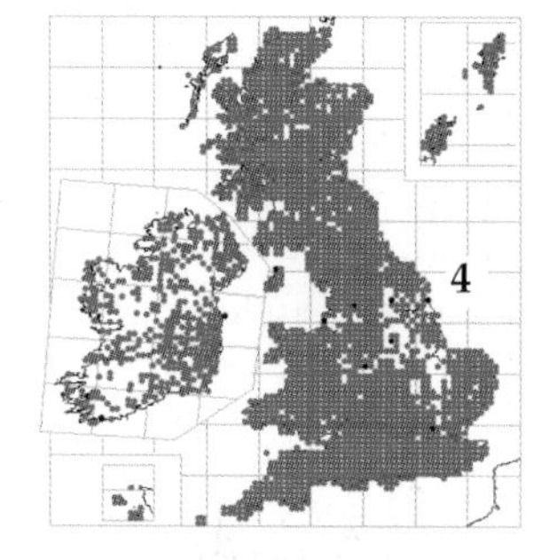

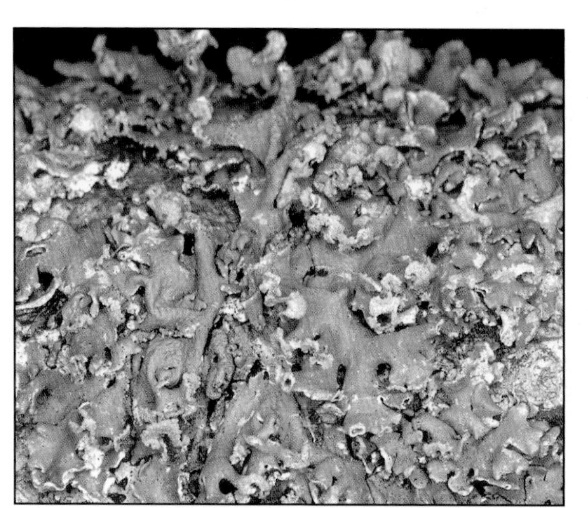
H. physodes x 3.

Reflexed, sorediate lobe tip of *H. physodes*.

2. H. tubulosa Resembles the previous species but has more erect, tubular, finger-like, rather than flattened, lobes. These darken at the tips and then the tops of these lobes become covered in farinose soredia.
Cortex: K+ yellow, UV+ purplish. Medulla and soralia: KC+red, P–, UV+ ice-blue.
Habitat: Common in similar situations to *H. physodes* but somewhat less resistant to air pollution than that species.

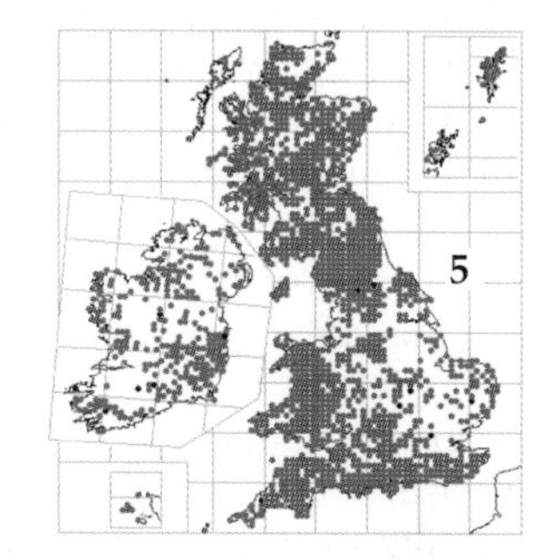

H. tubulosa x 3.

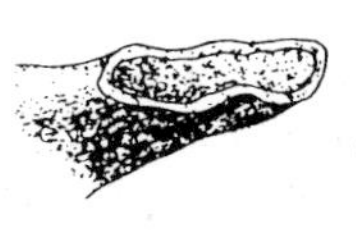
Cut lobe showing hallow thallus.

Lobe tip of *H. tubulosa*.

ICMADOPHILA ('lover of dampness' – from the situations in which it grows). **Thallus** crustose. **Photobiont** *Coccomyxa*. **Apothecia** lecanorine, but the thalline margin is soon excluded. The apothecia are sometimes on very short stalks, flesh-coloured with unbranched paraphyses. **Ascus** 8-spored, K/I blue, thin apical cap. **Spores** colourless, 1- to 3-septate. **Pycnidia** immersed, pale. There is only one British species.

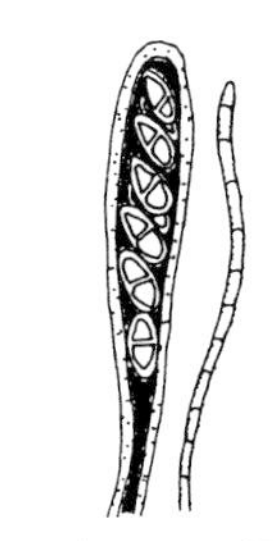
I. ericetorum x 250.

Icmadophila ericetorum Thallus light blue-grey, green when wet or shaded, granular. Apothecia flesh-pink, up to about 3 mm diam, sometimes short-stalked. The thick thalline margin becomes excluded, the disc contorted and often slightly pruinose. Apothecia in all stages of development are usually scattered over the thallus. Spores 13–27 x 4–6 µm.
P+ orange, K+ yellow, UV+ ice-blue. Apothecia: K+ yellow turning brown, UV–.
Habitat: Very common in Scotland, rarer in the rest of Britain. Found on damp peat and rotting wood. One of the first lichens to colonize freshly exposed peat. It may be confused with *Baeomyces roseus* (*Dibaeis baeomyces*) but lacks the mushroom-shaped apothecia of that species. Where sterile it resembles *Trapeliopsis granulosa,* which is found in similar habitats, but that species is C+ red and usually sorediate.

I. ericetorum x 4.

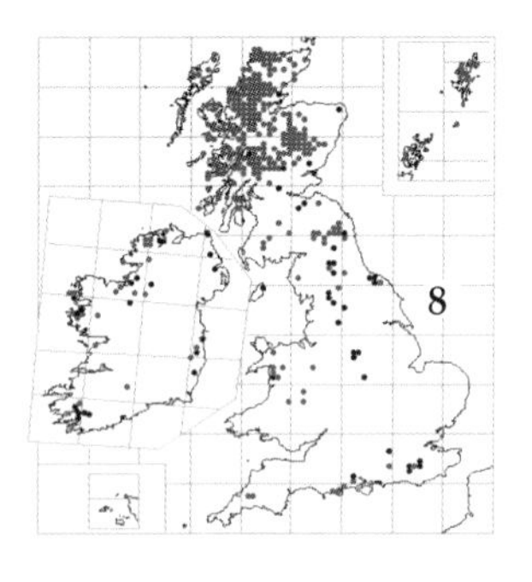

IMSHAUGIA (PARMELIOPSIS) (after the North American lichenologist Henry A. Imshaug, born 1925). **Thallus** foliose with simple rhizines on the pale fawn lower surface. **Photobiont** chlorococcoid. **Apothecia** lecanorine. **Ascus** 8–spored, *Lecanora*-type. **Spores** colourless, simple. **Pycnidia** laminal and marginal, black. Resembles a small *Parmelia*. There is only one British species. It differs from *Foraminella* in the pale lower cortex, oval spores and rod-like conidia.

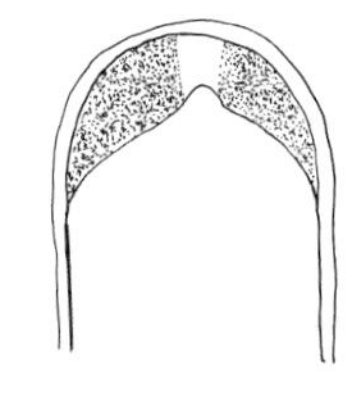
K/I reaction to the ascus tip.

Imshaugia aleurites Thallus pale grey, small (up to 5 cm), adpressed, rosette-shaped and much divided. Lobes to 3 mm wide. The thallus becomes covered in coralloid, grey isidia which soon erode. The lower surface is white or tan with sparse, simple, white rhizinae. Apothecia are rare, with brown discs. Spores 6–9 x 5–6 μm.
P+ yellowish orange, K+ yellow, UV–.
Habitat: Infrequent, on conifers, acid bark, wood, gritstone or peat in upland areas as well as palings in south-east England.

I. aleurites x 3.

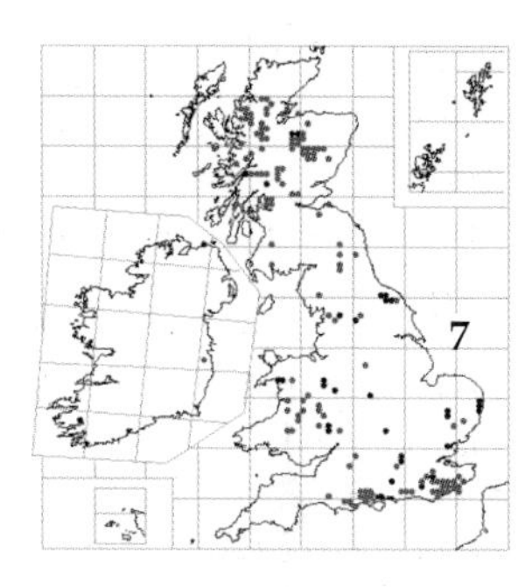

IONASPIS ('violet sign' – from the often violet tinge to the thallus). **Thallus** crustose. **Photobiont** *Trentepohlia*. (This helps separation from *Hymenelia* and *Aspicilia*.) The algal layer is poorly defined. **Apothecia** lecanorine, immersed. **Ascus** 8-spored, K/I blue outer coat. **Spores** simple, colourless, spherical to ellipsoid, frequently only immature spores can be found in the ascus. **Chemical reactions** negative.

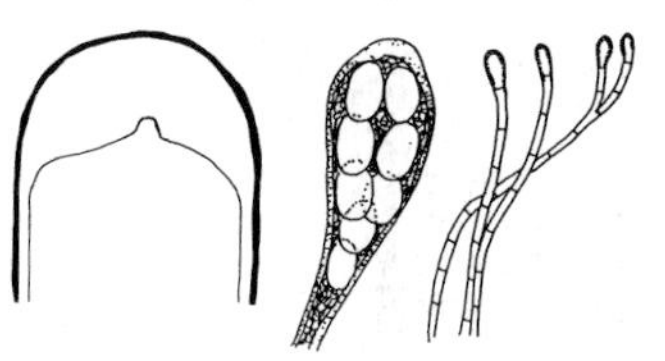

K/I reaction to the ascus tip.

I. suaveolens x 400.

1.	Apothecia pink to brown, on calcareous rocks	**1. I. epulotica**
–	Apothecia black, on acid rocks by streams	**2. I. suaveolens**

1. Ionaspis epulotica Thallus endolithic or cracked-areolate, yellowish to pinkish grey when fresh. Apothecia common, pink to brown when wet, usually with a thick margin, 0.3–0.8 mm diam, innate, concave but sometimes becoming convex and often separated from the thallus by a surrounding fissure. Hymenium 80–140 μm thick, colourless, K–, N–. Spores 13–22 x 5–12 μm.
Habitat: Locally common on damp calcareous rocks but it is also found on acid rocks where they are influenced by basic run-off. (See also the similar *Hymenelia prevostii*.) **I. odora** also has pink to brown apothecia but is found at altitude on acidic rocks by streams. The hymenium is 50– 70 μm thick, K+ violet, N–.

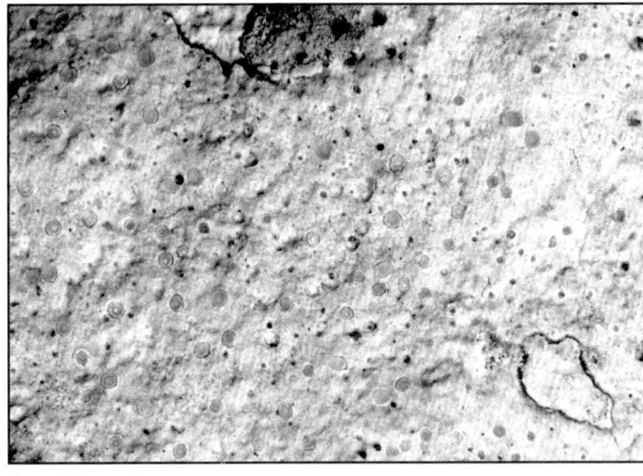

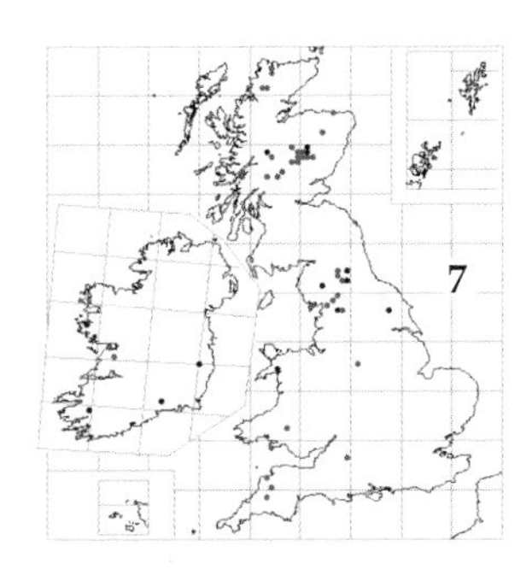

I. epulotica x 4.

2. I. suaveolens Thallus thin, dark green to olive-black, sometimes limited by a fimbriate prothallus. Apothecia black, 0.2–0.4 mm diam, innate with the margin becoming excluded. Hymenium 50–60 µm thick, blue-green in the upper part and K–, N–. Spores 6–10 x 5–7 µm.
Habitat: Infrequent on siliceous rocks in the splash zone of streams in upland regions. **I. cyanocarpa** is found in similar situations but the hymenium is 85–100 µm thick, K–, N+ reddish.
Two other rare species with blackish apothecia occurring on calcareous rocks in the North are: **I. heteromorpha**, hymenium 60–100 µm thick, K–, N+ reddish and **I. melenocarpa**, hymenium 120–150 µm thick. K–, N+ reddish.

I. suaveolens x 6.

LASALLIA (probably after a friend of Mérat de Vaumaroise). **Thallus** foliose, attached by a central holdfast. **Photobiont** *Trebouxia*. **Apothecia** lecideine, sessile and with a black disc. **Ascus** 1- (rarely 2-) spored (*Umbilicaria* has 8 smaller spores per ascus). Apical dome K/I blue. **Spores** muriform, brown. There is only one British species.

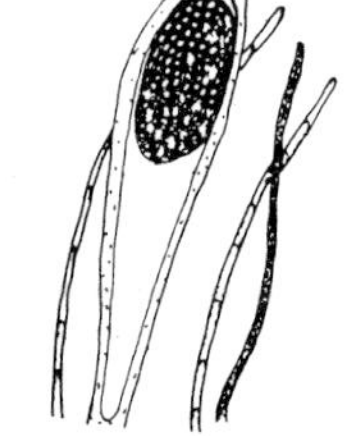

K/I reaction to the ascus tip.

L. pustulata x 250.

Lasallia pustulata Thallus mid- to dark brown when dry, up to about 8 cm diam. The surface is covered by large swollen pustules, which in the centre of the thallus are covered in a heavy pruina. The margins become tattered and often have numerous dark brown clusters of coralloid isidia. The under-surface of the thallus is brown or grey and finely reticulate, with depressions that correspond to the swellings on the upper surface. There are no rhizines. Rarely found fertile, apothecia lecideine, up to 3 mm diam, smooth, black, superficial, not gyrose. Spores 28–70 x 18–34 µm.
Medulla: C+ red, KC+ red, UV–.
Habitat: Common on nutrient-enriched rocks in upland situations where it may form extensive colonies, especially in enriched rain-tracks. Seldom growing with *Umbilicaria polyphylla* and *U. polyrrhiza* which prefer more acid, nutrient-poor habitats. This species has been used in dyeing and as a survival food (rock tripe).

L. pustulata x 3.

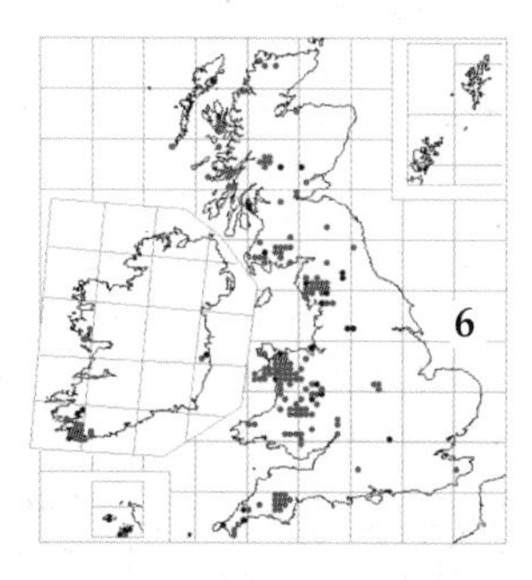

LECANACTIS ('shining, small bowl' – from the appearance of the apothecia). **Thallus** crustose. **Photobiont** *Trentepohlia*. **Apothecia** lecideine, carbonaceous, sessile, rounded or shortly elongate, often pruinose. **Ascus** 8-spored, K/I pale blue apical dome sometimes with a small darker ring. **Spores** colourless, 3- to 7-septate. **Pycnidia** either immersed or peg-like and pruinose.

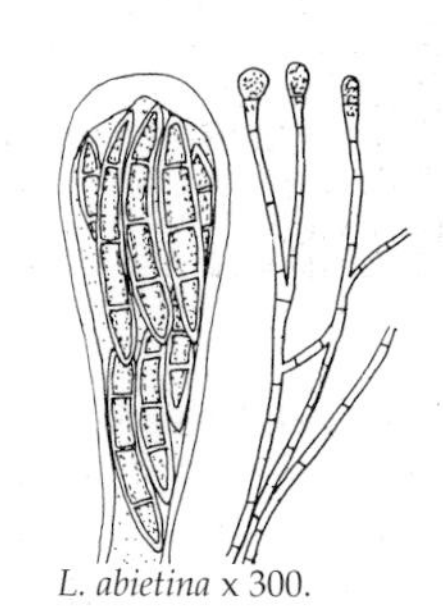

L. abietina x 300.

1.	Pycnidia black, usually absent	2
–	Pycnidia white, pruinose, abundant	4

2.	Apothecia round, angular or ellipsoid. Spores 2- to 5-septate	3
–	Apothecia short, lirellate. Spores 6- to 7-septate	**3. L. lyncea**
3.	Spores 5-septate	**4. L. premnea**
–	Spores 2- to 3-septate	**2. L. grumulosa**
4.	Pycnidial pruina C–, K+ pale yellow	**5. L. subabietina**
–	Pycnidial pruina C+ or–, K–	5
5.	Pycnidial pruina C+ red	**1. L. abietina**
–	Pycnidial pruina C–	**Opegrapha vermicellifera**

1. Lecanactis abietina Thallus white to dark grey, often with a mauve tinge, thin or leprose. Mostly infertile but nearly always with columnar pycnidia (about 0.2 mm wide) with white-pruinose tips, scattered over the surface. Apothecia brown, about 1–2 mm diam, usually covered with a thick, buff-grey pruina and with a thin proper margin. More commonly fertile in the south. Spores 3-septate, 28–45 x 3–6 µm, mainly curved.
Pruina on pycnidia: C+ red. Medulla: UV+ yellow or bluish.
Habitat: Widespread. On shaded sides of acid-barked trees, often in the large, dry cracks of rough bark. When infertile may be confused with *Opegrapha vermicellifera* which has conical pruinose pycnidia, the tips of which are C– and occurs on basic-barked trees. *L. subabietina* is C–, K+ pale yellow.

L. abietina x 4.

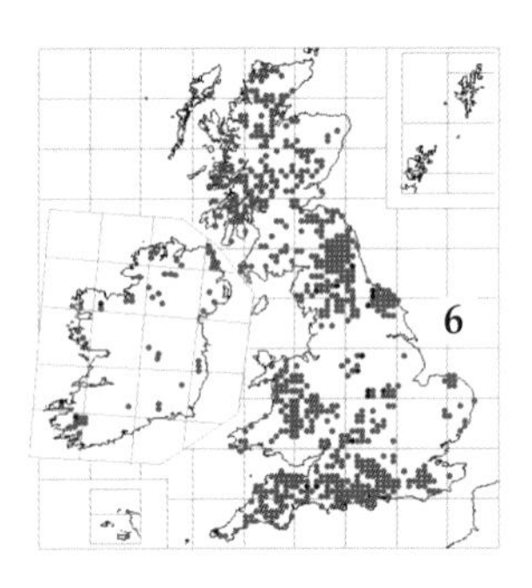

2. L. grumulosa. Thallus dull grey or brownish, often with a lilac tinge, cracked, thick, with a black prothallus. Apothecia usually present, up to 2 mm long, innate at first, often angular or shortly elongate with a persistent margin and a black, grey-pruinose disc. Spores 2- to 3-septate, 14–23 x 3–4 µm.
Thallus and pruina: C+ red.
Habitat: Infrequent, at northen limits of its range. On basic rock and mortar on walls. It prefers sheltered, shaded sites, especially beneath overhangs.

L. grumulosa x 3.

3. L. lyncea Thallus thick, glaucous white to snow-white, forming extensive, bright, powdery patches on the substratum. When infertile it can resemble *Arthonia impolita* (C+ red) but is separated by its C– reaction. Lirellae short and broad, up to 1.5 mm long, covered with a thin, very pale grey pruina. It is much more lirellate than *L. premnea*. Spores mainly 6- to 9-septate, 25–35 x 3–5 µm.
Spot reactions: negative. UV+ ice-blue.
Habitat: Locally frequent in parkland and woods in unpolluted areas. Almost entirely restricted to the dryest recesses and bough underhangs on ancient oaks.

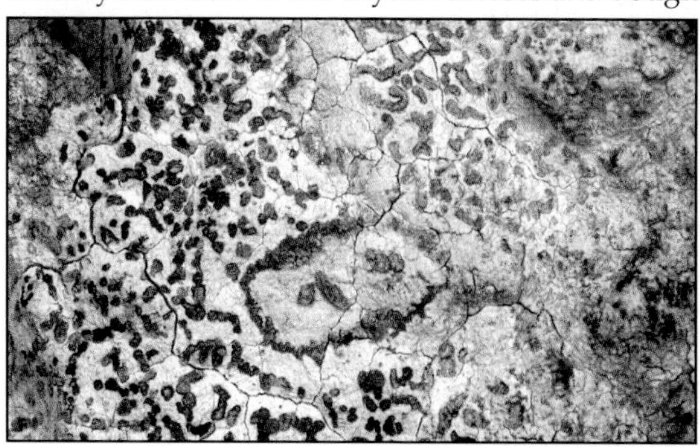

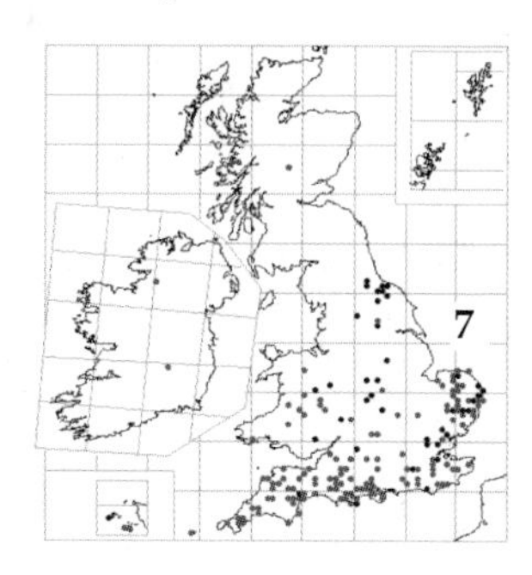

L. lyncea x 8.

4. L. premnea Thallus greenish-grey to grey, thin and smooth or immersed and almost evanescent. Apothecia usually present, black, 1–2 mm diam, often uneven in outline with a thick proper margin. The disc frequently has a light green-grey pruina and becomes convex when mature. Spores 5-septate and usually curved, 18–25 x 5–7 µm.
Spot reactions: negative.
Habitat: Frequent in the South. Usually on the north side of old, lightly shaded deciduous trees, particularly oak and holly. Rarely on shaded, acid rocks.

L. premnea x 6.

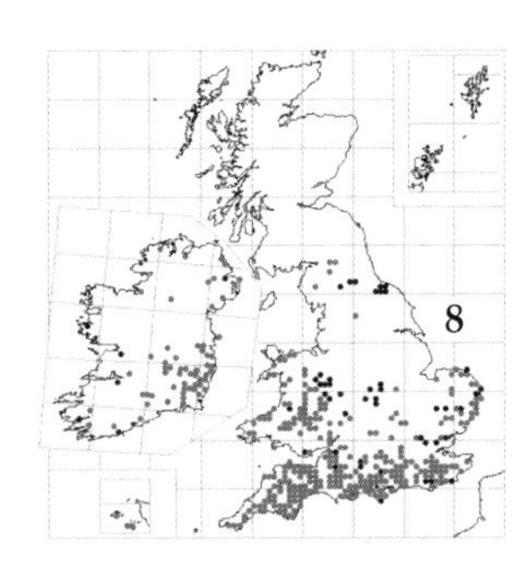

5. L. subabietina Thallus thin, pale grey and not known fertile. It normally has many globose pycnidia that often are wider at the tip than at the base, covered in a dense white pruina, sometimes tipped with pale yellow conidial gel. Conidia simple, 4–5 x 1–2 µm.
Pycnidial pruina C–, K+ light yellow (pruina on *L. abietina* C+ red, K–, *Opegrapha vermicellifera* C–, K–).
Habitat: Infrequent on the lower part of the trunks of old trees (usually oak) on the drier, shaded north side. It is also found on the stems of old ivy.

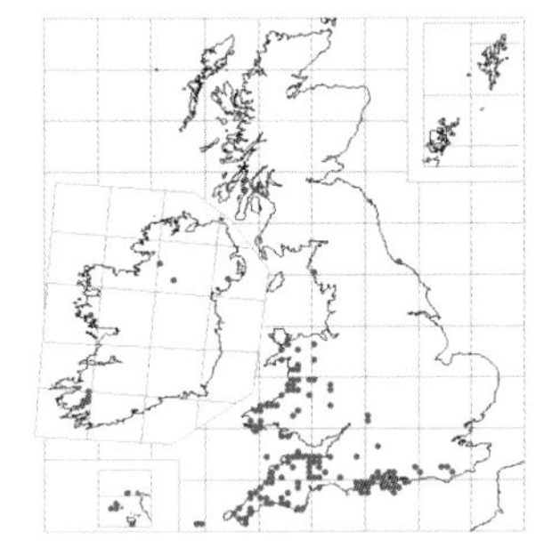

LECANIA ('small bowl' – from the shape of the apothecia). **Thallus** crustose or granular. **Photobiont** chlorococcoid. **Apothecia** orange-brown to black (redder when wet), lecanorine, but the thalline margin is often excluded early. **Ascus** 8- to 16-spored, *Bacidia*-type. **Spores** colourless, 1- to 7-septate, usually slightly bent. The following species have been found on many substances including old iron, bones and clinker.

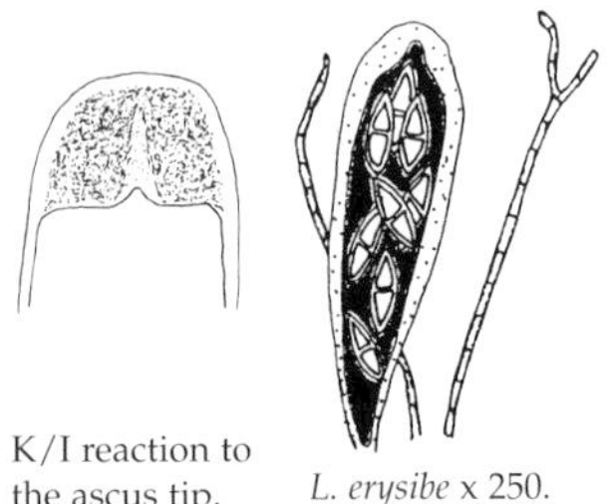

K/I reaction to the ascus tip. *L. erysibe* x 250.

1.	On bark	**3. L. cyrtella**
–	On rock	2
2.	Thallus papillate with apothecia on tips, coastal	**1. L. aipospila**
–	Thallus not papillate, not restricted to the coast	3
3.	Apothecia to 0.5 mm diam, spaced out, not pruinose	4
–	Apothecia to 1 mm diam, crowded, usually white-pruinose	**5. L. turicensis**

4. Thalline margin and thallus with granular blastidia — **4. L. erysibe**
– Thalline margin and thallus not with granular blastidia — **2. L. cuprea**

1. Lecania aipospila Thallus pale brown-grey (in shade) to dark grey, rough and warted, papillate towards the centre, often limited by a pale prothallus. Apothecia usually present often on the tips of the papillae, up to about 1 mm diam, disc red-brown to almost black, the margin usually persists and the apothecium only becomes slightly convex. Spores 1-septate, 9–15 x 4–6 µm.
Habitat: Frequent on nutrient-enriched coastal rocks, often in seepage tracks. Very variable; identification is not helped as it often grows on horizontal rocks where it is abraded by seated holiday-makers.

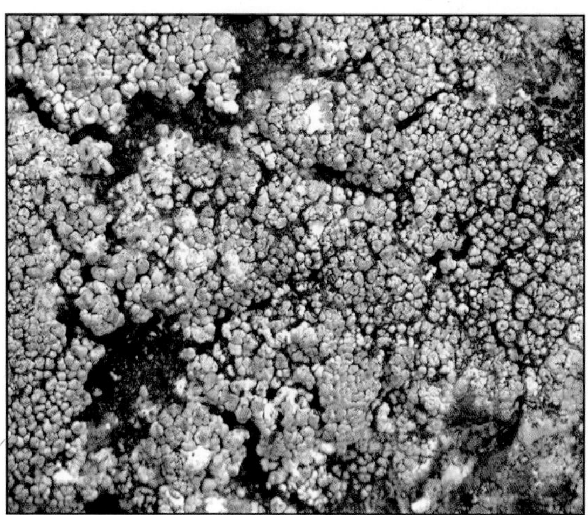

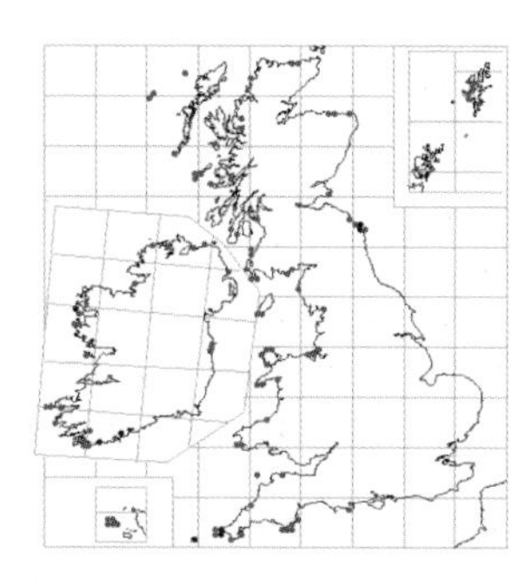

L. aipospila x 6.

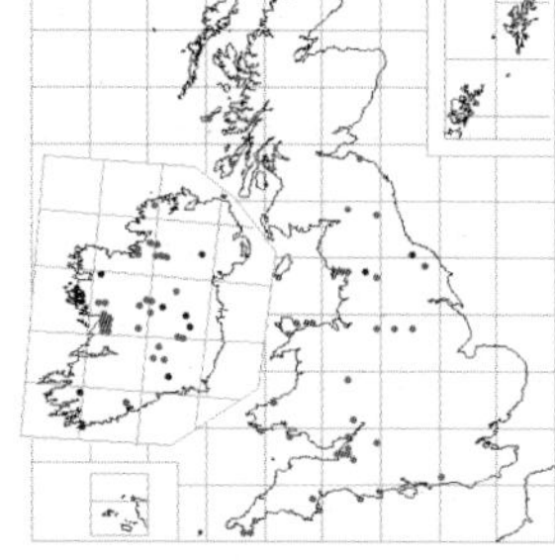

2. L. cuprea (Bacidia cuprea) Thallus grey to grey-green, warted to almost granulose, often covered in alien green algae. Apothecia up to 0.5 mm diam, buff to red-brown. Hymenium 40–50 µm thick. Hypothecium colourless to pale yellow. Spores 3-septate, 15–30 x 2–3 µm.
Habitat: Local, under overhangs and in deep, dry, very shaded cracks on hard limestone or scree.

3. L. cyrtella Thallus creamy grey to light grey, thin or slightly granular. Apothecia abundant, small (up to about 0.5 mm diam), pink-buff to dark brown with a thin, grey thalline margin which usually becomes excluded in mature apothecia and becomes convex, and often darker. Spores 1-septate when mature or more rarely 3-septate and curved, 10–15 x 4–5 µm, 8 or up to 16 per ascus.
Habitat: Frequent, mainly on rough, nutrient-rich or enriched bark.

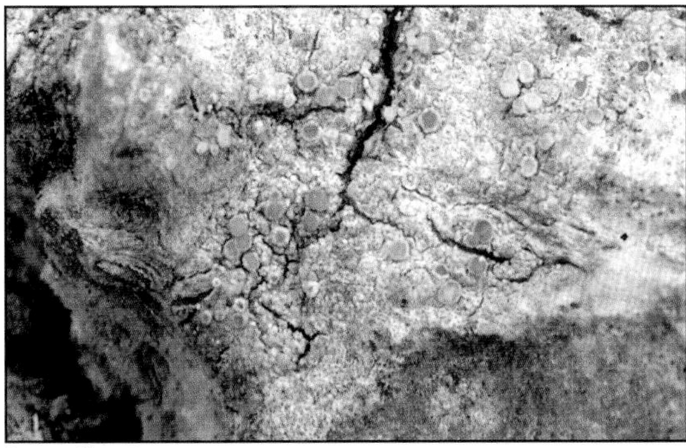

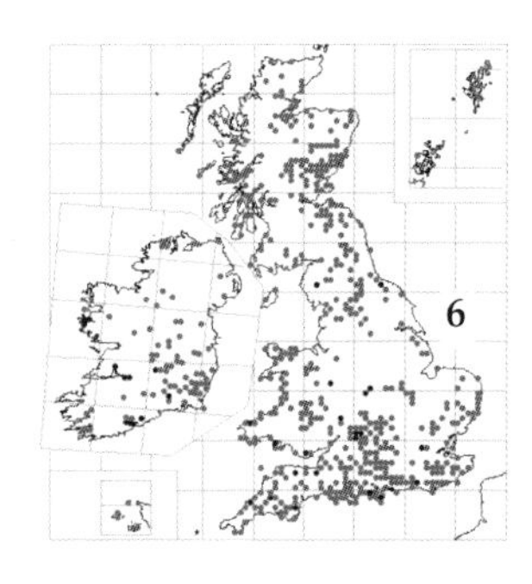

L. cyrtella x 6.

4. L. erysibe Thallus variable, yellowish grey to brown, thin, granular or cracked-areolate. The thallus surface is scurfy with minute clusters of algae surrounded by fungal hyphae (blastidia). Apothecia up to 0.5 mm diam, buff to black and becoming convex. The thin thalline margin is also covered in blastidia. Spores 1-septate when mature, 10–15 x 3–5 µm, 8 per ascus. It may have a superficial resemblance to *Lecanora helicopis* but that species is strictly maritime and has simple spores. It may be separated from *Rinodina gennarii* by the usually browner disc, thinner margin and colourless spores. There is a common pollution-tolerant sorediate form of *L. erysibe* which has small punctiform greenish soralia scattered over the surface of the thallus.
Habitat: Common on nutrient-enriched substrates, in cracks on calcareous rocks and on walls, asbestos-cement, and rarely on bark or decorticated wood. A notably urban species.

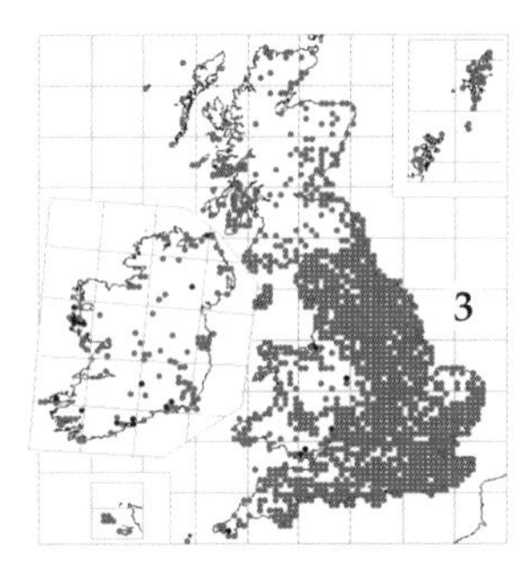

L. erysibe x 6.

5. L. turicensis Thallus white to grey, thin or with rounded, convex areoles. Apothecia usually crowded and therefore irregular in shape, up to 1 mm diam. Disc dark red-brown to black, usually white-pruinose. Disc convex, surrounded by a thin margin It resembles a large *Lecanora crenulata* but differs in the browner disc, the consistent presence of a coherent thallus and different spores. Spores 1-septate, 10–13 x 4–6 µm. **L. Rabenhorstii** is similar but with angular areoles and spores 11–15 x 4–7 µm.
Habitat. Common on many types of rock but best developed on calcareous stones and mortar on walls.

LECANORA ('beautiful small bowl' – from the shape of the apothecia). **Thallus** placodioid or crustose. **Photobiont** *Trebouxia*. **Apothecia** lecanorine. **Ascus** 8- or rarely up to 32-spored, *Lecanora*-type. **Spores** colourless, simple. **Pycnidia** immersed, usually with a dark ostiole. A large and widespread genus in which the thalline margin is usually readily visible, at least in the young apothecia.

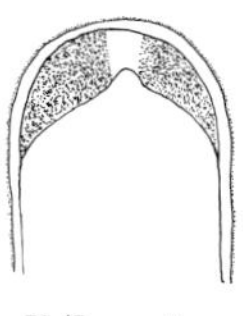

K/I reaction to the ascus tip.

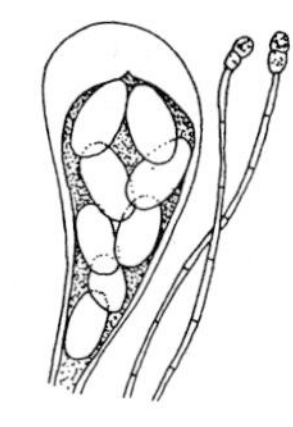

L. chlarotera x 400.

1.	Thallus placodioid. Greenish grey to yellow-grey	**1. L. muralis**
–	Thallus not placodioid. Colours various	2
2.	On rocks	3
–	On bark or wood	27
3.	Thallus sorediate	4
–	Thallus not sorediate	9
4.	Soredia white or yellow-green to green	5
–	Soredia greenish grey, granular, also found on the margins of apothecia	**11. L. conizaeoides**
5.	Soredia dull yellow-green, pale yellow or white	6
–	Soredia vivid lemon to apple-green	**13. L. epanora**
6.	K+ brownish yellow. Soredia pale yellow	**24. L. orosthea**
–	K– or K+ yellow	7
7.	K+ yellow, soredia white	**6. L. campestris** subsp. **dolmitica**
–	K–, soredia yellow-green	8
8.	Soralia on margins of squamules	**18. L. handelii**
–	Soralia laminal on squamules	**32. L. soralifera**
9.	Thallus K+ yellow or red	10
–	Thallus K–	15
10.	Apothecia pinkish buff or piebald or white-pruinose or brown	11
–	Apothecia black, never pruinose	14
11.	C+ yellow	**30. L. rupicola**
–	C–	11
12.	Apothecia pinkish buff, very pruinose	**33. L. subcarnea**
–	Apothecia shades of brown or piebald, pruinose or not	13
13.	Apothecia chestnut to red-brown	**6. L. campestris**
–	Apothecia pale brown to dark brown or piebald	**27. L. praepostera**

14. Thallus light to mid-grey. Thecium purple-brown **Tephromela atra**
- Thallus mid-grey to dark greenish grey. Thecium green-brown **17. L. gangaleoides**

15. Thallus grey, white, yellow-green or green-black 16
- Thallus brown, often thick and glossy. Apothecia dark red-brown to 2 mm diam **Protoparmelia badia**

16. Thallus yellow-green or green-black 17
- Thallus white, grey or buff 20

17. Thallus yellow-grey to yellow-green 18
- Thallus web-like, green-black in polluted areas. Apothecia with whitish margins **13. L. dispersa**

18. Apothecia yellowish becoming black and pruinose **34. L. sulphurea**
- Apothecia green to green-brown, not pruinose 19

19. Thallus squamulose to areolate. Apothecia green-brown, never convex, rather innate **21. L. intricata**
- Thallus scattered, often with a dark prothallus. Apothecia green to green-brown, becoming convex **26. L. polytropa**

20. Discs pale greenish grey to brown or buff, apothecia often pruinose 21
- Discs pinkish brown, orange or green-black, never pruinose (maritime) 25

21. Apothecia to 0.5 mm diam, margin regularly crenulate, hard calcareous substrata **12. L. crenulata**
- Apothecia over 0.5 mm diam, margins smooth or slightly crenulate, may be flexuose, many substrates 22

22. C+ orange 23
- C–, thallus white or absent, apothecia less than 1 mm diam 24

23. Thallus buff, apothecia usually over 1 mm diam. Maritime **16. L. fugiens**
- Thallus pale cream, apothecia 0.3–0.8 mm. Not maritime **9. L. conferta**

24. Thallus thin or absent, apothecia sessile **13. L. dispersa**
- Thallus thick, white, apothecia almost innate **4. L. albescens**

25. Thallus nodular, isidiate. Apothecia with nodular margins **25. L. poliophaea**
- Thallus not nodular or isidiate. Apothecia without nodular margins 26

26. Thallus leaden to yellow-grey. Disc brown-black, margin becoming excluded **19. L. helicopis**
- Thallus creamy white to grey. Disc green-black, margin not excluded **2. L. actophila**

27. C+ yellow or orange, at least in parts 28
- C– 31

28. Margins of apothecia C+ yellow, disc pruinose **7. L. carpinea**
– Margins of apothecia and thallus C+ orange, disc not pruinose 29

29. Thallus and margins of apothecia sorediate **15. L. expallens**
– Thallus and apothecia not sorediate 30

30. Pale margins often present in mature apothecia **10. L. confusa**
– Concolorous margins soon excluded even in young apothecia **35. L. symmicta**

31. Thallus and margins of apothecia granular sorediate **11. L. conizaeoides**
– Thallus not granular sorediate 32

32. Thallus grey, thin, with yellow-green punctiform soralia **23. L. jamesii**
– Thallus not sorediate 33

33. Apothecial discs pale buff, yellow-brown to green 34
– Apothecial discs brown, red-brown or black 36

34. P– Usually on bare wood 34
– P+ yellow, orange or red. Usually on bark 35

35. Thalline margin soon excluded, even in very young fruit **35. L. symmicta**
– Thalline margin persistent **31. L. saligna**

36. Apothecial discs pale buff, pruinose margins, P+ red.
On twigs of smooth-barked trees **3. L. albella**
– Apothecial discs yellow-brown to green. P+y, (usually on wood) **36. L. varia**

37. Apothecia to 2 mm diam **22. L. intumescens**
– Apothecia to about 1 mm diam 38

38. Apothecial margins P+ orange **28. L. pulicaris**
– Apothecial margins P– or very weak yellow 39

39. K– **20. L. horiza**
– K+ yellow 40

40. No granules on the epithecium **5. L. argentata**
– Granules on the epithecium 41

41. Thallus warted **8. L. chlarotera**
– Thallus of dispersed or granular areoles **29. L. rugosella**

THALLUS LOBATE AT THE MARGIN

1. Lecanora muralis Thallus greenish grey to yellow-grey, adpressed, large (up to about 10 cm across) and consisting of small lobules 1–2 mm wide which are often pruinose around their edges. The outer margin of the thallus becomes clearly lobate. Usually fertile with numerous apothecia. Discs creamy brown to brown, not pruinose, the margins often becoming crenulate when mature. The apothecia are confined to the centre of the thallus where they are often crowded together and angular in shape. Spores 9–15 x 5–7 μm. Often mistaken in urban areas for discarded chewing gum.
P± yellowish.

Habitat: Very common on man-made substrates, less common in the West and North. It is one of the more pollution-resistant species and is even found near the centre of large towns on basic substrates such as asbestos-cement, paving stones, asphalt, etc. (it is less common on the less well-lit, damper north side of roofs). Often on acid rocks, rarer in its natural habitat of bird-perching sites in uplands.

L. muralis x 4.

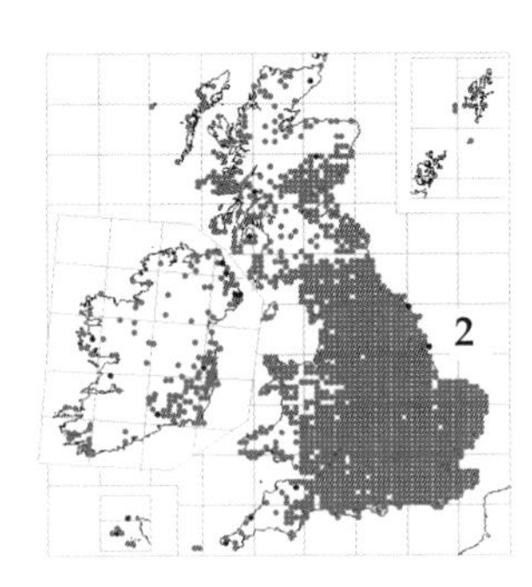

THALLUS NOT LOBATE AT THE MARGIN

2. L. actophila Thallus creamy white to green-grey, smooth, areolate, often with a white prothallus. Apothecia less than 1 mm diam, sessile, disc dark green-black (bluish when wet) with an entire margin which becomes contorted but not excluded as in *L. helicopis* with which it often grows. Spores 8–14 x 5–6 µm, often containing oil globules that may make them appear 1-septate.
K–, UV–.
Habitat: Very common on sunny, siliceous rocks above high-water mark.

L. actophila x 5.

3. L. albella (L. pallida) Thallus pale grey to almost white, smooth or warted, often with a white prothallus. Apothecia up to about 1.5 mm diam. Disc buff to pale mud-colour, usually densely white-pruinose. Margins entire but becoming

crenulate or excluded in mature apothecia. Spores 10– 12 x 6–8 µm.
Thallus: K+ yellow. Apothecia: C–, P+ yellow or red. UV+ pale orange.
Habitat: Frequent but becoming rarer in the North, on twigs and bark, mainly of smooth-barked, more acid (e.g. oak) trees than *L. carpinea*, but it is often small and easily overlooked.

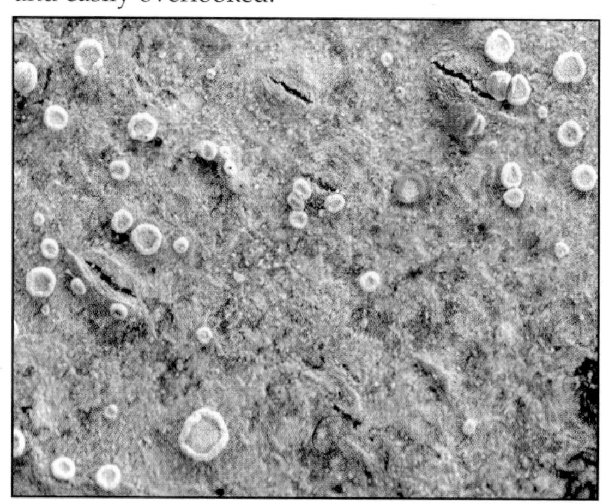

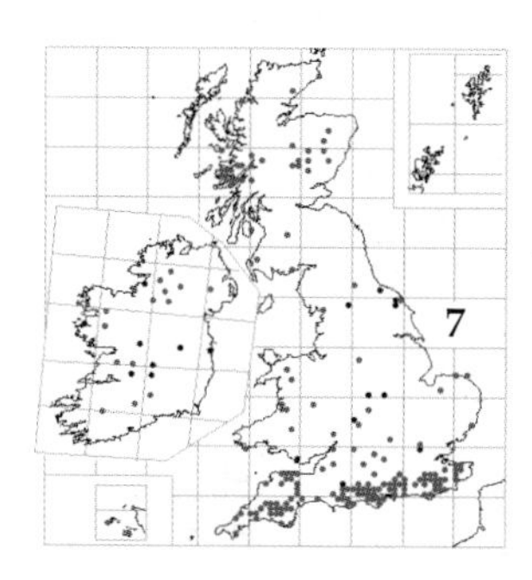

L. albella x 6 (showing P+ reaction).

4. L. albescens Thallus pure white and thick, cracked to areolate, sometimes almost placodioid. Apothecia crowded and almost innate, up to about 0.8 mm diam, with pinkish to greenish discs that are frequently heavily white-pruinose. Spores 8–15 x 4–6 µm. It resembles *L. dispersa* but with the apothecia set in the thick white thallus.
Spot reactions: negative.
Habitat: Common in unpolluted regions on sunny calcareous substrates, especially hard limestone, e.g. tombstones and hard concrete walls.

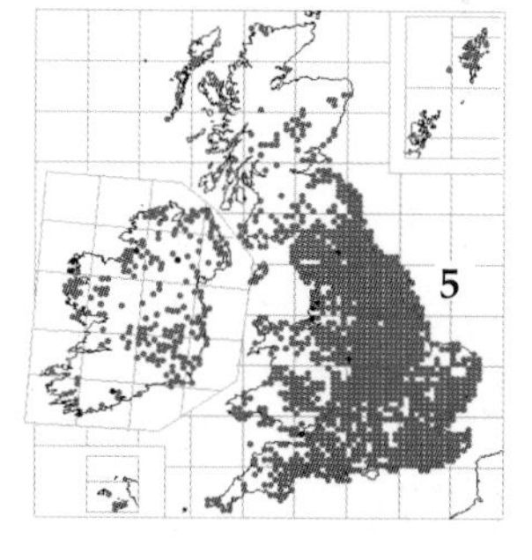

L. albescens x 6.

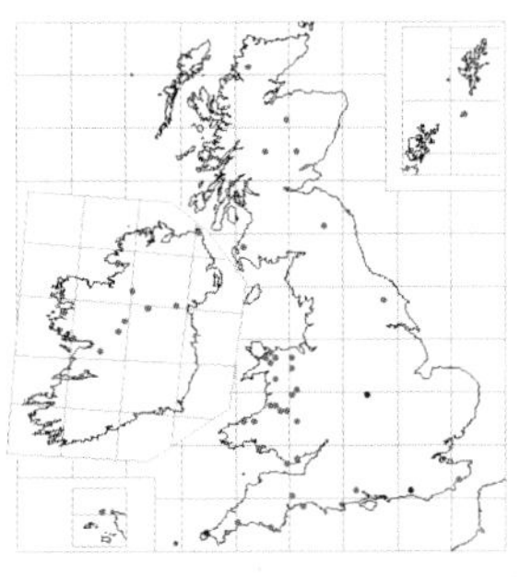

5. L. argentata Thallus creamy to greenish white, warted but with smoother margins surrounded by a black prothallus. Apothecia up to 1 mm diam, bright chestnut discs that are sometimes piebald. Thalline margin even to crenulate and containing massive crystals that do not dissolve in K. Epithecium lacks crystals. (see 'a' below) Spores 10–15 x 6–9 µm.
K+ yellow, sometimes P+ pale yellow.
Habitat: External appearance much like *L. chlorotera* and much under-recorded. probably common on bark.

Diagamatic sections of the apothecia of the *Lecanora subfusca* aggregate

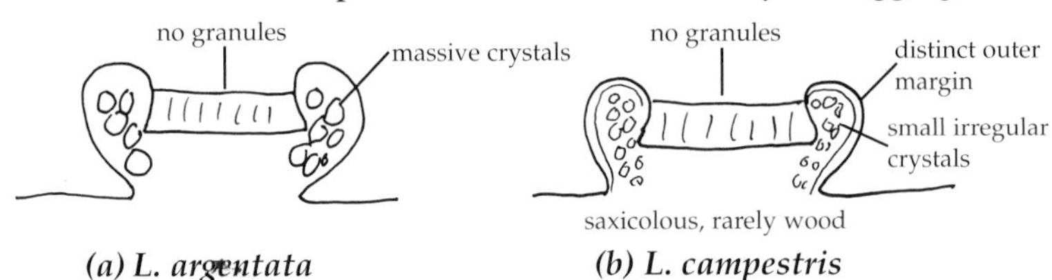

(a) L. argentata

(b) L. campestris

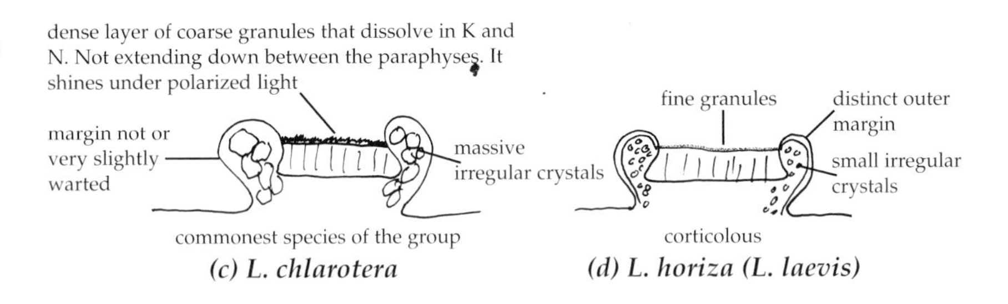

(c) L. chlarotera

(d) L. horiza (L. laevis)

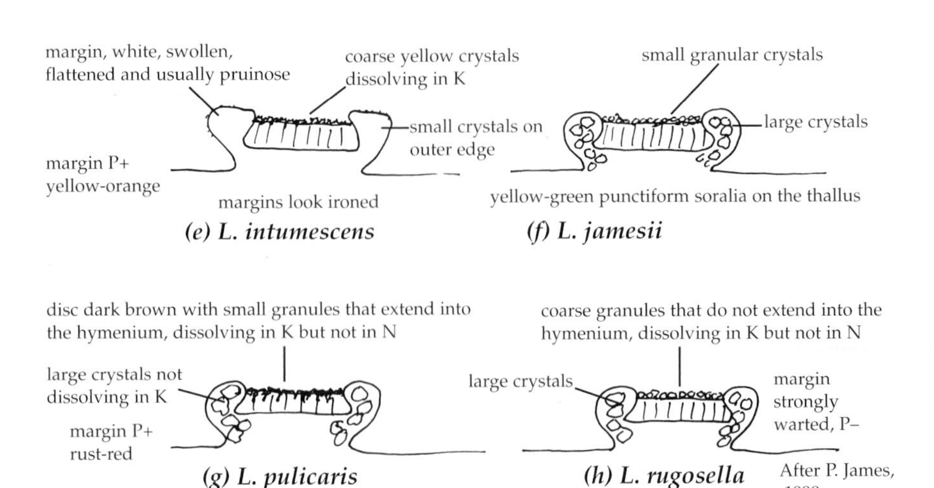

(e) L. intumescens

(f) L. jamesii

(g) L. pulicaris

(h) L. rugosella

After P. James, 1998.

6. L. campestris Thallus grey, warted or areolate, normally with a white, fimbriate prothallus. Usually fertile with the apothecia crowded in the centre. Apothecia large (up to about 1.5 mm), discs chestnut to very dark red-brown when dry, with a smooth margin that becomes contorted in mature apothecia. Small irregular crystals in the thalline margin and medulla (see 'b', p. 188). Spores 10–15 x 6–9 μm. It sometimes has pale, convex soralia on the surface and no granules in the epithecium (subsp. **dolmitica**).
K+ yellow, P– or very pale yellow, UV– or dull orange.
Habitat: Very common on somewhat basic to calcareous substrata, tombstones and walls, also on nutrient-enriched acid rocks and wood. Less common northwards.

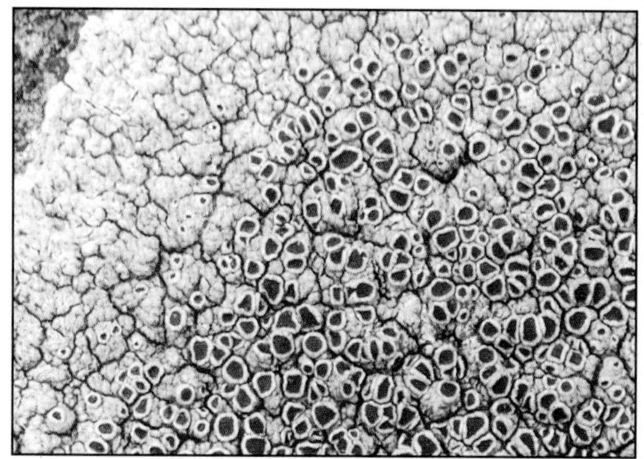

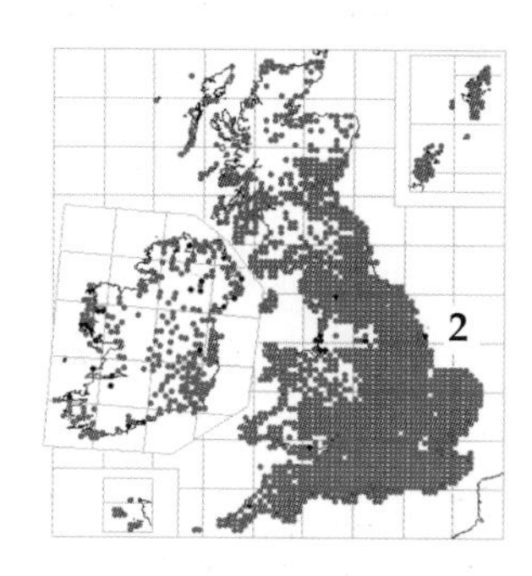

L. campestris x 3.

7. L. carpinea Thallus white to grey, thin but continuous (becoming cracked when old), limited by a white prothallus. Apothecia up to 1 mm diam, with a smooth margin that is sometimes is excluded in older apothecia. Disc brown-grey but this is often difficult to see due to the thick white pruina. Epithecium with yellowish granules that dissolve in K. Spores 10–13 x 6–8 μm.
Thallus: K+ yellow. Apothecia: C+ yellow, P– (*L. albella* P+ red), UV+ bright orange.
Habitat: Similar to *L. albella* but usually on smaller trees and branches. Rarely on stone.

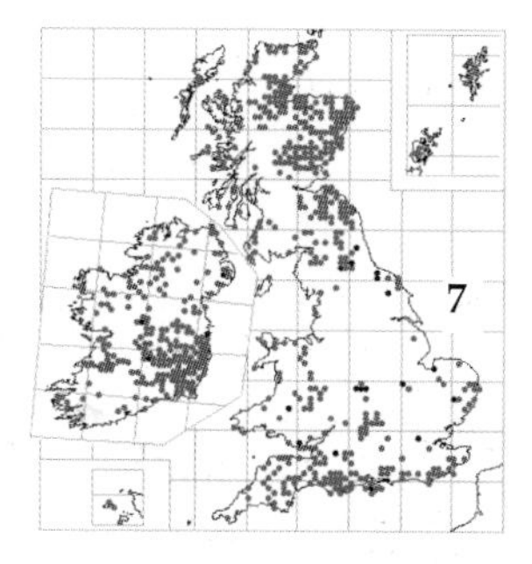

L. carpinea x 5.

8. L. chlarotera Thallus grey to creamy grey, smooth or warted, sometimes areolate. No prothallus. Apothecia up to about 1 mm diam, usually numerous, disc buff to red-brown, sometimes piebald (due to parasitic fungi, commonly of the genus *Vouauxiella*). Angular crystals, not dissolving in K, are found in the thick, smooth or slightly crenulate margins. (see 'c', p. 188). Spores 10–15 x 6–8 µm.
Thallus: K+ yellow, UV+ dull orange. Apothecia: margins P–.
Habitat: Very common on trees in unpolluted areas. It is the only common species with red-brown discs and a P– margin.

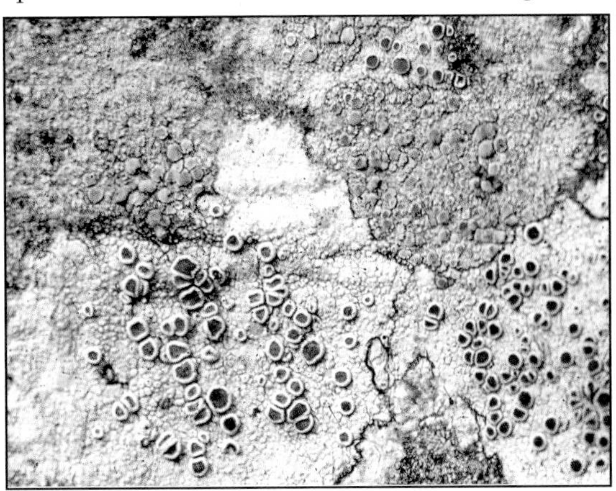

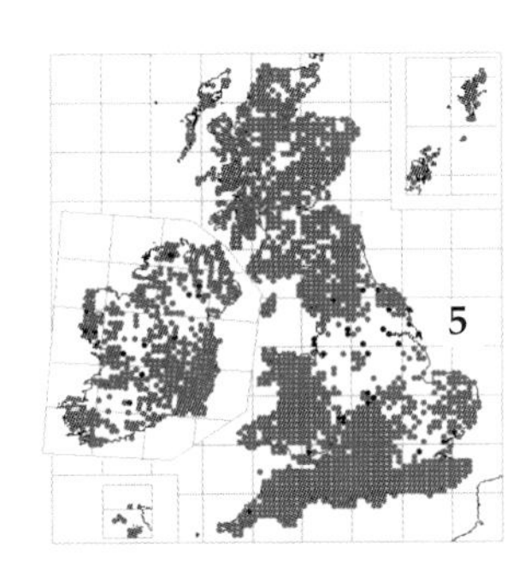

L. chlarotera x 4.

9. L. conferta Thallus whitish grey to creamy grey, variable from absent to thick and warted. Usually very fertile wth the apothecia often closely grouped. Apothecia up to 0.8 mm diam, usually very pruinose. Disc creamy brown to brown, margin becoming crenulate, sometimes excluded. Spores 8–12 x 4–7 µm.
Thallus and apothecia: C+ yellow to orange, discs deeper orange.
Habitat: Once considered very rare but now frequently found on the mortared walls of old churches, mainly in the South.

L. conferta x 5.

10. L. confusa Thallus green-grey, slightly granular to areolate, forming neat patches. Usually fertile. Apothecia small (less than 0.75 mm diam), often grouped, greenish yellow with a paler margin that stands out brightly against the thallus. This margin is frequently crenulate or becomes excluded. Spores 10–15 x 4–5 µm. Considered by some to be a merely a form of *L. expallens* but it differs in the lack of soredia and has a more scant thallus. *L. conizaeoides* has granular soredia and is P+ rust-red.
Thallus: K– (usually), C+ orange, P–.
Habitat: Common in unpolluted areas (particularly near the coast) on smooth-barked trees, especially ash and blackthorn. It is also common on fence palings.

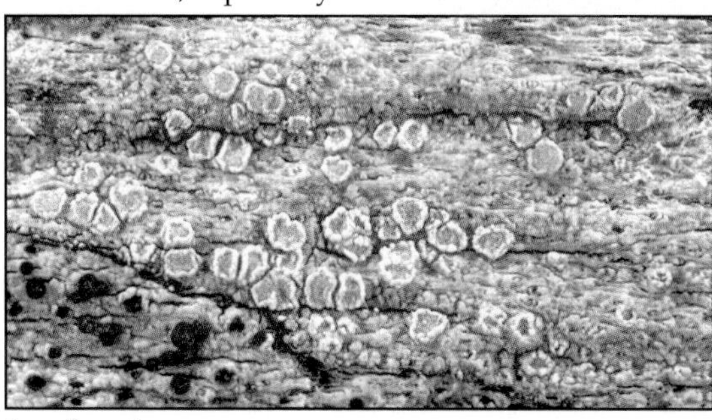

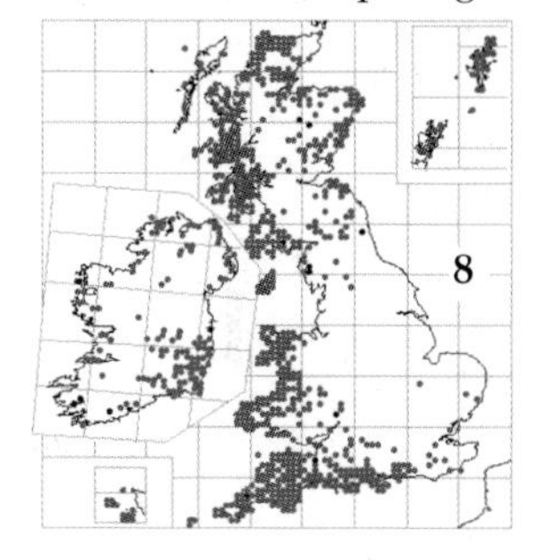

L. confusa x 6.

11. L. conizaeoides Thallus grey-green, thick and granular-sorediate, often forming a thick areolate crust that may cover extensive areas. Apothecia up to 1 mm diam with greenish buff to flesh-coloured (when dry) discs, slightly crenulate margins which become covered in similar granules to the thallus. It is often found with pale buff patches with white fimbriate edges where it has been attacked by the fungus *Athelia arachnoidea*. The apothecial discs are frequently black or piebald from infection by the fungus *Lichenoconium lecanorae*.
Thallus: P+ yellow turning rust-red.
Habitat: The commonest corticolous British lichen in polluted regions. It is found mainly on trees, sometimes on walls, rocks or soil. It was a very rare species until this century. It has replaced other lichens near the centres of industrial areas due to its affinity with sulphur dioxide pollution. With the recent reduction of the levels of sulphur dioxide it is becoming much less common. It is rare in unpolluted regions, where it is found on conifer twigs, heather stems and fences.

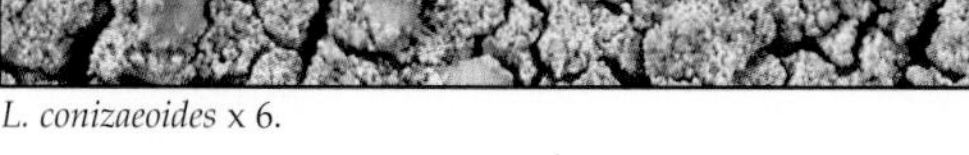

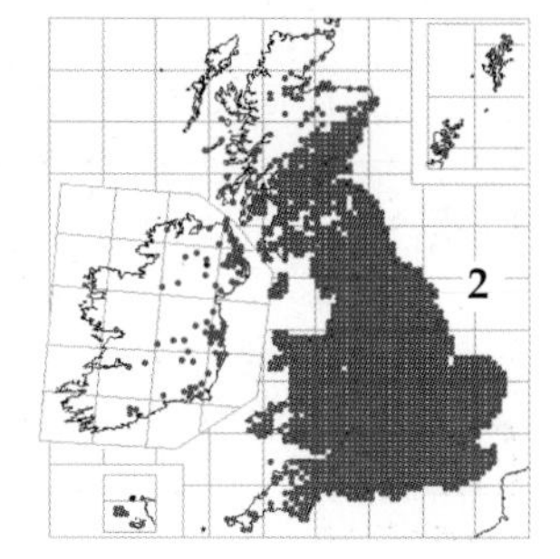

L. conizaeoides x 6.

12. L. crenulata Thallus immersed but scurfy, pale grey when on hard limestone. Apothecia (up to about 0.6 mm diam), may be grouped, but more usually scattered, with a brown to bluish, persistently pruinose, flat disc and a more crenulate, inrolled margin than *L. dispersa*. Epithecium brownish with fine crystals. Spores 6–10 x 4–6 µm. The lack of a coherent thallus helps to separate it in the field from *Lecania turicensis*. This is probably an aggregate of several species.
Spot reactions: negative.
Habitat: Common in the south east on limestone and mortar. Occasional in unpolluted regions but then usually only on hard calcareous rocks and walls.

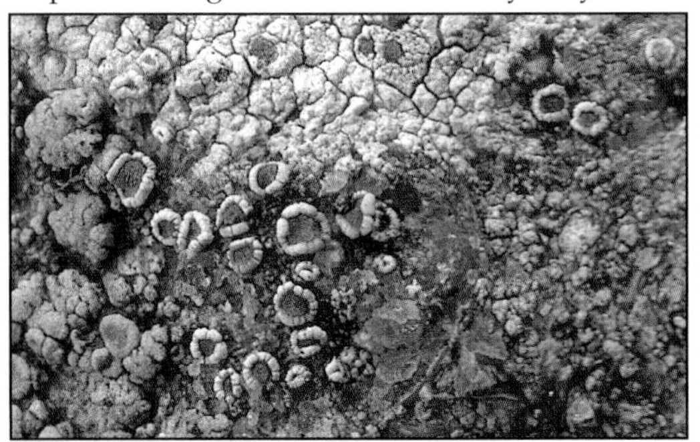

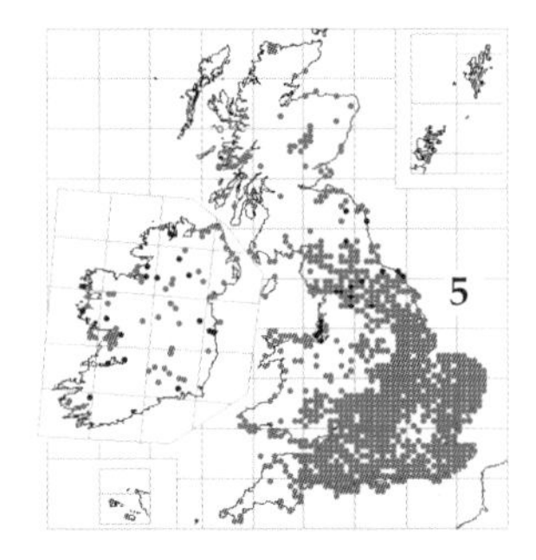

L. crenulata x 10.

13. L. dispersa Thallus very light grey or white, finely granular, thin or evanescent. In very polluted areas it becomes dark green-black (f. **dissipata**). Apothecia small, usually less than 1 mm diam, pale greenish grey to dark brown, often thinly white-pruinose. Margin entire, becoming slightly crenulate or flexuose. Epithecium brownish with numerous small granules. Spores 8–14 x 4–7 µm.
K+ yellow.
Habitat: Very common, very pollution-resistant and found even in city centres on nutrient-rich, basic substrates. In unpolluted areas it is also found on nutrient-rich bark and a wide range of other substrates such as iron, leather, etc.

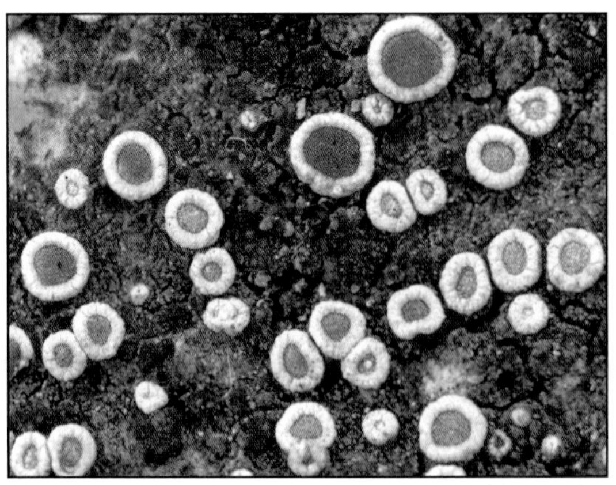

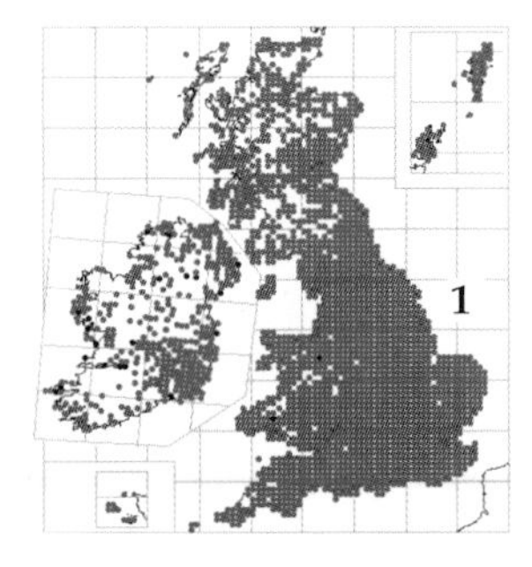

L. dispersa x 12.

14. L. epanora Thallus granular to convex-areolate, yellow-green to dull green, often limited by a black prothallus. Soralia arise towards the centre of the areoles, soredia yellow-green to bright yellow, often spreading to form a sorediate crust. Apothecia rare, up to 1.5 mm diam, disc yellow-brown to brown, margin persistent, often crenulate or flexuose. Epithecium yellow-green with yellowish granules. Spores 8–12 x 5–7 µm.
Spot reactions: negative. If on well-lit rocks, with the soredia arising from the margin of the areoles and P+ orange, it is likely to be **L. subaurea**.
Habitat: Frequent on shaded, acid rocks, especially where iron-rich, more rarely on fences. Most common in the southern Pennines and N. Yorkshire on mine spoil.

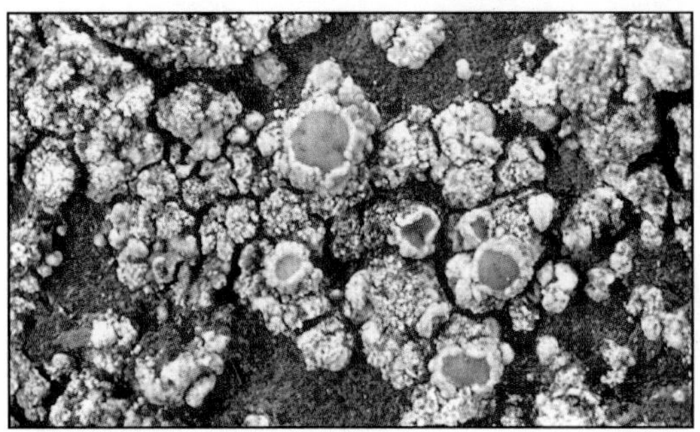

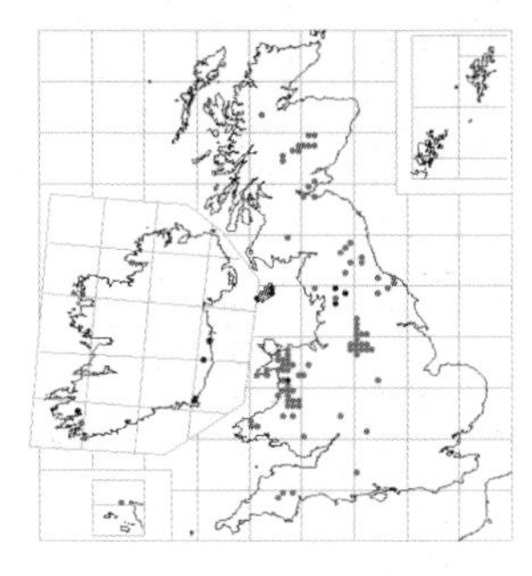

L. epanora x 8.

15. L. expallens Thallus granular or cracked, yellow-grey to yellow-green or green-grey with farinose soralia which may cover the thallus in an areolate crust. A pale grey, fimbriate prothallus is sometimes present. Usually sterile. Apothecia small (less than 0.8 mm diam) with flesh-coloured, convex discs and sorediate margins that soon become excluded. Spores 10–16 x 4–8 µm. When sterile it resembles *Pyrrhospora quernea* which has a slightly more ochre-coloured thallus and a distinct, much darker prothallus. See also *L. orosthea* (24).
K+ yellow, C+ yellow to orange-red.
Habitat: Very common, often on sheltered side of trunks and stumps of trees, fences and on decorticated wood. It is also found on rocks and walls and is not uncommon on church walls in the South.

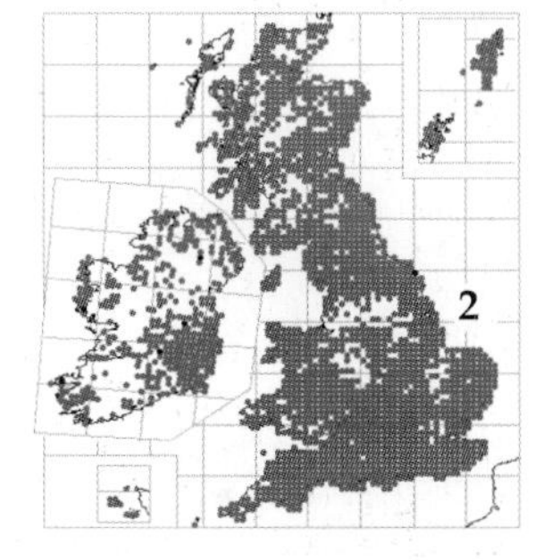

L. expallens x 8.

16. L. fugiens Thallus granular or a thin areolate crust, sometimes evanescent, light yellowish to tan. Apothecia 1–2 mm, disc yellow-brown, often fawn-pruinose, margin persistent, contorted, sometimes becoming crenulate. Epithecium brownish with minute crystals. Spores 9–12 x 5–6 µm.
Thallus: K+ pale yellow, C+ orange-red, UV+ orange. Apothecia: P+ orange-red.
Habitat: Locally common on well-lit maritime, acid rocks (often in shallow cracks), mainly in the South and West.

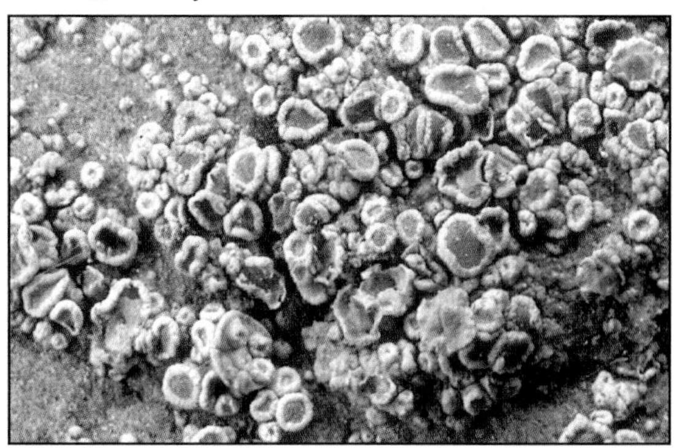

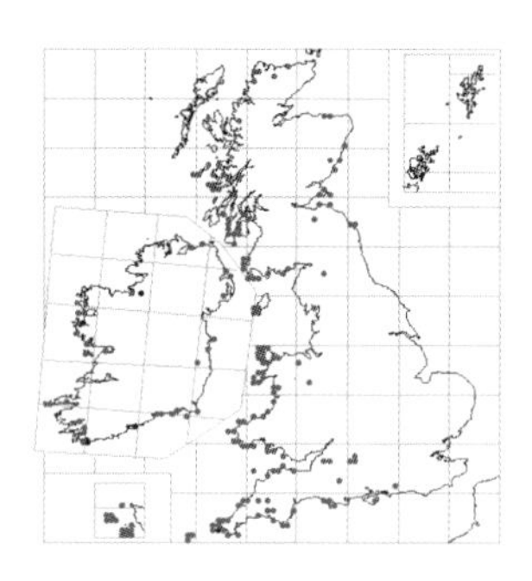

L. fugiens x 6.

17. L. gangaleoides Thallus smooth or warted, pale to mid-grey. Prothallus white. Usually fertile with apothecia to 2 mm diam with a black disc and a wide thalline margin.The thallus is frequently a darker green-grey and more warted than in the similar *Tephromela atra*. The discs of the apothecia are persistently convex and the margins do not usually become contorted. If cut open the thecium is dark green-brown and paler towards the hypothecium (purplish in *T. atra*). This colour may be hard to determine except under a microscope. If the thallus is picked away, orange anthraquinones (K+p) are exposed in the lowest part of the medulla. A very variable species in appearance.
K+ yellow, P+ orange, UV– (UV+ bluish in *Tephromela atra*).
Habitat: Common on acid rocks, especially near the sea, but also locally inland.

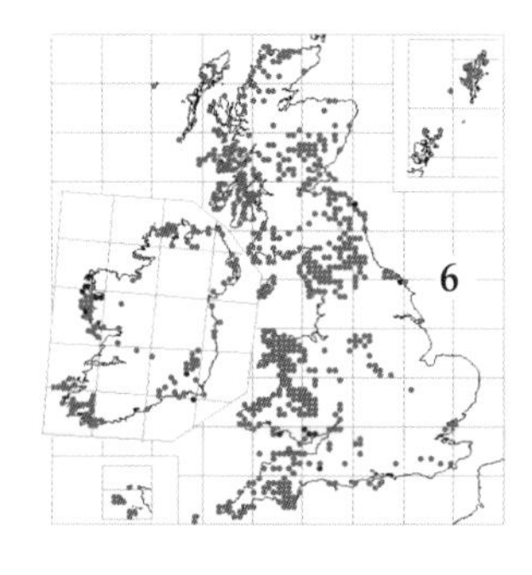

L. gangaleoides x 3.

18. L. handelii Thallus convex, subsquamulose to an areolate crust, green to grey. Concolorous soredia are produced in soralia on the margins of the areoles. No prothallus. Often infertile. Apothecia up to 0.5 mm diam, disc greenish brown to tan, rarely with a dark pruina. No spores have been found in the British Isles. A member of the *L. polytropa* group. See also *L. soralifera* (32).
KC+ yellow, UV–.
Habitat: Rare. On mine-spoil heaps and other metal-rich acid rocks.

19. L. helicopis Thallus very variable, smooth and cracked or slightly warted leaden to brown-grey. Prothallus white or dark bluish grey. Apothecia becoming sessile, up to 0.6 mm diam, very dark brown with a margin which becomes darker and then excluded. Epithecium brownish, K+ yellow. Spores 9–15 x 4–6 µm. They often contain two large oil globules and appear 1-septate. It then resembles **Halicania ralfsii** which grows in similar situations but that species has a P+ red medulla and a thicker, oily, blackish green thallus.
Spot reactions and UV: negative.
Habitat: Very common on acid coastal rocks. In slightly more shaded situations than *L. actophila*.

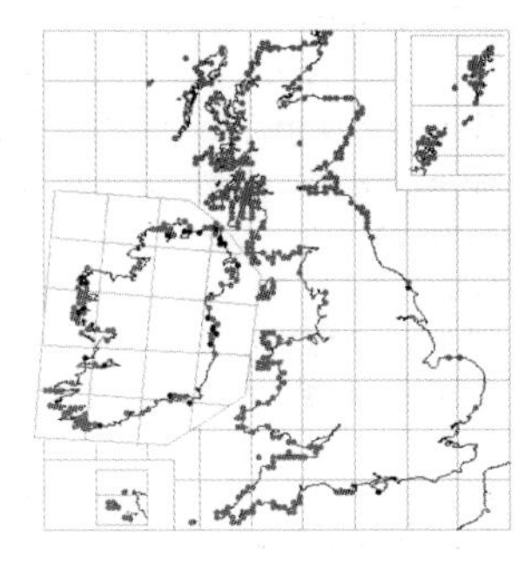

L. helicopis x 10.

20. L. horiza (including **L. laevis**) Thallus continuous to slightly cracked or warted, white to cream, sometimes with a pale prothallus. Apothecia up to about 1 mm diam, often crowded in groups. Disc orange to brown and sometimes pruinose with a persistent, flexuose margin. Epithecium with fine granules, medulla and margins with small crystals (see 'd', p. 188). Spores 12–15 x 6–9 µm.
Spot reactions: negative or slightly K+ yellow (*L. chlarotera* is K+ strong yellow).
Habitat: Locally frequent on deciduous bark.

21. L. intricata Thallus almost squamulose with crenulate margins to the areoles. These have a flat and slightly wrinkled top surface, yellow-green. Sometimes with a dark prothallus. Apothecia up to 1 mm diam, dark green-brown, emerald green when wet, not becoming very convex, more innate than *L. polytropa*. Epithecium greenish brown with granules that dissolve in K.
K– or K+ yellow, KC+ yellow, UV–.
Habitat: Common on similar habitats to *L. polytropa* such as acid rocks and sometimes sawn wood. Often in slight hollows on horizontal stones. Most common in upland areas.

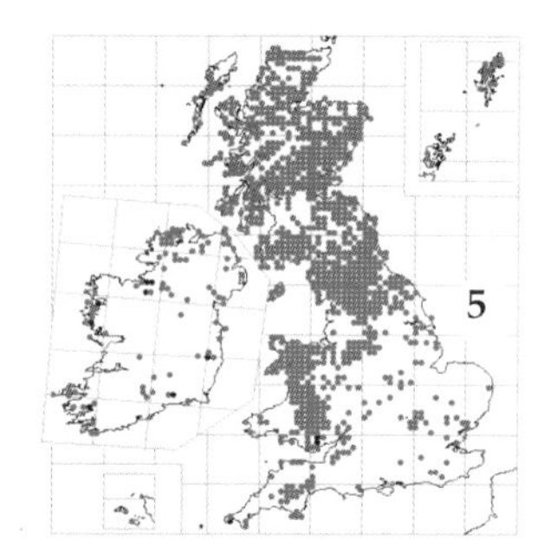

L. intricata x 5.

22. L. intumescens Thallus smooth to cracked, white to pale grey. A black prothallus is occasionally present. Apothecia up to 2 mm diam. The thalline margin may be pruinose and appears inflated and then ironed. Disc orange to red-brown, pruinose when young. Margin with small yellow crystals. Epithecium with large yellow crystals that dissolve in K. (see 'e', p. 188). Spores 11–18 x 5–8 µm.
Thallus: K+ yellow, UV+ yellow. Thalline margin: P+ bright orange.
Habitat: Infrequent, found on deciduous smooth-barked trees in coppices, woods and wayside trees.

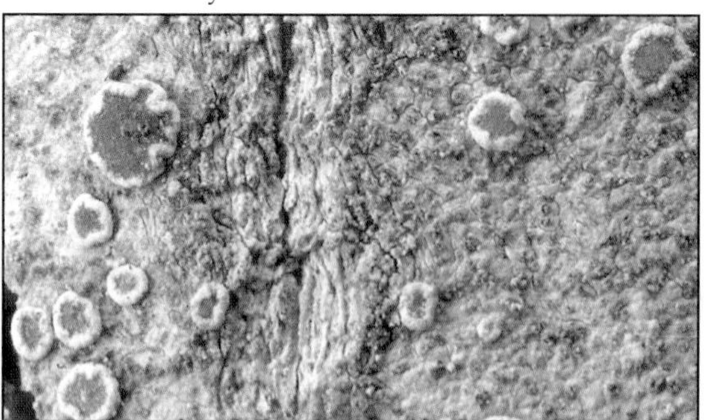

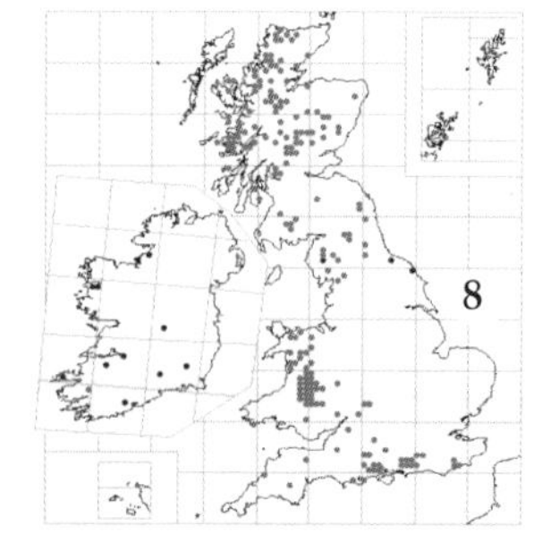

L. intumescens x 8.

23. L. jamesii Thallus forming orbicular patches up to 3 cm diam, light to mid-grey, thin and often slightly wrinkled, often with a black prothallus. Bright, yellow-green, punctiform soralia are scattered over the centre of the thallus. Apothecia rare, up to 0.8 mm diam with small green-brown discs. Thalline margin crenulate and containing large crystals. Epithecium yellowish with small granules (see 'f', p. 188). Spores 10–14 x 6–8 mm. When sterile, it may be separated from *Haematomma elatinum* as that species has greyish lemon-yellow soredia that become confluent and a K+ yellow thallus and P+ orange soredia.
Thallus: K–. Soralia: P–, UV+ dull orange.
Habitat: Frequent on smooth-barked trees in sheltered damp areas in the West.

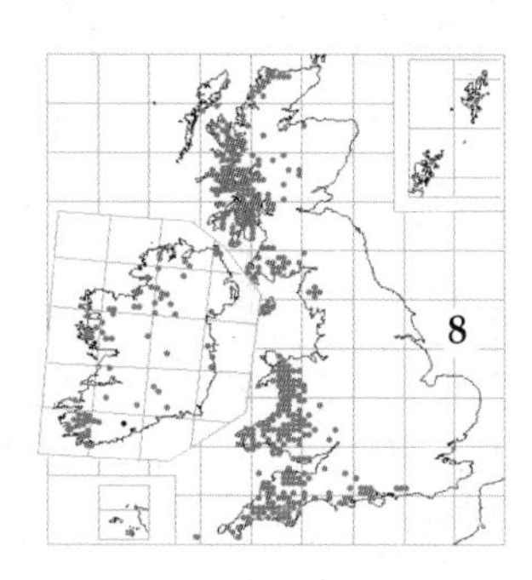

L. jamesii x 4.

24. L. orosthea Thallus diffuse to areolate, yellow-green to dull yellow, often limited by a pale prothallus. Pale yellow soredia form in soralia on the margins of the areoles but may soon cover the surface of the thallus. It can then resemble *L. expallens* but that species is C+ orange with a greyish thallus. Apothecia rare, up to 0.7 mm diam (it is probably the sorediate counterpart of *L. sulphurea*). Discs yellow-green to brown, with the margin soon excluded. Epithecium yellow-green with granules dissolving in K. Spores 9–16 x 4–6 µm.
K+ dirty yellow, KC+ yellow.
Habitat: Common on dry acid rocks and walls, often below overhangs.

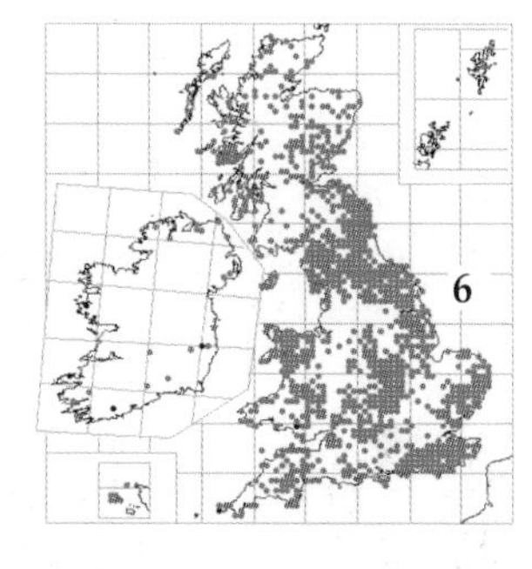

L. orosthea x 5.

25. L. poliophaea Thallus areolate, covered in granules, nodules and coarse isidia, bluish to brownish grey. Usually surrounded by a fimbriate prothallus with alternate light and dark bluish grey zones. Apothecia up to 1 mm diam, immersed in the isidia, becoming more sessile. Disc orange-brown with a crenulate, nodular margin. Epithecium yellow-brown, not granular. Spores 9–13 x 5–7 µm.
Spot reactions: negative. UV–.
Habitat: Common on the tops of acid rocks by water, especially on the coast. Found lower on the seashore than *L. praepostera*, usually on nutrient-enriched rocks, often in seepage tracks.

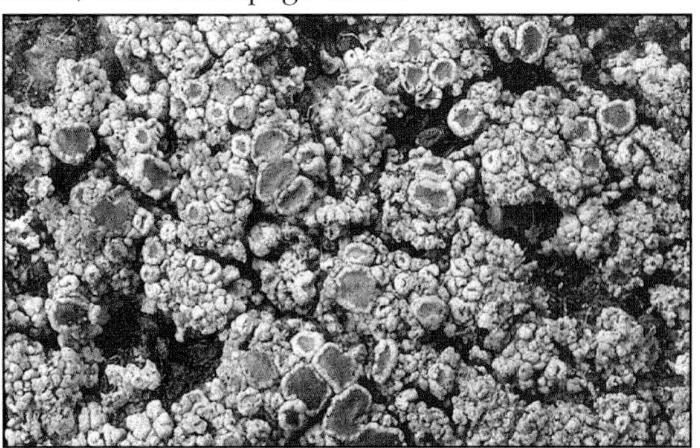

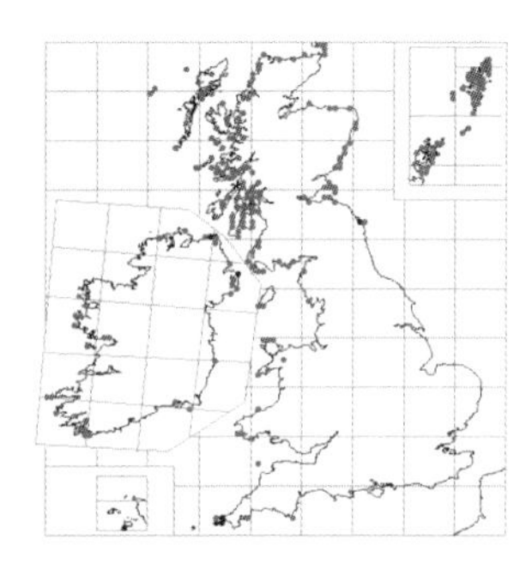

L. poliophaea x 6.

26. L. polytropa Thallus yellow-green, often of scattered granules or areoles, often with a dark prothallus, may be cconfined to small cracks in the substrata. The areoles have a flat, smooth surface and not the irregular edges of *L. intricata*. Usually fertile with the apothecia sometimes obscuring the surface of the thallus. Apothecia small (up to 0.5 mm diam), greenish brown to green and smooth so that they look as if carved from jade. The mature apothecia become strongly convex and soon exclude the margin. Epithecium colourless to reddish brown with granules that dissolve in K. Spores 10–14 x 5–7 µm. The similar **L. stenotropa** has a thallus that is granular, brownish to grey-green with brownish discs on the apothecia. Spores narrower, 8–12 x 3–4 µm.
K+ yellow, KC+ yellow, UV–.
Habitat: Common in less polluted areas on acid rocks, walls and stabilized shingle. It is occasionally found on sawn wood by railways, harbours, etc.

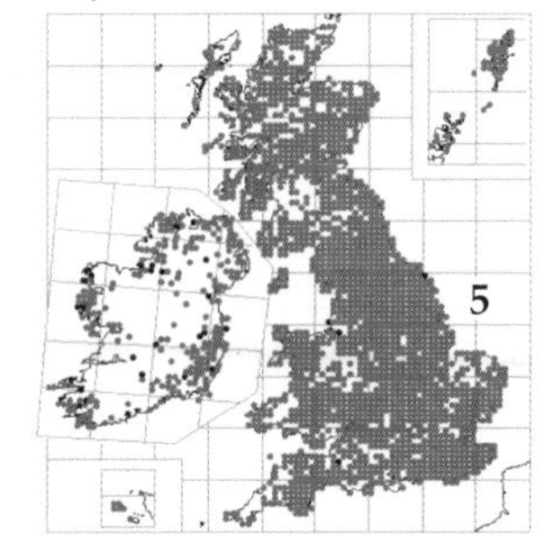

L. polytropa x 6.

27. L. praepostera (L. schistina) Thallus of flat to convex areoles, not warted, creamy green, often limited by a prothallus with light and dark zones. Apothecia up to 1.5 mm diam, sessile and neat in appearance. Disc tan to black and often piebald, sometimes pruinose. Thalline margin persistent but becoming crenulate. Epithecium colourless to greenish with granules, K+ red (with abundant needle-like crystals). Spores 11–15 x 6–8 µm.
K+ yellow turning blood red, P+ orange-red, UV–.
Habitat: On well-lit, but sheltered, often vertical, rocks on south-west coasts.

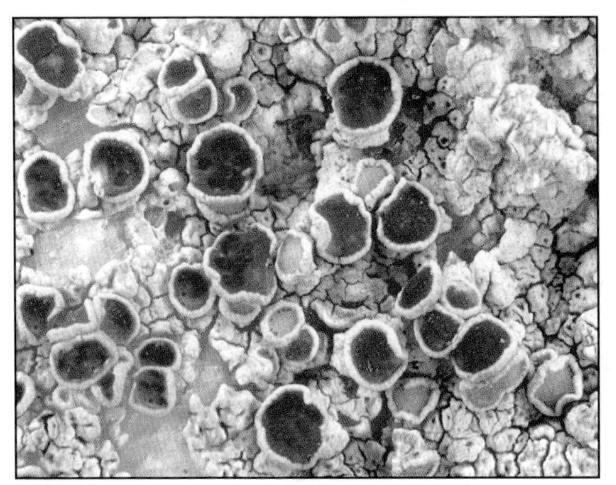

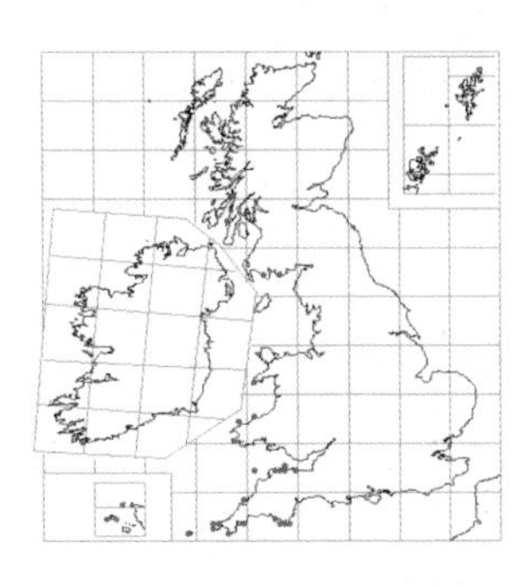

L. praepostera x 8.

28. L. pulicaris Thallus smooth or warted, grey to yellowish grey, it forms circular patches that may be limited by a light or dark prothallus. Very rarely with pale punctiform soralia. Apothecia up to 1 mm diam with a brown disc. Thalline margin persistent, thin, and, with the medulla, packed with large crystals not dissolving in K. Epithecium orange-red to brown with small granules which penetrate into the hymenium and dissolve in K (see 'g' p. 188). Spores 11–15 x 7–10 µm.
K+ yellow, P+ red, UV+ blue-white.
Habitat: Common on bark, mainly on twigs and small branches and fence palings.

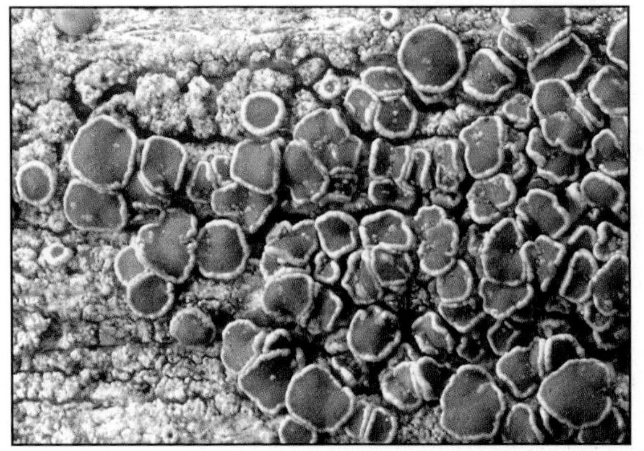

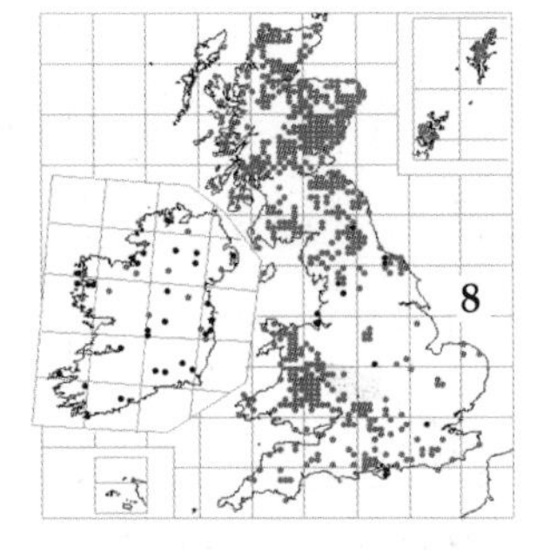

L. pulicaris x 8.

29. L. rugosella Thallus granular or of separate areoles, very lumpy in appearance, grey to yellow-grey. Apothecia up to about 1.3 mm. Disc pale brown to red-brown, often pruinose. Thalline margin thick and strongly warted. Margin and medulla packed with large crystals that do not dissolve in K. Epithecium colourless to brown with coarse granules on the surface that dissolve in K (see 'h', p. 188). Spores 12–17 x 7–10 µm.
K+ yellow.
Habitat: Probably overlooked as *L. chlarotera*. Found mainly on conifers and bare wood.

30. L. rupicola Thallus light grey, thick, smooth and cracked. Prothallus black. Rarely with punctiform soralia. Apothecia almost innate, up to 2 mm diam. Discs pinkish buff and white-pruinose, convex and contorted when mature. Epithecium buff to greenish with crystals that do not dissolve in K. Spores 9–15 x 5–7 µm. The apothecia often appear black as they are parasitized by *Arthonia varians.* Another parasite of this species is *Lecidea insularis* which forms small brown thalli, with a black prothallus, over the areoles of the host.
Thallus: K+ yellow. Apothecia: C+ yellow. Medulla: UV+ white.
Habitat: Very common on well-lit acid rocks in coastal regions, not uncommon inland in upland areas.

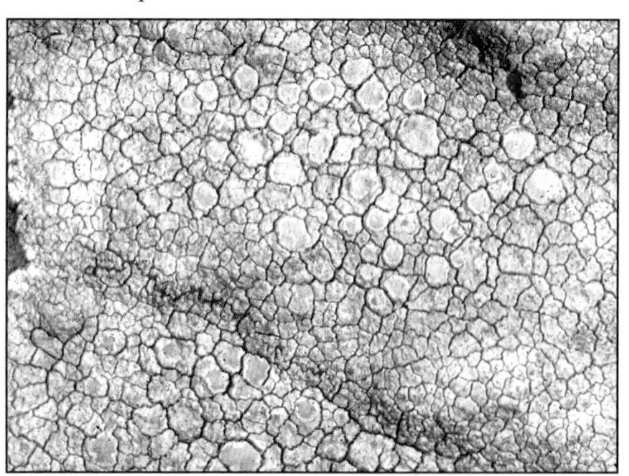

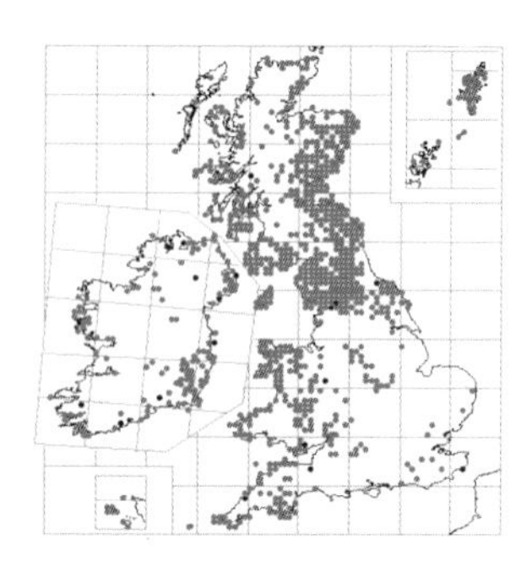

L. rupicola x 3.

31. L. saligna Thallus granular, often up to 5 cm or more, grey to yellow-grey. Prothallus poorly defined or absent. Usually very fertile. Apothecia up to 0.8 mm diam, disc pale reddish brown, sometimes thinly pruinose, with a thin, crenulate margin that becomes excluded. Epithecium greenish brown. Spores 7–10 x 4–6 µm. Usually with minute black pycnidia. Conidia 7–8 x 1–3 µm. Looks rather like *L. dispersa* but on wood.
Spot reactions: negative.
Habitat: Frequent on well-illuminated wood.

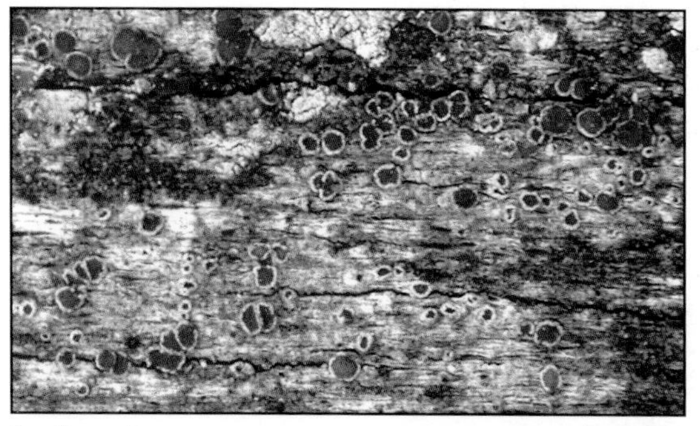

L. saligna x 5.

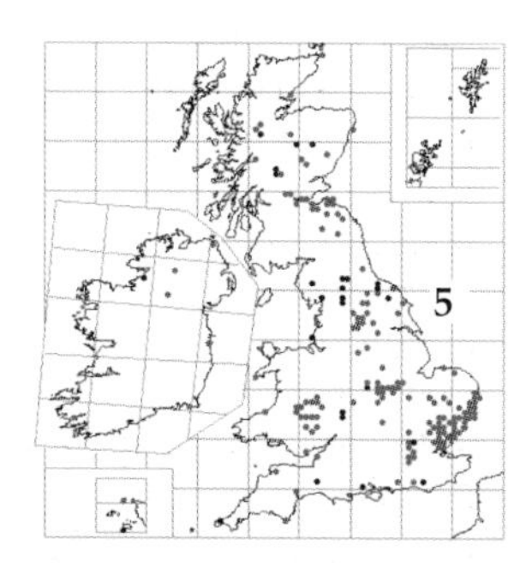

32. L. soralifera Thallus areolate or dispersed and subsquamulose, yellow-green, often greyish. Usually sterile with numerous yellow-green to green soralia forming delimited patches that arise from the centres of the squamules and may unite to cover much of the thallus. Apothecia up to 0.5 mm diam, disc greenish brown and convex. The thalline margin becomes excluded. Other members of this group that are found on metal-rich rocks are *L. handelii* (18) which differs in having soralia that arise from the margins of the squamules and *L. polytropa* (26) which is not sorediate.

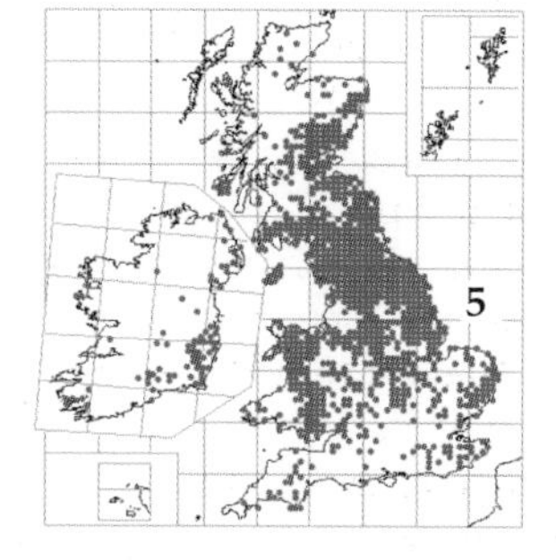

KC+ yellow.

Habitat: On exposed acid rock, often somewhat polluted walls and rarely wood.

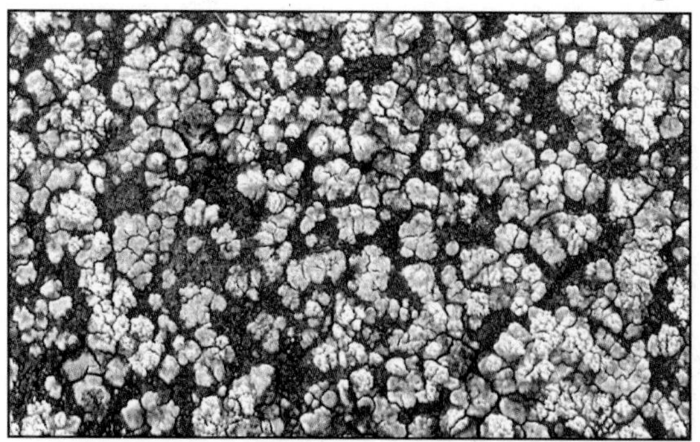

L. soralifera x 6.

L. soralifera

L. handelii

33. L. subcarnea (L. ochroidea) Thallus cracked to areolate, white to grey, thick with a warted surface, irregular in height and with irregular margins to the areoles. Thallus surrounded by a white fimbriate prothallus. Apothecia usually abundant, up to about 1 mm diam, immersed but becoming sessile. Disc very convex, pinkish or greyish brown but normally appearing white due to the dense pruina. Thalline margin paler than the thallus, thin and finally excluded.

Epithecium brown with granules that are K+ red with abundant needle-like crystals (visible under a microscope in a squash). Spores 10–14 x 6–8 µm.
K+ yellow turning red, P+ orange turning red, C–, UV+ dull orange.
Habitat: Local in sheltered underhangs on base-rich rocks. Mainly coastal where it sometimes spreads to more well-lit situations.

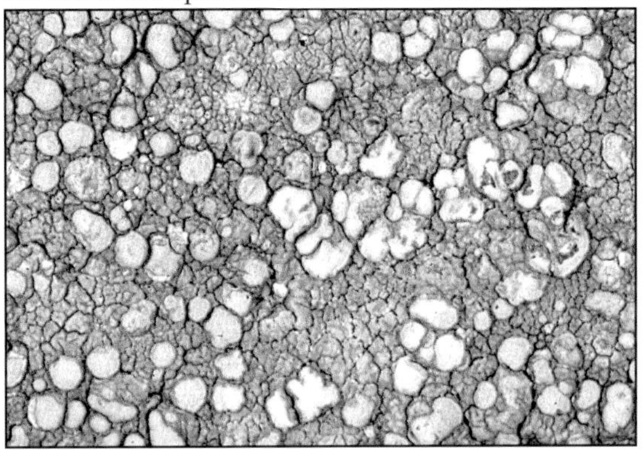

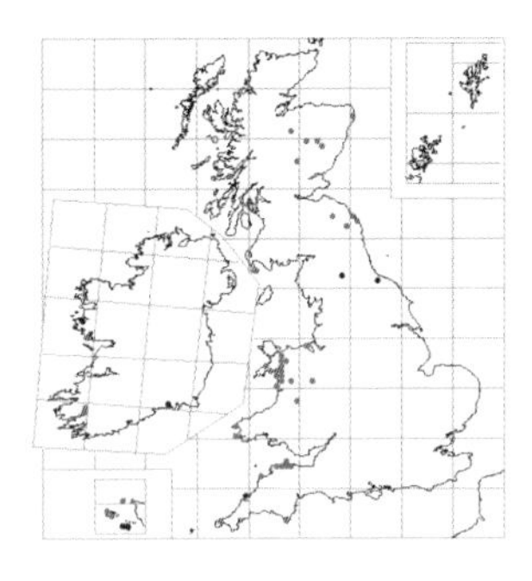

L. subcarnea x 6.

34. L. sulphurea Thallus yellow-grey to bright yellow-green. Thick, warted and cracked. Often limited by a greenish black prothallus which is also visible in the cracks. Apothecia usually present, up to 1.5 mm diam and immersed. When young they are pale yellow or concolorous with the thallus but becoming black with a pale grey pruina, convex and an irregular shape. Epithecium greenish with crystals that dissolve in K. Spores 9–13 x 4–6 µm.
K– or dirty yellow, KC+ yellow.
Habitat: On exposed nutrient-enriched, acid rocks and walls, often parasitising *Lecanora* or *Tephromelia* species when young.

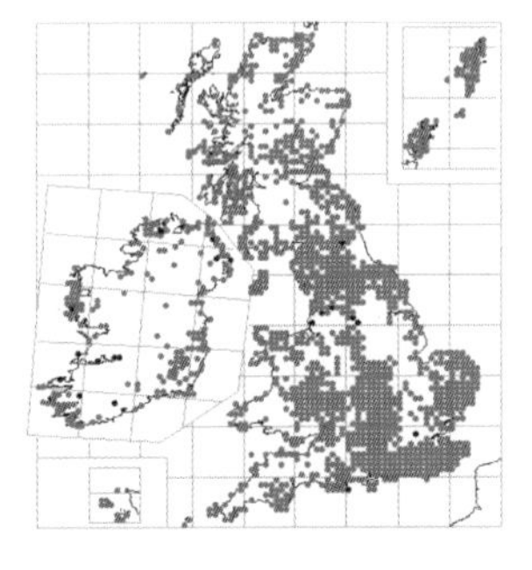

L. sulphurea x 3 (left).

35. L. symmicta Thallus thin and granular or areolate, pale yellowish green, forming neat patches with no, or only a diffuse, prothallus. It differs from a number of similar yellow-green species in that it lacks soralia and the margins of the apothecia become excluded very early. Apothecia up to 0.8 mm. Disc yellowish, becoming convex and darker with age. The specimens with red-

brown to green-black discs are referred to **L. aitema**. Epithecium various colours with yellow granules that dissolve in K. Spores 9–15 x 4–5 μm.
K–, C– or C+ orange.
Habitat: Common on acid-barked trees, rotting and decorticate wood, old palings. A common pioneer species of the rougher internodes of the young, well-lit twigs. In *L. confusa* the thalline margin is persistant and crenulate.

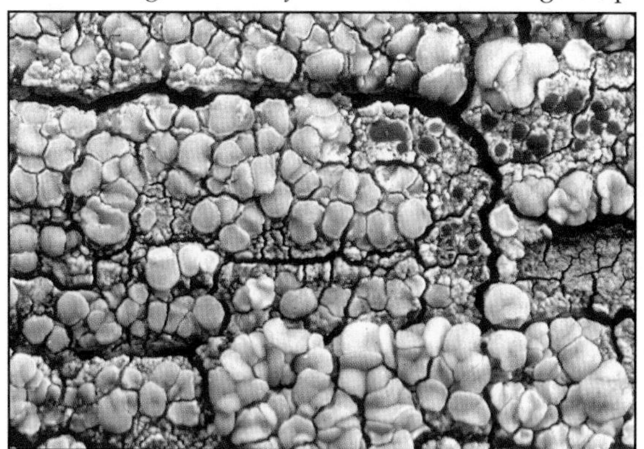

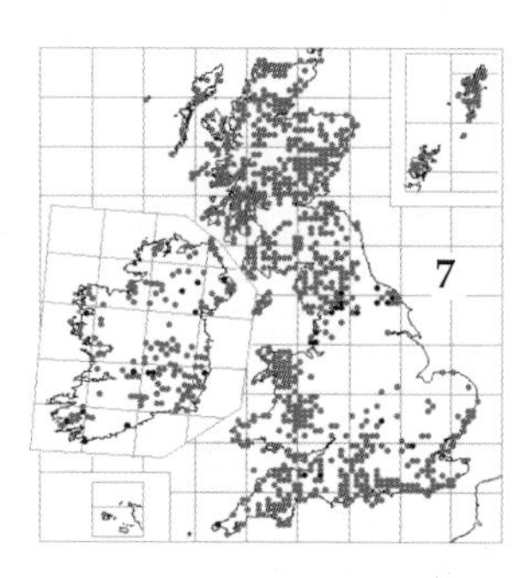

L. symmicta x 6.

36. L. varia Thallus usually of scattered rounded granules which may form an areolate crust, yellowish grey to grey-green. Apothecia common and often crowded, up to 1 mm, diam with a thin, distorted but persistent, thalline margin. Disc yellow-brown to green-brown (black discs are probably the parasite *Lecidea insidiosa*). It may be distinguished from *L. conizaeoides* by the P reaction and the lack of soredia. Epithecium colourless with small granules. Spores 9–12 x 5–7 μm.
K– or pale yellow, P+ yellow.
Habitat: Fairly common on trees and fences, only rarely found on living bark. Especially common in the East.

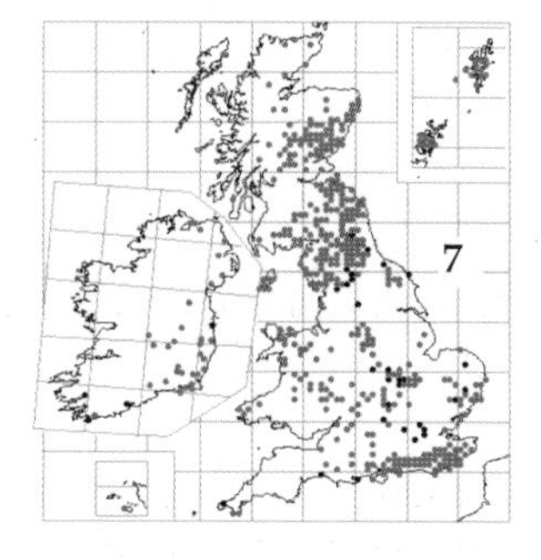

L. varia x 8.

Over the past twenty years the genus *Lecidea* has been much divided. Many of these divisions depend on the K/I reaction to the ascus tip and/or the form of the paraphyses. The following 'Lecidea' table covers those genera and species **in this book** that have:
green alga, lecideine apothecia and 8 simple, colourless spores per ascus

Genus	Habitat	Paraphyses	Isidia soredia	K/I type	Conidia	Chemistry	Hymen.	Epithec.
Carbonea	Si, Li	S, Con, Ssw	–	*Lecanora*	S, Thr	–	Cl, Br-G	B to G
Clauzadea	Ca	Bh, An, Ssw, P-T	–	*Porpidia*	Ba, S	–	Cl, Br	Br, R-Br
Fuscidea	Si, Bk	S, Sw, P-T	± Sor	*Fuscidea*	Ba, Thr	P+r, C+y	Cl	Br
Herteliana	Si	S, Br, Sw	± Sor	*Bacidia*	Thr	K+y	Cl, O	O, Br
Lecidea	Si	S, P-T	–	*Lecidea* or *Bacidia*	Ba	Various	Various	Br, G-B
Lecidella	Si, Bk	S, Sw, P-T	± Sor	*Lecanora*	Thr	K+y, C+o	Various	Br, G-B
Lecidoma	Si, T	Con, An, Sw, P-T	–	*Porpidia*	–	–	Cl	R-Br
Porpidia	Si, Ca	Bh, An, Ssw	± Sor	*Porpidia*	Ba	Various	Cl, Gr	Various
Schaereria	Si	S, Sw	Sor rare	*Schaereria*	Ba	C± pink	Cl	G, Br-G
Trapelia	Si, Bk	Bh, An	± Sor	*Trapelia*	Ba, Thr	C+r	Various	Various
Trapeliopsis	T, Bk	Bh, An, ±P-T	± Sor	*Trapelia*	Ba, Thr	C+r, K+p	Various	Various

Key: An = anastomosing, B = blue, Ba = bacilliform (cylindrical), Bk = bark, Bh = branched, Br = brown, Br–G = brown–green, Ca = calcarious, basic rock, Cl = colourless, Con = conglutinated (stuck together), G = green, G–B = greenish black, Gr = greenish, Li = lichens, O = orange, P-T = pigmented tip, Si = silica rich, acid rock, Sor = soredia (± Sor indicates that some species in the genus are sorediate), Ssw = slightly swollen, Sw = swollen, R-Br = red–brown, T = soil, Thr = thread-like, – = none.
Chemistry: o = orange, p = purple, r = red, y = yellow. An positive entry indicates that some species in this genus have this reaction.

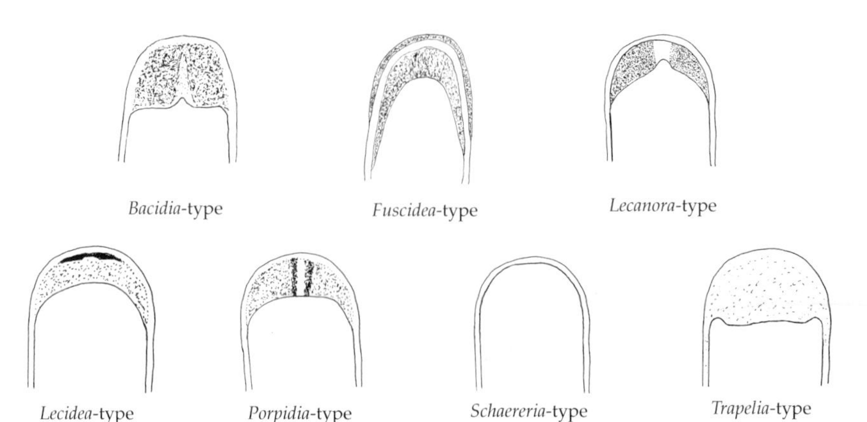

Bacidia-type
Fuscidea-type
Lecanora-type
Lecidea-type
Porpidia-type
Schaereria-type
Trapelia-type

LECIDEA ('shape of a little disc' – from the appearance of the apothecia). Many of the species are rare and difficult to separate except by microscopic examination. **Thallus** crustose or squamulose. **Photobiont** usually *Trebouxia*. **Apothecia** lecideine (lacking a thalline margin), usually with a dark-coloured disc. The proper margin consists of chains of swollen cells. **Ascus** usually 8-spored, mainly *Lecidea*–type. **Spores** colourless, simple. **Pycnidia** immersed, black. **Conidia** bacilliform. See p. 204 for a key to the 'Lecidea' group.

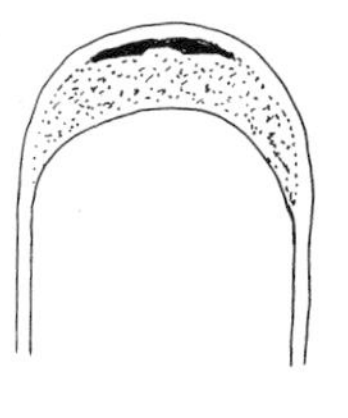

K/I reaction to the ascus tip.

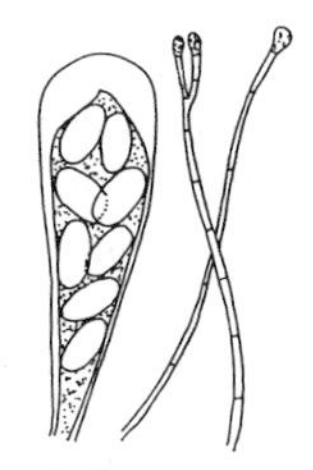

L. fuscoatra x 300.

1.	Apothecia up to 0.5 mm diam	2
–	Apothecia over 0.5 mm diam	3
2.	Apothecia in compact groups. On acid pebbles	**5. L. pycnocarpa**
–	Apothecia separate. On disturbed chalk	**3. L. lichenicola**
3.	Thallus C+ red	**2. L. fuscoatra**
–	Thallus C–	4
4.	Thallus cracked-areolate, often rust-stained	**4. L. lithophila**
–	Thallus dispersed granules or absent, not rust-stained	**1. L. auriculata** agg.

1. Lecidea auriculata agg. All the species of this group, **L. auriculata, L. diducens, L. sarcogynoides** have a thalus mostly reduced to a few scattered, pale areoles interconnected by a fimbriate prothallus. All are characteristic of crystalline granites. Apothecia black, ± shining, 0.5–1.2 mm diam (smaller in *L . sarcogynoides*) with a thin, persistent proper margin. Ascus with an I+ blue outer coat. Hymenium 30–50 µm tall. Epithecium green-black. Hypothecium thick, black-brown. Spores 7–11 x 2–3 µm, rather cylindrical. Proper margin in section: *L. auriculata*, C–, K– (upland species); *L. diducens*, C+ carmine (coastal species of western Britain); *L. sarcogynoides,* K+ violet (coastal species of south-west Britain). Pycnidia immersed, laminal. **L. inops** a related species has raised marginal pycnidia and is confined to copper-rich rocks.

L. auriculata x 6.

2. L. fuscoatra Thallus cracked into areoles to 3 mm wide, uniform, limited by a black prothallus, reddish brown to grey. Apothecia normally present, up to 2 mm diam, innate, with a black, often white-pruinose disc, sometimes convex with a persistent proper margin. Hymenium colourless. Hypothecium very dark brown. Spores 8–15 x 4–8 µm. This is the type species of the genus *Lecidea*.
Upper cortex only: C+ red.
Habitat: Common on nutrient-enriched acid rocks and brick walls.

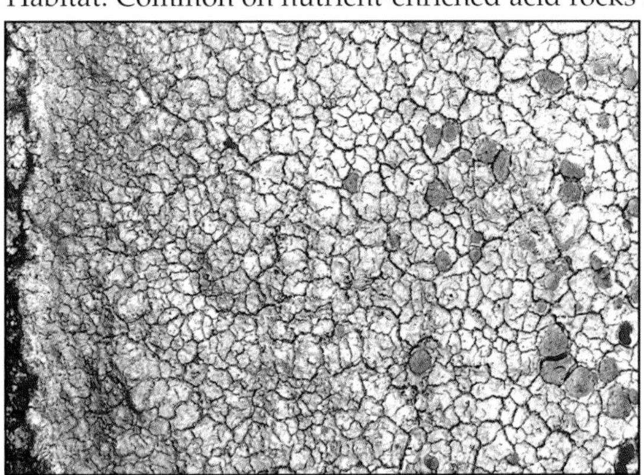

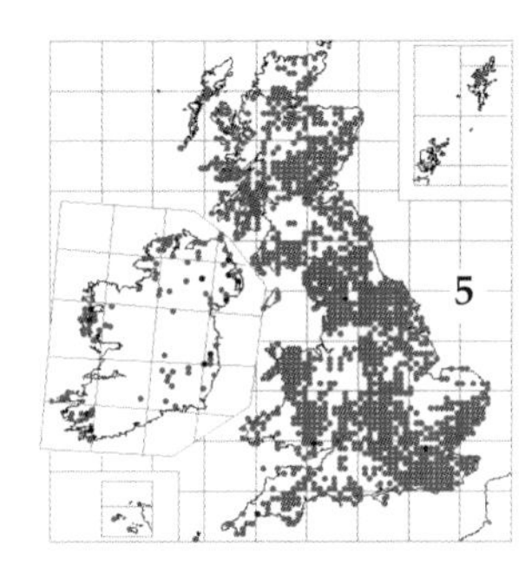

L. fuscoatra x 3.

3. L. lichenicola Thallus endolithic or slightly granular. Apothecia dark red-brown, pinkish when young or wet. Very small (0.1–0.2 mm diam). Outer coat of ascus K/I blue. Spores 16–19 x 6–8 µm. It is a very difficult species to locate in the field and it is probably overlooked.
Habitat: It is included in this book as it is an interesting species that colonizes the unstable substratum of disturbed chalk pebbles around rabbit burrows, etc.

4. L. lithophila Thallus cracked-areolate, grey, usually stained rust-red in patches. Apothecia large (up to 2 mm diam), becoming somewhat sessile. Disc very dark brown to black (browner when wet), almost flat. Epithecium brown, hymenium colourless to brownish. Spores 10–15 x 5–6 µm. (In **L. plana** the thallus is thinner and dispersed. Epithecium greenish. Spores 8–11 x 3–5 µm.)
Reactions: negative except in var. **lactea** which is K+ yellow becoming red.
Habitat: Common on acid rocks (especially iron-rich) in the North and West.

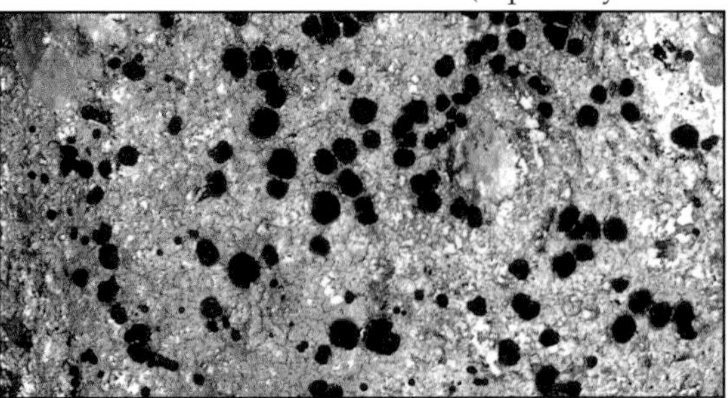

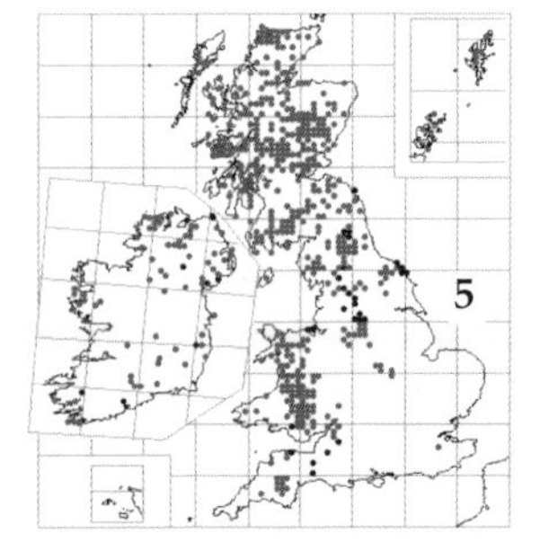

L. lithophila x 3.

5. L. pycnocarpa Thallus immersed or of dispersed areoles with a black, fimbriate margin. Apothecia up to 0.3 mm diam in blackberry-like, close-packed clusters of up to about 20 fruits. Epithecium and hymenium greenish brown to bluish. Hypothecium dark reddish brown. Ascus *Bacidia*-type. Spores 10–18 x 4–6 µm. **L. p.** f. **sorediata** has pale areoles with very dark soralia.
P± yellow, K+ yellow.
Habitat: Frequent on rough, acid rocks in upland regions.

L. pyconocarpa x 6.

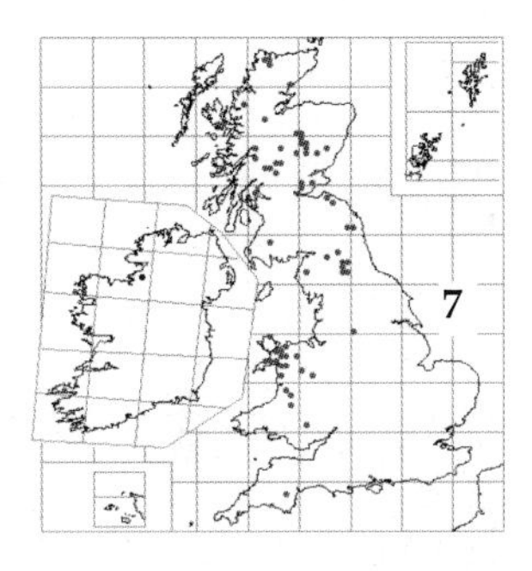

LECIDELLA (diminutive of *Lecidea*). **Thallus** crustose. **Photobiont** chlorococcoid. **Apothecia** lecideine. **Ascus** 8-spored, *Lecanora*-type. **Spores** colourless, simple. *Pycnidia* immersed. **Conidia** thread-like. This genus is close to *Lecidea* but differs principally in that: The paraphyses are lax in K solution, the conidia are thread-like, the asci are *Lecanora*-type.

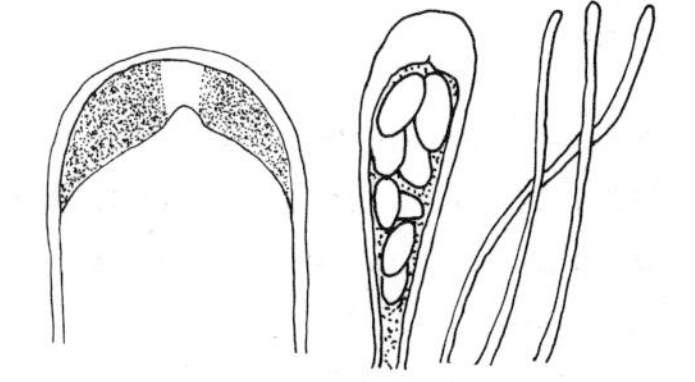

K/I reaction to ascus tip. *L. elaeochroma* x 500.

1. On bark. Thallus yellow-grey to yellow-green, sometimes sorediate. C+ orange **2. L. elaeochroma**
– On rock. C+ orange or C– 2
2. Soralia delimited, yellow-green to green. Thallus greenish grey **3. L. scabra**
– Not sorediate. Thallus buff to yellow-grey 3
3. Thallus warted or granulose. On maritime siliceous rocks **1. L. asema**
– Thallus areolate or evanescent. Mainly on calcareous substrates, not strictly maritime **4. L. stigmatea**

1. Lecidella asema (L. subincongrua) Thallus thick, usually very granulose but may be almost areolate and warted, limited by a black prothallus, buff to yellow-grey or greenish yellow. Apothecia up to 1 mm diam, appear almost innate,

becoming sessile and convex with excluded margins. Disc brown to black and contrasting strongly against the lighter thallus. Hypothecium red-brown. Spores 10–13 x 6–9 µm.
K+ yellow, C+ orange.
Habitat: Common on well-lit, hard, siliceous, maritime rocks.

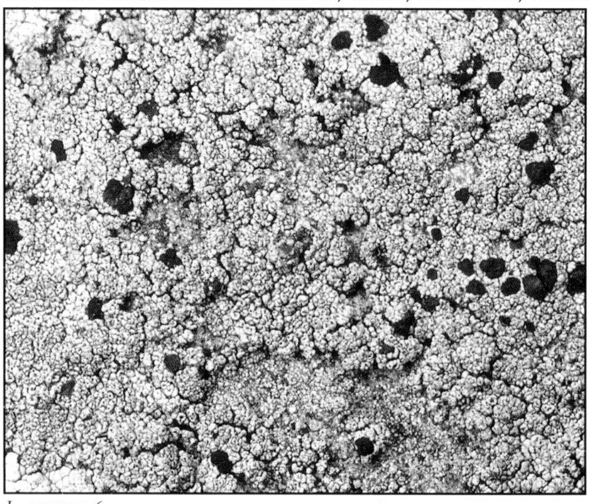

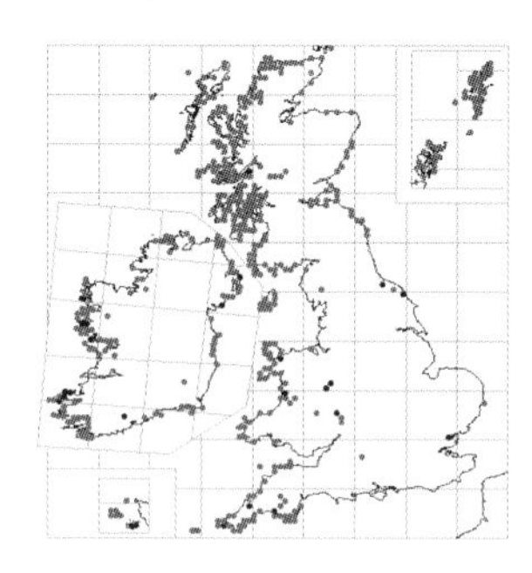

L. asema x 6.

2. L. elaeochroma Thallus smooth to slightly granular, usually shiny, not sorediate, often limited by a black prothallus and forming extensive mosaics (often with *Lecanora chlarotera*), yellow-grey to grey (lighter and more grey when in shade). Usually fertile with black (reddish or piebald in shade) apothecia, up to 1 mm diam. Disc concave with a smooth black margin which is excluded as the apothecia become convex. Hypothecium orange-brown. Spores 10–17 x 6–9 µm. It may be confused with *Fuscidea lightfootii* which is sorediate, C– and has 1-septate spores. A very variable species.
C+ orange (in most cases), KC+ yellow.
Habitat: Very common on smooth-bark trees, shrubs and fences.
L. e. f. **soralifera** has yellow- or green-farinose soralia scattered over the surface (apothecia are also normally present). Mainly in the West.

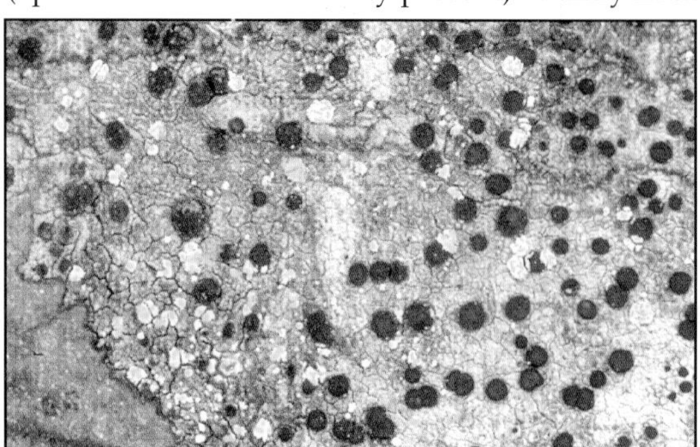

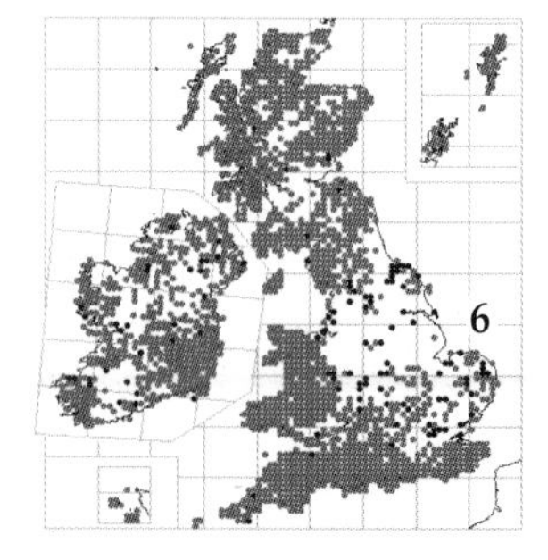

L. elaeochroma f. *soralifera* x 4.

3. L. scabra Thallus greenish grey, granular, rough with delimited areas of pale yellow-green or bluish green soralia which may become confluent. If the surface of the thallus is rubbed this disturbs the soredia and gives the soralia a distinctive lighter colour. Apothecia rare, with slightly convex, black discs and contorted margins. Hypothecium yellow to red-brown. Spores 10–15 x 6–8 µm. C+ orange.
Habitat: Common on hard, acid rocks and walls, rarely on weathered or dust-impregnated wood and tree bases.

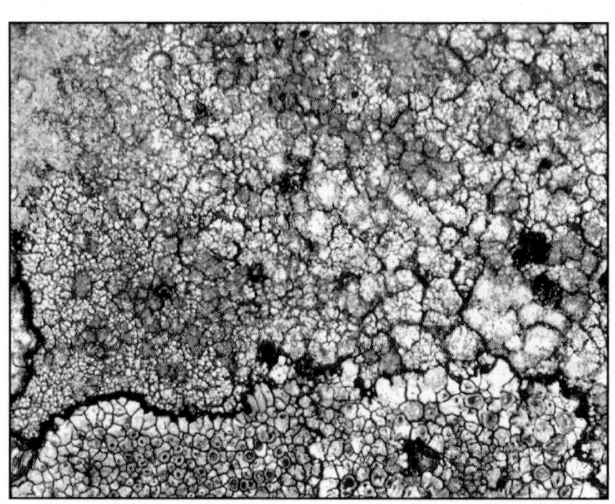

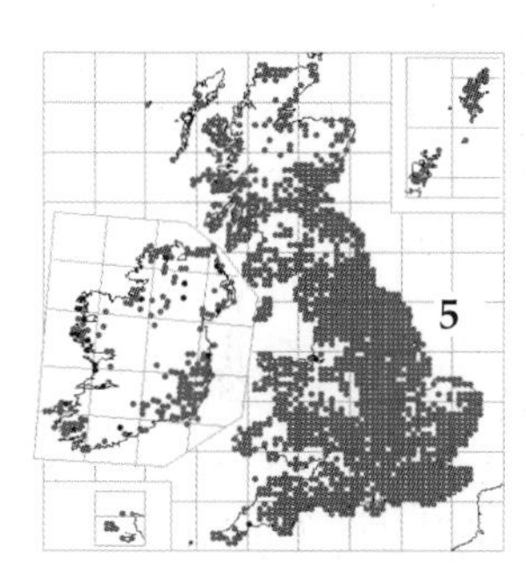

L. scabra x 5.

4. L. stigmatea Thallus very variable, pale green-grey, reddish brown or white, areolate, cracked or almost evanescent. Apothecia sessile, up to about 1 mm diam. Discs plane, occasionally becoming convex, very dark brown or black with glossy margins that become excluded. Epithecium purplish brown. Hypothecium colourless to straw-coloured.
K+ yellow or K–, UV–.
Habitat: Common on ± calcareous rocks, asbestos-cement or mortar. A thinner thallus is usually formed on siliceous substrates. Often confused with *Clauzadea monticola* which has a distinctive red-brown hypothecium.

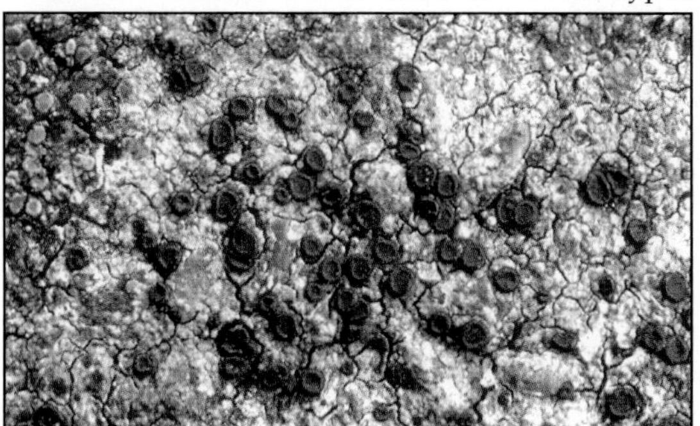

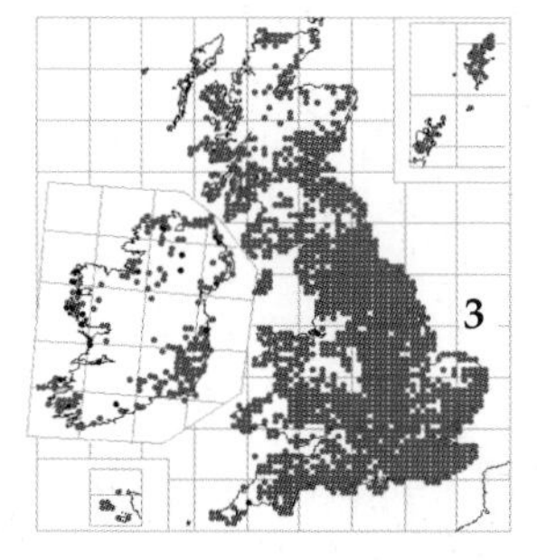

L. stigmatea x 6.

LECIDOMA (from its resemblance to *Lecidea*). **Thallus** crustose, areolate to almost squamulose. **Photobiont** chlorococcoid. **Apothecia** lecideine. Ascus 8-spored, *Porpidia*-like. **Hymenium** colourless, I+ blue. **Spores** simple, colourless. **Pycnidia** not found. **Chemical reactions** negative.

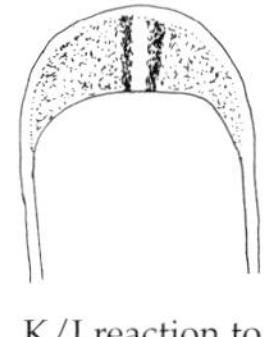

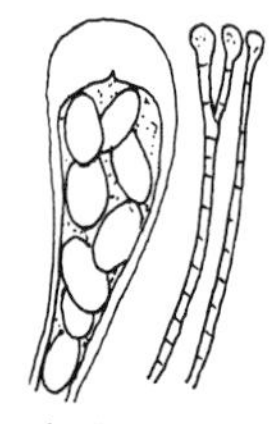

K/I reaction to the ascus tip.

L. demissum x 400.

Lecidoma demissum Thallus almost squamulose with large areoles, 1–2 mm wide. The whole thallus up to about 8 cm wide, brown to brown-grey, frequently surrounded by a black prothallus and actually looking like its English name 'cow-pat lichen'. Lower surface dark. Apothecia frequent, often crowded, red-brown, lighter when wet, up to 1 mm diam with a thin margin that soon becomes excluded. Spores 12–16 x 5–7 µm.
Habitat: Fairly common on acid soil and pebbles in exposed montane sites.

L. demissum x 4.

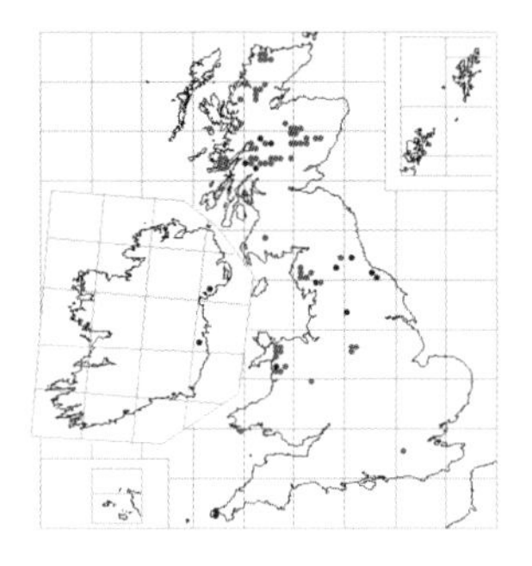

LEPRARIA ('scurfy' – from the structure of the thallus). **Thallus** leprose, consisting of a network of fungal hyphae with the photobiont cells scattered amongst them. Some species do, however, have a medulla and some an almost lobate margin to the thallus. **Fruiting bodies** unknown. This is a 'dust-bin' genus. If a specimen is found with a fruiting body, that species is can then be allocated to its correct genus. Identification of many species can only be done with certainty by the use of thin-layer chromatography or similar techniques. The appended distribution maps must therefore be consulted with caution.

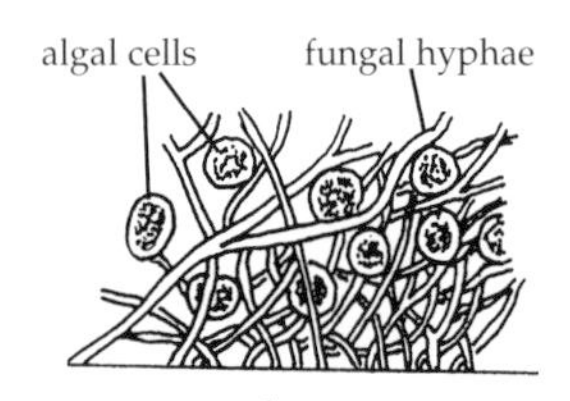

Diagramatic section x 80.

View from above x 10.

1.	Thallus coarse-granular, pale grey, in well-lit situations	2
–	Thallus powdery, green to grey or white, mainly in shade	3
2.	C+ reddish orange	**5. L. neglecta**
	C–	**1. L. caesioalba**
3.	Pale grey to green-grey, dull, with bluish tinge	**2. L. incana**
–	Green to grey, never with a bluish tinge	4
4.	Thallus apple green. In limestone caves and crevices	**3. L. lesdainii**
–	Thallus greenish grey or whitish	5
5.	Thallus whitish. On limestone	**6. L. nivalis**
–	Thallus usually bright greenish grey	**4. L. lobificans**

1. Lepraria caesioalba Thallus rosette-forming, grey, granular, not powdery, granules up to 0.2 mm diam. The thallus forms neat, rather circular patches which are slightly darker in the centre giving a zoned appearance.

Usually K+ faint yellow, C–, P+ orange but reactions vary.

Habitat: Scarce but locally common on well-lit, not nutrient-enriched, siliceous rocks and especially over associated mosses, mostly in upland Britain.

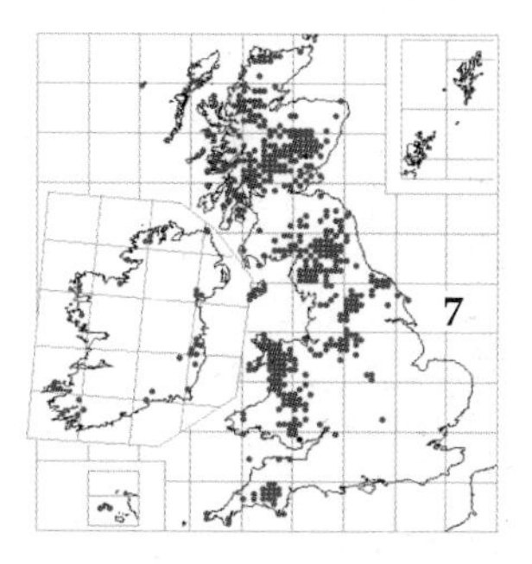

2. L. incana Thallus pale grey to green-grey with a glaucous tinge, often thick and consisting of minute fluffy granules, without a clearly differentiated medulla or marginal lobes. It may cover large areas.

Spot reactions: negative.

Habitat: Very common on shaded acid rocks, trees and mosses. It is one of the commonest lichens in eastern Britain. In the West it is less common being replaced by *L. lobificans*. It frequently grows on trees near the centre of cities where it may be separated from the ubiquitous alga, *Desmococcus*, by its blue-grey, not bright yellow-green colour.

L. incana x 6.

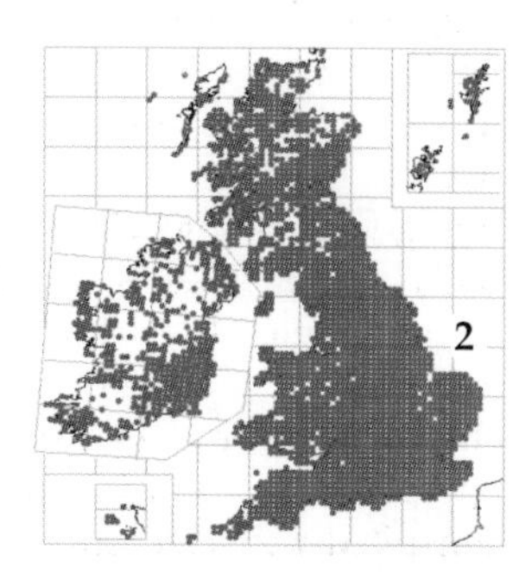

3. L. lesdainii [Botryoleproma lesdainii] Thallus of very fine fluffy granules (up to 0.1 mm). Projecting hyphae cover the surface like a cobweb. It is a distinctive bright apple-green (greener than *Leproloma vouauxii* and never blue-green), thin or thick and spongy, without a differentiated medulla or marginal lobes. It usually forms neat patches like green cotton wool.
Spot reactions: negative, UV–.
Habitat: Infrequent on damp shaded limestone and mortar often growing over associated mosses.

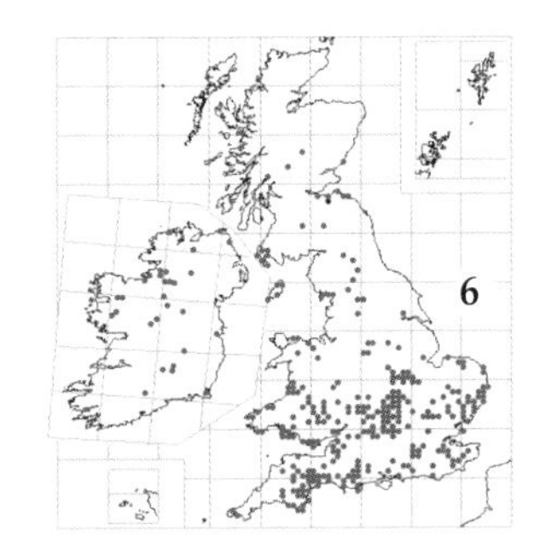

4. L. lobificans Thallus of fluffy greenish grey granules which are variable in size but mainly larger (up to 0.5 mm) than in *L. lesdainii*, thick with a white medulla. These granules often become enveloped in hyphae or become eroded giving the thallus a pale, leprose appearance with indistinct marginal lobes.
K– or faint yellow, C–, P+ orange.
Habitat: Common throughout Britain and possibly the commonest lichen in the West. It occurs on a wide range of shaded habitats, including calcareous rocks, trees and soil where sheltered from direct rainfall.

L. lobificans x 8.

6

5. L. neglecta Identical in its appearance to *L. caesioalba* having a pale grey, hard, granular appearance, but but differing in its chemistry.
K– or K+ yellow, C+ orange-red, P+ yellow. The only completely definitive reaction is the KC+ orange-pink colour of an extract of the lichen with acetone on filter paper.
Habitat: Rare, growing over mosses and on peaty soil, sometimes on siliceous rocks, in northern Britain. Found above 300 m. The only map available is omitted as it merely shows a few recently confirmed records.

L. neglecta x 5.

6. L. nivalis (L. crassissima) Thallus white or very pale grey, soft and thick, forming delimited, membraneous patches which are fluffy in the centre and weakly lobed at the margin.
K– or faint yellow, C–, P+ orange.
Habitat: Locally abundant on shaded hard calcareous rocks (e.g. cliffs) where protected from direct rain. May also occur on acid rocks near the coast. It also rarely occurs on consolidated calcareous soils.

L. nivalis x 1.

LEPROCAULON ('scurfy stalk' – from the thallus structure). **Thallus** leprose granules from which secondary pseudopodetia develop. **Photobiont** *Trebouxia*. Not known fertile. There is only one British species which was previously included in *Stereocaulon*.

Leprocaulon microscopicum Thallus initially of glaucous-green, leprose granules. The secondary pseudopodetia are whitish, about 2 mm high (rarely up to 4 mm), frequently branched towards the tips which are covered in pale green, leprose granules.
Spot reactions: negative, UV–.
Habitat: Frequent on acid soil on cliffs, roadsides etc. Rarely on acid bark. Most common in coastal areas.

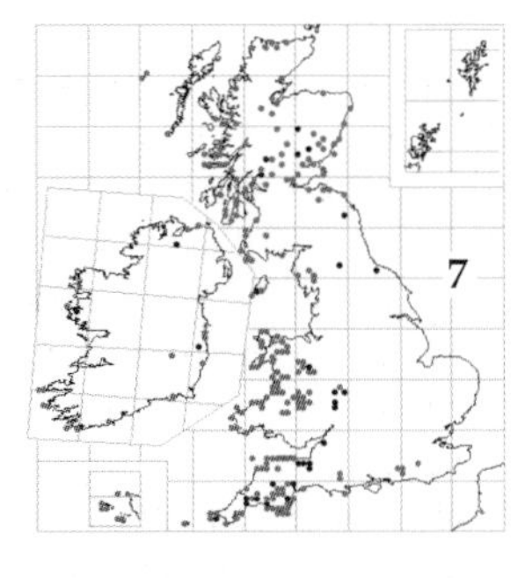

L. microscopicum x 5.

LEPROLOMA ('scurfy edges' – from the form of the thallus margins). **Thallus** leprose, usually with slight puckered marginal lobes and a white medulla. **Photobion**t chlorococcoid. **Apothecia** not known fertile.

1. Definite lobes and hypothallus, an upland species **1. L. membranaceum**
– Ill-defined lobes and hypothallus, many habitats **2. L. vouauxii**

1. Leproloma membranaceum Thallus yellow-white, thick, finely granular and forming roughly circular patches. Margins pale, often distinctly lobed and usually slightly raised. The lower surface consists of a darker mat of hyphae. Apothecia up to 2 mm diam were recorded in Britain in the 18th century but it is now considered that this record is probably erroneous.
P+ reddish orange, K± yellow.
Habitat: Fairly common in upland Britain on dry shaded rocks especially on vertical acid rocks, also over mosses and on shaded deciduous trees.

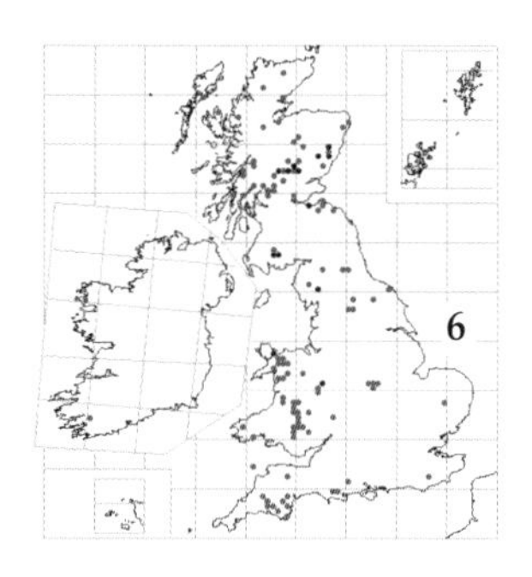

L. membranaceum x 6.

L. vouauxii Thallus yellow-white to pale grey-green, thick, puckered, consisting of powdery granules up to 0.5 mm across, often eroded and then showing the white medulla. It differs from *L. membranaceum* in that the margin is not or only weakly lobed, and the undersurface has only a poorly developed hypothallus.
Habitat: Frequent, mainly in lowland Britain, on shaded rocks, walls, tombstones, mortar and trees (especially ash).

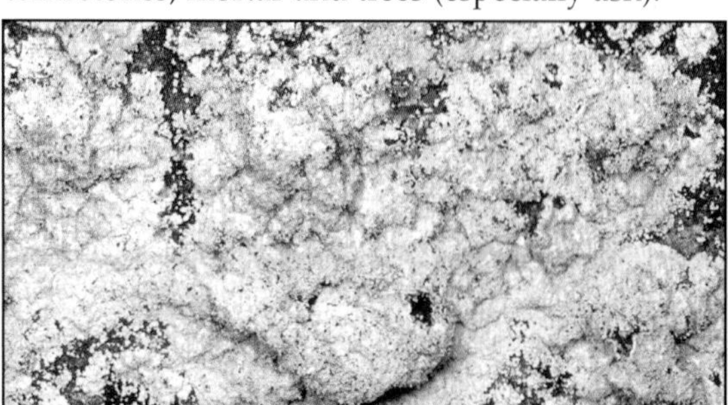

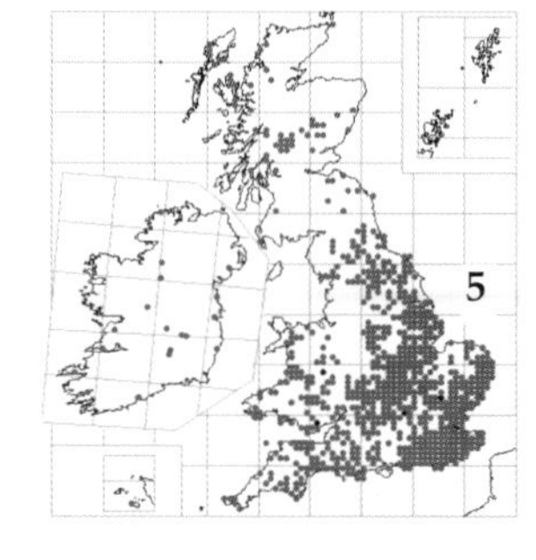

L. vouauxii x 4.

LEPROPLACA (from the combination of the names *Lepraria* and *Caloplaca*). Separated from the genus *Lepraria* and placed in the *Teloschistaceae* by the K+ purple reaction. **Thallus** leprose. **Photobiont** chlorococcoid. Not found fertile in Britain. Superficially similar to *Chrysothrix*, but that genus is K–. Separated from *Caloplaca* by the leprose thallus. Most authorities now consider that the genus is best reunited with *Caloplaca*.

1. Thallus deep mustard-yellow to brownish. Not lobate **1. L. chrysodeta**
– Thallus mustard to green-yellow, white medulla. Lobate at margin **2. L. xantholyta**

1. Leproplaca chrysodeta Thallus powdery, more or less continuous, deep mustard to brownish orange, consisting of very small (about 0.1 mm diam) spherical granules. Not lobate at the margins.
K+ purple.
Habitat: Locally common in the dry, sheltered crevices of hard calcareous rocks and mortared walls, often overgrowing mosses.

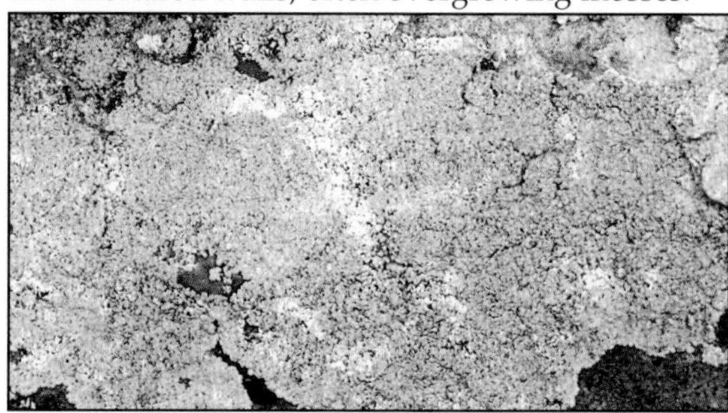

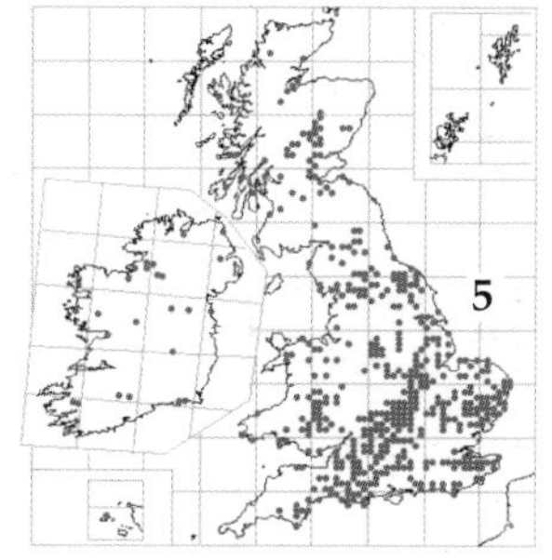

L. chrysodeta x 3.

2. L. xantholyta Thallus powdery, often fragmented, mustard-yellow to green-yellow with a white medulla and delimited by a white prothallus. Distinctly lobate at the margins.
K+ purple.
Habitat: Frequent in sheltered crevices of damp, hard calcareous rocks.

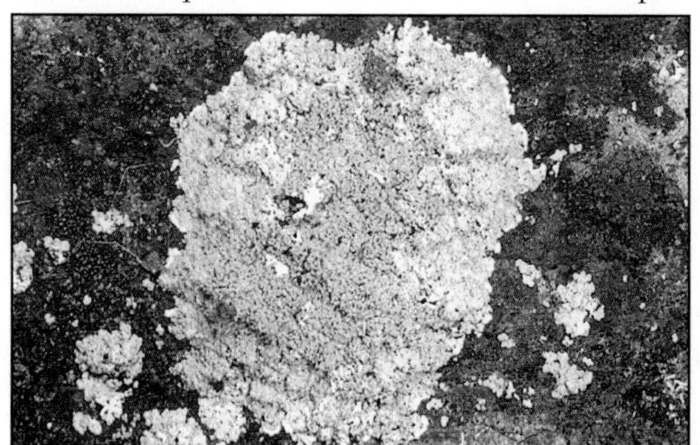

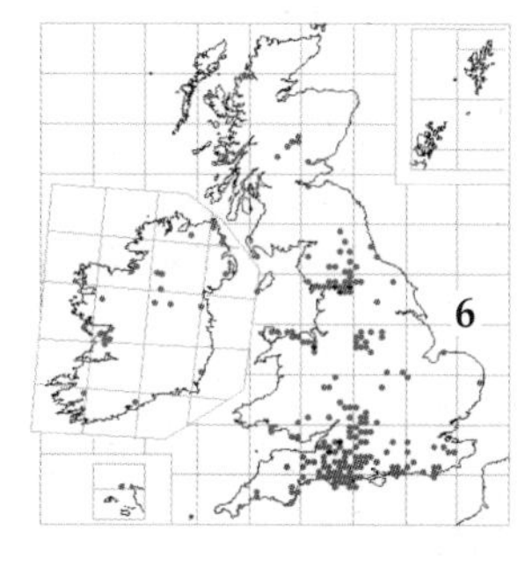

L. xantholita x 3.

LEPTOGIUM ('thin' – from the paper-like thallus when dry). **Thallus** crustose to foliose, homoiomerous but unlike *Collema* the apical cells of the hyphae near the surface form a single-celled cortical layer. Usually brown-black, not green-black, more papery and less swollen, when moist, than *Collema*. **Photobiont** *Nostoc*. **Apothecia** lecanorine often with a double margin. **Ascus** 4- to 8-spored, K/I+ blue outer wall and paler apical dome containing a darker central tube. **Spores** colourless to pale brown, 3- to 5-septate or muriform. **Chemical reactions** negative. Many species are difficult to identify.

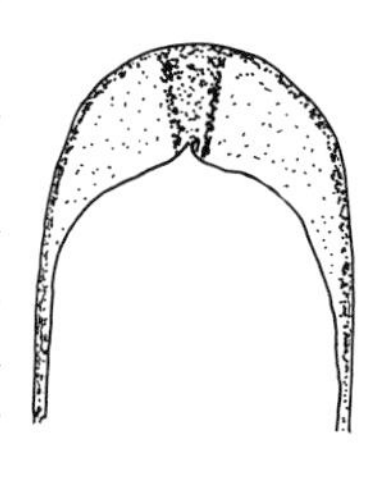

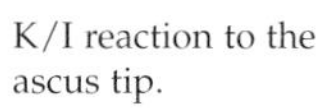

K/I reaction to the ascus tip.

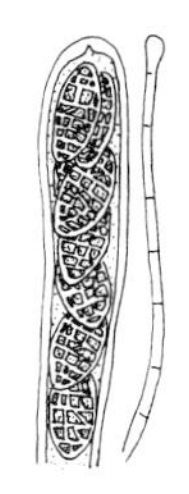

L. lichenoides x 200.

1. Thallus almost crustose, lobes up to 1 mm wide — 2
– Thallus foliose, lobes over 1 mm wide — 3

2. Thallus to 5 mm high, 1 mm wide — **6. L. schraderi**
– Thallus almost crustose, lobes to 1 mm diam — **7. L. teretiusculum**

3. Isidiate — 4
– Lacking isidia — 6

4. Lobes forming a dense mat 2–5 mm high, striated, margins with thin digitate isidia — **4. L. lichenoides**
– Lobes to 1 cm across, with laminal flat, coralloid or wart-like isidia — 5

5. Lobes to 1 cm wide, overlapping, mainly flattened isidia — **2. L. cyanescens**
– Lobes to 3 mm wide, contorted, coarse, wart-like isidia — **5. L. plicatile**

6. Lobes wrinkled when dry, erect, green-brown. Usually fertile — **3. L. gelatinosum**
– Lobes not wrinkled when dry, less erect, green-grey to blue-grey. Rarely fertile — **1. L. britannicum**

1. Leptogium britannicum Thallus translucent dark green-grey when wet, pale blue-grey when dry. The lobes are very thin and papery with a smooth edge and wrinkled when dry. Lower surface paler grey and without rhizinae. The lobes are frequently almost circular, up to 1 cm across. It often forms extensive tufted patches up to 10 cm wide or may consist of rather scattered lobes. It is rarely fertile. Apothecia top-shaped on a short, pale stalk and with reddish brown discs, about 1 mm diam. The thalline margin is soon excluded. Spores 3- to 4-septate often with a single longitudinal septum, 20–30 x 6–7 µm.
Habitat: Local on the coast above high-water mark in western Ireland and Scotland but occasionally found in the South-West and West. Often in soil pockets and amongst mosses on exposed rocks, more rarely on the tops of walls on or near the coast.

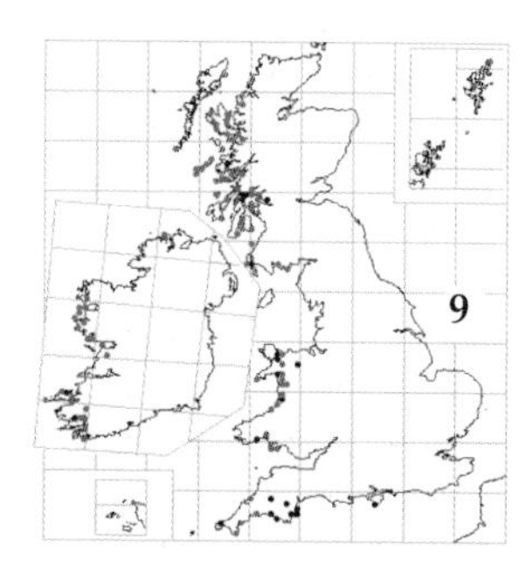

L. britannicum x 4.

2. L. cyanescens Forms large, loose patches to 10 cm or more wide but often of rather dispersed lobes. The lobes up to 1 cm wide, overlapping, not erect. Upper surface pale grey with numerous flat or pin-like, laminal isidia which become flattened and overlapping towards the centre of the thallus. Lower surface paler grey without rhizinae. Apothecia very rare. Spores 19–23 x 7–9 µm, becoming muriform.

Habitat: Locally common (possibly the commonest of the blue-grey species), mainly in the West, often near water amongst mosses on trees and on rocks.

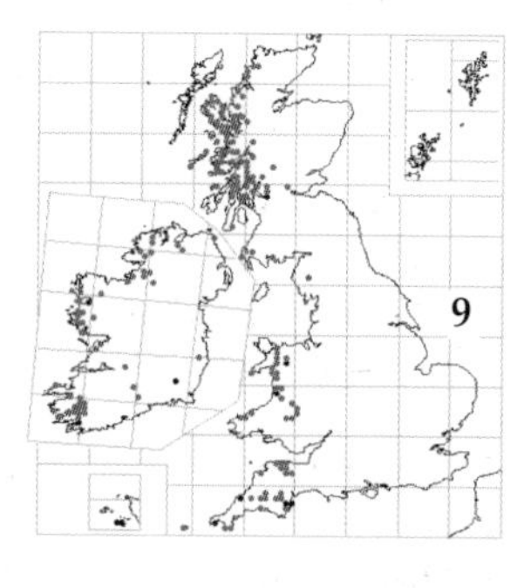

L. cyanescens x 4.

3. L. gelatinosum (L. sinuatum) Thallus green-brown to brown, erect or rarely adpressed, wrinkled, either with entire margins or regularly lacerate, never isidiate. Very variable in form. Usually abundantly fertile with apothecia up to 1.5 mm diam with red-brown to brown discs. Spores muriform.

Habitat: Common amongst mosses on trees and rocks, calcareous soils and mortar. It is the commonest and most variable species of *Leptogium* in southern Britain and when the lobes are finely divided, it is easily confused with the much rarer *L. lichenoides*.

L. *gelatinosum* x 6.

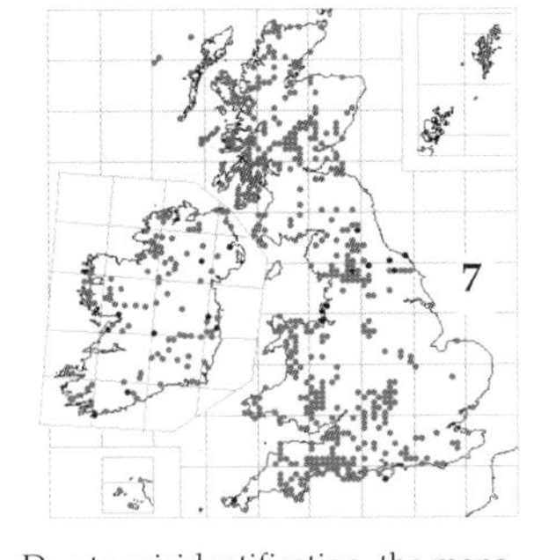

Due to misidentification, the maps of *L gelatinosum* and *L. lichenoides* do not depict the true situation. *L. lichenoides* has a narrower habitat preference and is over-represented in the map below.

4. L. lichenoides Thallus dark brown or grey-brown, usually consisting of a dense mat of more or less erect lobes about 2–5 mm high. Each lobe is thin and striate when dry, the margins normally bearing numerous, fine, digitate isidia. It is these terete projections that help differentiate it from *L. gelatinosum*. Lower surface with vertical ridges. Usually infertile. Apothecia when present with chestnut-brown discs with a lighter margin. Spores 33–45 x 12–15 µm, persistently muriform. Habitat: Local, on mossy old trees (often at the base), rarely calcareous rocks, or with mosses on damp calcareous soils.

L. *lichenoides* x 10.

5. L. plicatile Thallus rosette-shaped and adpressed. Pleated when dry. Lobes up to 3 mm wide, dark red-brown even when wet, bearing coarse isidia-like, granular warts. The thallus is tough (wet or dry) with a contorted appearance, firmly attached to the substratum. Apothecia small, up to 1.5 mm diam, with a persistant thalline margin and a concave disc. Spores 18–30 x 8–16 µm, becoming muriform. Looks like a *Collema* but is dark red-brown and has an upper cortex. Habitat: Common on hard, damp, calcareous rocks, especially common in churchyards on horizontal stones.

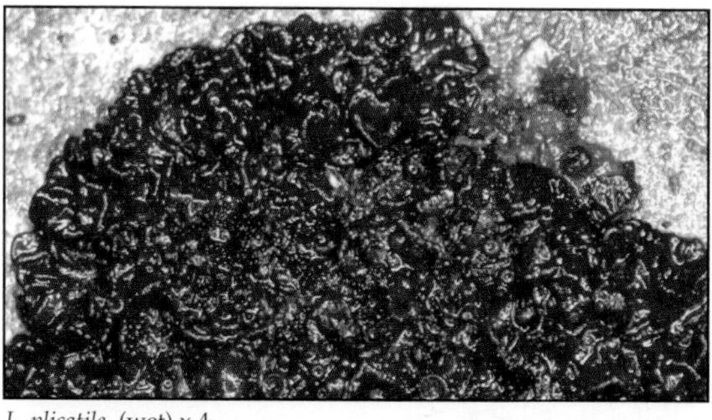

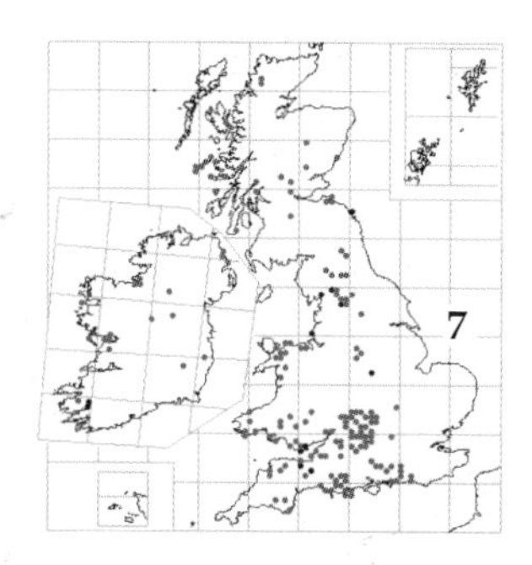

L. plicatile (wet) x 4.

6. L. schraderi Thallus dark red-brown, of compacted, wrinkled, glossy, cylindrical (not flattened) lobes about 1 mm wide to 5 mm long, branching from the base with a few granular isidia. It looks somewhat like a giant *Placynthium nigrum*. Apothecia are uncommon, about 1.5 mm diam. Spores 23–33 x 10–12 µm, muriform. If it is fertile with numerous globose isidia, it is probably the similar **L. turgidum.**
Habitat: Frequent on mosses, mortar and calcareous soils.

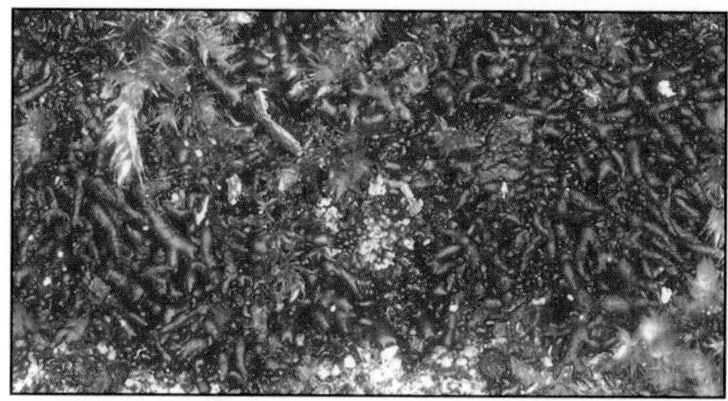

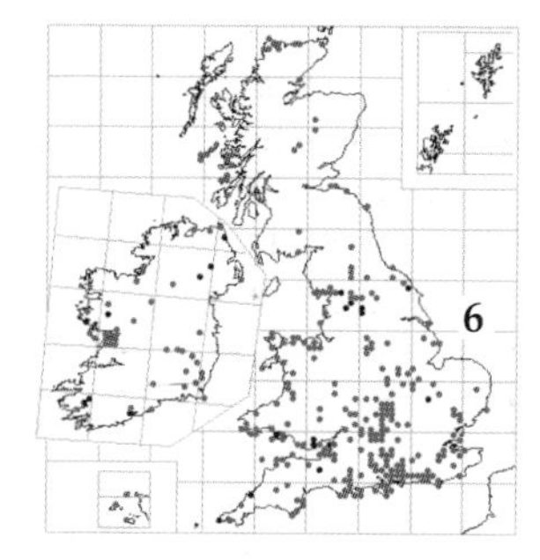

L. schraderi (wet) x 6.

7. L. teretiusculum Thallus dark red-brown (greyish in shade), consisting of small, short, cylindrical to coralloid lobes about 0.1 mm wide and to 1 mm long. Especially when dry, its coralloid, knobby, crustose appearance makes it look very like *Placynthiella icmalea* which has simple spores. Apothecia are rare, up to 1 mm diam. Spores to 5-septate becoming muriform, 20–25 x 10–12 µm.
Habitat: On shaded bark of old deciduous trees and calcareous soil, rocks and grassland. A southerly species.

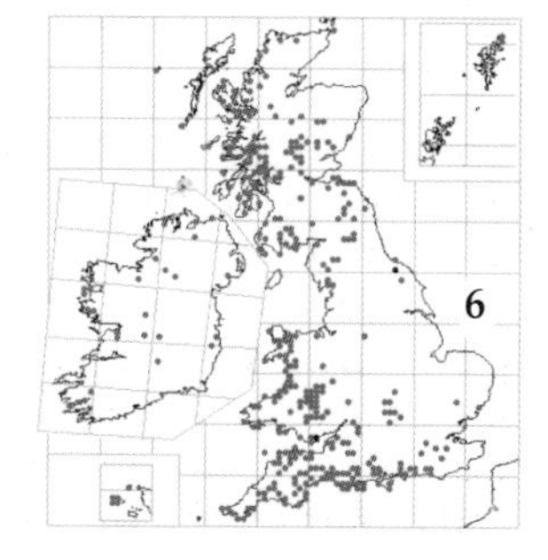

L. teretiusculum x 4.

LEPTORHAPHIS ('thin needle' – from the shape of the spores). **Thallus** endophloeodal, if visible it appears as a whitish stain. **Photobiont** possibly *Trentepohlia*, but it is not or only slightly lichenized. **Perithecia** are innate, becoming more prominent. **Ascus** cylindrical-clavate, normally 8-spored. **Spores** colourless, 1- to 3-septate and curved.

L. epidermis spore x 1000.

Leptorhaphis epidermidis Thallus usually absent with alga occasionally around the perithecia which are oval and 0.3–0.5 mm diam. The dark brown involucrellum appears as a spreading dark ring around the base of the perithicium. Spores curved, 25–35 x 2–4 µm. Minute dark pycnidia are also normally present.
Habitat: Only on birch. Most common in the North and West.

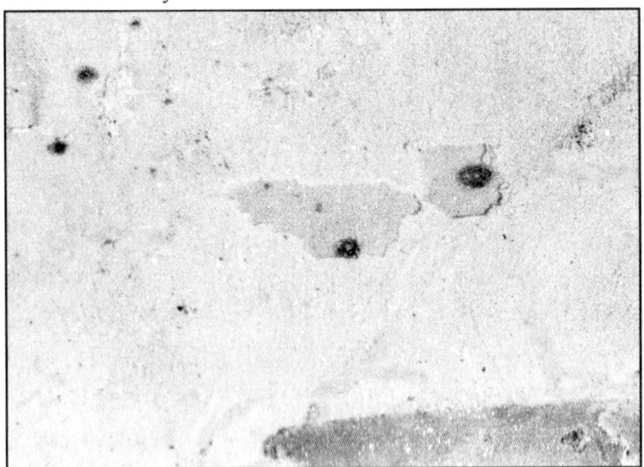

L. epidermidis x 10.

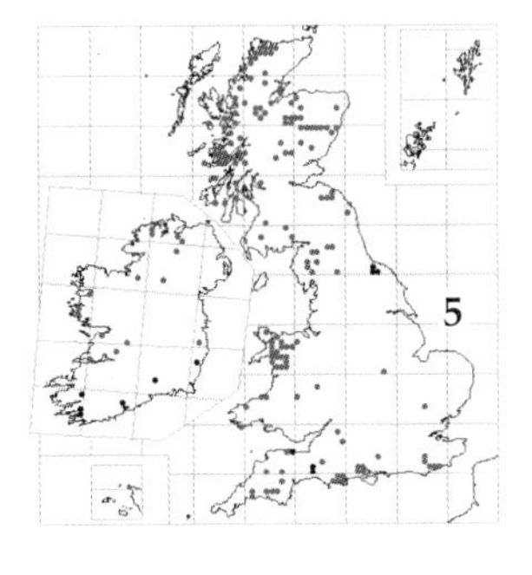

LICHINA ('lichen'). **Thallus** fruticose, dark brown to black. The fungal hyphae usually form a central core and also a cortical layer one or two cells thick. **Photobiont** *Calothrix*. **Apothecia** apical. **Ascus** thin-walled with a K/I+ blue outer coat, 8-spored. **Spores** colourless, simple. **Ecology** saxicolous and maritime. **Chemical reactions** negative. They look like small, brown-black seaweeds.

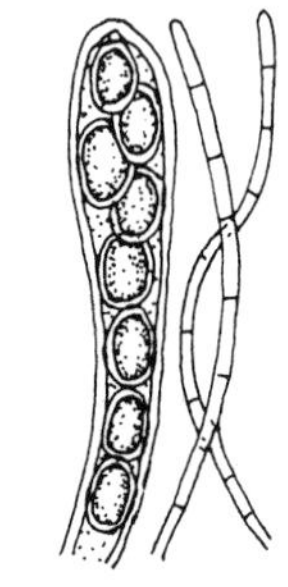

L. confinis x 300.

1. Thallus less than 5 mm high. Lobes more or less terete. Usually around high-water mark **1. L. confinis**
– Thallus to 1 cm high. Lobes flattened. Below high-water mark **2. L. pygmaea**

1. Lichina confinis Thallus dark brown to black, matt, much smaller than *L. pygmaea* (less than 5 mm high) and more richly branched, lobes terete (about 0.3 mm diam), forming a short, dense mat which often originates in sheltered crevices. Apothecia spherical, about 0.5 mm diam, on the tips of the branches. Spores 12–18 x 10–15 µm.
Habitat: Very common on rocks on well-lit, sheltered shores, or in crevices on exposed shores, just above high-water mark (above *L. pygmaea*).

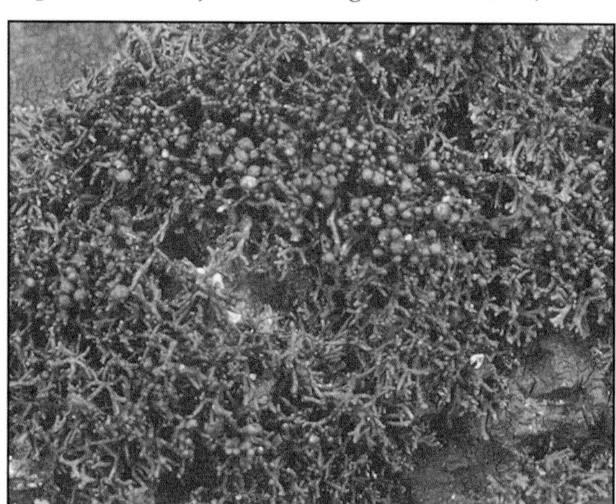

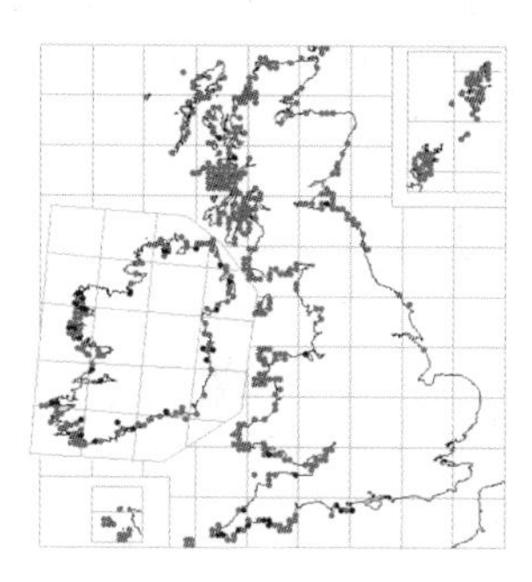

L. confinis x 8.

2. L. pygmaea Thallus matt dark brown to black, sometimes with some yellow-brown branches, lobes flattened except towards the tips which may be terete. It forms extensive mats up to about 1 cm high. Apothecia spherical, up to 2 mm diam, on the tips of the branches. Spores 22–29 x 11–16 µm. When dry and crushed between the fingers it smells of embrocation, a feature that separates it from the similar looking seaweed, *Catenella opuntia*.
Habitat: Common on rocks on exposed shores in the upper part of the tidal region below high-water mark, below *L. confinis*.

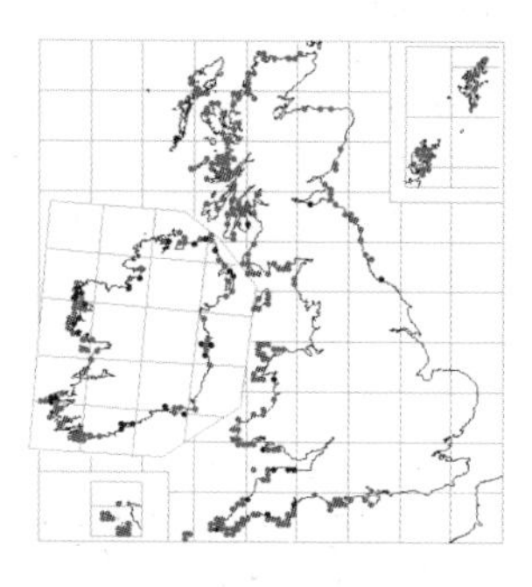

L. pygmaea x 10.

LOBARIA ('lobed' – from the thallus shape). **Thallus** foliose, lower surface tomentose. **Photobionts** *Trebouxia* or *Myrmecia,* or cyanobacteria *Nostoc* and *Scytonema.* **Apothecia** lecanorine. Ascus 8-spored, *Peltigera*-type. **Spores** colourless or brown, septate. **Pycnidia** wart-like with a dark ostiole. These large species flourish in moist, unpolluted regions and are therefore commonest on the western side of Britain. Due to air pollution and the destruction of ancient woodland they have disappeared from many parts of the country where they were once common. They appear to have a very slow ability for recolonization and even where conditions again become suitable, it will be many years before they become reestablished in these areas. They differ from *Sticta* species in the absence of cyphellae on the under-surface.

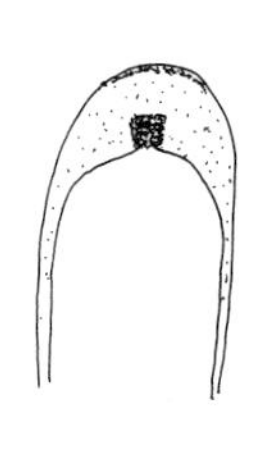

K/I reation to the ascus tip.

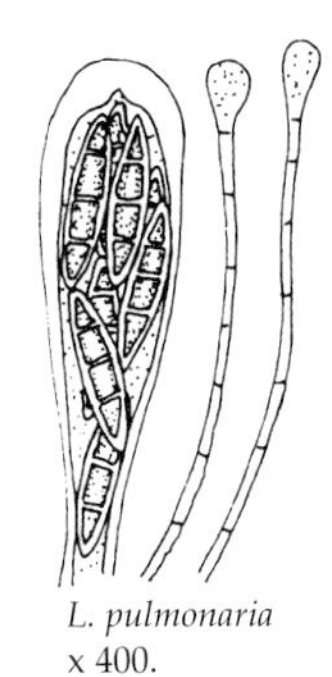

L. pulmonaria x 400.

1.	Thallus sorediate, isidiate or with black coralloid outgrowths	3
–	Thallus lacking soralia, isidia or black outgrowths	2
2.	Thallus silver-grey to pale buff, green-grey when wet, sometimes wrinkled	**1. L. amplissima**
–	Thallus green to grey-brown, bright green when wet, lobes more or less smooth	**4. L. virens**
3.	Thallus silver-grey with black coralloid outgrowths	**1. L. amplissima**
–	Thallus blue-grey, khaki, or green, sorediate or isidiate	4
4.	Lobes ridged, bright green or khaki. Isidia or soralia on ridges	**2. L. pulmonaria**
–	Lobes smooth, blue-grey to yellow-grey. Dark blue-grey, globose soralia or isidia towards the lobe tips	**3. L. scrobiculata**

1. Lobaria amplissima Thallus white to brownish when dry, pale green-grey when wet. Lobes adpressed, large, smooth towards the rounded, notched and wavy tips, wrinkled in the centre of the thallus. Lower surface pale, with a brown tomentum, paler towards the margins. Large, mature specimens (up to 1 m wide) sometimes have brown-black, coralloid outgrowths (cephalodia) up to 2 cm wide containing a blue-green photobiont. These probably assist the plant with fixing atmospheric nitrogen and are an example of how the form of the lichen is modified with a change of photobiont. Sometimes these outgrowths break off and continue an independent existence. They have been called *Dendriscocaulon umhausense. L. amplissima* is usually sterile. Apothecia red-brown. Spores 1- to 3-septate, 40–60 x 6–7 µm. Pycnidia are found in wart-like protrusions (up to 1 mm across) on the surface of the thallus. Conidia 5–1 µm.
Medulla: K+ yellow or K–, KC+ pinkish red or KC–.
Habitat: As *L. pulmonaria* on old trees and rarely rocks, but much rarer; only frequent in north-west Scotland, although it is still just present in the rest of west Britain.

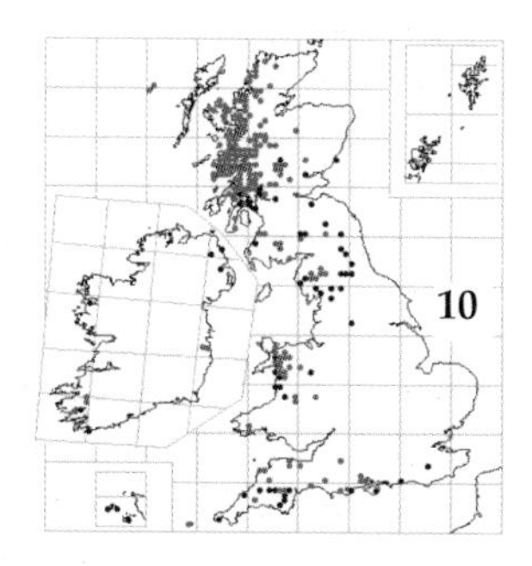

L. amplissima x 3.

2. L. pulmonaria Thallus khaki to green-grey when dry, bright clear green when wet. Upper surface shiny, wrinkled and pustulate. Lower surface light tan with a darker tomentum which is absent on the raised parts of the thallus. Lobes up to about 25 cm long, the ends are often incised. Soralia, which may become isidiate, form along the ridges on the upper surface. Internal cephalodia with *Nostoc* are frequently present. Apothecia fairly rare, red-brown, with a thin margin. Spores 1- to 3-septate, 18–30 x 5–9 µm.
This species used to be common and was collected in large quantities as 'lungwort' and due to its lung-like appearance was sold as a cure for lung diseases. It has even been used, as an alternative to hops, for brewing ale.
Medulla: K+ yellowish orange, P+ orange.
Habitat: Frequent in the West on deciduous trees and is an 'old forest' indicator species. Sometimes on mossy rocks and occasionally on heather stems. It is found throughout Britain, but is now rare in the East.

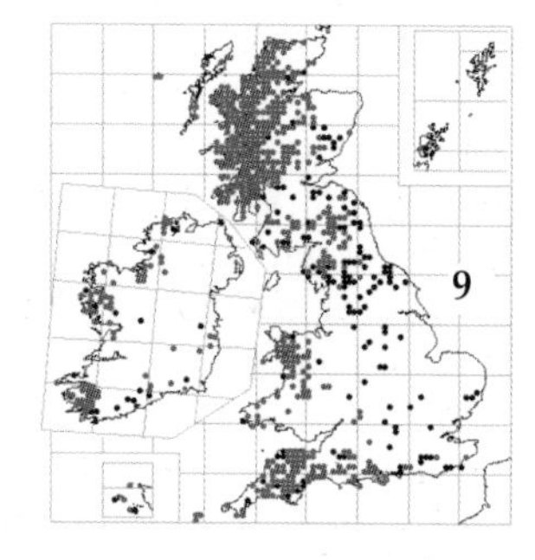

L. pulmonaria x 1.

3. L. scrobiculata Thallus yellowish green when dry, blue-grey to almost black when wet. Lobes up to 10 cm long, weakly ridged, attached only towards the centre. Under-surface tomentose, brown-black in the centre and pale tan at the margin, with small, white, naked areas which look like cyphellae and could cause confusion with *Sticta* species. It is the only British species of *Lobaria* with a cyanobacterium as the main photobiont. Coarse, blue-grey soralia or isidia form dark, almost globose areas mainly on the ridges near, or on, the lobe margins. Apothecia very rare, with a red-brown disc. Spores colourless, becoming brown, 1- to 3-septate, 50–80 x 6–7 µm.
Medulla: K+ yellow, P+ orange.
Habitat: As *L. pulmonaria* on 'old forest' trees, rarely on *Calluna*. Much rarer and decreasing, except in north-west Scotland.

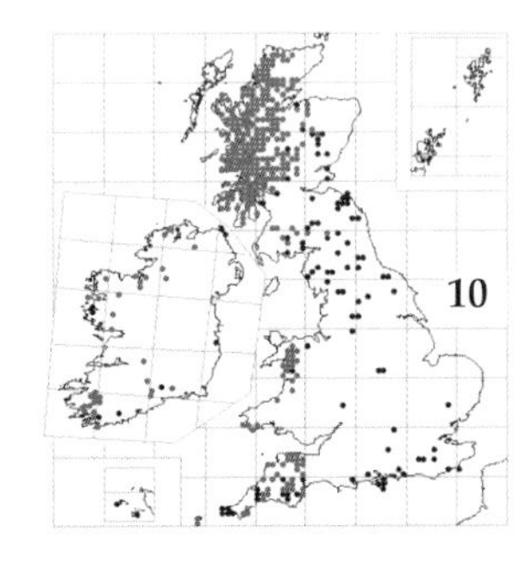

L. scrobiculata x 2.

4. L. virens (L. laetevirens) Thallus green-grey to grey-brown when dry with a smooth, almost oily, appearance, green when wet. Under-surface almost white with a fine, brown tomentum. Lobes short, narrow and unridged (looking like a *Parmelia*), overlapping and more adpressed than in the previous species, the inner lobes incised and contorted, the marginal lobes rounded and smooth. No soralia or isidia, rarely with few to numerous marginal folioles. Usually with abundant apothecia which, when young, appear as a volcano-like swelling which opens out to expose a brown disc with a warted margin. Spores colourless, becoming brown when mature. Spores persistently 1-septate, 25–45 x 8–11 µm.
Spot reactions negative but sometimes K+ faint yellow and KC+ faint pink.
Habitat: As *L. pulmonaria*, but almost always in shade. This is the most oceanic of the British *Lobaria* species. It occurs on more acidic substrata, at pH 5 or slightly lower, than other species in the genus.

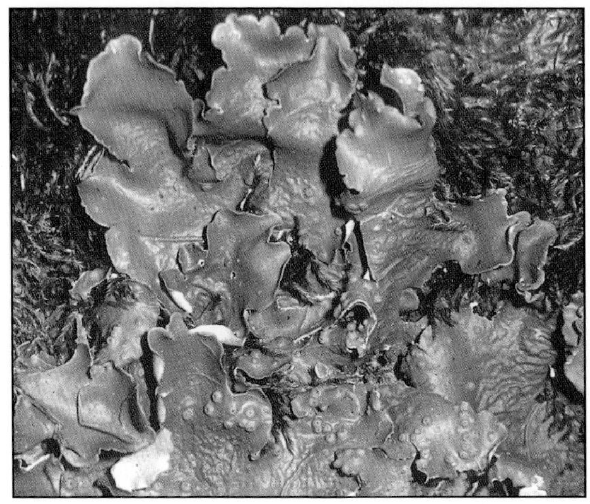

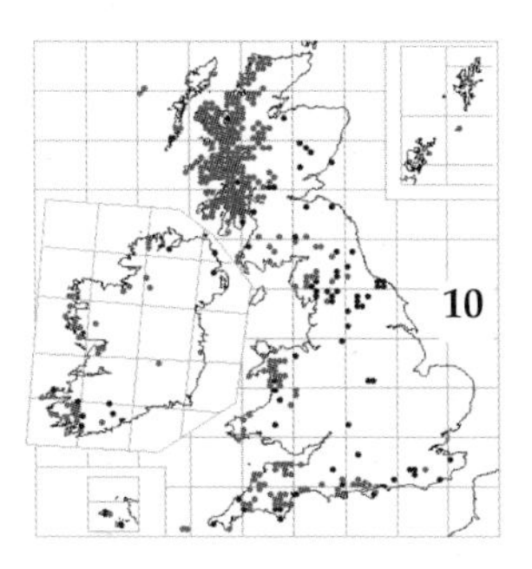

L. virens x 3.

LOXOSPORA ('crooked spore' – from its shape). **Thallus** crustose. **Photobiont** trebouxioid. **Apothecia** lecanorine. **Ascus** 8-spored, K/I+ blue apical dome. **Spores** colourless, septate, spirally coiled in the ascus. **Pycnidia** immersed or in thalline warts.

Loxospora elatina (Haematomma elatinum) Thallus light to dark grey, thin, or warted with pale yellow to blue-yellow, covex soralia which may become confluent. Apothecia very rare, up to 1.5 mm diam with a blood red disc. Epithecium red-brown with numerous crystals that dissolve K+ yellow. Spores 35–50 x 4–5 µm, 3–5 septate.
Thallus and soralia: K+ instantly yellow, C–, P+ orange. Apothecia: K–.
Habitat: Widespread in Scotland on shaded, mainly rough-barked trees, less common in the East. May be separated from some superficially similar *Pertusaria* species and *Lecanora jamesii* by the P+ yellow reaction and the colour of the soralia, from *Ochrolechia androgyna* which usually has a thinner thallus and is C+ scarlet.

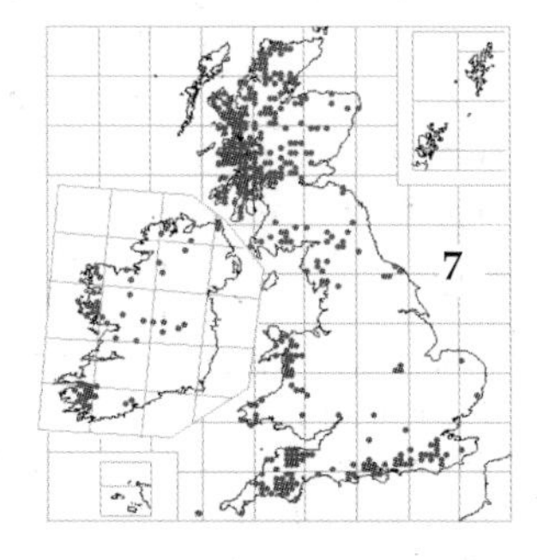

L. elatina x 6.

MASSALONGIA (after the Italian lichenologist A.B. Massalongo, 1824–1860). **Thallus** foliose to squamulose. **Photobiont** *Nostoc*. **Apothecia** sessile to stalked. **Ascus** 8-spored, *Peltigera*-type. **Spores** colourless, septate. **Pycnidia** common, brown but lower part paler. **Conidia** often slightly constricted in the centre. **Chemical reactions** negative. There is only one British species.

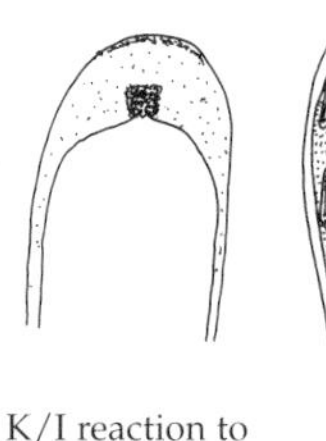
K/I reaction to the ascus tip.

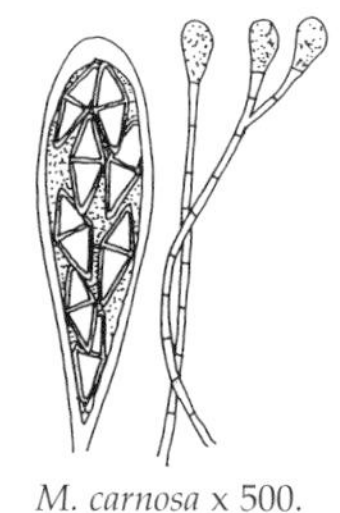
M. carnosa x 500.

Massalongia carnosa Thallus forming small rosettes (up to about 3 cm wide) of narrow (0.5–1.5 mm), overlapping lobes. Dark reddish brown or greyish when dry, greener when wet. It looks rather like a brown *Parmeliopsis ambigua* but with warted to granular isidia instead of soralia. On the pale lower surface there are small rhizines. Apothecia are uncommon, stalked, with chestnut discs and a paler margin. Spores 1-septate, 11–13 x 4–7 µm.
Habitat: Not uncommon in the West on damp, mossy acidic boulders, usually near water.

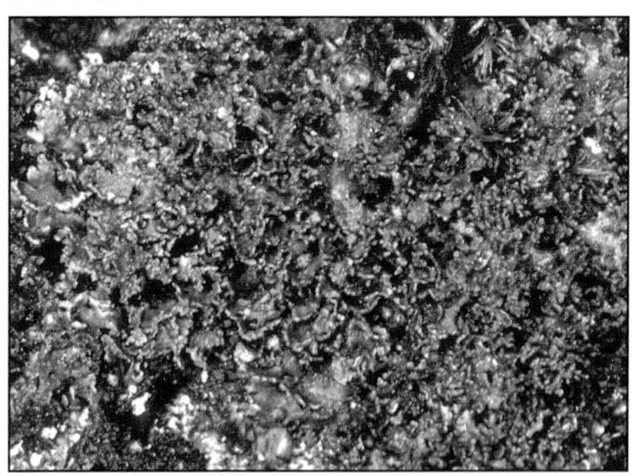
M. carnosa x 6.

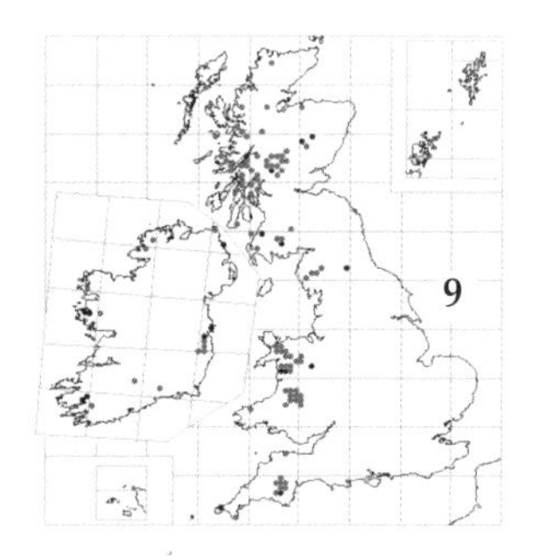

MEGALARIA ('very large' – from the size of the spores). **Thallus** crustose and lacking a cortex. **Photobiont** *Trentephohlia*. **Apothecia** lecideine, sessile. **Ascus** 8-spored, *Lecanora*-type. **Spores** colourless, 1-septate, with a thick wall. **Chemical reactions** negative. There is only a single British species.

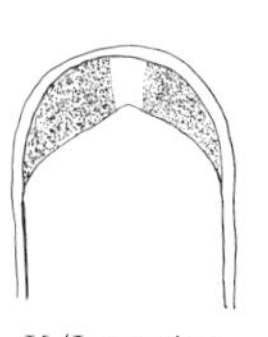
K/I reaction to the ascus tip.

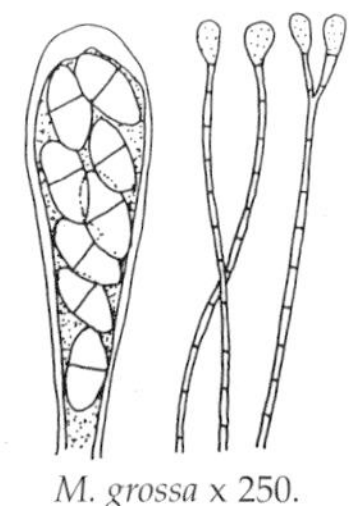
M. grossa x 250.

Megalaria grossa (Catinaria grossa) Thallus greenish grey to almost white, more or less smooth, usually with a black prothallus. Apothecia large (up to 2 mm diam), often in small groups. Disc matt but with a thick shiny proper margin which becomes excluded as the apothecium becomes convex. Hypothecium dark bluish green, K+ green. The 1-septate spores are slightly constricted at the septum, 20–30 x 8–15 µm. It resembles a *Lecanactis premnea* but

that species has 5-septate spores, apothecia with smooth, not glossy, margins and is usually found on more acid-barked trees such as oak. *Armandinea punctata* has smaller fruits (less than 1 mm) and brown, 1-septate spores.
Habitat: Uncommon, in old woods on nutrient-enriched, basic-barked trees such as ash or lime. Very rarely on basic rocks.

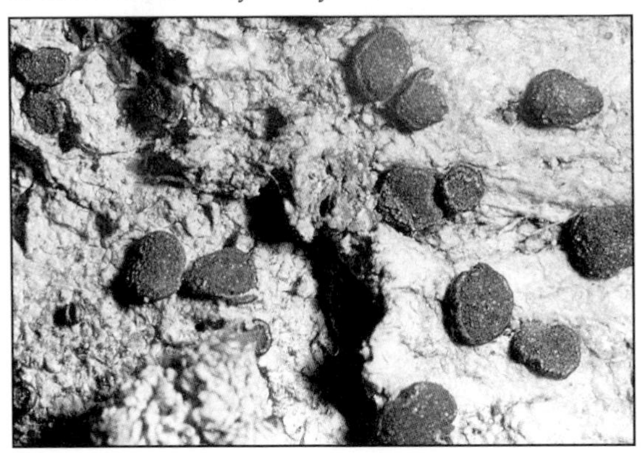

M. grossa x 6.

MEGASPORA ('very large spores'). **Thallus** crustose. **Photobiont** chlorococcoid. **Apothecia** lecanorine, in thalline warts. **Ascus** 8-spored, K/I+ pale blue apical dome. **Spores** simple, colourless with thickened walls. **Pycnidia** not known. **Chemical reactions** negative.

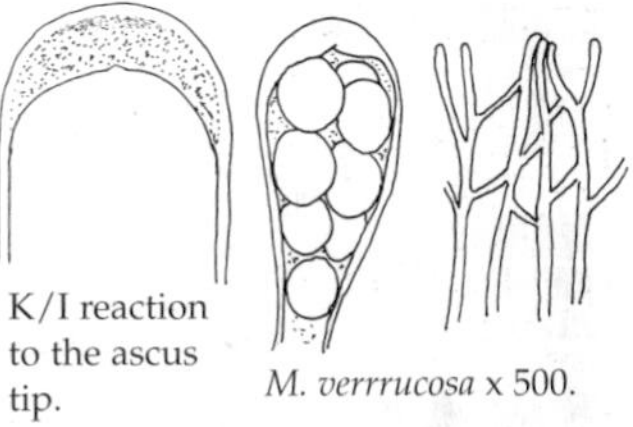

M. verrucosa x 500.

Megaspora verrucosa Thallus uneven, granular or scurfy, often dispersed, white, usually heavily pruinose. Apothecia up to 1.5 mm diam, sunk in thalline warts, expanding when mature to show the small (0.2–0.5 mm diam) black disc, encircled by a narrow, dark ring adjacent to the thallus. Spores 35–50 x 25–40 µm.
Habitat: Rare but may be locally common, on basic soils in limestone areas and on shell-rich dunes, mainly growing over mosses and plant debris.

M. verrucosa x 6.

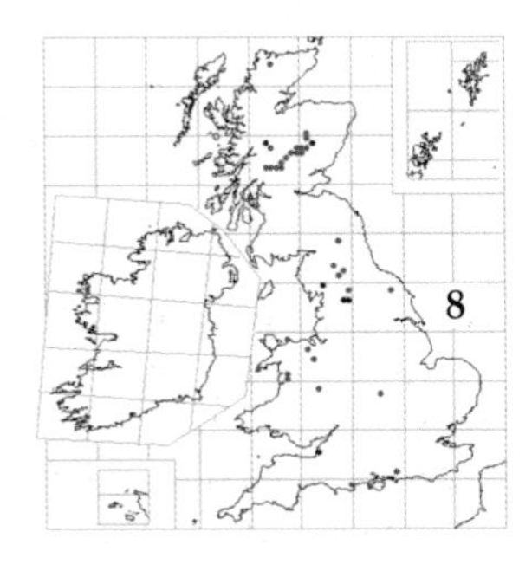

MENEGAZZIA (after Luigi Menegazzi, a friend of Massalongo). **Thallus** foliose, hollow. **Photobiont** chlorococcoid. **Apothecia** lecanorine, stalked. **Ascus** 2-spored. **Spores** colourless, simple, thick-walled. **Pycnidia** immersed with a pigmented tip. Similar to the genus *Hypogymnia*, it has the same inflated foliose thallus but differs in the upper surface being perforated with small holes and soralia which are laminal, not terminal. There is only one British species.

M. terebrata x 6.

Menegazzia terebrata Thallus grey, smooth, adpressed and hollow, up to 7 cm diam. Lobes to 1.5 mm wide. Upper surface perforated by small holes and usually edged with globose soralia which may be on short stalks . The lower surface is black, wrinkled and without rhizines. Apothecia are very rare with chestnut-coloured discs. Spores 50–70 x 30–36 µm.
Cortex: K+ yellow. Medulla: K+ yellow, P+ yellowish orange.
Habitat. Rare on damp shaded trees, heather stems and rocks in the West. It is an 'old forest' indicator species but it may occasionally occur on the coast.

M. terebrata x 4.

MICAREA ('minute granules' – from the thallus structure of many species). **Thallus** crustose. **Photobiont** green and in all the species below except *M. bauschiana* and *M. sylvicola*, 'micareoid'. This alga is globose, small (4–7 µm) and has thin walls. It reproduces by developing a thin dividing wall inside the original cell forming clusters (goniocysts). **Apothecia** lecideine, usually convex and immarginate. **Ascus** 8-spored, mainly K/I+ blue outer layer and apical dome.

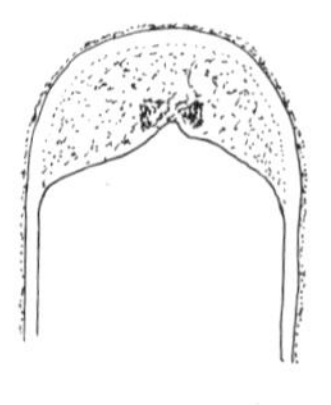

K/I reaction to the ascus tip.

M. prasina x 400.

Paraphyses (strictly paraphysoids) branched and anastomosing (separating this genus from *Catillaria*). **Spores** colourless, simple to septate. **Conidia** colourless, three types: ***macroconidia*** thread-like or twisted, mainly septate, rarely ellipsoid; ***mesoconidia*** bacilliform to ellipsoid, simple; ***microconidia*** bacilliform, simple. **Chemical reactions** mainly negative or C+ red. The colour of the hypothecium is often an important aid to identification.

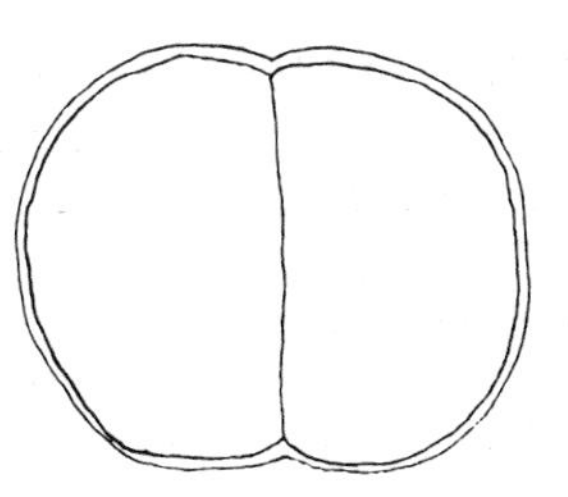

'Micareoid' alga dividing.

1.	Thallus C–	2
–	Thallus C+ yellow, orange or red	9
2.	Spores simple	3
–	Spores septate	4
3.	Hypothecium brownish green to green-black	**3. M. bauschiana/3a. M. sylvicola**
–	Hypothecium dark brown	**6. M. erratica**
4.	Spores 1-septate	5
–	Spores more than 1-septate	7
5.	Thallus smooth or scurfy, often looks waxy	**1. M. adnata**
	Thallus granular or areolate	6
6.	Thallus of discrete granules up to 60 µm diam	**10. M. prasina**
–	Thallus areolate, areoles 60–200 µm wide	**5. M. denigrata**
7.	Thallus P+ red	**8. M. lignaria**
–	Thallus P–	8
8.	Hypothecium purple-brown	**9. M. melaena**
–	Hypothecium colourless to pale yellow	**10. M. prasina**
9.	C+ yellow to orange	**8. M. lignaria** var. **endoleuca**
–	C+ red	10
10.	Hypothecium purple-brown. P–	**9. M. melaena**
–	Hypothecium colourless to yellow–brown. P– or + red	11
11.	P+ red. Hypothecium yellow to brown	**7. M. leprosula**
–	P–. Hypothecium colourless	12
12.	Spores mainly 7-septate. Apothecia pale blue-grey	**4. M. cinerea**
–	Spores mainly 3-septate. Apothecia white to pale cream	**2. M. alabastrites**

1. Micarea adnata Thallus smooth and often appearing waxy, grey-green to green. Apothecia pale brown, becoming convex, often in clusters, small, 0.2–0.6 mm diam. Hymenium and hypothecium colourless. Spores becoming 1-septate, 9–16 x 3–5 µm.

Often without apothecia but with white, convex, sporodochia (up to 0.25 mm diam) containing macroconidia, 6–10 x 2–3 µm. Immersed mesoconidia may also be present, 4–6 x 1–2 µm.
Habitat: Infrequent, on bark, wood and tree stumps, rarely peat.

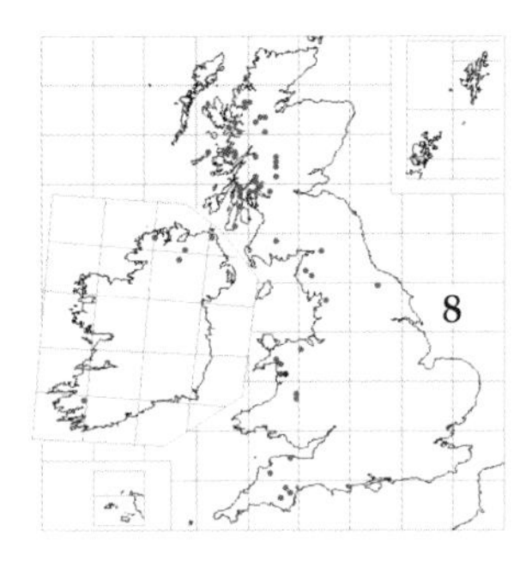

M. adnata x 6.

2. M. alabastrites Thallus scurfy to areolate, grey-green. Apothecia colourless to pale cream, 0.2–0.7 mm diam. hymenium greenish, 40–55 µm tall. Hypothecium colourless. Spores mainly 3-septate, 18–26 x 4–5 µm.
Habitat: Uncommon, found in damp woodlands on bark or wood or over mosses, very rarely on rock.

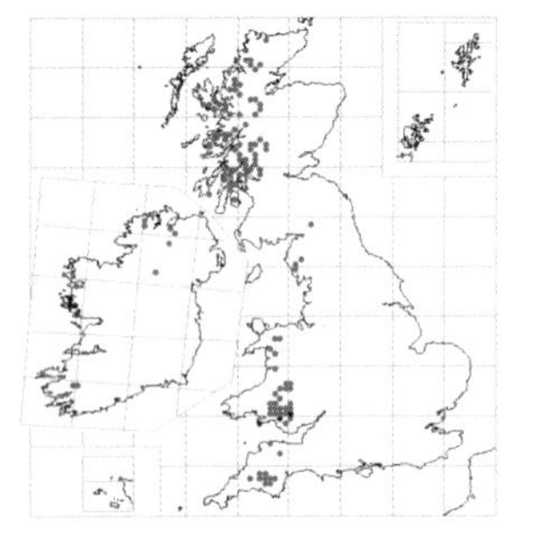

M. alabastrites x 6.

3. M. bauschiana Thallus scurfy or cracked, greenish grey, sometimes with yellow to brown patches when on iron-rich rocks. The thallus is often covered in a layer of green algae. Apothecia common, very convex, pale grey to almost black, sometimes piebald and often lumpy like a small blackberry, about 0.3 mm diam. Hypothecium 80–150 µm, colourless or pale brownish green. Spores simple, 6–10 x 3–4 µm.
Habitat: Frequent in dry underhangs on rocks (often metal-rich), soil and roots, often on stones embedded in dry sandy slopes.

3a. M. sylvicola is similar but has a bluish grey, areolate thallus and a dark blue to green-black hypothecium. It is confined to upland areas and may be found on rock and pebbles in damper situations, rarely on old sawn wood.

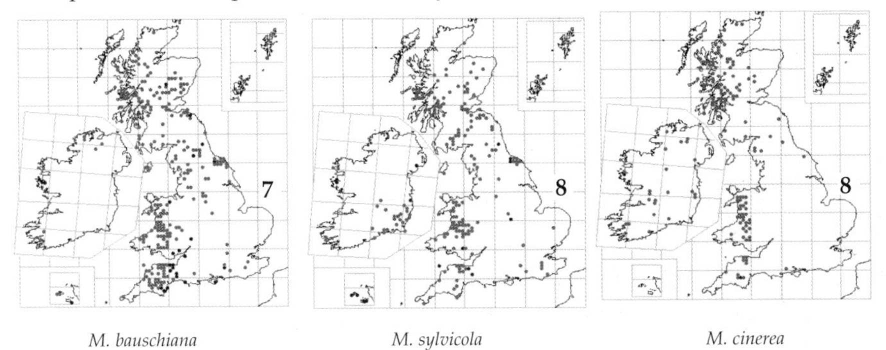

M. bauschiana *M. sylvicola* *M. cinerea*

4. M. cinerea Thallus of separate or continuous, very pale green to a darker glaucous-grey, globose, smooth-surfaced, areoles. Apothecia usually numerous, from innate to shortly stalked, cream (in shade) to almost black, plane to convex (in *M. lignaria* they become globose). Disc 0.3–0.7 mm diam with a thin, smooth margin. Hypothecium colourless, 40–70 µm thick. Spores 5- to 7-septate, 20–35 x 4–6 µm.
Thallus: C+ red. Apothecia: C+ red (in section).
Habitat: Infrequent, mainly on trees and mosses, rarely on rocks, wood or fences. In high rainfall regions in the West.

5. M. denigrata Thallus immersed, or of convex areoles, 60–200 µm diam, pale green to grey, often just a black crust, especially in polluted areas. Apothecia numerous, small (0.15–0.5 mm diam), grey to black, brown in shade. The disc soon convex excluding an indistinct margin. Hypothecium colourless to pale straw, 60–110 µm tall. Spores 1-septate, often slightly curved, 10–15 x 2–3 µm.
Apothecia: C+ orange-red (in section), often parasitized when they may be C–.
Habitat: Frequent on decorticated trees and stumps in light shade, especially common on weathered fences and benches, roof shingles, sheds, etc. When on man-made wooden substrates, the number of apothecia is often reduced. It can then be recognized by the numerous pycnidia (up to 0.15 mm diam) with white tips formed by the extruded conidia. Macroconidia 12–24 x 1 µm, 3-septate, curved.

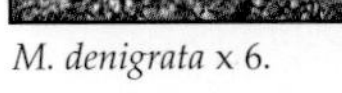
M. denigrata x 6.

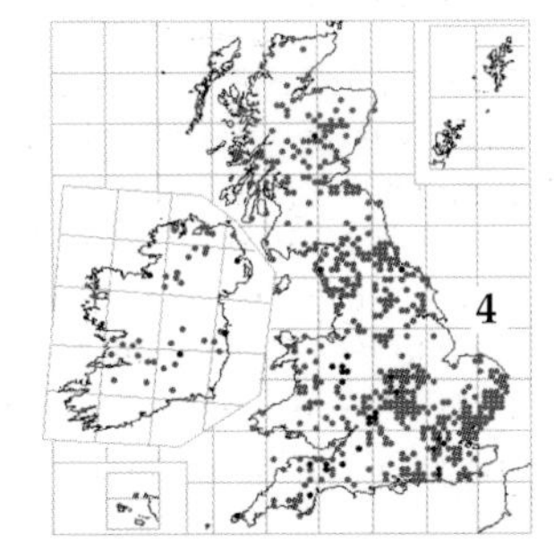

6. M. erratica (Lecidea erratica) Thallus pale grey, thin, often immersed when on wood, may be reduced to small scattered patches with apothecia and/or be studded with numerous dark pycnidia. Surrounded by a dark grey, fimbriate prothallus when on rock. Apothecia small (less than 0.4 mm diam), dark brown to black, often leaving a dark ring when the apothecia fall out. Epithecium dark greenish blue. Hypothecium dark brown. Spores 7–10 x 3–4 µm. Often only very small (80–150 µm diam) pycnidia are present.
Habitat: Common on siliceous pebbles on fixed shingle beaches in the East and South West, rarely on old fences and wood. Other species commonly found on pebbles are *Armandinea punctata*, *B. aethalea* (brown, 1-septate spores), *Catillaria chalybeia* (colourless, 1-septate spores), *Rhizocarpon reductum* (almost colourless, muriform spores) and, on more calcareous substrates, *Verrucaria nigrescens.*

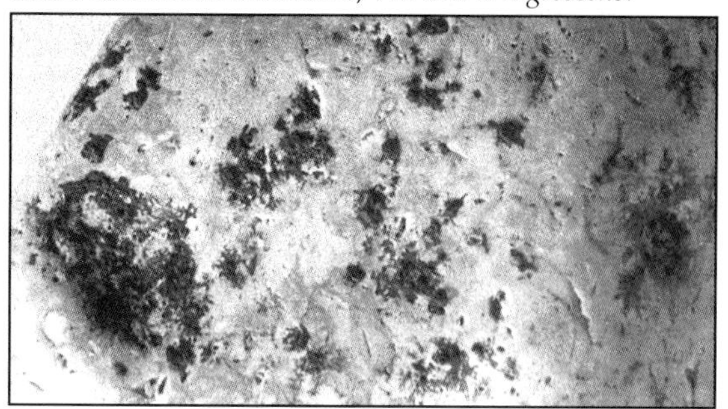

M. erratica x 8.

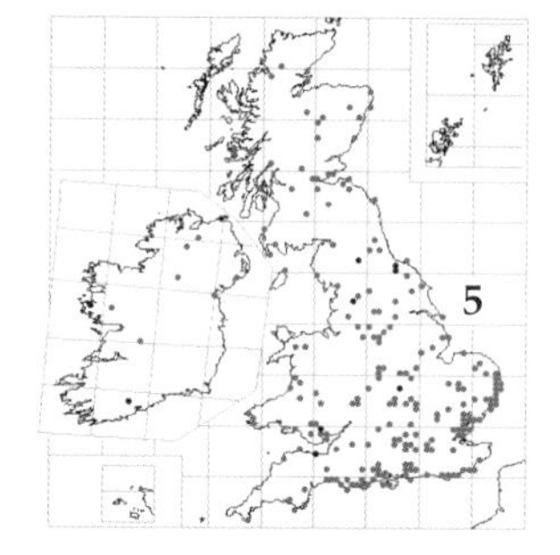

7. M. leprosula Thallus of convex areoles up to about 0.4 mm wide, usually glaucous grey to brown-grey, lighter in colour in the depressions in the thallus, sometimes forming a thick crust which partially breaks down into a yellowish green, sorediate crust. Apothecia are infrequent, about 0.4 mm diam, dark grey to black, convex. Hypothecium usually 35–45 µm tall, pale yellow to brown. Spores 3-septate with blunt ends, 15–25 x 4–6 µm.
Thallus: C+ red, P+ red. Apothecia: C+ red (in section).
Habitat: Not uncommon in the North and West on dead mosses in exposed, often boggy or moorland sites, rarely on wood.

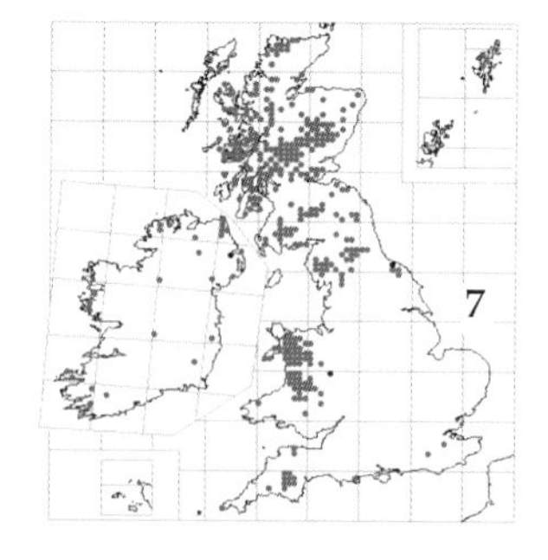

8. M. lignaria Thallus of convex granules about 0.25 mm diam, pale grey, rarely brown-grey. Apothecia usually abundant, sessile or sometimes on short stalks, very globose, black, about 0.5 mm diam. Hypothecium 100–250 µm tall, upper part bluish to olive, lower part pale brown to colourless. Spores 3- to 7-septate, sometimes slightly curved, 16–36 x 4–6 µm. **M.** var. **endoleuca** is similar but is rarer, more oceanic and is C+ deep yellow, P–.
P+ red.
Habitat: Common on many substrates such as mosses, peat, shaded acid rocks, walls, tombstones, etc. Especially common in metal-rich, mine spoil heaps.

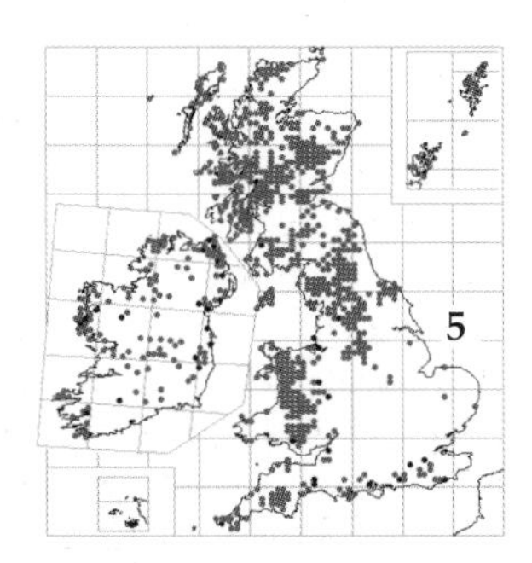

M. lignaria x 8.

9. M. melaena Thallus of granules about 0.1 mm diam, pale green to dark green, yellowish white in dry, shaded sites. Often forms a black crust on tree stumps and peat. Apothecia abundant, convex, black, up to 0.5 mm diam. Hypothecium 80–160 µm tall, dark purple-brown (more purple in K) becoming more green in the centre. Spores usually 3-septate (rarely to 5-septate) with blunt ends, 12–21 x 4–5 µm.
C+ red, more rarely C–.
Habitat: Common, especially in upland, moorland regions in the North and West. Found in well-lit and shaded sites, on tree stumps, decorticated trees, peat, fences and trees. It is resistant to SO_2 pollution.

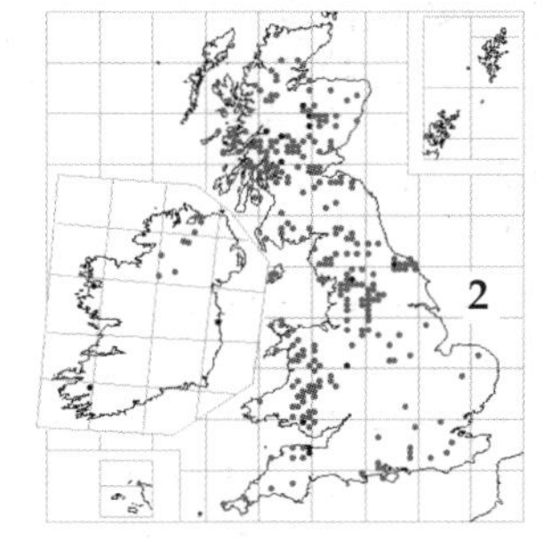

10. M. prasina Thallus very variable, of small, discrete globose granules (goniocysts) up to about 60 µm diam, straw-coloured, or pale green to dirty olive -green, becoming swollen and gelatinous when wet. Apothecia usually abundant, to 0.5 mm diam, pale pink-buff, but usually grey to almost black, hypothecium 40–170 µm thick, colourless to pale yellow. Spores usually 1- (3-) septate with one lower cell slightly longer and narrower, 8–15 x 2.5–5 µm. It is the only species of *Micarea* (except for two very rare species) which consists of very small, discrete globose granules.
Spot reactions: usually negative, very rarely C+ orange. Greenish pigment found on the thallus surface K+ violet.
Habitat: The commonest species and due to its very variable nature it will be found that many 'unknown' specimens will turn out to be this species. On shaded trees, wood, soil, fallen debris, especially in rock crevices in coastal regions. It occurs even towards the centre of towns in sheltered cracks on basic substrates.

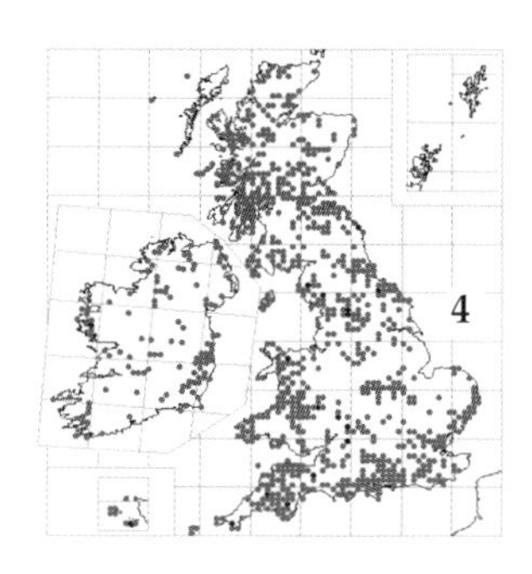

M. prasina x 6.

MIRIQUIDICA (after the Latin name of the area where the type specimen was found). **Thallus** crustose. **Photobiont** chlorococcoid. **Apothecia** lecideine. **Ascus** 8-spored, K/I+ very weak blue, *Lecanora*-type. **Spores** simple, colourless, rarely 1-septate when old. **Pycnidia** immersed. **Conidia** simple, colourless, thread-like. On a t.l.c. plate miriaquidic acid appears as a kingfisher-blue spot.

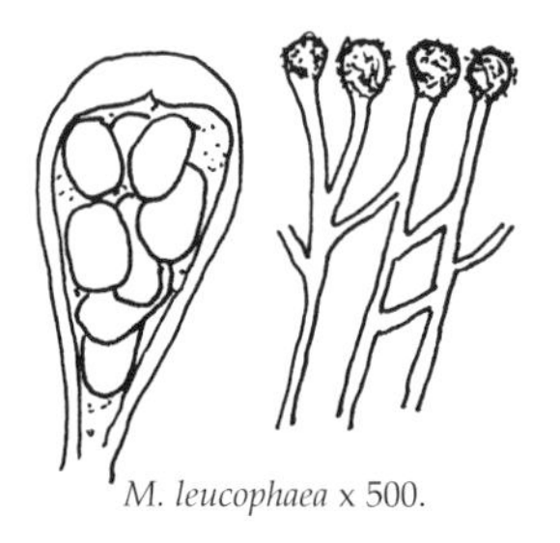

M. leucophaea x 500.

Miriquidica leucophaea Thallus areolate, flat to warted, often glossy, pale grey to pale brown-grey. Apothecia usually abundant, up to about 1 mm diam, becoming sessile and convex, disc very dark brown to black, paler when wet, with a thin, slightly darker margin, even when wet. Spores 8–15 x 4–7 µm.
Apothecia: C± faint pink (margin in section).
Habitat: Mainly upland on well-lit acid rocks especially if metal-rich. Rarely on sawn wood.

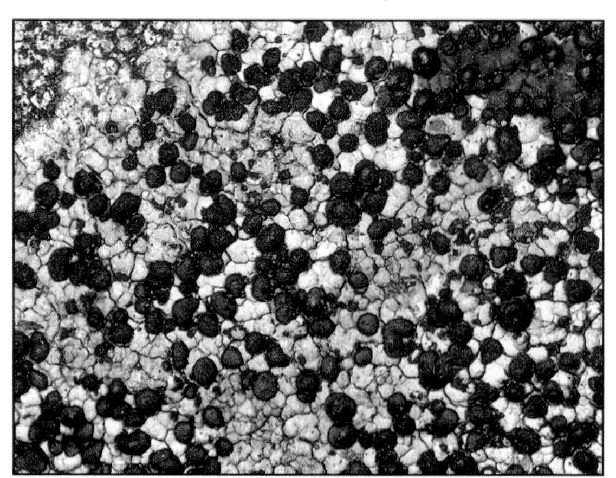

M. leucophaea x 6.

MOELLEROPSIS (after the Swedish bryologist Hjalmar Möller, 1866–1941 plus 'opsis' as a word-filler). **Thallus** crustose. **Photobiont** *Nostoc*. **Apothecia** lecanorine. **Ascus** 8-spored, K/I+ blue apical dome. **Hymenium** K/I+ blue. **Spores** colourless, simple. **Chemical reactions** negative.

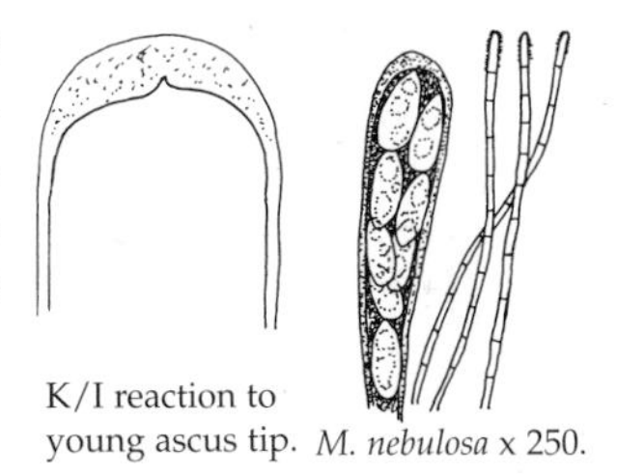
K/I reaction to young ascus tip. *M. nebulosa* x 250.

Moelleropsis nebulosa Thallus a bluish grey, coarsely granular crust formed by clusters of *Nostoc* mixed with the fungal hyphae. Usually fertile, apothecia about 1 mm diam, chestnut-brown with a granular thalline margin. Spores 15–20 x 6–10 µm, containing oil drops. *Pannaria pezizoide*s consists of pale brownish grey squamules, is found on damp mosses, has larger spores and a warted epispore. Habitat: Infrequent, mainly in coastal regions in the West. On light, well-drained, often recently disturbed soil, especially on wall tops.

M. nebulosa x 5.

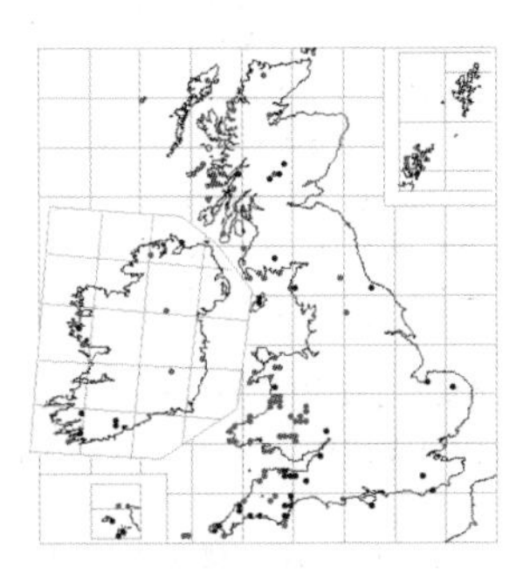

MYCOBLASTUS ('spreading fungal shoot'). **Thallus** crustose, granular, sometimes with red areas in the medulla and hypothecium. **Photobiont** chlorococcoid. **Apothecia** lecideine. **Ascus** 1- to 3-spored, K/I+ blue apical dome with a thickened dark blue cap. **Spores** colourless, simple, very large, thick-walled. Each spore contains many nuclei.

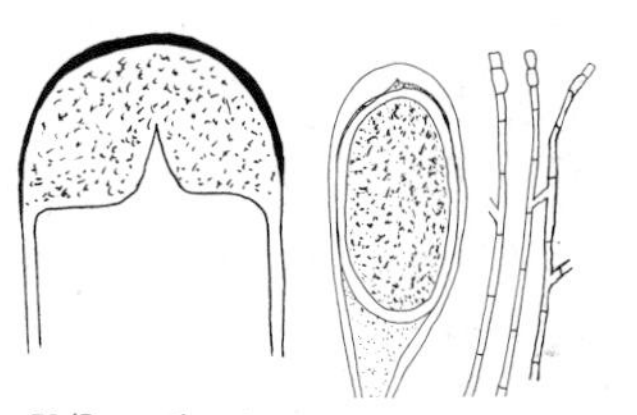
K/I reaction to the ascus tip. *M. sanguinarius* x 200.

1.	Apothecia black with a red hypothecium, not sorediate	**2. M. sanguinarius**
–	Apothecium absent but with yellowish to bluish soredia	2
2.	Soralia K+ yellow, P+ orange-red, UV–	**3. M. fucatus**
–	Soralia spot reations negative, UV+ white	**1. M. caesius**

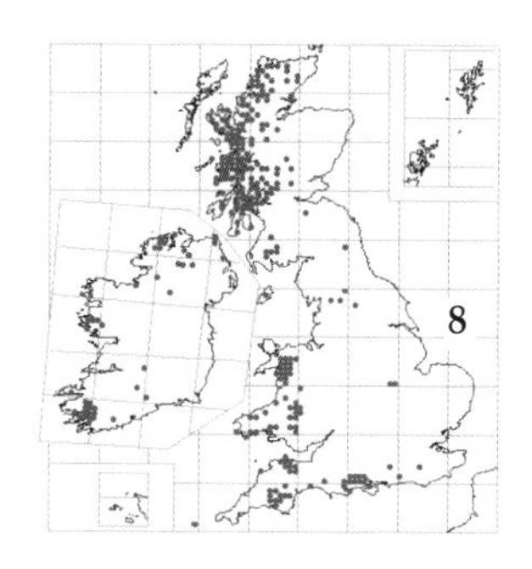

1. Mycoblastus caesius (Haematomma caesium) Thallus thin but sometimes areolate, bluish grey with a dark blue-grey prothallus (on smooth bark the thallus may be reduced to the blue-grey stain of the prothallus). The surface has discrete patches of pale grey soralia that may spread over the surface. The surface of the soralia usually have deep blue flecks (use x 20 lens) giving the soralia a verdigris colour. It has only been found sterile.
Spot reactions: negative, UV+ white.
Habitat: Infrequent, found on both rough and smooth bark, rarely on wood and very rarely on acid rocks.

2. M. sanguinarius Thallus grey, thick, either granular or warted, or thin when growing over mosses. Prothallus grey. Medulla red under apothecia and often, if scraped, showing red through the cortex at the site of apothecial initials. Usually fertile. Apothecia up to 2.5 mm diam. Discs black, becoming strongly convex, sometimes innate. Spores 70–100 x 30–50 µm, usually 1, but up to 3, per ascus. Rarely found with convex soralia (**M. s.** f. **leprosus**).
Cortex: K+ yellow, P+ yellow. Medulla (where red): K+ red, UV–.
Habitat: Common in upland areas on hard siliceous rocks, over mosses or directly on deciduous trees. Most common in Scotland.

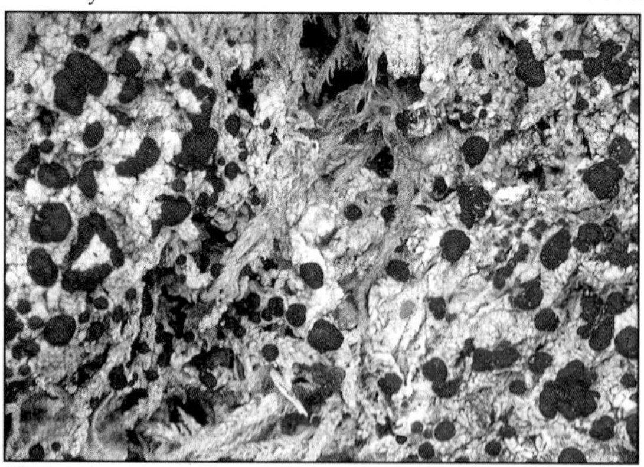

M. sanguinarius x 3.

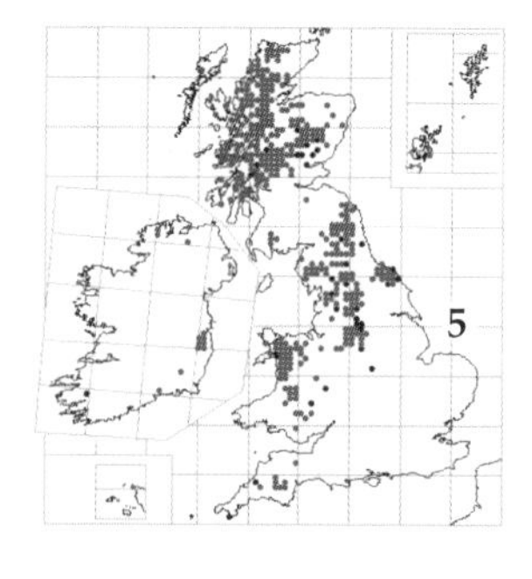

3. M. fucatus (M. sterilis) Thallus thin or areolate, grey with lighter patches and often delimited by a black prothallus. Punctiform soralia may become confluent with bluish surface, giving it the appearance of *Porpidia tuberculosa* growing on bark. It may be separated from *Buellia griseovirens* which is P–. Apothecia very rare, internally violet-purple, K+ vivid blue. Spores usually 2 per ascus.
K+ yellow, P+ red, UV–.
Habitat: Fairly common on smooth bark or smooth patches of rough-barked trees, rarely on wood where it may be fertile.

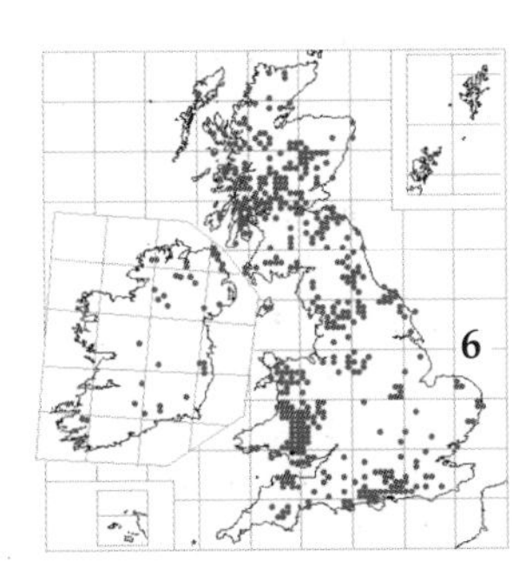

M. fucatus x 6.

MYCOGLAENA ('fungal slime' – from the thallus form?). **Thallus** very thin. **Photobiont** probably not lichenized. **Perithecia** circular to ellipsoid. **Involucrellum** green, N+ red. **Paraphyses** simple and anastomosing. **Ascus** 8-spored, cylindrical, K/I–. **Spores** colourless, septate, becoming slightly muriform. **Chemical reactions** negative.

Mycoglaena myricae Thallus immersed. Perithecia 0.2–0.4 mm diam, often ellipsoid from the growth of the host. Spores 3-septate, middle cell often largeest, 16–20 x 4–7 µm.
Habitat: Common in the North and West, mainly on the stems of bog myrtle

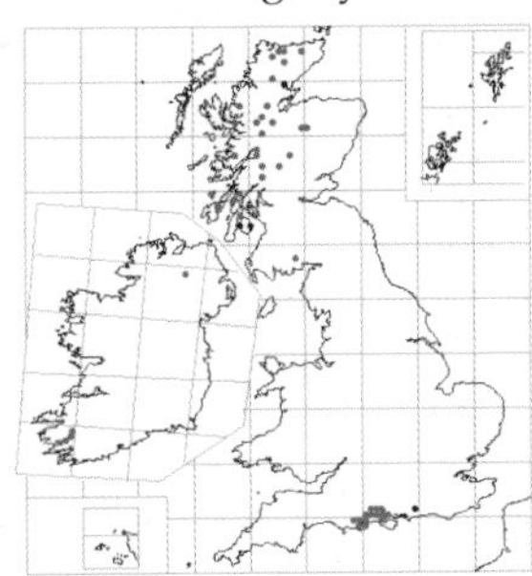

M. myricae x 8.

MYCOPORUM ('fungal opening' – from the way that the perithecia penetrate through the host). **Thallus** very thin, usually immersed. **Photobiont** probably not lichenized. **Perithecia** often irregular in outline and frequently gathered into a stroma. **Ascus** 8-spored, K/I–. **Spores** colourless, septate, becoming slightly muriform, slightly constricted at the septum and somewhat tapered at one end. Pycnidia not known. **Chemical reactions** negative.

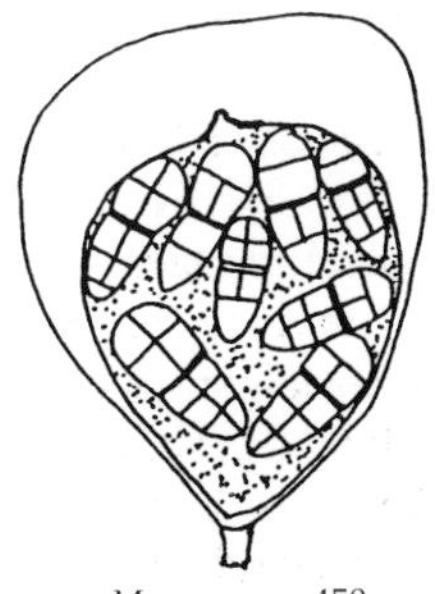

M. quercus x 450.

Mycoporum quercus (Cyrtidula quercus) Thallus as a faint stain on the bark. Perithecia small, about 0.3 mm across but often irregular in shape with up to about 5 gathered together into a stroma. Spores 10–20 x 4–5 μm, up to 4-septate, becoming muriform.
Habitat: Frequent on young branches of oak or, more rarely, hazel.

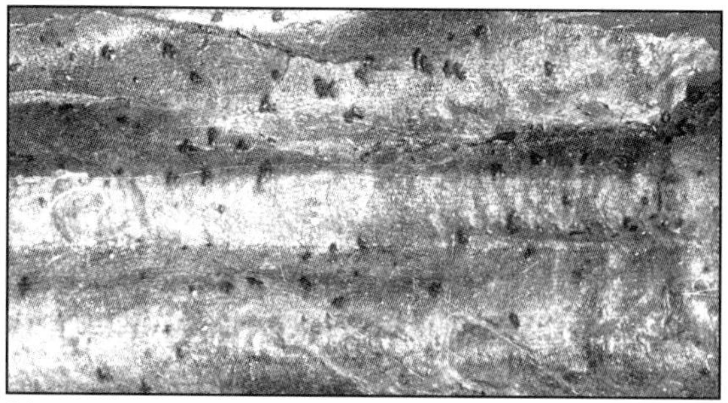

M. quercus x 10.

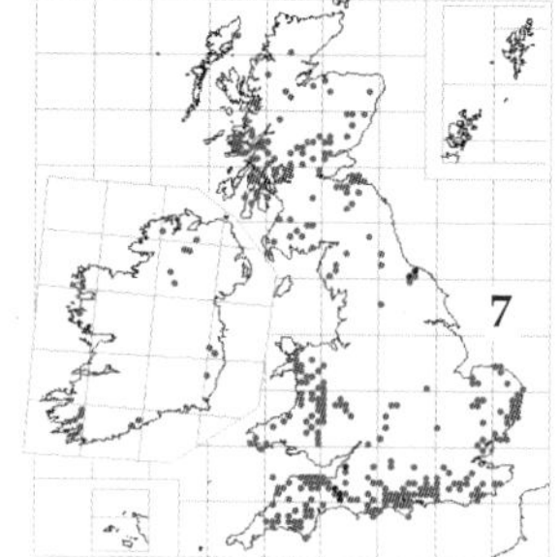

NEPHROMA ('kidney' – from the shape of the apothecia). **Thallus** foliose. **Photobiont** green – *Coccomyxa* or blue-green – *Nostoc* (also in cephalodia). **Apothecia** lecanorine and borne on the under-surface of the lobe ends. This, together with the bare lower surface, separates this genus from related *Peltigera* and *Solorina*. **Ascus** 8-spored, similar to *Peltigera*. **Spore**s at first colourless but becoming brownish, 3-septate. **Pycnidia** immersed in warts along the lobe margins, ostiole black. **Conidia** colourless, bacilliform.

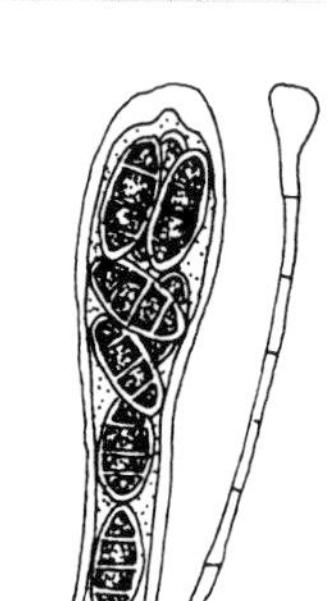

N. laevigatum x 400.

1.	Medulla pale yellow, normally fertile, no soredia	**1. N. laevigatum**
–	Medulla white, normally not fertile, soredia marginal	**2. N. parile**

1. Nephroma laevigatum Thallus large, up to 10 cm diam, brown-grey to red-brown, shining, the lobes up to 1 cm wide, short and sometimes with small lobules where the edge of the lobe has been damaged. Under-surface buff, darker towards the centre, bare and wrinkled. Medulla pale yellow. Photobiont *Nostoc*. It lacks soredia but is usually fertile. Apothecia on the lower surface of the lobe tip. These lobes are often longer than the infertile lobes and recurved to reveal the apothecia. Smaller apothecia have distinct margins which are entire but become crenulate. Sometimes there may be several apothecia on one lobe. Some apothecia may be up to 1 cm or more wide, broader than the lobe on which they grow. Spores 3-septate, 17–20 x 5–7 μm.
Medulla: K+ purple.
Habitat: Locally abundant in the West on mossy trees, also on walls and rocks in damp oceanic situations. An 'old forest' species indicator.

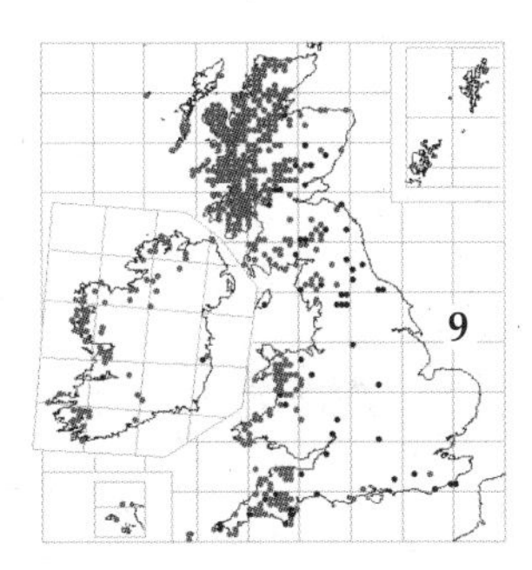

N. laevigatum x 3.

2. N. parile Similar to *N. laevigatum* but with a white medulla and bluish grey to brownish soredia along the margins of the lobes and, less commonly, also on the upper surface. The lower surface is usually smooth but occasionally finely tomentose. Photobiont *Nostoc*. It is only very rarely found fertile but may have vestigial apothecia. Spores 18–20 x 6–7 µm. It may be separated from *Peltigera collina* by the lack of rhizines and veining on the lower surface.
Medulla: K– rarely K+ yellowish.
Habitat: Similar to the previous species but much rarer and often more upland and less oceanic. It is found in ancient woodlands and forms part of the *Lobarion* association.

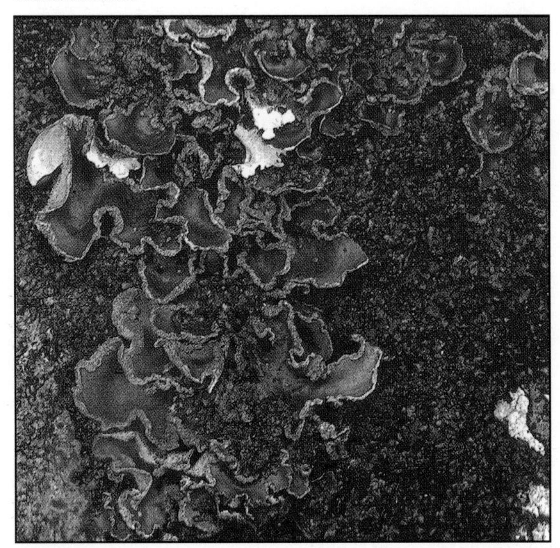

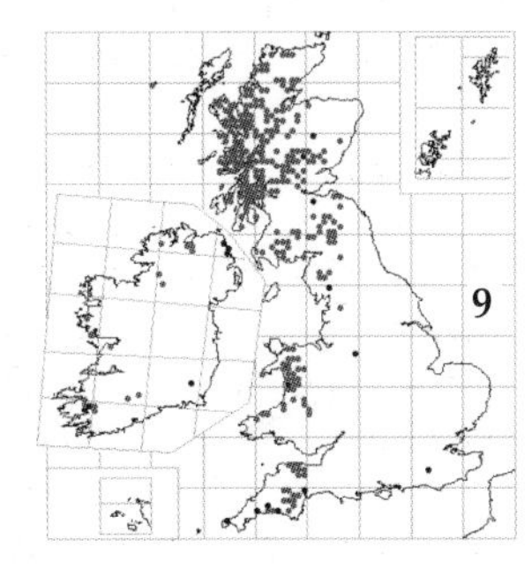

N. parile x 3.

NORMANDINA (after the French naturalist Seb. René Lenormand, 1796–1871). **Thallus** of small squamules that become sorediate. **Photobiont** *Trebouxia.* Fruiting bodies are unknown and it was once incorrectly suggested that the single species in the genus was a lichenized basidiomycete. **Chemical reactions** negative.

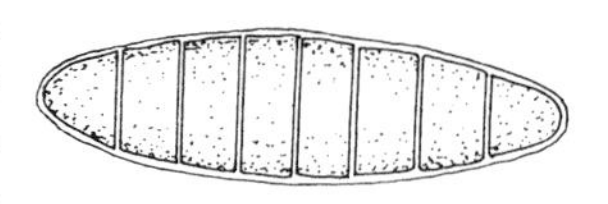

Lauderlindsaya borreri x 1000.

Normandina pulchella Thallus pale glaucous, green-grey or pruinose, rounded with raised margins or oyster shell-shaped squamules. Lower surface white. The squamules are usually less than 1 mm wide but may be up to 3 mm. They become sorediate around the raised margin and the soredia may spread to cover the whole of the squamule. They may form extensive colonies. It has never been found fertile. The perithecia which are sometimes found in the thallus were originally thought to be from the lichen but they are now known to belong to a parasitic fungus. This fungus, *Lauderlindsaya borreri*, appears to be specific to *N. pulchella*.
Habitat: Common on mosses on trees or rocks, especially in light shade. Sometimes found growing on other lichens in very damp situations.

N. pulchella x 8.

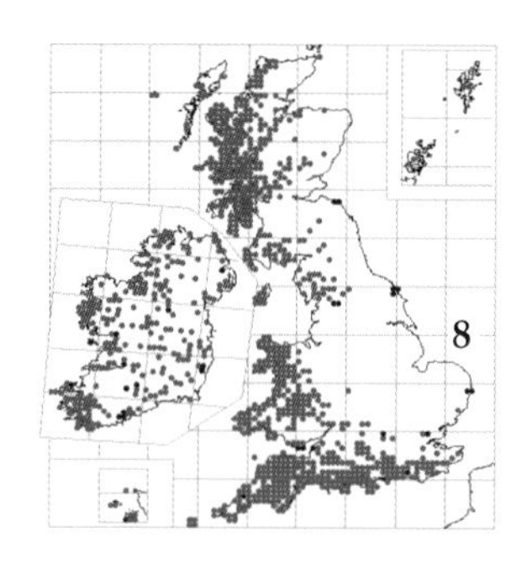

OCHROLECHIA ('sallow-coloured couch or marriage bed' – from the colour of the apothecia in the type species). **Thallus** crustose. **Photobiont** trebouxioid. **Apothecia** lecanorine, with buff to orange-brown discs. **Ascus** 2- to 8-spored, *Pertusaria*-like. **Spores** colourless, simple, very large, two or more per ascus. This genus is very closely related to *Pertusaria* but has more open discs and thinner-walled spores. Up to the end of the last century they were of importance for dyeing and were collected in large quantities for this purpose.

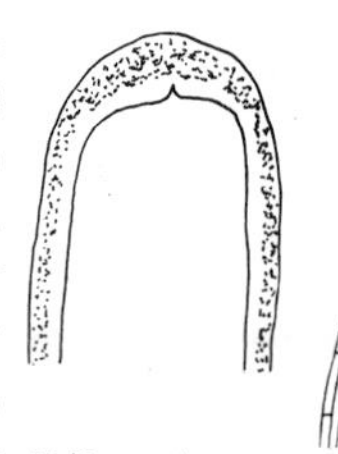

K/I reaction to the ascus tip.

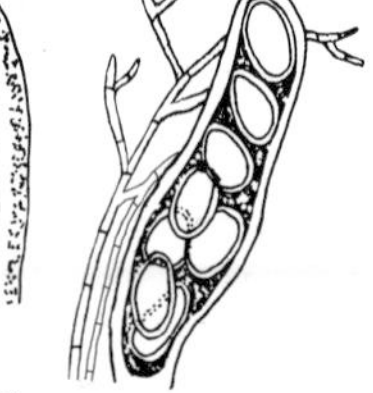

O. parella x 100.

1.	With isidia or soredia or long spikes	2
–	Lacking isidia, soredia or long spikes	8
2.	Isidiate or with long spikes	3
–	Sorediate	5
3.	C+ red. Delicate coralloid isidia or long spikes	4
–	C–. Coarse granular isidia	**7. O. turneri**
4.	Isidia delicate and massed	**5. O. subviridis**
–	Spike-like extensions on thallus	**2. O. frigida**
5.	Soralia yellow-green or yellowish grey	6
–	Soralia pale grey to greenish grey	7
6.	Thallus pale grey or green-grey, warted crust, C+ red	**1. O. androgyna**
–	Thallus yellow-grey, thin, C+ orange	**3. O. inversa**
7.	Soralia from isidia, coarse, grey or greenish grey, C+ red	**5. O. subviridis**
–	Soralia coarse, like isidia, pale grey, C– or pale yellow	**7. O. turneri**
8.	Thallus white to pale grey, coarsely granular, prothallus indistinct. Cortex and disc C+ rose	**6. O. tartarea**
–	Thallus fawn to grey, not coarsely granular, prothallus white. Cortex C–, disc KC+ red	**4. O. parella**

1. Ochrolecia androgyna Thallus grey or yellowish grey forming a thick warted crust often with a distinct white prothallus. Yellowish grey soralia up to several millimetres wide are scattered over the surface, sometimes becoming confluent. Usually infertile except in the SouthWest and the western highlands of Scotland where it may be abundantly fertile. Apothecia frequent, up to 4 mm diam. Disc flat, flesh-coloured to tan, with a pale, smooth or sorediate, entire margin. Spores 30–45 x 12–20 µm. It was used in the production of cudbear for dyeing.
Cortex and soralia: C+ scarlet, UV–.
Habitat: Widespread on acid-barked trees and siliceous rocks, often growing over mosses. It becomes rarer in the South and East. Very variable.

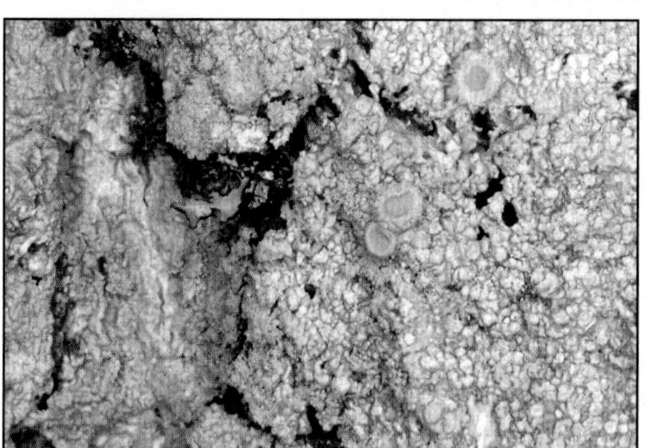

O. androgyna x 5.

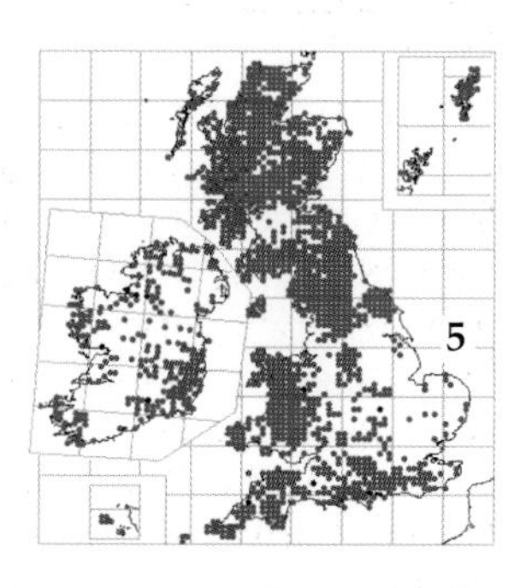

2. O. frigida Thallus grey or cream, granular. These granules develop long spiky growths that are usually tipped with narrow, splayed and frayed ends. The appearance of the thallus resembles a pile of fish bones. Apothecia infrequent, up to 5 mm diam, flat, brown with a smooth, thin margin. Spores 25–40 x 15–26 µm. C+ red, UV–.
Habitat: Overgrowing mosses and other vegetation at altitude, rarely coastal.

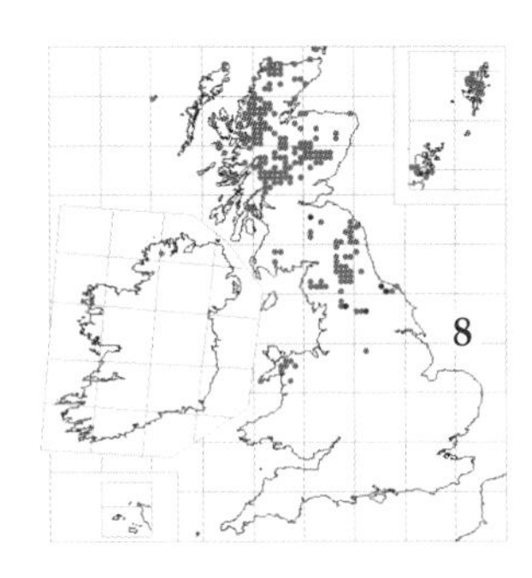

O. frigida x 10.

3. O. inversa Thallus smooth to finely areolate, greenish grey, often with a dark prothallus. Yellowish to ochre soralia dot the surface and often become confluent to form a sorediate crust. Very rarely fertile in Britain.
Thallus and soralia: C+ orange (*O. androgyna* is C+ scarlet), UV+ orange.
Habitat: On acidic bark of old trees in damp areas, rarely rocks, occurs particularly in the South and West, where it is widely distributed but rarely abundant.

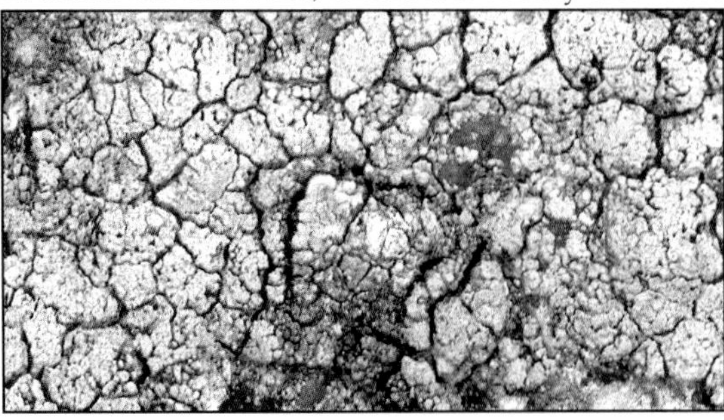

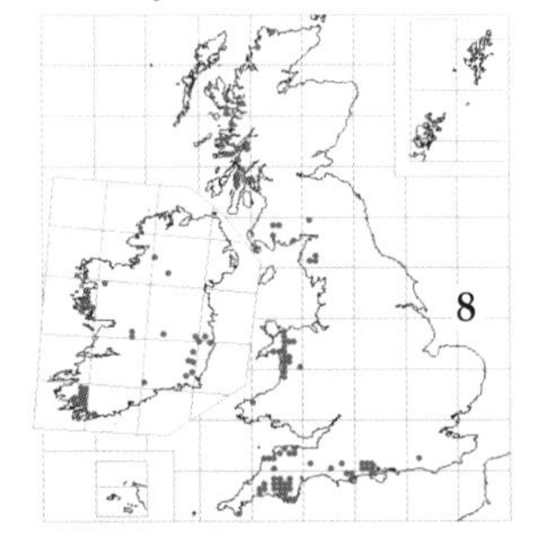

O. inversa x 6.

4. O. parella Thallus grey to buff-grey with a white prothallus. It forms large patches up to 20 cm across often, with zoned 'growth-rings' towards the margin which may be much thickened where it meets other lichens. Thick and warted in the centre, but sometimes smoother when on trees. There are no soralia. Usually abundantly fertile. Apothecia 2–3 mm diam, margins thick and swollen. Discs flesh to pink. Spores 45–75 x 25–45 µm. When on rocks the disc is usually

covered in a thick, white, often cracked, pruina that appears almost papillose. It was used for dyeing and was the source of the purple dye 'parelle'.
Cortex: C– (rarely C+ yellow), UV –.
Disc: C+ red, KC+ red, UV+ white.
Habitat: Very common on hard, smooth siliceous rocks and walls, especially slates and schists. It is also more rarely found on trees. Rather variable.

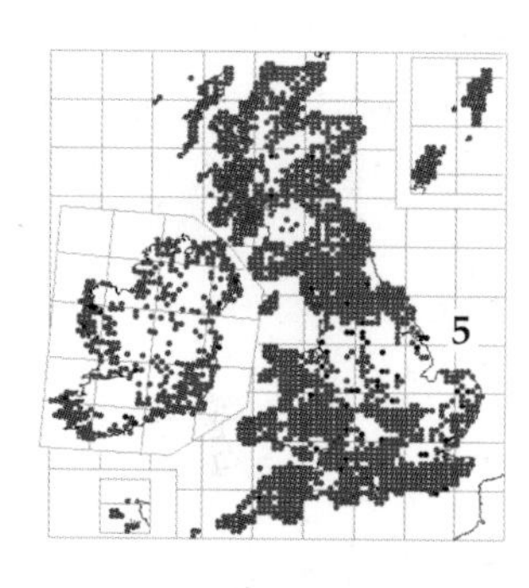

O. parella x 4.

5. O. subviridis Thallus smooth to warted, grey to green-grey, covered with distinct, delicate, short, soft, massed isidia that may break down and become sorediate in old specimens. (*Pertusaria coccodes* has smooth isidia that are usually brown-tipped, *O. turneri* is more coarsely 'isidiate'. Both are C–.) Apothecia rare, only found in unpolluted areas in the West. Disc pink, often pruinose and usually with an isidiate margin. Spores 30–68 x 25–35 µm.
Isidia: C+ red, UV+ bluish or yellowish.
Habitat: Frequent on nutrient-rich, rough-barked deciduous trees.

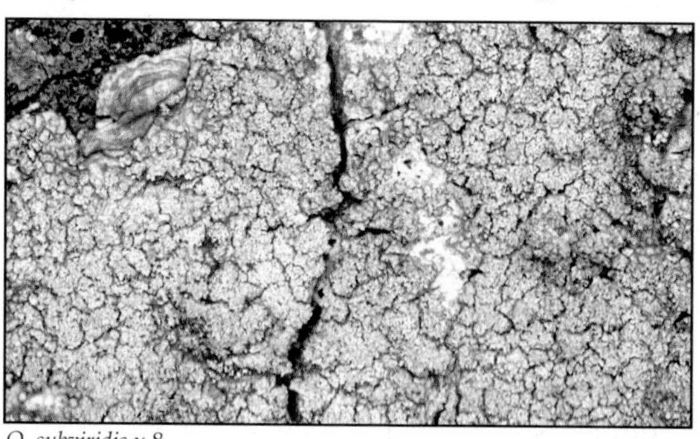

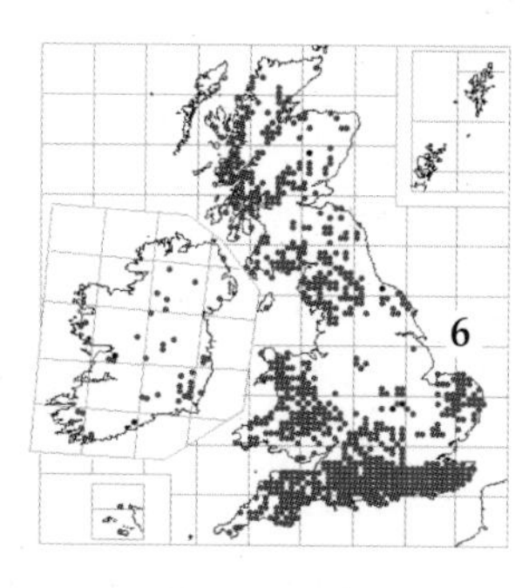

O. subviridis x 8.

6. O. tartarea Thallus yellowish grey or creamy, large, of compacted convex granules or warted, often up to 4 mm thick with a pale, zoned prothallus. Apothecia usually abundant with a thick, notched margin, 3–6 mm diam, rarely up to 1 cm diam. Disc flesh-pink to brown, rough with a flexuose margin. Spores 40–70 x 20–40 µm. This species was used to produce dyes called 'cudbear'. This

process was patented in 1758 in Scotland. The name is derived from Cuthbert, the maiden name of the mother of the inventor.
Cortex: C+ orange-red. Disc: C+ rose-red, UV–.
Habitat: Common on trees, rocks and mosses in high rainfall areas, mostly in exposed upland regions. Often confused with the sorediate *O. androgyna*.

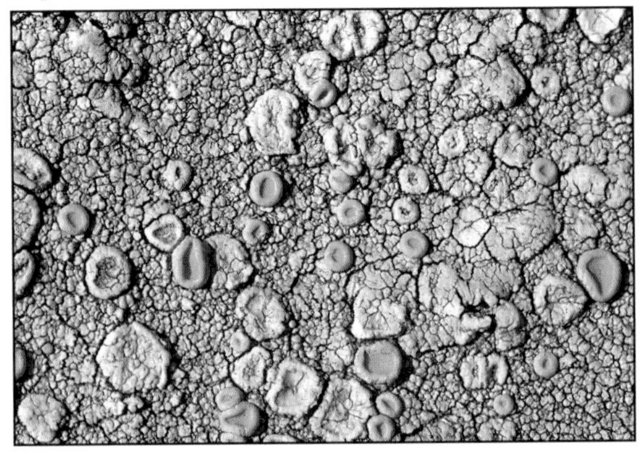

O. tartarea x 2.

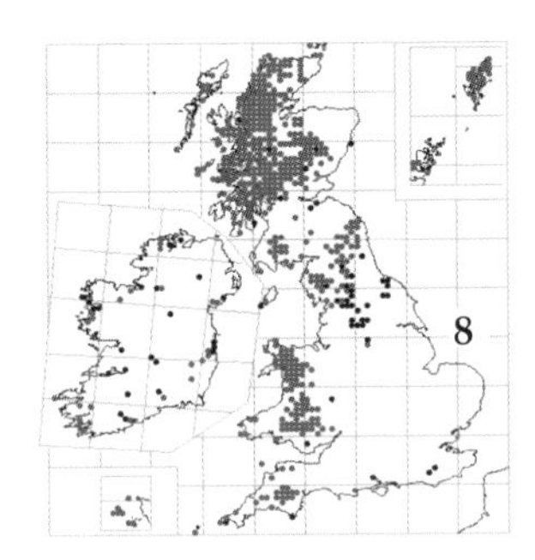

7. O. turneri Thallus smooth to granular-wrinkled, pale grey, smooth or granular with coarse, pale soredia (often looking isidiate) bursting from low warts, sometimes resembling eroded *Pertusaria amara* or the lines of soralia that occur in *Phlyctis argena*. The soredia often form a powdery crust towards the centre of the thallus. Apothecia scarce, up to 3 mm with a wavy, sorediate margin. Disc yellow to flesh-coloured, usually pruinose with a sorediate margin.
Thallus: C+ pale lemon-yellow, UV+ bluish. Disc: KC+ red.
Habitat: Frequent on trees and wood, rarely on acid rocks.

OMPHALINA ('navel' – from the shape of the fruit body). This genus is a member of the *Basidiomycota* and the spores are, therefore, borne on a club-like basidium instead of the sac-like ascus of the other British genera treated here.
Thallus granular or squamulose. **Photobiont** *Coccomyxa*. **Fruiting body** agaricoid, mushroom-like. **Basidium** 2- or 4-spored. **Spores** simple, colourless. **Spore print** white (use shed spores for measurements). **Chemical reactions** negative.

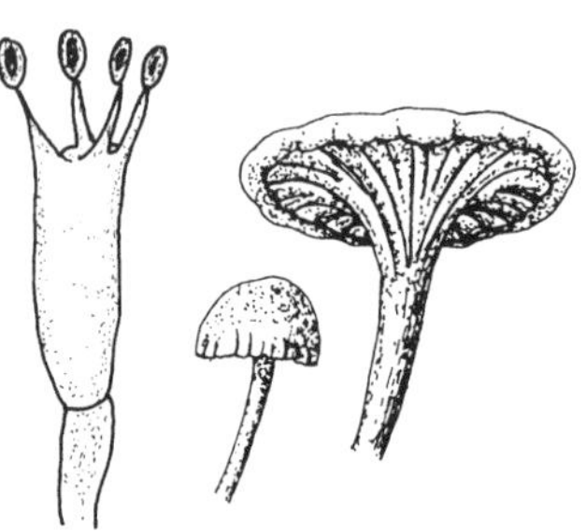

A basidium. *O. hudsoniana* x 2.

1.	Thallus of small, blue-green squamules	**2. O. hudsoniana**
–	Thallus of small, dark green granules	2
2.	Cap cream to light tan	**1. O. ericetorum**
–	Cap bright yellow	**3. O. luteovitellina**

1. Omphalina ericetorum Thallus dark green, consisting of small, clustered granules up to 0.25 mm diam. Cap up to 20 mm diam, light brown, becoming much paler as it ages, often with radiating darker lines. Gills white to pale yellow. Stem up to 30 mm tall, 1–2 mm diam. Spores 4 per basidium, 7–10 x 6–7 µm.
Habitat: On soil and rotting wood in damp situations, rarely on trees or *Sphagnum*.

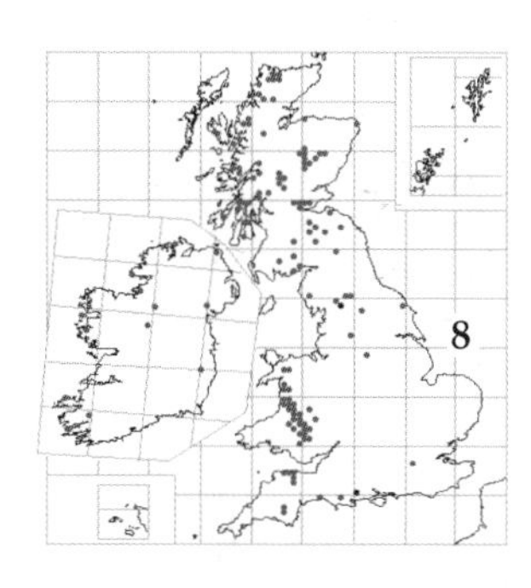

O. ericetorum x 10.

2. O. hudsoniana (Coriscium viride) Thallus glaucous-green, consisting of ± circular squamules with raised margins. The squamules resemble *Normandina pulchella* but are larger (up to about 2 mm diam) and lack soredia. The fruiting body is toadstool-shaped, up to 20 mm high and about 30 mm diam, cream to light tan, often with a pinkish tinge at the top. Stem about 3 mm diam, pale violet above when young, becoming paler. Spores 4 per basidium, 8–10 x 4–5 µm.
Habitat: Frequent on wet peat moors and rotting vegetation in western Scotland, but also found in southern England.

O. hudsoniana x 6.

O. hudsoniana squamules x 6.

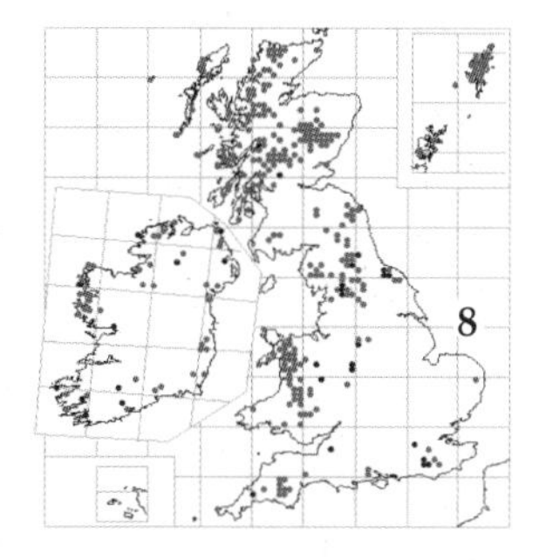

3. O. luteovitellina is similar to *O. ericetorum* but has a bright yellow stem and cap which is 5–15 mm diam with a crenulate edge. Stem matt to tomentose, almost white or concolorous with the cap, about 2 mm diam. Spores 4 per basidium, 6–10 x 3–5 µm.
Habitat: Fairly common on peaty soils and rotting vegetation in upland areas.

OPEGRAPHA ('hidden writing' – from the small lirellae). **Thallus** crustose. **Photobiont** *Trentepohlia*. **Ascocarps** carbonaceous lirellae. **Ascus** 8-spored, K/I– except for a very small apical ring. **Spores** colourless, becoming darker with age, fusiform or clavate, 3- or more septate, 8 per ascus. It differs from *Graphis* in having branched, often anastomosing, paraphyses. Care should be taken to avoid confusion with the fungal genus *Hysterium*, the common species of which have brown 3-septate spores, slightly constricted at the septa. Due to the soft nature of the thallus, there are very few fossil lichens. However, an early record of a lichen is probably an *Opegrapha* species, found in Mesozoic chalk.

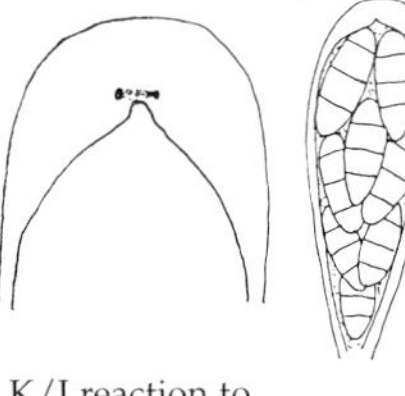

K/I reaction to the ascus tip.

O. herbarum x 500.

1.	Corticolous	2
–	Saxicolous	9
2.	Lacking soredia or prominent pruinose pycnidia	3
–	Sorediate or with papilla-like white pruinose pycnidia	7
3.	Lirellae opening widely	4
–	Lirellae not opening widely	5
4.	Thallus white to greenish. Lirellae to 1.25 mm long. Spores 3-septate	**2. O. herbarum**
–	Thallus brown to grey or evanescent. Lirellae to 3 mm long. Spores 4- to 6-septate	**4. O. varia**
5.	Thallus white to grey. Spores 3- or 8- to 14-septate	6
–	Thallus brown. Spores 4- to 8-septate	**6. O. vulgata**
6.	Thallus grey to greenish grey. Spores 8- to 14-septate	**3. O. prosodea**
–	Thallus grey, lirellae numerous often crowded in the centre of the thallus. Spores 3-septate	**1. O. atra**
7.	Sorediate, not with white pruinose pycnidia	8
–	Thallus pinkish-grey, not sorediate but with papilla-like, white, pruinose pycnidia	**5. O. vermicellifera**
8.	Thallus red-brown, soralia orange	**8. O. gyrocarpa**
–	Thallus greenish grey, soralia yellowish green	**8a. O. corticola**
9.	Parasitic on other lichens	**9. O. parasitica**
–	Not parasitic on other lichens	10
10.	With soralia	11
–	Without soralia	12
11.	Thallus red-brown. Soralia buff to orange. Spores 3-septate	**8. O. gyrocarpa**
–	Thallus purplish brown. Soralia brownish to mauve. Spores 5- to 10-septate	**Enterographa zonata**

12.	On acid rock	13
–	On basic rock	14
13.	Thallus white to lilac grey. Spores 4- to 5-septate	**7. O. cesareensis**
–	Thallus brown. Spores 3-septate	**12. O. saxigena**
–	Thallus grey. Spores 3-septate	**10. O. saxatilis/O. conferta**
14.	Lirellae to 1 mm long, often in heaps	**10. O. saxatilis**
–	Lirellae to 2 mm long, scattered but often contorted	**11. O. saxicola**

CORTICOLOUS

(see also *O. gyrocarpa*)

1. Opegrapha atra Thallus light grey or white, delimited or sometimes almost evanescent. Lirellae short (up to about 2 x 0.3 mm), slit-like, often densely crowded in the centre. It can resemble *Graphis scripta* but the smaller, more prominent lirellae, the 3-septate spores (14–20 x 3–5 µm) and I+ blue hymenium, separate the species. Habitat: This is the commonest of the British *Opegrapha* species and the most easily recognised. It is found on trees, especially those lightly shaded and/or with smooth bark, also on twigs and rarely on fences.

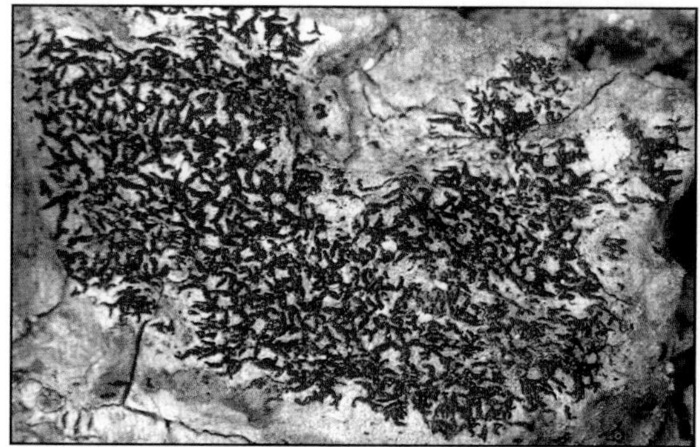

O. atra x 6.

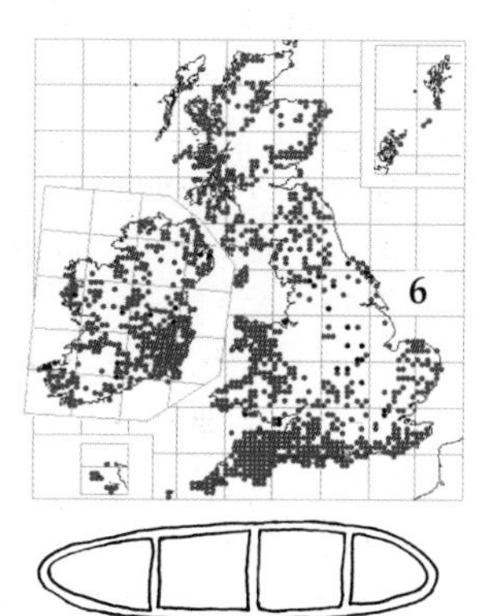

O. atra spore.

2. O. herbarum Thallus pale grey to greenish. Lirellae small, up to about 1.25 mm long, sometimes branched. The disc is open but not as widely as in *O. varia*, rarely green-pruinose. Hymenium 70–90 µm tall, I+ red. Epithecium brown. Spores 3-septate, 15–18 x 5–7 µm with a perispore, remaining colourless longer than with most other *Opegrapha* species.
Habitat: Widespread on shaded smooth bark, plant stems and, rarely, sandstone.

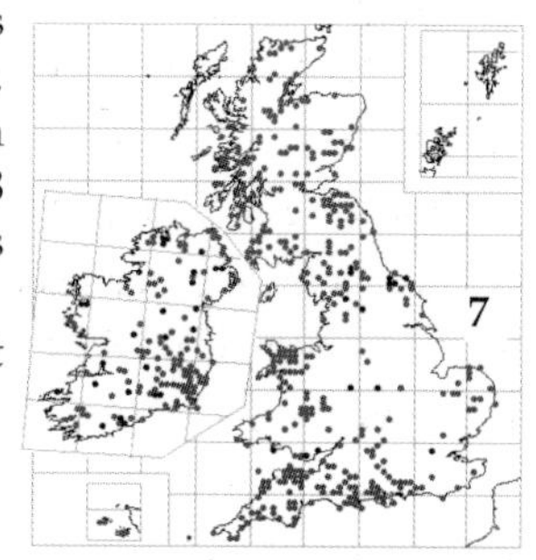

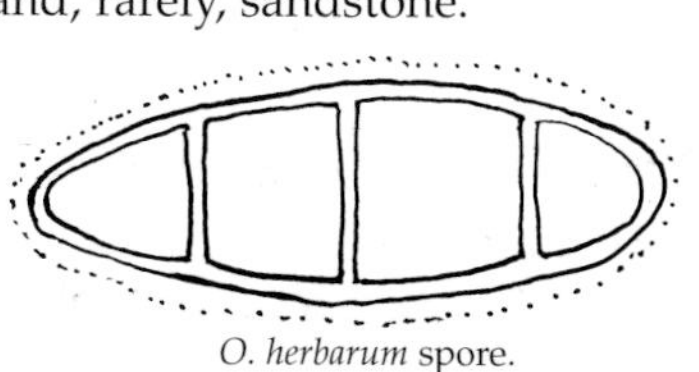

O. herbarum spore.

3. O. prosodea Thallus thin, grey, sometimes dark greenish grey, smooth or finely cracked. Lirellae scattered or clustered and interlocked, sessile, wavy, sometimes forked, long, up to 3 mm, with a narrow slit that does not become open. Hymenium 90–100 µm tall, I+ red. Spores 8- to 14-septate, 45–75 x 6–8 µm with a thin perispore.
Habitat: Infrequent, southern, mainly on the sides of shaded, vertical cracks of old oaks and yews in parkland and churchyards.

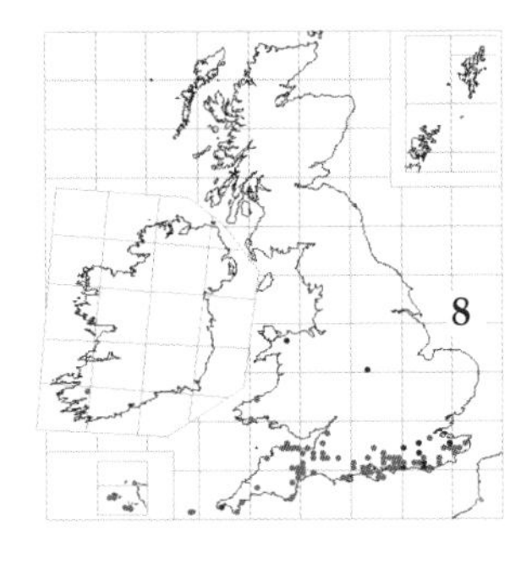

4. O. varia (O. lichenoides) Thallus thin, usually grey but sometimes with a brown tinge. Lirellae up to 3 mm long, usually simple but sometimes branching with a more open disc than in other species, the centre may become grey to green pruinose. Hymenium 60–80 µm tall, I+ red. Spores 4- to 6-septate, with a thin perispore, 20–35 x 5–8 µm, becoming reddish brown. Pycnidia often pruinose.
Habitat: Common on rough, basic-barked trees in shade.

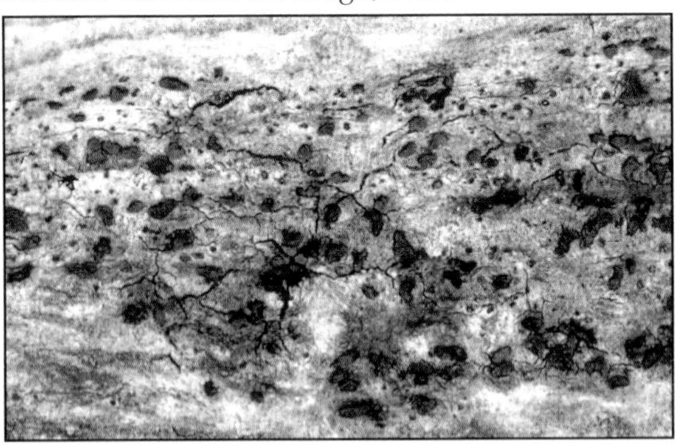

O. varia x 5.

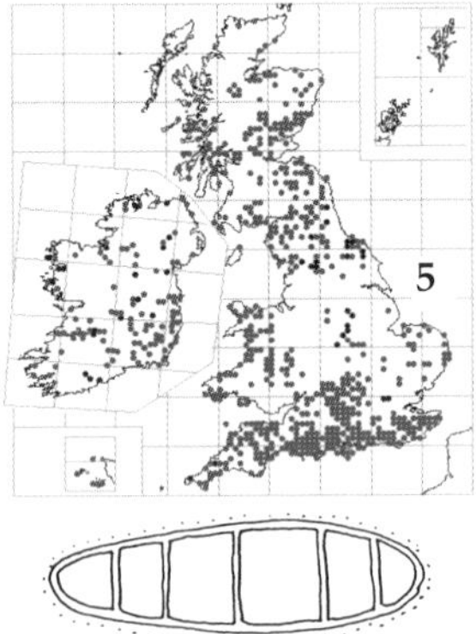

O. varia spore.

5. O. vermicellifera Thallus light grey, smooth. Usually sterile, when it can be recognized by the small (about 0.25 mm tall) papilla-like pycnidia which are covered in a white or pale grey pruina. Lirellae in patches, slender and only about 1 mm long, with a pruinose, more open disc than *O. vulgata*. Spores 5-septate, 15–25 x 3–4 µm.
The C–, UV– reaction of the pycnidial pruina separates it from superficially similar sterile *Lecanactis abietina* which has larger pycnidia and C + red. UV+ glaucous pycnidial pruina.
Habitat: Frequent in dry recesses on shaded basic-barked trees. This the superficially similar *Lecanactis subabietina* often occurs at the base of acid-barked trees, spreading on to ivy, stones, etc.

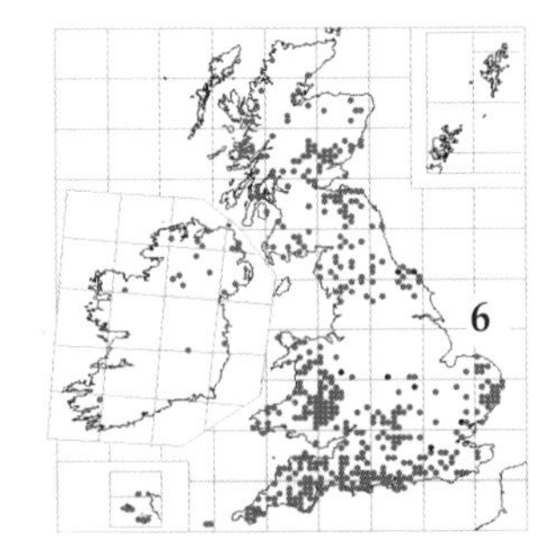

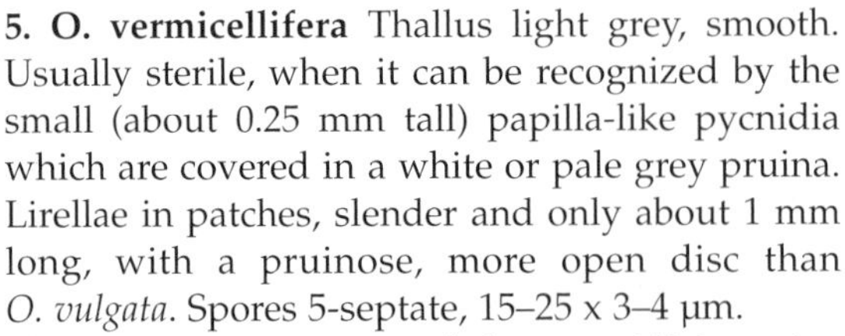

6. O. vulgata Thallus grey or brown, thin, with more separated lirellae than in *O. atra*. The lirellae are slender, to 2.5 mm long, straight, curved or sometimes stellate, disc usually remaining slit-like. Black dot-like pycnidia are often scattered amongst the lirellae. Hymenium 45–60 µm tall, I+ red. Spores 4- to 8-septate, mainly 6-septate, thin-walled and sometimes curved, 20–35 x 3–4 µm. Habitat: Very common on shaded, smooth-barked, or smooth areas of trees.

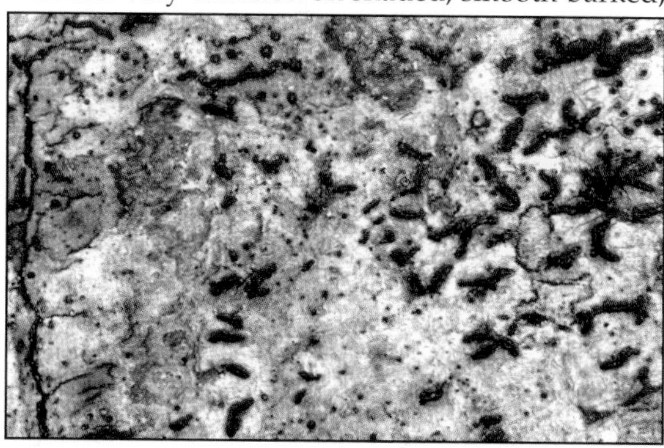

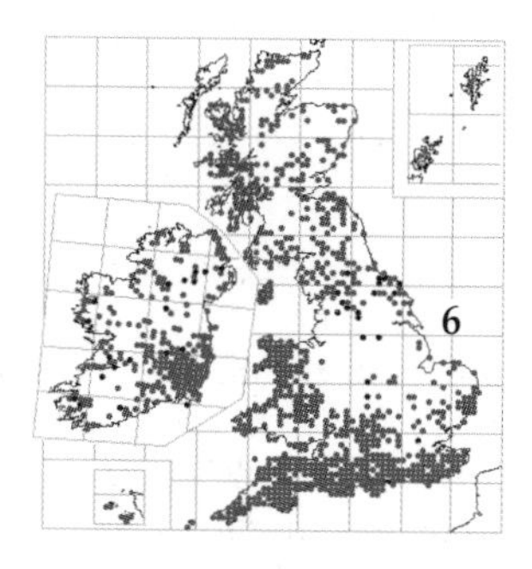

O. vulgata x 6.

SAXICOLOUS OR PARASITIC

(see also *O. herbarum*)

7. O. cesareensis Thallus white or grey, often slightly purple, thin and smooth or thicker and cracked, limited by a dark prothallus. Lirellae up to 2 mm long and very prominent, usually dispersed and mainly unbranched. Hymenium 80–90 µm tall, I+ blue in upper layer. Spores 4- or 5-septate, 15–22 x 4–5 µm.
Habitat: Not infrequent on shaded, or under overhanging, often on ± damp, siliceous rocks in coastal areas.

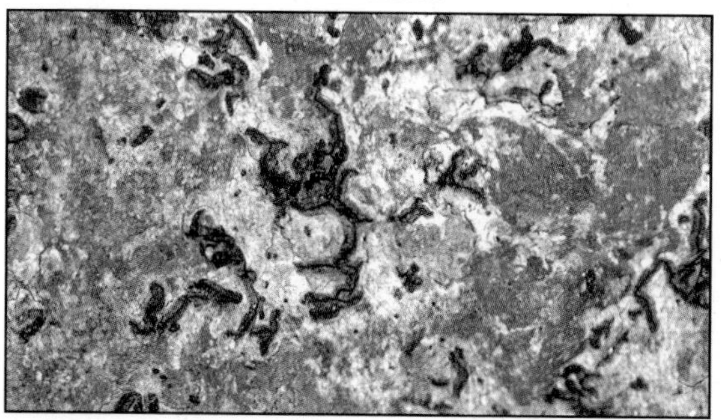

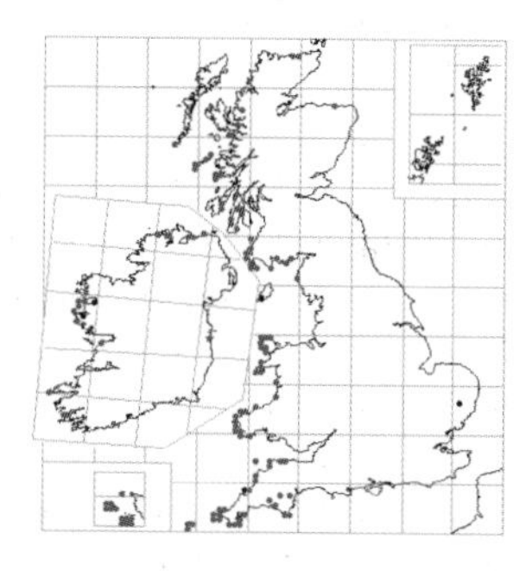

O. cesareensis x 8.

8. O. gyrocarpa Thallus tan to deep red-brown, fairly thick with a leprose or cracked surface and black prothallus. It often forms extensive mosaics. Yellow-buff to light orange soralia, which may become confluent, are dotted over the surface. Lirellae rare, up to about 1.5 mm long, contorted so as to appear gyrose. Hymenium 80–120 µm tall, I–. Spores 3-septate, 18–25 x 3–5 µm.
Soralia: C+ red.

Habitat: Frequent in shaded recesses and underhangs of siliceous rocks. Rarely on trees. A very similar species, **8a. O. corticola,** has a grey thallus and is C–. It is found on shaded trees in the South of England. *Enterographa zonata* often forms dark purplish brown mosaics with *O. gyrocarpa* and has lilac, punctiform soralia and, occasionally, small (0.25 mm long) lirellae. Spores 5- to 10-septate. See also *O. saxigena.*

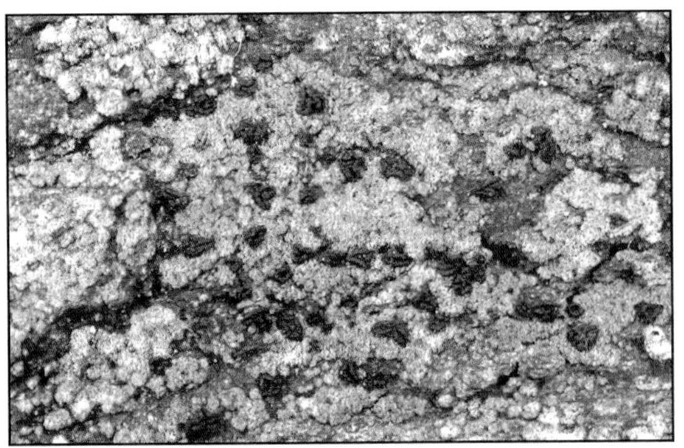

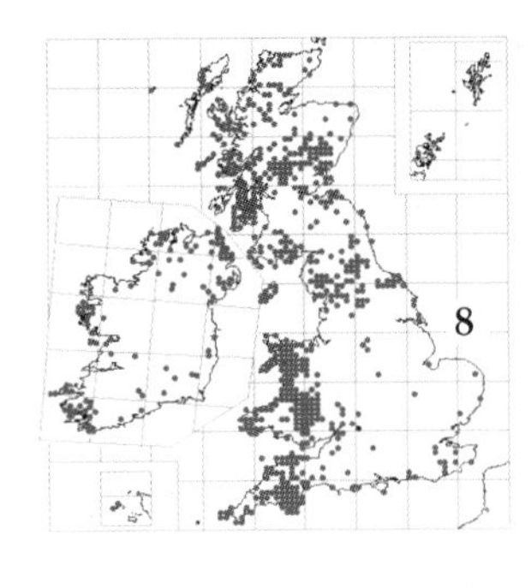

O. gyrocarpa x 6.

9. O. parasitica (O. persoonii) A parasitic species with small but wide rounded lirellae which have a persistently narrow slit. Spores 3-septate, 13–20 x 5–8 µm.
Habitat: Parasitic on crustose lichens (especially *Verrucariaceae*) growing on limestone. A related species, **O. physciaria**, is sometimes found on *Xanthoria parietina*.

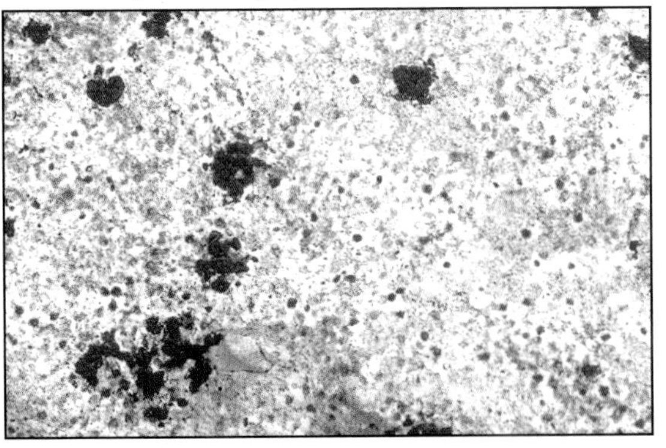

O. parasitica x 8.

O. parasitica spore.

10. O. saxatilis Thallus white or light to dark brown, rough and scurfy or sometimes endolithic (especially on calcareous rocks). Lirellae about 1 mm long, unbranched or stellate, sometimes piled up in heaps. Hymenium 80–100 µm tall. Spores 3-septate, 15–20 x 4–6 µm.
Habitat: Frequent on damp, shaded calcareous substrata, mainly near the coast. Included in this species are: **O. calcarea** with pink, immersed thallus found on shaded, hard limestone; **O. conferta**, with a grey thallus and lirellae usually in piled in heaps, is found in cracks on acid to slightly basic rock near the coast; and

O. chevallieri, with a thick, pure white thallus and piles of lirellae up to 5 mm wide. Occurs especially on man-made basic substrates such as cement and mortar.

O. saxatilis x 6.

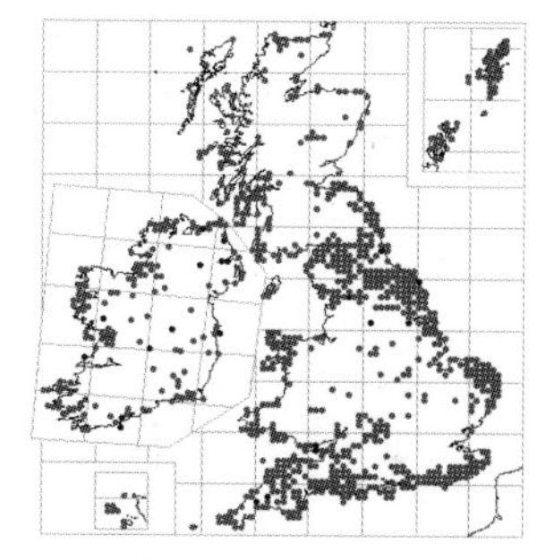

11. O. saxicola Thallus white to brown and may be thick and smooth or immersed. Lirellae scattered and often twisted, contorted and furrowed, up to 2 mm long. Hymenium 90–120 mm tall. Spores 3-septate, 20–25 x 5–7 µm. The slit-like disc sometimes becomes slightly open.
Habitat: Frequent on sheltered, damp, soft calcareous substrata, also on clints in limestone.

12. O. saxigena Thallus dark brown, cracked, with a dark prothallus. Lirellae scattered, up to about 1 mm. Hymenium 80–120 µm tall, I+ red. Spores 3-septate, 15–20 x 4–5 µm.
Habitat: Frequently forming mosaics, often with *O. gyrocarpa*, on damp, very shaded acid rocks.

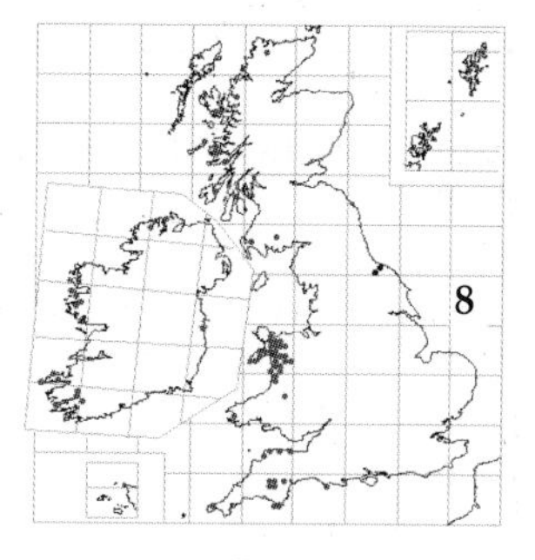

O. saxigena.

OPHIOPARMA ('snake-like shield' – from the serpentine undulations of the margins of the apothecia). **Thallus** crustose, not sorediate. **Photobion**t trebouxioid. **Apothecia** lecanorine with a prominent proper margin. **Paraphyses** with club-like, swollen tips, rarely anastomosing (in *Haematomma* the paraphyses do not have thickened tips and are anastomosing). Ascus 8-spored, K/I+ blue apical dome. **Spores** colourless, usually septate. There is only one British species.

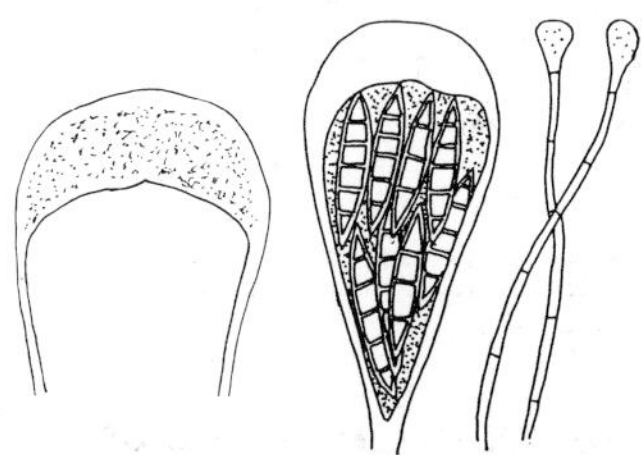

K/I reaction to the ascus tip. *O. ventosum* x 250.

Ophioparma ventosa (Haematomma ventosum) Thallus areolate to very warted, either grey (f. *subfestiva* without usnic acid) or yellow-grey (f. *ventosa* containing usnic acid), usually delimited by a rather fimbriate prothallus. Apothecial disc blood-red to dried blood colour, up to 4 mm wide, scattered or

in groups, with a prominent margin that may become excluded. Hymenium 60–70 µm tall. Spores usually curved, 3- to 7-septate, 40–55 x 4–5 µm.
Thallus: K+ yellow, P+ orange. Apothecia: K+ purple to crimson.
Habitat: Common in upland areas on exposed, nutrient-poor, rough, siliceous rocks and boulders. Both chemical racees may occur together.

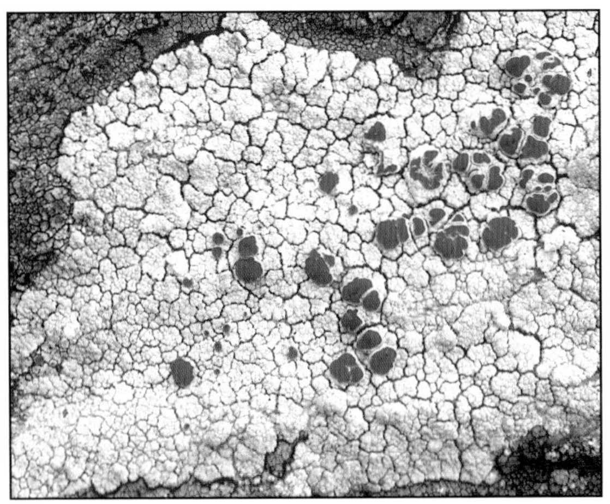

O. ventosa x 3.

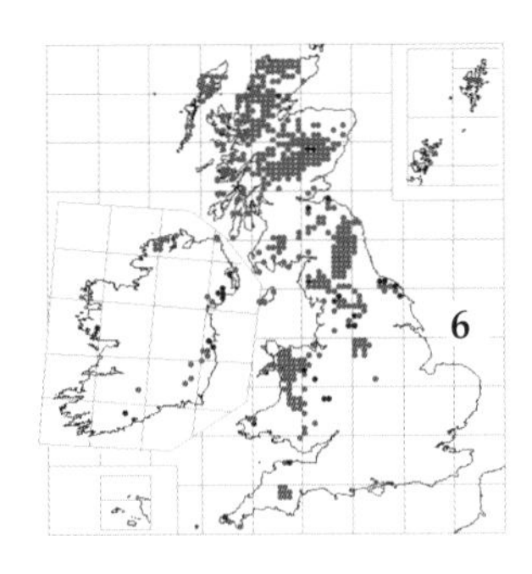

PACHYPHIALE ('thick bowl' – from the thick margin and dish-shaped apothecia). **Thallus** crustose. **Photobiont** *Trentepohlia*. **Apothecia** lecideine. **Ascus** 16- to 48-spored, I+ blue wall. **Spores** colourless, multi-septate. **Pycnidia** brown, innate.

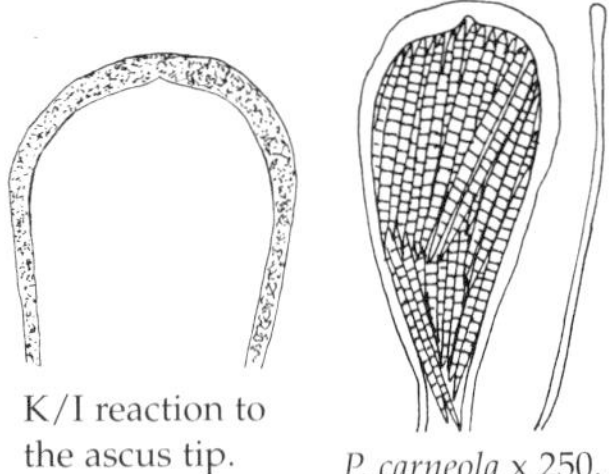

K/I reaction to the ascus tip.

P. carneola x 250.

Pachyphiale carneola (P. cornea) Thallus thin, light buff-grey. Apothecia about 0.5 mm diam, becoming sessile, light buff when young, becoming dark reddish brown, translucent when wet. Margin pronounced and entire giving it the appearance of a very small wine-gum. Spores up to 40 per ascus, 40–80 x 3-5 µm.
Habitat: Locally abundant on somewhat shaded, rough-barked deciduous trees in long established woodlands. An ancient woodland indicator species.

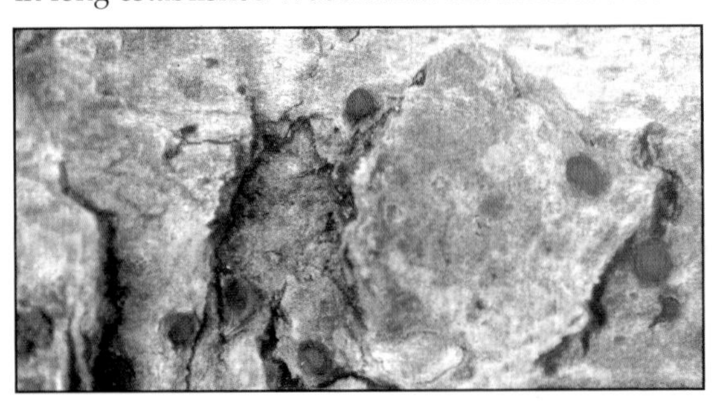

P. carneola x 6.

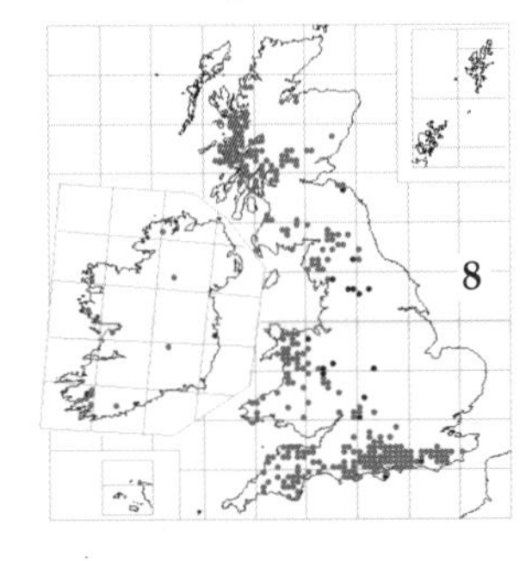

PANNARIA ('a piece of cloth' – from the shape of the thallus). **Thallus** squamulose to crustose. Under-surface a dark-felted hypothallus. **Photobiont** *Nostoc*. **Apothecia** lecanorine. **Ascus** 8-spored, K/I reactions various. **Spores** simple, colourless, 8 per ascus. The species may be separated from similar *Parmeliella* species by the presence of the thalline margin on the apothecia. There are a number of British species, but most are rare.

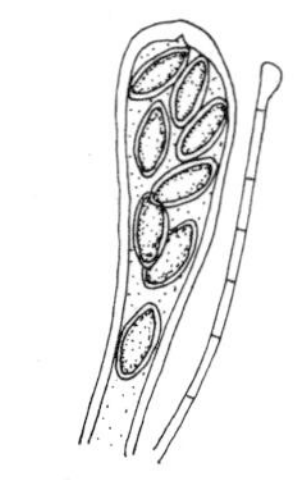
P. rubiginosa x 300.

1. Thallus sorediate or isidiate. Not usually fertile — 2
– Thallus without soredia or isidia. Usually fertile — 3
2. Thallus of pale brown squamules on a dark hypothallus. Cream-coloured marginal and laminal soralia — **4. P. sampaiana**
– Thallus of dark to blue-grey, elongate, separate squamules. Margins sorediate to knobby isidiate — **1. P. conoplea**
3. Thallus a rosette of imbricate squamules, appearing foliose. Thalline margin smooth to uneven-crenulate — **3. P. rubiginosa**
– Thallus small-squamulose, often appearing coarsely granular. Thalline margin crenulate to granular — **2. P. pezizoides**

1. Pannaria conoplea Thallus blue-grey or yellowish grey, consisting of long, ± contiguous squamules (not in rosettes), up to about 8 mm long, imbricate, adpressed and deeply incised, often pruinose. Coarse granular or coralloid isidia are formed on the ascending margins and may spread over the surface to form a complete crust. Under-surface tomentose, grey-brown to black. Rarely fertile. Apothecia with chestnut discs and isidiate margins. Spores 15–22 x 10–12 µm. P+ reddish orange.
Habitat: Similar to *P. rubiginosa,* but less strongly oceanic, on damp, sheltered, mossy, basic bark; commonest in the West. It is an 'old forest' indicator species.

P. conoplea x 5 (moist).

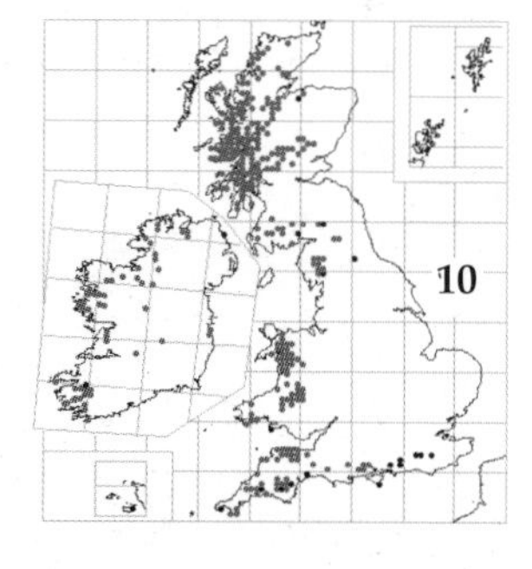

2. P. pezizoides Thallus grey to grey-brown, of squamules up to 1 mm long which are often compacted into an almost solid, granular mass. Undersurface with an indistinct, dark hypothallus. Usually very fertile with an orange-brown disc and a persistent nodular to granular margin. Spores 13–16 x 7–8 µm, with a warted epispore. *Psoroma hypnorum* appears similar but has green algae and cephalodia.
Habitat: An upland species found on sheltered, damp rocks, trees and mosses; frequently occurs on the ground amongst low vegetation.

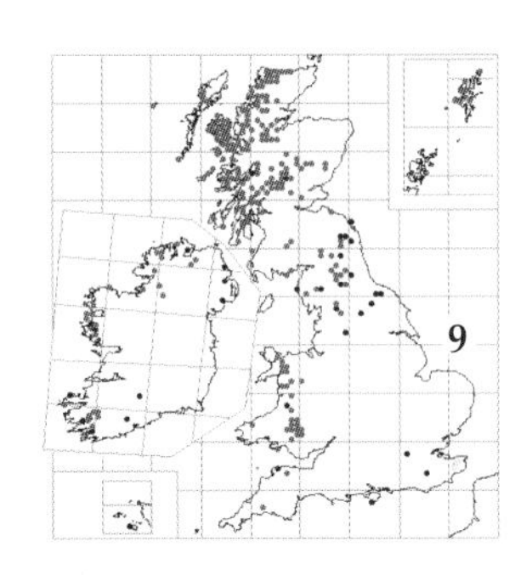

P. pezizoides x 3.

3. P. rubiginosa Thallus bluish grey to green-brown, forming rosettes up to about 3 cm wide. Consisting of imbricate squamules, 1–4 mm wide, much incised and with a paler margin and sometimes slightly pruinose. Under-surface with a grey to black, hairy hypothallus, usually visible at the edges of the thallus. Normally fertile. Apothecia up to 2 mm across with a crenulate margin. Disc chestnut-red, paler when young, becoming darker red when wet. Spores 15–20 x 9–10 µm.
P+ orange-red.
Habitat: An oceanic species now only found in the extreme west of Britain and Ireland, usually overgrowing damp mosses on trees and rocks.

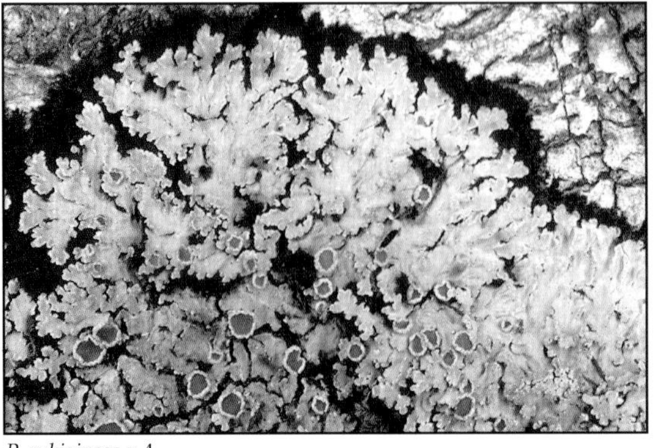

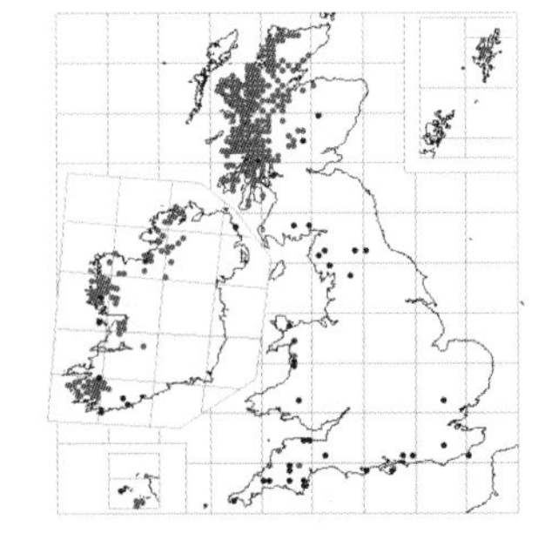

P. rubiginosa x 4.

4. P. sampaiana Thallus of tan to red-brown squamules, up to 4 mm wide, set on a blue-black hypothallus. Coarse, granular, concolorous or pale cream soredia spread over the surface of the squamules. Not known fertile.
Habitat: Mossy bark or smooth patches on old trees in ancient woodland or on wayside trees. Very local, mainly confined to W. Scotland.

P. sampaiana x 3.

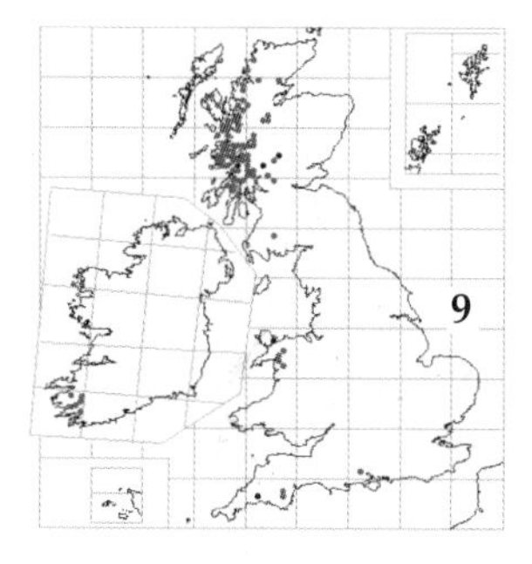

PARMELIA ('embedded fruit bowl' – from the shape of the apothecia). **Thallus** foliose, lobate, attached by rhizines. **Photobiont** trebouxioid. **Apothecia** lecanorine, sessile or stalked. Ascus 8-spored, K/I+ blue, *Lecanora*-type. **Spores** simple, colourless. This is a large genus of world-wide distribution. Some of the species were important sources of dyes. The spot reactions are very useful in the identification of the species. The upper cortex of the grey species is nearly always K+ yellow. Many attempts to subdivide this large genus have been made in recent years but the limits of some of these subdivisions are not yet clear or universally accepted by specialists. A broad view is therefore taken here. However, a summary of the characteristics of the generally accepted new genera is included below together with assignment of all the British species (reproduced by kind permission of P. W. James).

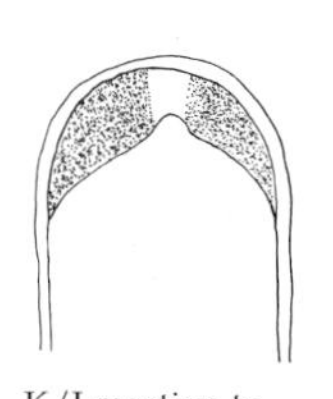

K/I reaction to the ascus tip.

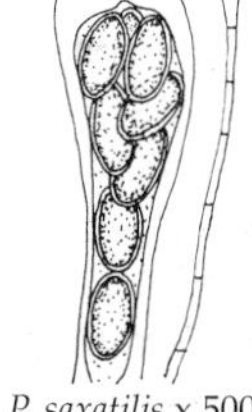

P. saxatilis x 500.

Arctoparmelia Hale
Thallus closely appressed, upper surface yellow-green, pseudocyphellae and cilia absent; lower surface finely pubescent, rhizines sparse, simple. Saxicolous. Arctic-boreal, Europe, Northern Asia, N. America.
P. incurva.

Flavoparmelia Hale
Thallus more or less closely appressed, wide-spreading, upper surface yellow-green (usnic acid), lobes broad, rounded, pseudocyphellae and cilia absent; lower surface naked towards the margins, rhizines simple. Saxicolous and corticolous, rarely terricolous. Cosmopolitan; mainly temperate and subtropical.
P. caperata, P. soredians.

Hypotrachyna (Vain.) Hale
Thallus loosely to ± closely appressed, wide-spreading, upper surface grey or yellow-green, lobes discrete to overlapping, ends truncated with sinuate axils, pseudocyphellae and cilia absent; lower surface rhizinose to the margins, rhizines regularly dichotomously branched. Chemically diverse. Saxicolous, corticolous, rarely terricolous. Cosmopolitan; mainly subtropical and montane-tropical, few temperate.
P. endochlora, P. laevigata, P. revoluta, P. sinuosa, P. britannica, P. taylorensis.

Melanelia Essl.
Thallus ± closely appressed, lobes discrete to crowded-imbricate, upper surface brown (N–), often with pseudocyphellae, more rarely ± finely pubescent, cilia absent; lower surface ± rhizinose to the margin, rhizines simple. Saxicolous and corticolous. Cosmopolitan; temperate-boreal, N. and S. America, Australasia and Eurasia.
P. disjuncta, P. elegantula, P. exasperata, P. exasperatula, P. glabratula subsp. *glabratula, P. glabratula* subsp. *fuliginosa, P. laciniatula, P. septentrionalis, P. stygia, P. subargentifera, P. subaurifera.* Also *Cetraria commixta, C. hepatizon.*

Neofuscelia Essl.
Thallus foliose, wide-spreading to subcrustose, upper surface brown (N+ bluish green), pseudocyphellae and cilia absent, soredia absent; lower surface mainly rhizinose, rhizines mostly simple. Chemically very diverse. Mainly saxicolous, sometimes lignicolous or terricolous. Cosmopolitan; temperate to semi-arid boreal, particularly S. Africa and Australia.
P. delisei, P. loxodes, P. pulla, P. verruculifera.

Parmelia Ach.
Thallus compact to ± wide-spreading, upper surface grey to brown, with white linear or comma-shaped pseudocyphellae, cilia absent; lower surface rhizinose to the margin, rhizines simple, sometimes furcate or squarrose-branched. Saxicolous and corticolous. Cosmopolitan; temperate to boreal.
P. submontana (=*P. contorta*), *P. omphalodes, P. omphalodes* subsp. *discordans, P. saxatilis, P. sulcata.*

Parmelina Hale
Thallus ± closely appressed, wide-spreading, lobes rounded, upper surface grey, finely white-maculate (when wet), cilia present, mainly in lobe axils, simple; lower surface ± rhizinose to the margin, rhizines simple; medulla C+ red (lecanoric acid). Corticolous, sometimes saxicolous. Cosmopolitan; temperate.
P. pastillifera, P. quercina, P. tiliacea.

Parmelinopsis Elix & Hale
Thallus compact to wide-spreading, lobes narrow and ± apically truncate, cilia present, marginal or laminal, simple; lower surface rhizinose to the margin, rhizines simple or rarely weakly dichotomously branched. Corticolous and saxicolous. Cosmopolitan; temperate to tropical.
P. horrescens, P. minarum.

Parmotrema A. Massal.
Thallus often large, wide-spreading, sometimes loosely attached in part, lobes broad, grey (rarely yellow-green in a few non-British species), broadly rounded, often undulate, cilia often present, marginal or, more rarely, also laminal, simple, rarely branched at the base, lower surface naked towards the margin, rhizines simple, sometimes sparse. Spores large, 20–35 x 12–18 µm, thick-walled. Chemically diverse. Corticolous and saxicolous. Cosmopolitan; mostly tropical, less frequently temperate.
P. arnoldii, P. perlata (=Parmotrema chinense), P. crinita, P. robusta.

Pleurosticta Petrak
Thallus ± closely attached, ± wide-spreading, lobes rounded, often undulate, upper surface green to brownish (N+ violet) (oily deep green when wet), pseudocyphellae and cilia absent; lower surface ± densely rhizinose often naked towards the margins, rhizines simple. Corticolous, rarely saxicolous. Asia, Europe, N. Africa; temperate-boreal.
P. acetabulum.

Punctelia Krog
Thallus ± closely appressed, rosette-forming, lobes neatly rounded, upper surface grey, rarely brownish, pseudocyphellae white, punctiform, often numerous, cilia absent; lower surface ± rhizinose to the margin, rhizines simple, sometimes in bundles. Corticolous and saxicolous. Cosmopolitan; temperate, tropical.
P. borreri, P. reddenda, P. subrudecta, P. ulophylla.

Rimelia Hale & A. Fletcher
Thallus ± closely appressed, widespreading, lobes rounded-undulate, upper surface grey, with a fine mosaic of maculae often apparent as hair-line cracks (x 10 lens), cilia present, simple; lower surface ± rhizinose to the margin, rhizines simple to squarrose-branched. Corticolous and saxicolous. Cosmopolitan; temperate, tropical.
P. reticulata.

Xanthoparmelia (Vain.) Hale
Thallus radiating-foliose to sub-crustose, lobes discrete to overlapping, upper surface yellow-green (usnic acid), pseudocyphellae and cilia absent; lower surface variously rhizinose, rhizines simple. Saxicolous, more rarely lignicolous or terricolous; chemically diverse. Cosmopolitan; temperate, tropical (particularly arid areas in S. Africa and Australia)
P. conspersa, P. mougeotii, P. protomatrae, P. tinctina.

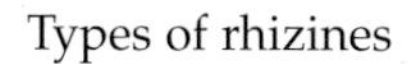
Types of rhizines

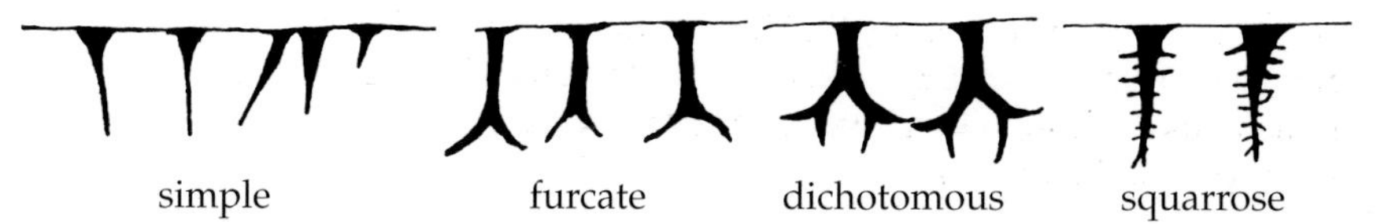

1. Thallus grey or green-grey 2
- Thallus green-brown to dark metallic brown, or yellow-green to yellow-grey 16

2. Thallus with soredia or isidia. Medulla C+ red or C– 3
- Thallus lacking soredia or isidia. Medulla C+ red 15

3. Thallus sorediate 4
- Thallus isidiate 12

4. Medulla C+ red 5
- Medulla C– 8

5. Soralia mainly marginal or apical. Thallus lacking pseudocyphellae 6
- Soralia laminal and punctiform. Thallus with white dot-like pseudocyphellae 7

6. Thallus light grey, lobes ascending, bent down at the tips. Soredia concolorous to creamy yellow-grey **26. P. revoluta**
- Thallus mid-grey, lobes adpressed, ends ± ascending, soredia with blue-black speckles **3. P. britannica**

7. Under surface light brown **31. P. subrudecta/ 31a. P. ulophylla**
- Under surface black (towards the centre) **2. P. borreri**

8. Thallus with white pseudocyphellae in dots and lines, often on ridges, or forming a net of fine white lines (x 10 lens) 9
- Thallus without white pseudocyphellae 11

9. Thallus with fine net of white lines (use lens), often with black cilia on the margins **25. P. reticulata**
- Thallus with coarser, white pseudocyphellae. No cilia 10

10. Soralia not on ridges. Punctiform to confluent. Medulla P– **24. P. reddenda**
- Soralia on pale ridges. Linear to confluent. Medulla P+ red. **32. P. sulcata**

11. Lobe tips rounded. Rhizines simple, not reaching margin **21. P. perlata**
- Lobe tips truncated. Rhizines dichotomously branched, reaching to, or beyond the margin **16. P. laevigata/ 16a. P. endochlora**

12. Thallus with white pseudocyphellae or black cilia. Medulla C– 13
- Thallus without pseudocyphellae or cilia. Medulla C+ red 14

13. Pseudocyphellae, as white lines and dots. Grey to brown coralloid isidia, growing from lines. No marginal cilia **27. P. saxatilis**
- No pseudocyphellae. With laminal and marginal cilia and scattered clumps of coralloid isidia **6. P. crinita/ 6a. P. horrescens**

14. Isidia mid-brown, coralloid **34. P. tiliacea**
- Isidia dark brown to blue-black, bun-shaped head **20. P. pastillifera**

15. Thallus grey with a green tinge, lobes decending, overlapping. Rhizines branched. Very rarely fertile. Trees and rocks **33. P. taylorensis**
– Thallus whitish grey, adpressed, not very overlapping. Rhizines simple. Usually fertile. Occurs mainly in the upper tree canopy **23. P. quercina**

16. Thallus green-brown to dark metallic-brown 17
– Thallus yellow-green to yellow-grey 29

17. Thallus isidiate, sorediate or with many small warts 18
– Thallus without isidia, soredia or small warts 24

18. Medulla C+ red 19
– Medulla C– 21

19. Thallus dark brown to black with dense coralloid isidia. On rocks **13. P. glabratula** subsp. **fuliginosa**
– Thallus green-brown. Mainly on trees, rarely on rocks 20

20. Thallus glossy, isidia coralloid, breaking off to leave white scars **12. P. glabratula** subsp. **glabratula**
– Thallus often slightly matt, isidia more granular and having pale yellow scars **30. P. subaurifera**

21. Thallus adpressed with numerous small volcano-like warts (x 10 lens). Isidia absent **10. P. exasperata**
– Thallus with isidia. warts absent 22

22a Isidia simple, spoon-shaped. Under-surface pale brown **11. P. exasperatula**
22b.Isidia often branched, cylindrical. Under-surface pale/mid-brown **9. P elegantula**
– Isidia not spoon-shaped. Under-surface black 23

23. Lobes pale brown, convex, ridged. Isidia almost spherical and in groups **17. P. loxodes**
– Lobes dark brown to black, adpressed, more or less smooth. Isidia flattened and scattered **35. P. verruculifera**

24. Medulla K+ yellow, orange or red 25
– Medulla K– 26

25. Thallus brown with purple tinge, with a well defined reticulum of raised, pale-coloured lines. Mainly on siliceous rocks. **19. P. omphalodes**
– Thallus leaden to greenish, no pale lines. Mainly on bark in the East **1. P. acetabulum**

26. Thallus brown with a clear reticulum of pale lines **8. P. discordans**
– Thallus chocolate to mid-brown with no, or only a very faint, pale reticulum (x 10 lens) 27

27. Lobes less than 1 mm wide, in dense overlapping tufts. Under-surface pale **15. P. laciniatula**

– Lobes more than 1 mm wide. Under-surface black in centre ... 28

28. Thallus chocolate-brown. Medulla KC– ... **22. P. pulla**
– Thallus mid-brown. Medulla KC+ red. ... **7. P. delisei**

29. Thallus with massed delicate coralloid isidia ... **5. P. conspersa**
– Thallus sorediate not isidiate ... 30

30. Thallus to 5 cm across. Lobes to 3 mm wide. Soralia farinose and globose ... 31
– Thallus to 10 cm across. Lobes to about 1 cm wide. Soralia coarse, rather granular ... 33

31. Lobe tips adpressed or curved under. Rhizines simple ... 32
– Lobe tips ± ascending. Rhizines dichotomously branched ... **28. P. sinuosa**

32. Lobes not stongly convex. Thallus dark and granular in the centre. Soralia laminal, K+ yellow ... **18. P. mougeotii**
– Lobes convex and curved under at the tips. Soralia ± apical, K– ... **14. P. incurva**

33. Medulla and soralia K+ yellow ... **4. P. caperata**
– Medulla and soralia K+ red ... **29. P. soredians**

1. Parmelia acetabulum [*Pleurosticta acetabulum*] Thallus grey-green, sometimes pruinose, green when wet, adpressed though inclined to be more erect, wrinkled and warted in the centre of mature specimens. Lobes up to 15 mm wide, rounded and widening at the apices which are deeply notched. Under-surface light brown with rather stout, simple rhizines that expand at the tip to form a holdfast. Frequently very fertile. Apothecia brown-red with a contorted and inflexed, uneven margin. Spores 14–17 x 7–9 μm.
Medulla: K+ red, P+ orange, UV–.
Habitat: Local and decreasing, on well-lit, somewhat nutrient-rich bark, rarely on rock. Mainly in southern and eastern England.

P. acetabulum x 5 (damp and showing P+ orange reaction).

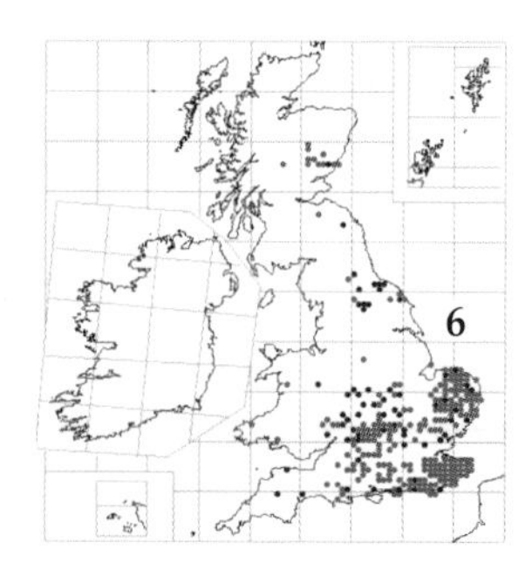

2. P. borreri [*Punctelia borreri*] Thallus grey to green-grey, closely adpressed except for the tips. Lobes rounded and only slightly notched. Lower surface black towards the centre, rhizines simple and absent towards the margins of the lobes. Widely scattered, irregular-shaped, punctiform pseudocyphellae on the upper surface often becoming coarsely sorediate. Sometimes fertile with red-brown discs, up to 5 mm diam, margin with pale pseudocyphellae. Spores 15–18 x 12–15 µm.
Very similar in appearance to *P. subrudecta* (31) except for its black (away from lobe margin) under-surface, less numerous and less rounded pseudocyphellae, coarser soredia and C+ orange-red reaction. It may be separated from *P. reddenda* (24) (C–) by the C+ orange-red reaction.
Cortex: K–. Soralia and medulla: C+ orange-red, P–.
Habitat: Not common, but overlooked for *P. subrudecta*. Found mainly in the South on well-lit, nutrient-rich trees and moss-covered rocks.

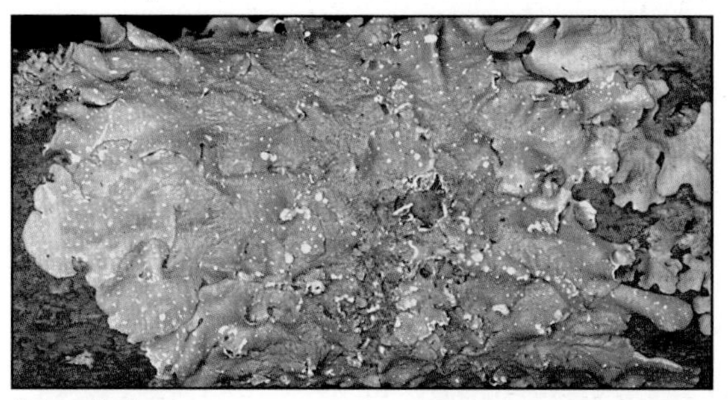

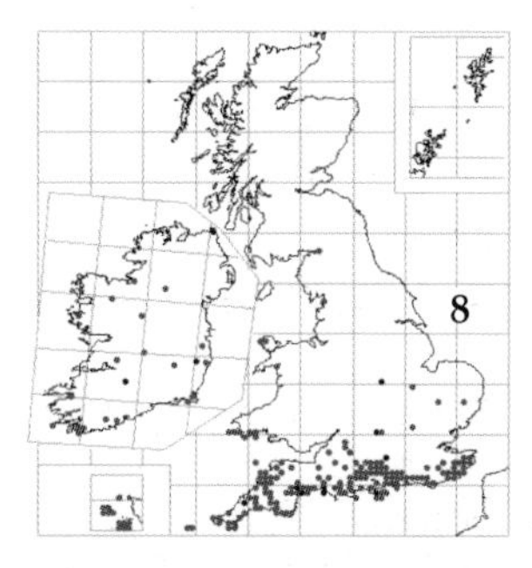

P. borreri x 4.

3. P. britannica [*Hypotrachyna britannica*] Thallus up to about 5 cm diam, dove-grey, smooth, very rarely with a few marginal cilia. Lobes are rounded and sometimes indented with rounded axils. Lobe tips ± ascending, extreme edge often tan-coloured like singed paper. Lower surface black with simple rhizines. Towards the lobe tips there are coarse, dark, blue-grey to indigo soralia. Not known fertile. Resembles *P. revoluta* (26) but with longer, narrower (less than 3 mm wide) lobes that are not revolute but raised at the tips and with dark blue-grey soredia.
Medulla and soralia: C+ red, UV– or dull orange.
Habitat: Infrequent in the West on well-lit acid rocks, usually near the coast.

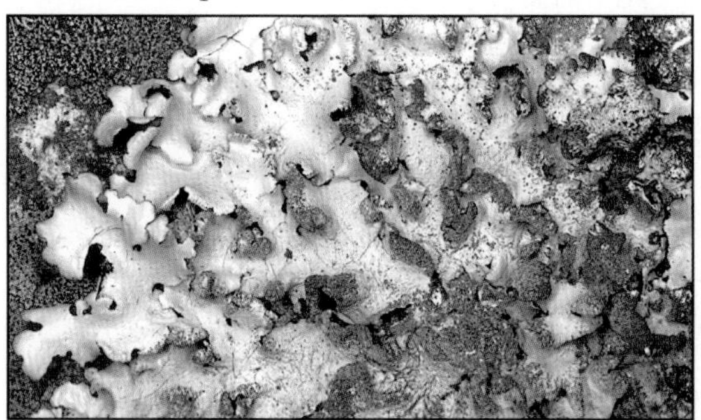

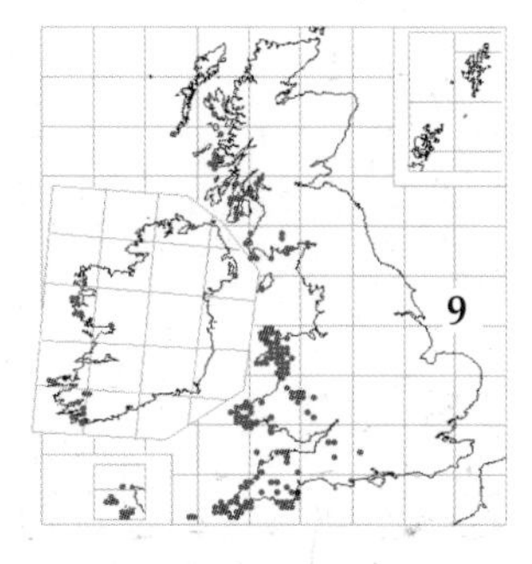

P. britannica x 3.

4. P. caperata [*Flavoparmelia caperata*] Thallus large, up to 20 cm across, yellow-grey when dry, becoming a very distinctive, almost apple-green when wet. Lobes up to 1 cm wide, expanding at the apices. Lobes transversely wrinkled and much contorted when mature, the surface becoming covered in coarse soralia that arise from shallow pustular areas. Under-surface black with simple rhizines that are often widely spaced. The lobe margins are light brown with white rhizines that turn black as they mature. Apothecia occasionally present, with sorediate margins. Spores 15–20 x 9–10 µm.
Cortex: KC+ yellow. Medulla and soralia: P+ orange-red, KC± red.
Habitat: Very common on acid-barked deciduous trees in the South but decreasing northwards. Also on well-lit rocks and roofs and overgrowing mosses. It is recolonizing many areas with the falling levels of SO_2. It has even been recently found in the grounds of Buckingham Palace.

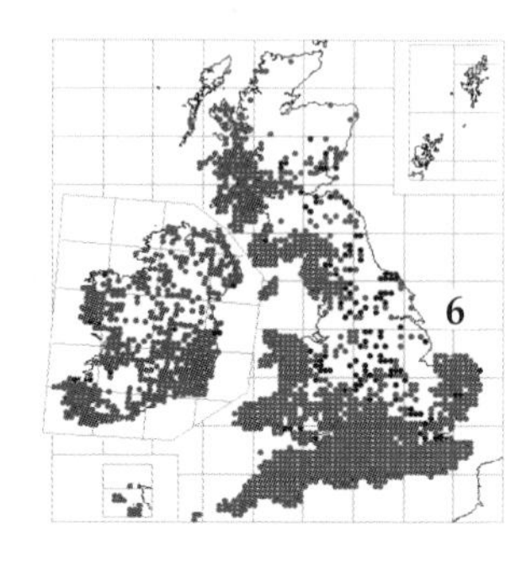

P. caperata x 2.

5. P. conspersa [*Xanthoparmelia conspersa*] Thallus yellow-green to yellow-grey, usually glossy. Lobes overlapping, narrow, up to 3 mm wide and much divided with delicate coralloid isidia which may be sparse or cover the whole surface. Under-surface dark brown to black, paler brown towards the margin, with widely spaced, simple rhizines almost to the margins. Commonly fertile. Disc brown, margins thin, contorted and often isidiate. Spores 6–10 x 4–5 µm.
Medulla: K+ yellow-orange, P+ orange.
Habitat: Common on exposed acid rocks, walls and roofs. It is also frequently found on drier rocks in nutrient-enriched, streams and lakes.

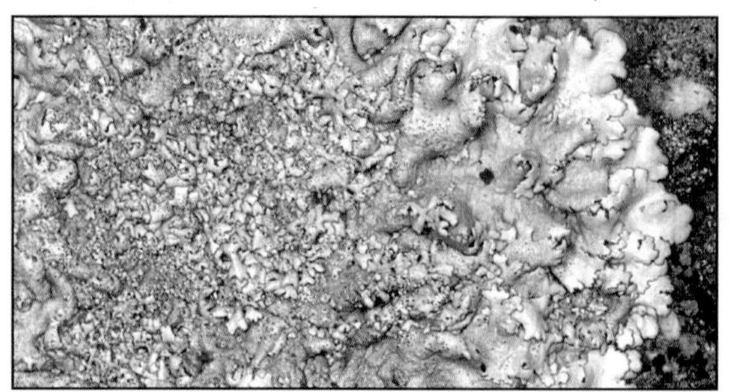

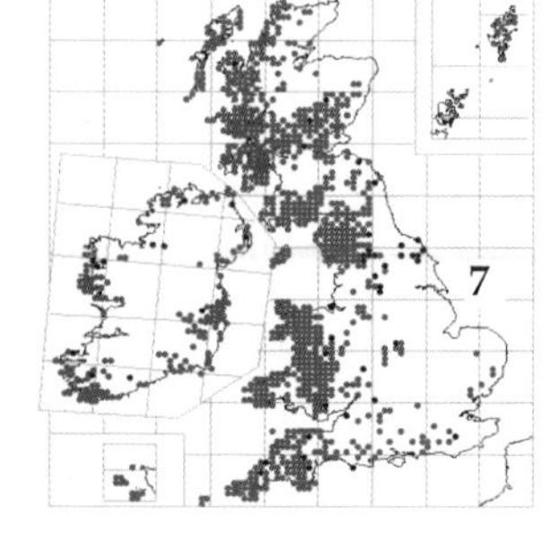

P. conspersa x 4.

6. P. crinita [*Parmotrema crinitum*] Thallus often loosely attached, glaucous-grey with crisped, overlapping, broad rounded lobes to 1.5 cm wide which are frequently much divided along the margin like an incised *P. perlata* (21). Black cilia and clusters of coralloid isidia (which are often eroded) are scattered over the surface and along the margins. Under-surface black in the centre, with fine, simple rhizinae, the margins are brown without rhizinae. Apothecia are rare. Discs brown with crenulate and isidiate margins. Spores 21–31 x 11–15 µm.
Medulla: P+ yellow-orange, K+ orange, UV–.
Habitat: Locally common in the West on well-lit, mossy trees and rocks. An 'old forest' species. *P. perlata* (21) is sorediate: **6a. P. horrescens** is smaller and K–.

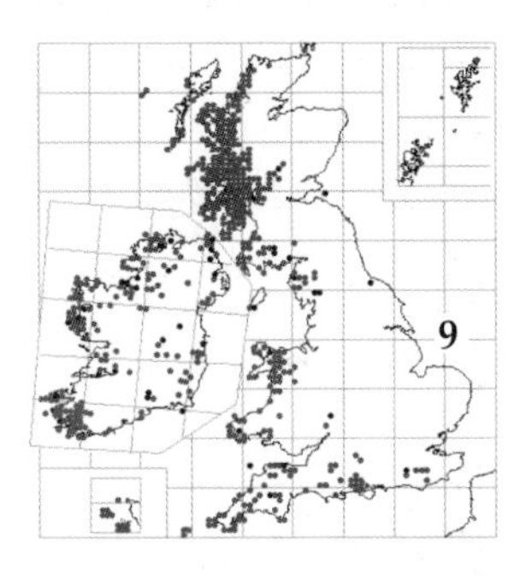

P. crinita x 5.

7. P. delisei [*Neofuscelia delisei*] Has the general appearance of *P. pulla* (22) in being fertile but is a paler milk-coffee brown. It is the fertile form of *P. loxodes* (17) and is doubtfully distict from it as specimens may be found with both apothecia and isidia.
Medulla: KC+ orange-red, C ± red, UV+ white.
Habitat: Common on well-lit, acid rocks on the coast.

8. P. discordans Very similar in appearance to *P. omphalodes* (19) but usually darker brown with less conspicuous white pseudocyphellae on the narrower (usually about 1 mm wide), overlapping lobes.
Medulla: P+ orange-red, UV+ blue-white.
Habitat: Nutrient-poor, well-lit acid rocks, mainly in upland regions.

9. P. elegantula [*Melanelia elegantula*] Thallus adpressed, brown to olive-green, up to 5 cm diam. Lobes to 2 mm wide. The centre of the thallus is covered in coralloid, often branched, solid isidia. The isidia are separate and rather evenly spaced on the younger lobes. Under-surface pale brown with simple rhizines. Seldom fertile, apothecia with isidiate margins. Spores 8–11 x 4–7 µm.
Spot reactions: negative.

Habitat: Frequent mainly on twigs and horizontal branches of nutrient-enriched trees, rarely on rocks. Often with *P. lacinatula* (15), seldom with *P. exasperatula* (11).

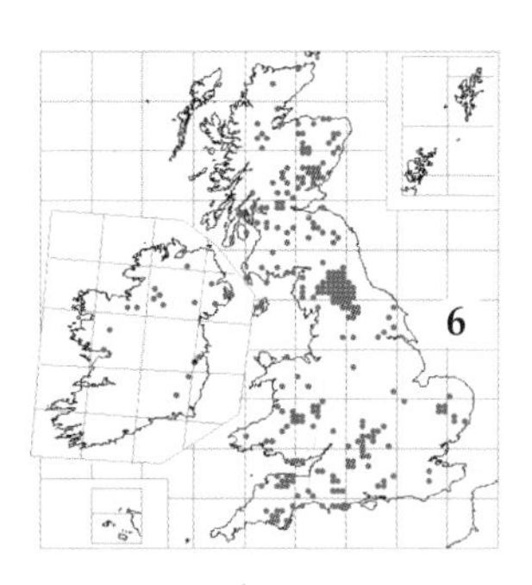

P. elegantula x 8.

For *P. endochlora* see under *P. laevigata* (16).

10. P. exasperata *[Melanelia exasperata]* Thallus to 5 cm diam, brown to olive-brown, often shiny. Lobes adpressed, short, often widening at the apices, which are rounded and only slightly notched. The lobes often have longitudinal wrinkles and numerous warts with a distinct, pale, apical crater (use hand lens). Under-surface light buff with very pale simple or squarrose rhizines. Usually fertile. Discs reddish brown with thick margins with warts. Spores 9–12 x 5–6 µm. Spot reactions: negative.
Habitat: Once common but now decreasing. Found especially in the West, on fairly well-lit, acid-barked twigs and smooth branches of deciduous trees. In other European countries it is normally found growing amongst pine needles, but it has yet to be found in this habitat in Britain.

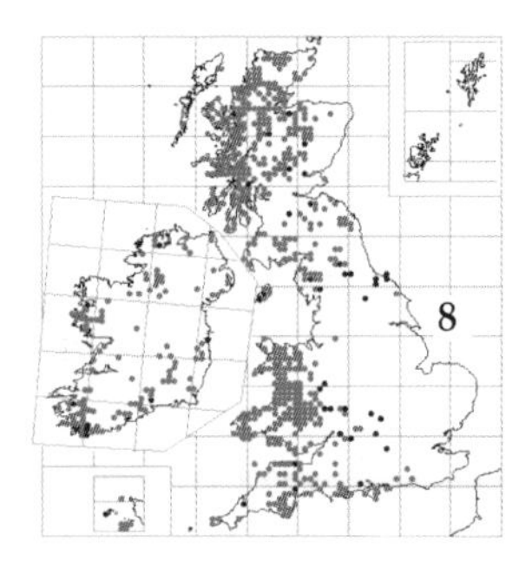

P. exasperata x 5.

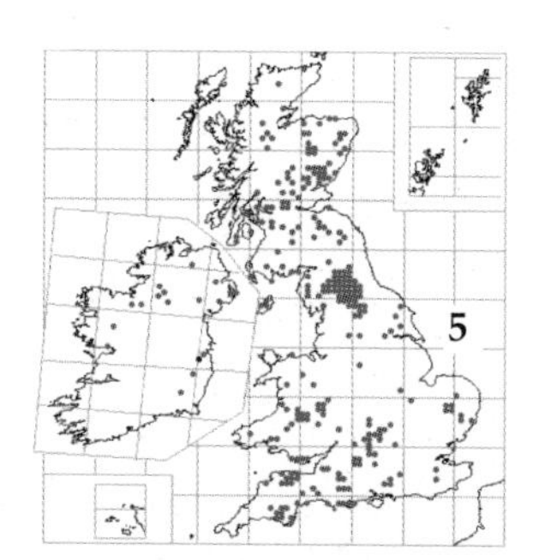

11. P. exasperatula [*Melanelia exasperatula*] Similar to *P. glabratula* (12) but differs in the pale under-surface and the negative reactions. The margins are more loosely attached to the substratum. Isidia mainly simple, larger, often randomly decumbent, hollow, shaped like the bowl of a spoon.
Spot reactions: negative.
Habitat: On both trunks and branches of trees, rarely on rocks (especially in northern England), usually on slightly nutrient-enriched substrata.

12. P. glabratula subsp. **glabratula** [*Melanelia glabratula*] Thallus green-brown, shining, adpressed, lobes short, up to about 3 mm wide, widening at the apices which have shallow notches. Under-surface black in the centre with simple rhizines, light brown and bare at the apices. Isidia simple or coralloid and neater and more regular in shape than in *P. subaurifera* (30), often becoming crowded in the centre of the thallus. If eroded, leaving white scars. Apothecia infrequent, with isidiate margins. Spores 10–14 x 5–8 µm.
Medulla: K–, rarely K+ violet, C+ red, KC+ red, UV–.
Habitat: Common throughout Britain. Mainly on trees (more usually on the trunk) or fences, rarely on rocks.

13. P. glabratula subsp. **fuliginosa** is very similar but dark green-brown (when wet) to almost black, with densely packed, glossy small isidia in the centre, which can almost obscure the lobes. Common on rocks and acid gravestones.

P. glabratula subsp. *fuliginosa* x 4.

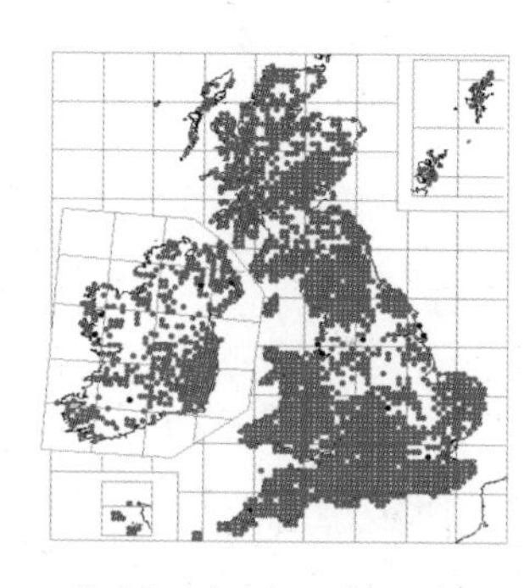

P. glabratula subsp *glabratula*

14. P. incurva [*Arctoparmelia incurva*] Thallus yellowish grey, small (up to about 5 cm), orbicular, consisting of long, narrow (about 3 mm wide), radiating, convex, contorted lobes which curve under at the tips and overlap. The inner lobes have large, rather yellow, globose soralia on their tips. Under-surface pale brown, lighter at the margin, with simple rhizines.

Medulla and soralia: KC+ pink, P– or rarely P+ rust-red, UV+ blue-white.
Habitat: Locally abundant on well-lit siliceous rocks in upland regions. It is rarely found on wood but appears to be increasing on man-made substrata.

P. incurva x 3.

15. P. laciniatula [*Melanelia laciniatula*] Thallus green to green-brown, adpressed, up to 5 cm diam. Lobes narrow (less than 3 mm wide), the marginal lobes being flat and smooth, the centre of the thallus becoming covered in numerous, overlapping, flattened folioles. Lower surface pale with simple rhizines. Not known fertile.
Spot reactions: negative.
Habitat: Well-lit branches and, rarely, trunks of deciduous trees, most frequent in south-east England. Like *P. elegantula* it appears to have spread from Dorking in Surrey where it was first recorded in about 1930.

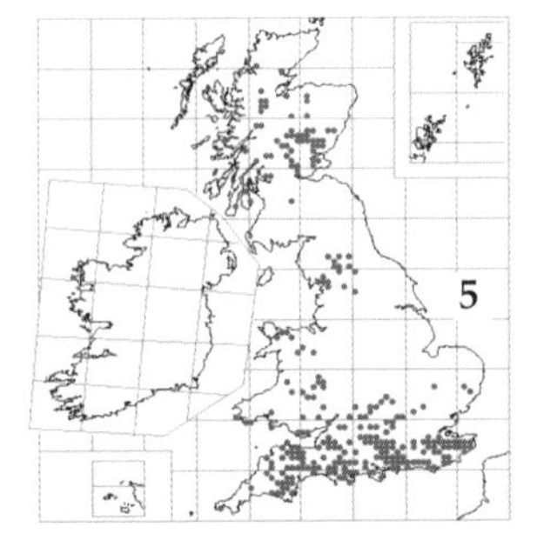

P. laciniatula x 7.

16. P. laevigata [*Hypotrachyna laevigata*] Thallus light bluish grey, large, up to 15 cm diam, orbicular and loosly attached. Lobes smooth, long and relatively narrow (up to 6 mm wide), rather rectangular with square cut tips and curved axils so that the lobe tips often overlap giving 'pseudo-holes' between the lobe tip and lobe axil. The lobe tips have delimited greenish to dark grey soralia. Under-surface black with repeatedly dichotomously branched rhizines that look like small trees. These reach right to the margin of the lobes. Medulla white. It

may be separated from *P. perlata* (21) , which it often replaces in high rainfall areas, by the lobe shape, the lack of a bald area near the lobe tips on the under-surface, and the shape of the rhizines. It is also P–. *P. revoluta* (26) is found on more basic substrates and is C+ red. Rarely fertile, apothecia with a smooth or ± sorediate margin. Spores 18–21 x 9–13 µm.
Medulla and soredia: C+ orange, KC+ orange.
Habitat: Common in high rainfall areas in the West, growing over mosses on trees or rocks.
16a. P. endochlora is similar but rarer. It has a pale yellow medulla and is found in the West and SouthWest. It is most common in coastal western Scotland.

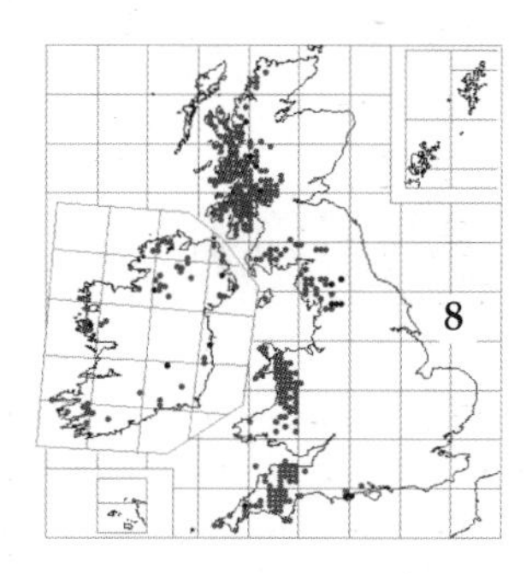

P. laevigata x 3.

17. P. loxodes [*Neofuscelia loxodes*] Thallus large, up to 20 cm across, yellowish brown to brown, slightly shiny, lobes long and narrow (2–5 mm wide), somewhat convex, parallel-sided, not, or only slightly widening at the tips which are rather square cut. The lobe surface with slight transverse wrinkles. Under-surface black with simple or furcate rhizines, bare towards the tips of the lobes. Coarse spherical isidia form conspicuous laminal clusters that may become confluent and erode to leave prominent white scars. Often fertile with often isidiate margins to the apothecia. Spores 8–10 x 4–5 µm.
Medulla: KC+ orange-red, C ± red, UV+ white.
Habitat: Frequent in maritime regions on well-lit siliceous rock, rarer inland.

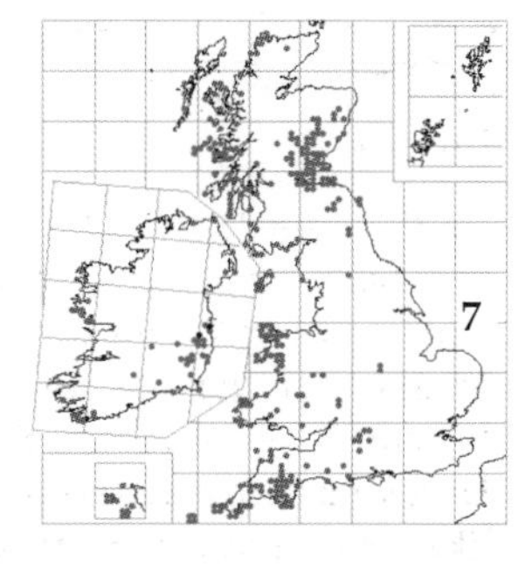

P. loxodes x 4.

18. P. mougeotii [*Xanthoparmelia mougeotii*] Thallus yellowish grey, small, up to 4 cm diam, adpressed, rosette-forming with narrow (up to about 3 mm wide) lobes that are radiating and separate. The centre of the thallus is dark from the numerous dark brown granules on the surface. Large, yellowish grey, convex to excavate soralia are scattered over the surface (not limited to the tip as in *P. incurva*). Under-surface dark brown to black with simple rhizines, lighter brown at the margin with rhizinae extending almost to the edge of the lobe. It is rarely found fertile. Apothecia with sorediate margins. Spores 6–9 x 4–5 µm. It superficially resembles *Parmeliopsis ambigua* on rocks but that species has squarer tips to the lobes and the medulla is P–, UV+ white.
Medulla: K+ orange, P+ orange, UV– (*P. incurva*, K–, UV+ blue-white).
Habitat: Common and increasing, on siliceous rocks and on the flat tops of tombstones and chippings on graves. It is even found on glass and roofing felt; it is a pioneer species on these substrates.

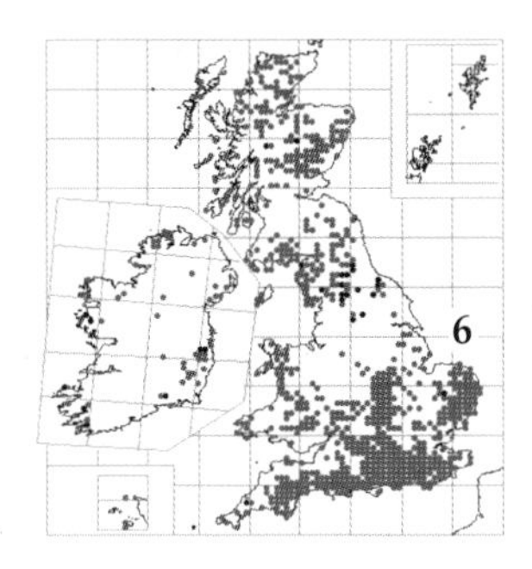

P. mougeotii x 3.

19. P. omphalodes Thallus up to about 15 cm wide, dark brown to grey-brown with a purple, almost metallic, hue, but often appears lighter as the upper surface is covered in a coarse reticulum of white or pale grey lines. Lobes rather small and expanded at the apices which are square cut and notched to give a palmate effect. Under-surface black with simple or furcate, rather sparse, rhizines which grow to the margins of the lobes. Apothecia fairly frequent especially in the North and West. Discs dark brown with a thin, lighter margin. May be separated from *P. saxatilis* (27) and *P. sulcata* (32) by the colour and the lack of soralia or isidia. (The much rarer *P. discordans* (8) is mainly westerly and has a less marked reticulum, is less shiny with narrower (less than 1 mm wide), more adpressed lobes and the medulla is K–.)
Medulla: K+ orange-red, P+ orange.
Habitat: Very common on nutrient-poor, well-lit, siliceous rocks, especially in upland areas, but extending down to sea-level. Very rarely found on bark and wood. It was commonly used in dyeing.

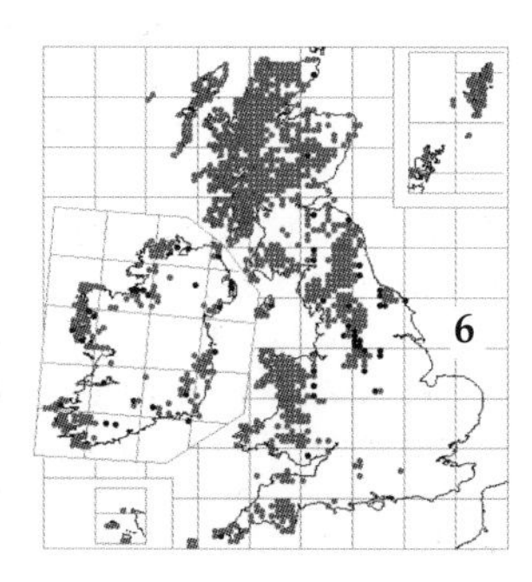

P. omphalodes x 4.

20. P. pastillifera [*Parmelina pastillifera*] Thallus to 10 cm diam, blue-grey, smooth, rather adpressed, ridged towards the centre. Under-surface black, brown towards the margin, rhizines simple or furcate. The isidia expand to form very blue-black to black, bun-shaped heads which may be sessile, up to 0.3 mm and several times wider than their stalks. These are more scattered and less crowded than in *P. tiliacea* (34). When fertile but not isidiate, see *P. quercina* (23). Medulla: C+ red.
Habitat: Frequent in the damper West and South of Britain, less common in the SouthEast. Found on well-lit, nutrient-enriched trees and rocks.

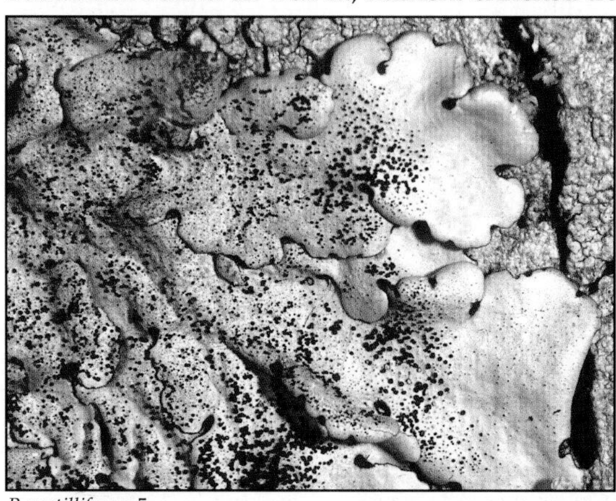

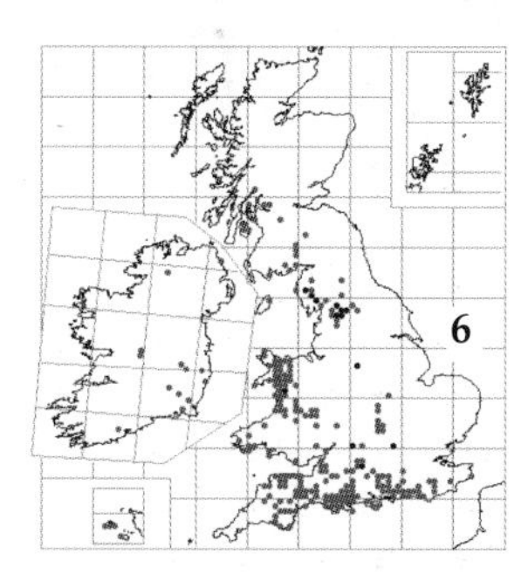

P. pastillifera x 5.

21. P. perlata [*Parmotrema chinense*] Thallus light pearl-grey, orbicular, up to 15 cm diam. Lobes smooth, up to 1.5 cm wide, with ascending, incised and undulating margins which have delimited soralia on the margins. Black cilia, up to about 2 mm long, are often found around the margin (*P. crinita* (6) is isidiate with laminal cilia among the isidia). Under-surface black in the centre with

simple rhizines, tan-coloured towards the margins which are devoid of rhizines. It may be easily detached from the substrate. Rarely fertile. Apothecia with sorediate margins. Spores 21–28 x 13–15 µm. It has been used to produce a brown dye. Closely related species are eaten in curries in India.
Medulla and soralia: K+ yellow-orange, P+ orange, UV–.
Habitat: Common in the South and West but becoming rarer northwards. Found on trees and rocks. It is pollution sensitive but is returning sooner than expected to many areas as pollution levels fall.

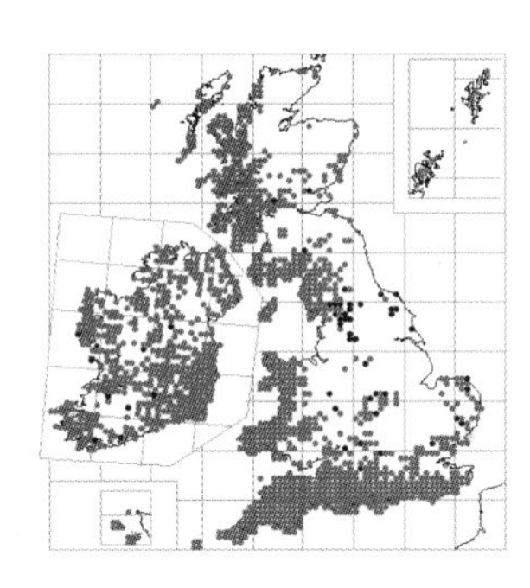

P. perlata x 1.

22. P. pulla [*Neofuscelia pulla*] Thallus large, up to 15 cm diam, brown, spreading, slightly shiny, transversely wrinkled, lobes adpressed and not widening at the apices, often covered with a faint reticulum. Under-surface black with sparse, simple rhizines that sometimes become branched, light brown and bare towards the margins. Apothecia almost always present, dark brown with entire margins when young, becoming thin and much distorted when mature. It resembles a fertile *P. loxodes* (17) or *P. verruculifera* (35), but lacks isidia. *P. delisei* (7) is lighter brown with flattened, wider, less rounded lobes.
Medulla: P–, K–, KC+ pinkish red, C± pinkish red, UV+ white. Reactions may vary.
Habitat: Common on sunny supralittoral rocks , more rarely in upland areas.

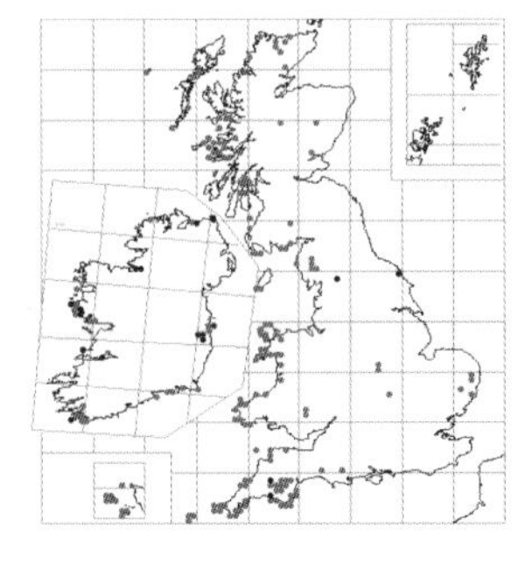

P. pulla x 4.

23. P. quercina [*Parmelina quercina*] Thallus grey, smooth and more or less shiny, adpressed. Lobes rounded with crenulate tips. Under-surface black with simple rhizines which grow almost to the tips of the lobes. Usually fertile. Apothecia with red-brown discs and thick margins. The under-surface of the apothecia frequently has black rhizines (remove apothecium to see clearly). This is the fertile counterpart of *P. pastillifera* (20).
Medulla: C+ red, UV–.
Habitat: A very rare and decreasing species. Found on mainly horizontal, well-lit branches, usually in the upper canopy of deciduous woodland.

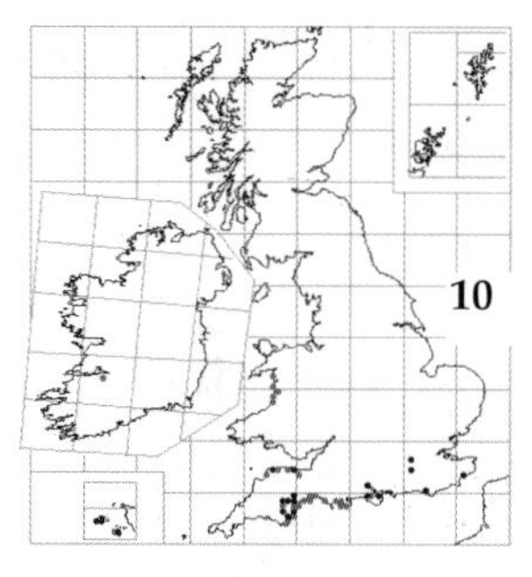

P. quercina x 4.

24. P. reddenda [*Punctelia reddenda*] Thallus grey, lobes less than 1 cm wide. The upper surface has white pseudocyphellae, which often produce soralia with granular soredia that may spread over the surface of the lobes. Frequently small folioles are present. Under-surface black with a lighter margin. Differs from *P. subrudecta* (31) in the black under-surface and C– reaction of the medulla.
Medulla and soredia: spot reactions and UV negative.
Habitat: An 'old forest' species of humid sites that is rather local. Found on shaded trees (often on horizontal branches) and moss-covered rocks.

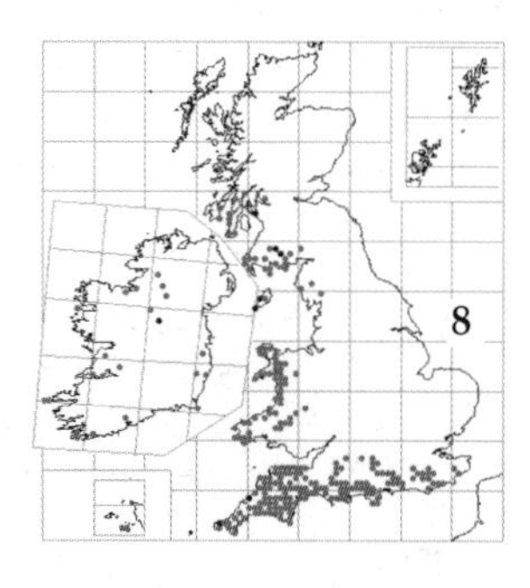

P. reddenda x 4.

25. P. reticulata [*Parmotrema reticulatum, Rimelia reticulata*] Thallus glaucous-grey, up to 15 cm or more diam and loosely attached, smooth, with very small, white reticulations giving it the appearance of cigarette paper (visible with a hand

lens). Ascending lobes which frequently turn down at the crenulate apices. Soralia and black cilia are usually present on the tips and margins of the lobes. Under-surface dark brown to black with simple rhizines (which, unlike *P. perlata* (21), extend to the margin), slightly lighter towards the margin. Apothecia very rare, brown, with an entire or partially sorediate margin. Spores 13–19 x 8–10 µm.
Medulla: K+ yellow turning red, C–, P–, UV–.
Habitat: Widespread but rarely abundant in low rainfall areas of the South on exposed trees (rarely on moss-covered rocks).

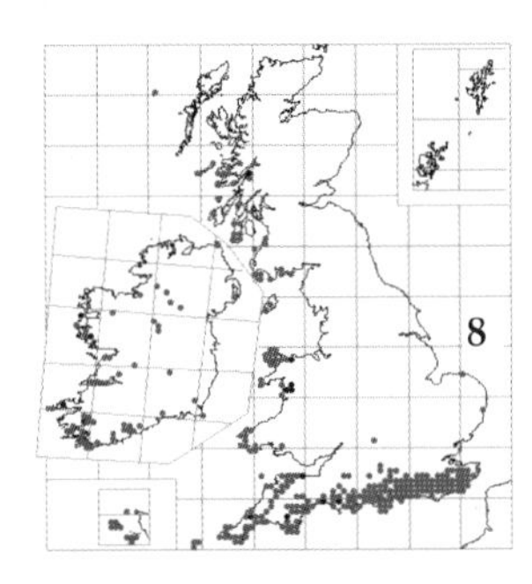

P. reticulata x 8.

26. P. revoluta [*Hypotrachyna revoluta*] Thallus light grey, orbicular, up to 5 cm diam. Lobes short, incised and turned down at the tips, usually with a light yellow-brown edge so that the lobes look slightly burnt around the margin. Very rarely with marginal cilia. Soralia, with concolorous or darker soredia occur towards the apices. The soralia spread over the lobe and are not sharply delimited. Under-surface dark with short simple or slightly branched rhizines towards the centre, tan and sometimes with rhizines to the margins. Apothecia rare. It may be separated from *P. laevigata* (16) by the smaller size, the more rounded revolute lobes and the C+ red reaction. It has shorter, wider lobes and lighter soredia than *P. britannica* (3).
Medulla: C+ red, UV– or dull orange.
Habitat: Widespread and fairly common on trees, rocks and memorials.

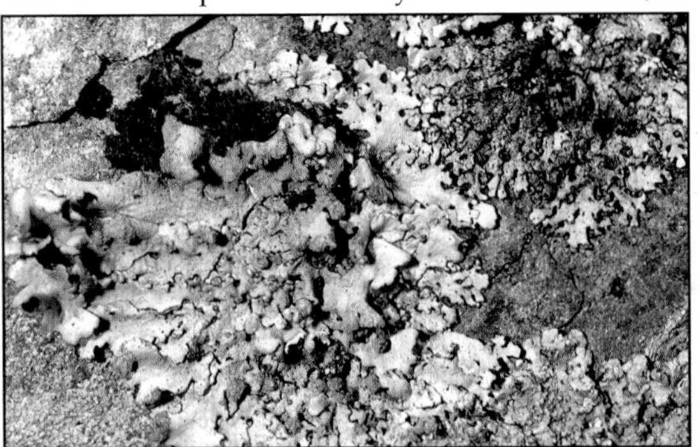

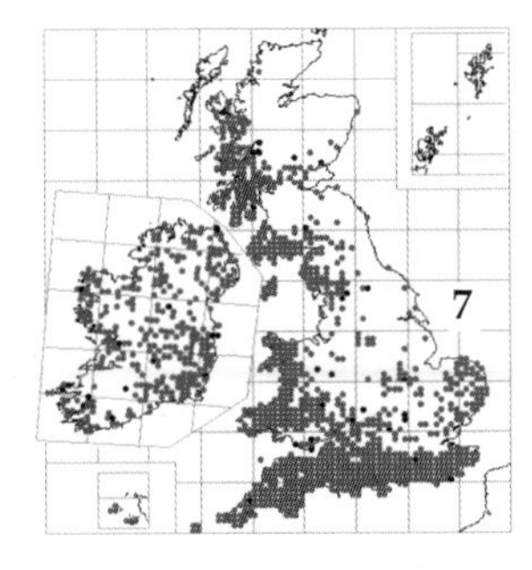

P. revoluta (left) *P. britannica* (top right) x 2.

27. P. saxatilis Thallus pale grey to green-grey in shade, often with brownish tips. Lobes to 3 mm wide, ridged, widening slightly at the tips. Pseudocyphellae forming a coarse reticulum of white lines in the upper cortex (see *P. sulcata* (32), *P. discordans* (8) and *P. omphalodes* (19)). Grey-brown isidia are formed on the reticulum and become confluent. Under-surface black, lighter at the margins. The under-surface, out to the margin, is covered in simple or rarely squarrose rhizines. Apothecia infrequent, up to about 1 cm diam. Disc dark red-brown, margins thin and frequently isidiate or crenulate. Spores 16–18 x 9–11 µm. It is frequently parasitised by the coral–red fungus, *Marchandiomyces corallinus*.
Medulla: K+ orange turning red, P+ orange, UV–.
Habitat: Very common throughout Britain on trees, stone walls and rocks. Specimens growing on human bones used to be considered to have medicinal properties. The most prized were said to grow on the skull of a hanged man. This species was also much used to produce a reddish brown dye.

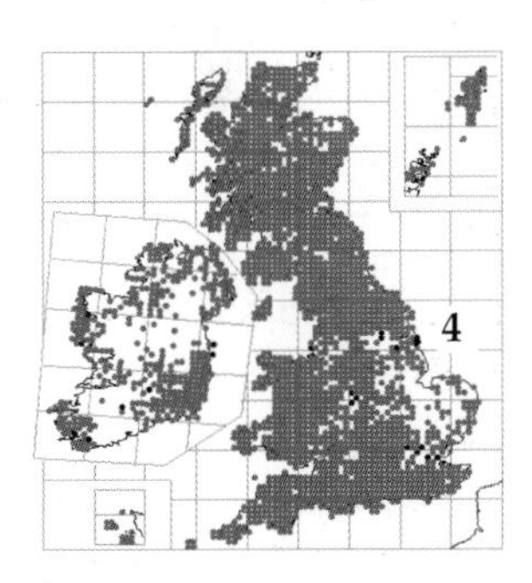

P. saxatilis x 5.

28. P. sinuosa [*Hypotrachyna sinuosa*] Thallus yellow-grey, smooth, up to 5 cm diam with separate, narrow, sinuate lobes, about 3 mm wide. The tips of the lobes are often ascending and develop farinose soralia. Lower surface black, crowded dichotomously branched rhizinae often extend beyond the edge of the lobes. Apothecia not known. Resembles a yellowish *P. laevigata* (16) which is C+ orange.
Medulla and soredia: K+ orange, P+ orange, C–, UV– or white.
Habitat: Frequent in north-west Scotland on well-lit trees, twigs, horizontal branches and acid rocks, rare in the rest of western Britain.

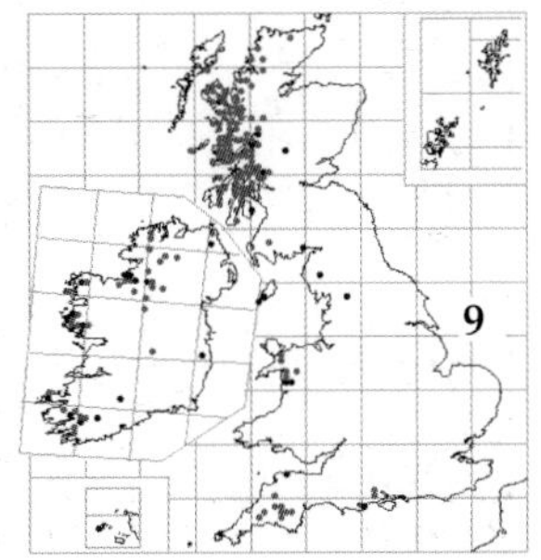

P. sinuosa x 4.

29. P. soredians [*Flavoparmelia soredians*] Thallus yellow-green to green or yellow-grey. Very similar to *P. caperata* (4) but rather more adpressed. The lobes are narrower, only up to 7 mm wide, more incised with farinose, rather than coarse, soredia.
Medulla: K+ yellow turning red, UV–. *P. caperata* remains K+ yellow.
Habitat: Locally common on trees, fences and exposed acid rocks. Frequently found on the tops of tombstones. Especially common near the coast.

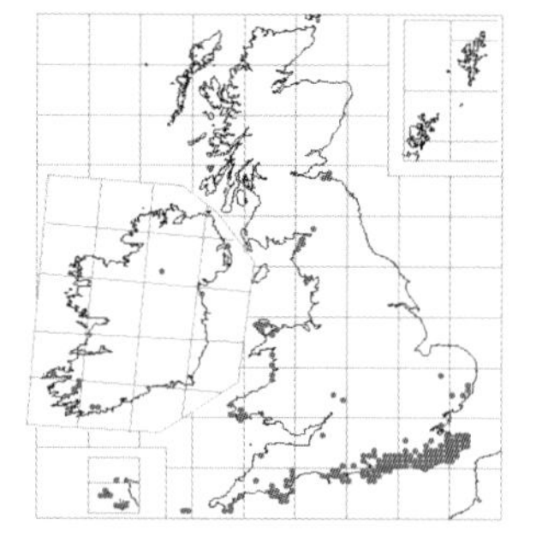

P. soredians x 2.

30. P. subaurifera [*Melanelia subaurifera*] Thallus brown to green-brown, adpressed, lobes to 5 mm wide. Under-surface black with simple rhizines. Similar in appearance to *P. glabratula* (12) but lobes often with a more matt surface. The isidia are simple and shorter, in clumps and less coralloid. They often break down to form soredia which easily erode leaving abrasions which are often very pale yellow-white (rub finger over surface of isidia/soralia).
Medulla: C+ red, UV–.
Habitat: Very common throughout Britain on smooth-barked trees, fences and sometimes rocks. More frequent on twigs and branches than *P. glabratula* and also more pollution tolerant.

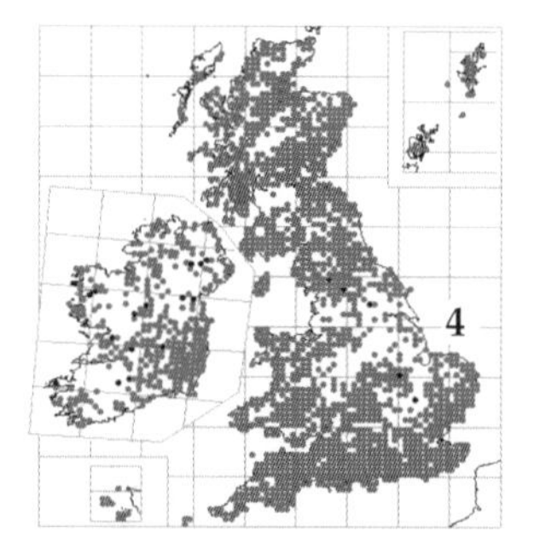

P. subaurifera x 5.

31. P. subrudecta [*Punctelia subrudecta*] Thallus grey, orbicular, to about 7 cm across, rather adpressed, with smooth or nearly smooth rounded lobes, sprinkled with delimited soralia containing farinose soredia which arise from white punctiform pseudocyphellae. Under surface light brown to white, darker

in the centre with simple rhizines. Very rarely fertile. Spores 14–17 x 12–15 µm. **P. ulophylla (31a)** differs in being greenish to brownish grey, with pruinose tips to the lobes and soralia along the ascending margins of the lobes. It is found on shaded trees and especially horizontal branches. *P. reddenda* (24) has a black lower surface and is C–, *P. borreri* (2) has a black lower surface but is C+ orange-red. *Cetrelia olivetorum* has minute, non-sorediate pseudocyphellae (use lens).
Medulla and soredia: C+ pinkish red, KC+ red, UV– or dull orange.
Habitat: Common but becoming rarer in the north. On well-lit trees and moss on acid rocks and memorials.

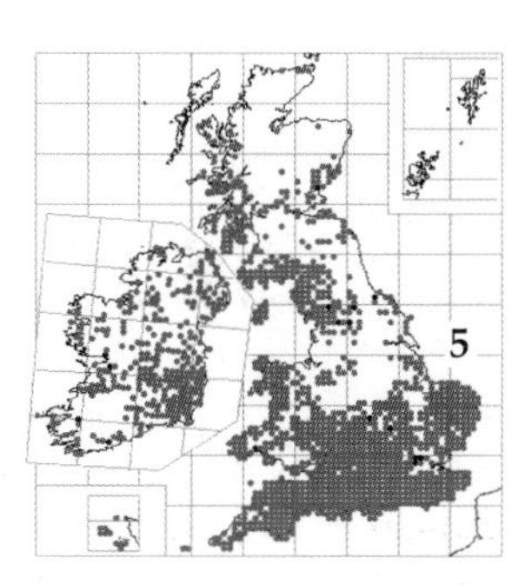

P. subrudecta x 2.

32. P. sulcata Thallus orbicular, grey to glaucous white with brownish tips, consisting of overlapping, ridged lobes, normally with a faint, coarse, white reticulum along which soralia develop, these may spread covering the centre of the thallus. Lower surface black with simple, or more rarely, squarrose rhizines. Usually infertile except in the North and West. Apothecia with a sorediate margin. Distinguished from *P. saxatilis* (27) by having soralia, not isidia.
Medulla and soredia: K+ orange-red, P+ orange, UV–.
Habitat: Very common on trees and rocks, especially in lowland areas.

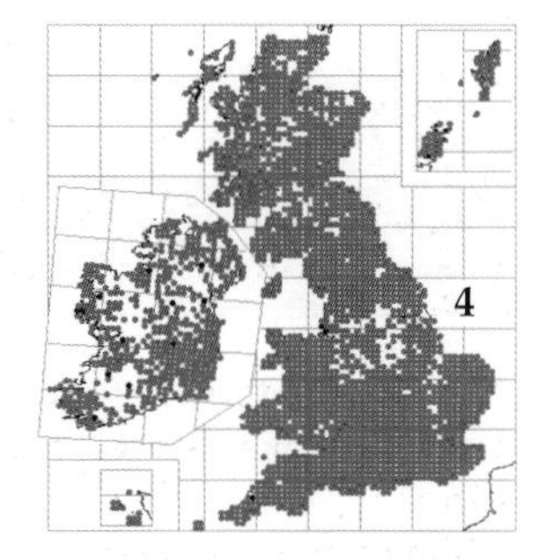

P. sulcata x 3.

33. P. taylorensis [*Hypotrachyna taylorensis*] Thallus up to 12 cm across, pale grey, often with a green tinge. Lobes rounded with sinuate axils. Upper-surface often white-maculate and crumpled. Upper cortex peeling in places, the torn fragments being the main means of distribution as soralia and isidia are absent. Lobe tips may be down-turned and brown as in *P. revoluta*. but that species and *P. laevigata* (16) are sorediate. Lower surface black in the centre, brown at the margin. Dichotomous rhizines cover the lower surface almost to the margins of the lobes. It is seldom fertile. Spores 9–12 x 5–10 µm. In large specimens the lobes towards the centre of the thallus overlap and point more in the same direction looking like the ripples of waves on a sandy beach.
Medulla: C+ red, UV± blue-white.
Habitat: Local, on mossy trees and rocks in old woodlands.

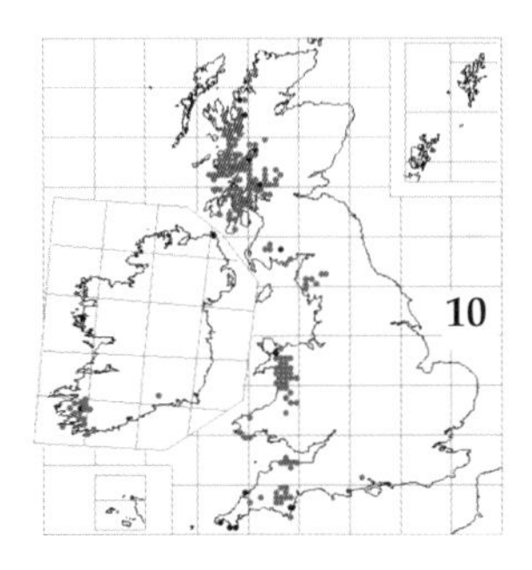

P. taylorensis x 3.

34. P. tiliacea [*Parmelina tiliacea*] Thallus pale blue-grey, smooth and sometimes slightly pruinose. Lobes rounded, slightly erect, becoming notched at the tips. Lower surface black with simple rhizines in the centre, light brown at the margin. The lobes bear simple or branched, coralloid isidia which have brown tips. The isidia may cover the centre of the thallus. Apothecia very rare, margins isidiate, rhizines frequently occurring on their undersides (see also *P. pastllifera*).
Medulla: C+ red, UV–.
Habitat: Widespread. On nutrient-rich trees, roofs and rocks.

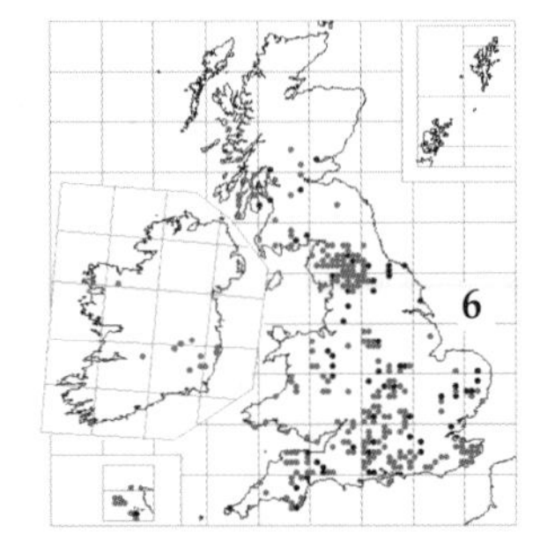

P. tiliacea x 3.

35. P. verruculifera [*Neofuscelia verruculifera*] Thallus brown to very dark brown, large, up to 15 cm diam, transversely wrinkled, with coarse isidia thinly or thickly dispersed over the thallus. Lower surface black with simple rhizines. Apothecia with isidiate margins. Has coarser, more clumped isidia than *P. glabratula* subsp. *fuliginosa* (13). *P. pulla* (22) is fertile and not isidiate, *P. loxodes* (17) has pustulate clumps of isidia, *P. delisei* (7) is paler brown and normally fertile. These last three species are mainly coastal.
Medulla: C± red, UV+ white.
Habitat: Found on well-lit acid rocks and especially on horizontal surfaces such as the top of chest-tombs both inland and on the coast..

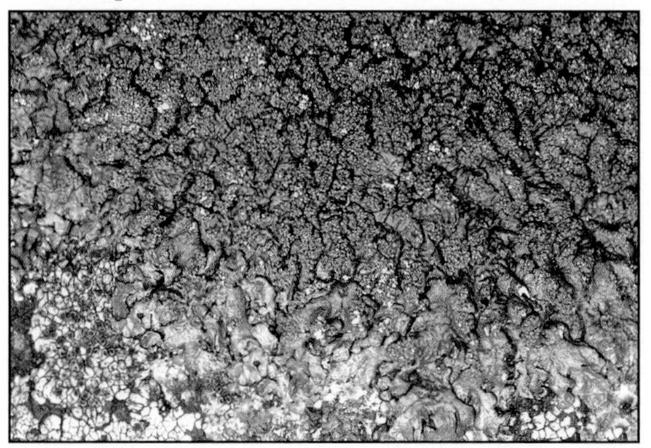

P. verruculifera x 3.

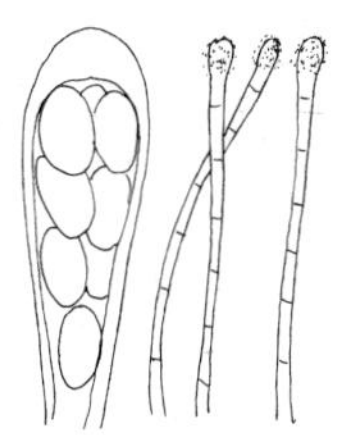

P. parvula x 300.

PARMELIELLA (diminutive of *Parmelia*) **Thallus** foliose or squamulose, usually with a black hypothallus. **Photobiont** *Nostoc*. **Apothecia** lecideine. **Ascus** 8-spored, with a K/I+ blue apical plug. **Spores** simple, colourless, ellipsoid. **Chemical reactions** none known.

Parmeliella parvula (P. jamesii) Thallus of blue-grey to olive-brown squamules with crenulate edges, up to 2 mm long, forming colonies up to 2 cm diam. The lobe margins are covered in coarse, rather granular, bluish isidia that may spread to cover the whole surface. Apothecia very rare, red-brown with a pale margin.
Habitat: Rare, in damp old woodland on mossy trees and rocks.

P. parvula x 6.

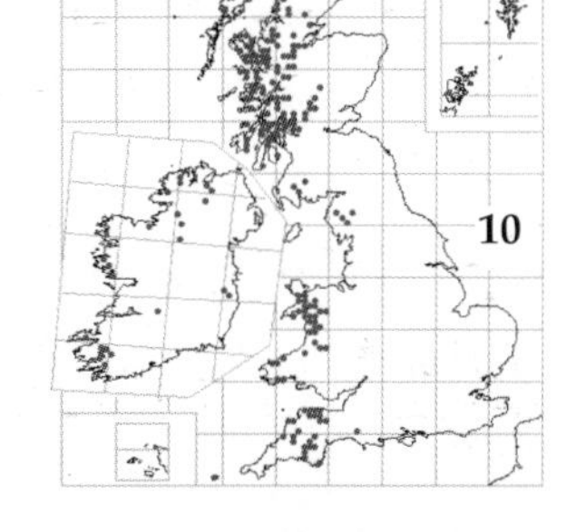

PARMELIOPSIS (resembles *Parmelia*). **Thallus** foliose with a dark lower surface and small simple rhizines. **Photobiont** chlorococcoid. **Apothecia** lecanorine with chestnut-brown discs. **Ascus** 8-spored. **Spores** simple, colourless and slightly curved. *Parmeliopsis* species resemble a small *Parmelia*, but are all closely adpressed and have curved spores whilst *Parmelia* has straight spores.

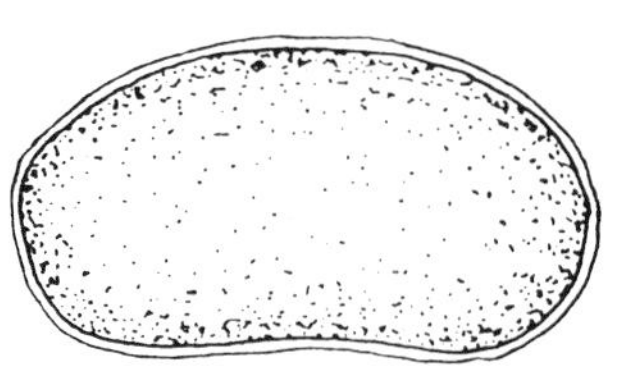

Spore of *P. ambigua* x 4000.

1. Thallus yellow-grey, soralia yellowish — **1. P. ambigua**
– Thallus grey, soralia white to pale grey — **2. P. hyperopta**

1. Parmeliopsis ambigua (Foraminella ambigua) Thallus yellow-grey to greenish, up to about 4 cm across. Lobes flat, closely adpressed, up to 1 mm wide and rather palmately divided. The lobe tips have discrete soralia and they and centre of the thallus become covered with concolorous powdery soredia. Lower surface black in the centre with stout, simple rhizines that adhere firmly to the substratum. Becoming light brown towards the lobe tips and lacking rhizines. Apothecia very rare in Britain, with light brown discs. Spores 7–11 x 2–3 µm. Cortex: K+ very pale yellow, KC± yellow. Medulla: UV+white. The similar *Parmelia mougeotii* is P+ orange, K+ yellow and has more convex and shiny lobes with coarser soralia.
Habitat: Common on coniferous trees and wood in Scotland, extending southwards on air-polluted acidified bark of deciduous trees, wood and even rocks. The species was increasing due to the spread of acid rain but, with the present lower levels of pollution, it is declining rapidly, especially in the South.

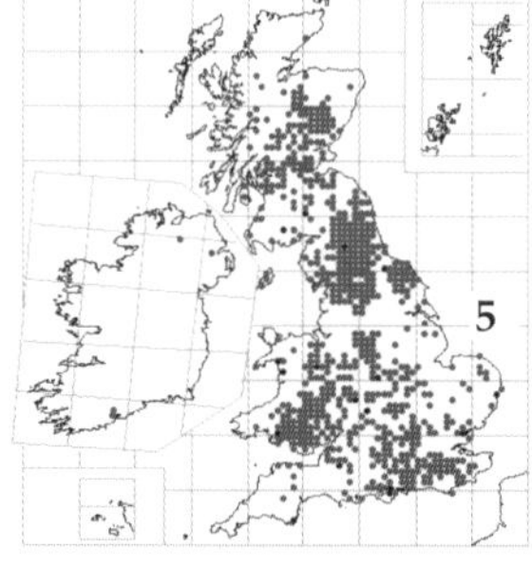

P. ambigua x 6.

P. hyperopta (Foraminella hyperopta) Thallus light grey, small, with light-coloured, small, globose soralia. Lower surface dark brown to black. Apothecia rare. Cortex: K– or pale yellow. Medulla: UV+ white.
Habitat: Mainly in upland areas on coniferous trees and wood, it can be locally abundant. Rarer elsewhere, sometimes found on deciduous trees and rocks.

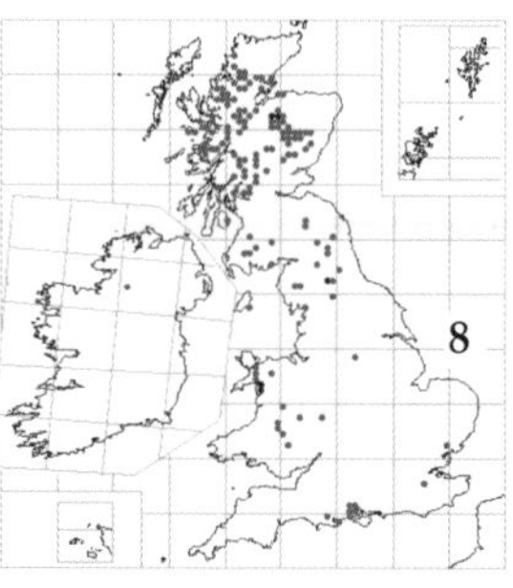

PELTIGERA ('carrying a light shield' – from the shape of the apothecia). **Thallus** foliose, usually large. Lower surface felted, frequently with various stout, tooth-like rhizines and veins which can be very useful for identifying the species (see table below which includes all British species). **Cephalodia** occur on the upper or lower surface of some species. **Photobiont** chlorococcoid or *Nostoc*. **Apothecia** lecanorine and arising on the upper surface of the lobe ends (in *Nephroma* the apothecia are on the under-surface of the lobe ends). **Ascus** 8-spored, *Peltigera*-type. **Spores** colourless, multiseptate. Although most species are large, many are not easily identified if the specimens are not in good condition. The simple chemical spot tests are of no assistance.

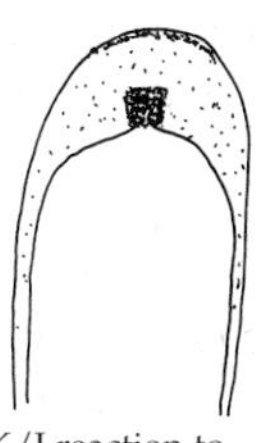
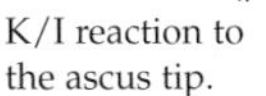

K/I reaction to the ascus tip.

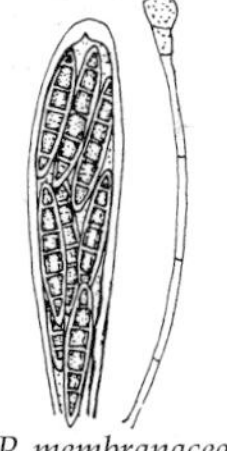

P. membranacea x 200.

PELTIGERA VEINS AND RHIZINES

Photobiont green and with cephalodia

Name	Rhizine shape	Rhizine arrangement	Vein colour	Vein shape	Notes
britannica	bottle-brush	in clusters	concolorous	indistinct or absent	Cephalodia dish-shaped, easily detached from upper surface. Mossy trees, walls and rocks in the North and West.
leucophlebia	simple	mostly scattered, discrete	brown-black, paler at margins	net-like	Cephalodia wart-like on upper surface, not easily detached. Mossy trees and rather calcareous rocks in upland Britain.
venosa	tomentose	not present	light to dark brown	fan-shaped	Often a single lobe to 2 cm diam. Cephalodia wart-like on veins on lower surface, not easily detached. Calcareous uplands in the North.

Photobiont blue-green and without cephalodia

Upper surface tomentose (at least in part)

Name	Rhizine shape	Rhizine arrangement	Vein colour	Vein shape	Notes
canina	bushy, like a shag-pile carpet	confluent at base	concolorous	flattened	Thallus bullate. Nutrient-poor calcareous, sandy soils.
didactyla	simple to stranded or bottle-brush	separate and often evenly arranged	cream to pale tan	net-like	Thallus to 3 cm diam. Lobes ascending. Laminal soredia when young. Often urban.
lactucifolia	simple, often with split ends, pale to tan	separate, widely dispersed	pale to dark tan with pale interstices	flattened, often indistinct	Soils, grass, rocks, etc. where damp. Common.
lepidophora	simple	separate	cream to pale tan	net-like	Thallus to 2 cm diam with flattened, button-like isidia. V. rare, river rocks. E. Scotland.

Name	Rhizine shape	Rhizine arrangement	Vein colour	Vein shape	Notes
membranacea	simple, becoming bottle-brush	separate	concolorous	raised and rounded, net-like	Thallus bullate. Common. Grass, mossy rocks and trees.
praetextata	simple, becoming slightly fluffy	separate	concolorous to tan	flattened, sometimes indistinct	Has folioles (schizidia) on margins and surface. Mossy trees, stumps, soil. Common.
ponojensis (species needs investigation)	simple, becoming rope-like	separate, widely dispersed	concolorous	raised	Calcareous sites in SW England, Derbyshire and Scotland.
rufescens	branched and - ± contiguous, usually brown	becoming confluent	concolorous, darker in centre	raised	Thallus brownish, ± bullate. On basic, mainly dry, nutrient-poor soils. Frequent.
		Upper surface matt to glossy			
collina	simple to fluffy	separate, numerous	light brown	indistinct	Only *Peltigera* with sorediate margins. Mossy trees and rocks. N. and W. Britain.
degenii	simple, smooth, narrow, white to tan	separate, widely dispersed	white to yellow-brown	narrow, raised	Often marginal isidia/lobules. Mossy trees, rocks, stumps. Scotland and N. Ireland.
elisabethae	clustered and rope-like, thick, dark brown	separate to clustered	felted, brown-black with small pale patches	absent or obscure	Margins crisped, curled, with folioles. Lobe surface cracked. Mossy rocks, central Scotland.
horizontalis	clustered and rope-like, thick, dark brown	separate to clustered	brown to black with white interstices	flattened, netted, sometimes indistinct	Apothecia rounded, horizontal. Mossy trees, rocks, etc., in old woodlands in the West.
lactucifolia	simple, often with split ends, pale to tan	separate, widely dispersed	pale to dark tan with pale interstices	flattened, often indistinct	Soils, grass, rocks, etc. where damp. Common.
malacea	absent to many hair-like, bushy	clustered, forest-like	absent. Lower surface brown	absent but hyphal net	Nutrient-poor soils, conifers, mosses in Scotland. Rare.
neckeri	poorly formed, simple	sparse and often in groups	ochre to black, with white interstices	flattened, wide, rather indistinct	Apothecia black-brown. Metal-rich and basic soils, rocks and grass. Local.
polydactyla	simple, pale to dark brown	confluent	dark brown to margins, with pale interstices	net-like and prominent	Lobe ends contorted, crisped. Mosses on trees and rocks in N. England and Scotland.

Peltigera rhizines

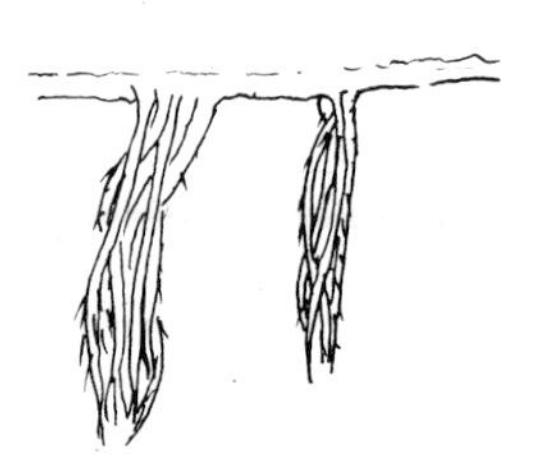

P. canina *P. didactyla* *P. horizontalis*

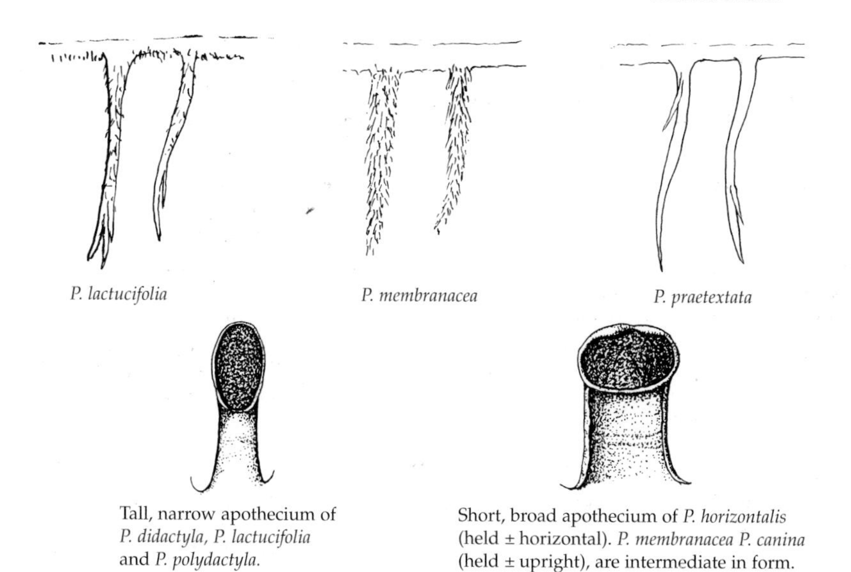

P. lactucifolia *P. membranacea* *P. praetextata*

Tall, narrow apothecium of *P. didactyla, P. lactucifolia* and *P. polydactyla.*

Short, broad apothecium of *P. horizontalis* (held ± horizontal). *P. membranacea P. canina* (held ± upright), are intermediate in form.

Note that the tomentose and matt species appear glossy when wet. If a lobe is squeezed between the fingers to press out moisture, the true nature of the upper surface can be seen.

1.	Upper surface tomentose or at least matt in parts	2
–	Upper surface glossy or slightly matt, not tomentose	9
2.	Thallus with isidia or soredia	3
–	Thallus without isidia or soredia	5
3.	Thallus with soredia	4
–	Thallus with foliose isidia	**10. P. praetextata**
4.	Thallus with laminal soredia	**4. P. didactyla**
–	Thallus with marginal soredia	**3. P. collina**
5.	Apothecia longer than broad.Thallus not bullate	6
–	Apothecia wider than long (often absent). Thallus bullate	7
6.	Lobes to 1 cm wide. Wall tops, disturbed soil. Tomentose	**4. P. didactyla**
–	Lobes to 2 cm wide. Damp mosses, rocks and lawns. Matt	**6. P. lactucifolia**
7.	Lobes to 3 mm wide, bullate. On grass or dunes	8
–	Lobes to 1 cm wide, slightly bullate. On calcareous substrates	**11. P. rufescens**
8.	On trees, mosses and rocks. Rhizines do not meet at base, loose fibres, rather bottle-brush shape	**8. P. membranacea**
–	On sandy soils. Rhizines meet at base, matted, bushy	**2. P. canina**
9.	Thallus bright green when wet, grey-brown dry. Cephalodia on upper surface	10
–	Thallus olive-green to grey when wet. No cephalodia	11

10.	Cephalodia not easily removed. Mossy calcareous sites	**7. P. leucophlebia**
–	Cephalodia easily removed. Mossy acidic sites	**1. P. britannica**
11.	Lobe margins grey sorediate	**3. P. collina**
–	Not sorediate	12
12.	Lobe tips digitally upturned. Apothecia ± vertical	13
–	Lobe tips not upturned. Apothecia borne horizontally	**5. P. horizontalis**
13.	Thallus with or without cracks. Tan-coloured veins	**6. P. lactucifolia**
–	Thallus with cracks. Dark veins	**9. P. neckeri**

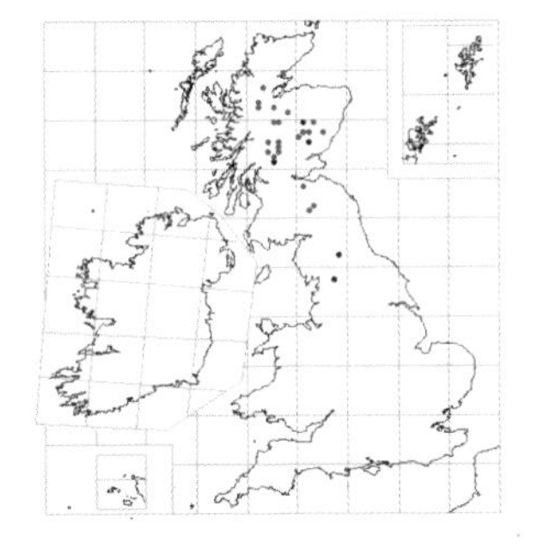

1. Peltigera britannica Thallus smooth, grey to brown when dry, bright green when wet. Lobes to 4 cm wide, rounded, wavy edged with distinctive dark, dish-shaped cephalodia on the upper surface that are easily removed to leave white scars. Lower surface dark brown to black in the centre, with indistinct veins and a few scattered groups of rhizines. Apothecia rare in Britain. Spores 3- to 7-septate, 45–100 x 5–7 µm.
Habitat: On acidic sites where ± consistantly damp, such as mossy trees and rocks.

2. P. canina Thallus grey to brown-grey, forming large patches up to 20 cm diam. Lobes to 2.5 cm wide and covered (at least towards the tips of the lobes) in a white tomentum, bullate, usually with down-turned tips. Under-surface almost white and differing from *P. membranacea* (8) in the flatter veins and the much branched, woolly rhizines that meet at the base so that the tops of the veins appear to be covered in a shaggy layer. Apothecia saddle-shaped. Spores 3- to 5-septate. It was at one time used to try to treat rabies due to the canine tooth-like appearance of the rhizines.
Habitat: Much rarer than *P. membranacea* (8) and found mainly on rather basic impoverished dunes and sandy soils.

P. canina x 4 (lower surface left, upper surface right).

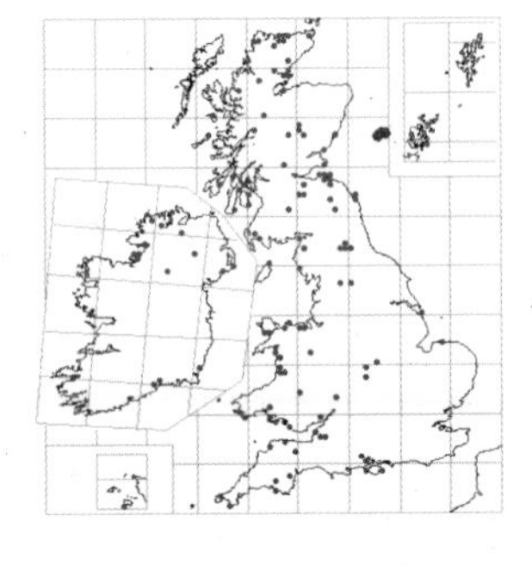

3. P. collina Thallus medium, to 10 cm diam, blue-grey to brownish, smooth to slightly pruinose, adpressed but with ascending tips and margins and a rather membranous appearance. Lobes to about 1 cm wide with edges usually covered in bluish grey soredia. This is the only *Peltigera* with strictly marginal soralia. Lower surface almost white with light tan veins and simple rhizines. It may be separated from *Sticta limbata* by the lack of cyphellae on the lower surface. *Nephroma parile* lacks veins and rhizines. Apothecia rare and only about 2 mm diam, dark brown and on ascending lobe ends. Spores 3-septate, 65–85 x 4–5 µm.
Habitat: On mossy trees and rocks in sheltered woodland.

P. *collina* x 3.

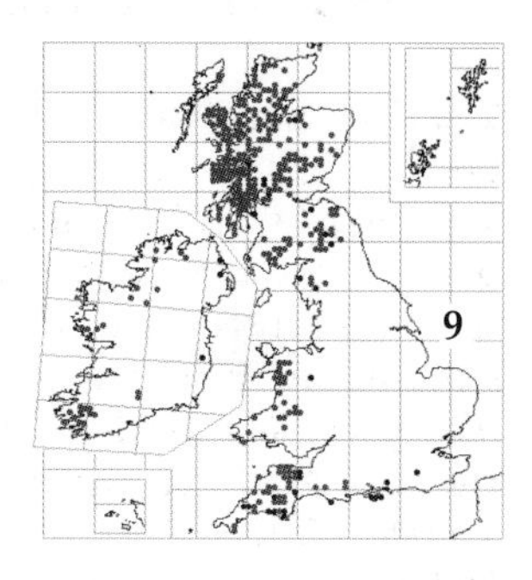

4. P. didactyla (P. spuria) Thallus grey, small, rarely larger than 3 cm diam, with narrow (to about 1 cm wide), white-tomentose, rounded, more erect, much less bullate lobes than *P. membranacea* (8). Lower surface with cream to light tan anastomosing veins with simple to bottle-brush-shaped rhizines.The young plants are clearly differentiated from other species by laminal soralia containing coarse grey soredia that may spread to cover the surface. Uniquely these soralia disappear as the thallus matures and produces apothecia on the ends of the erect narrow lobes. The margins of the red-brown apothecia are very crenulate. Spores 4- to 7-septate, 55–75 x 4–5 µm.
Habitat: Locally abundant on dry, well-lit soil or sand, especially where disturbed, such as paths, wall tops, old fire sites and spoil tips.

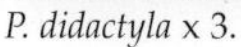

P. didactyla x 3.

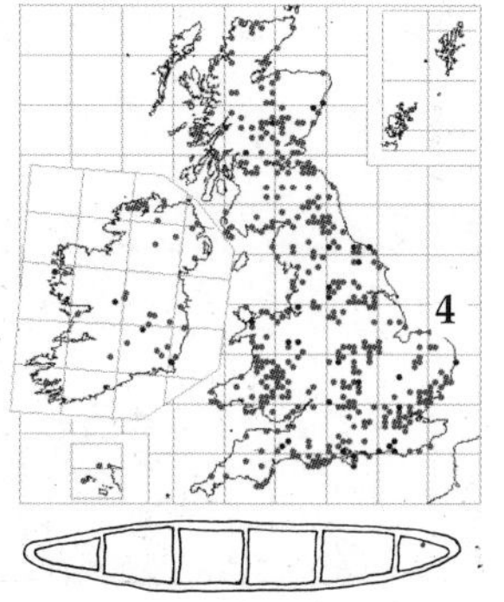

P. didactyla. 4- to 7-septate.

5. P. horizontalis Thallus large, smooth, dark grey, brown when dry. Lobes to 2 cm wide. Under-surface pale at the margins, much darker in the centre where the dark brown veins become netted and confluent. The area between the veins is starkly white and contrasts with the dark veins. Rhizines are grouped in clusters and are almost rope-like. Apothecia rounded or broader than long and held horizontally. Spores 3-septate, 30–46 x 6–7 µm.
Habitat: Locally abundant, often in damp areas. It is a characteristic species of trees, stumps and moss-covered rocks in ancient woodlands.

P. horizontalis x 3.

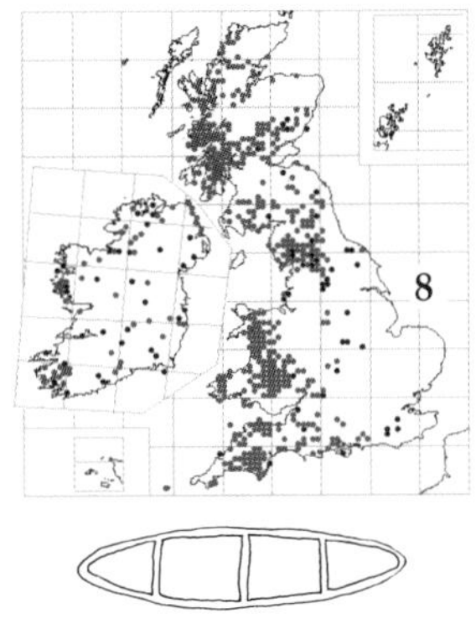

P. horizontalis. 3-septate.

6. P. lactucifolia (P. hymenina) Thallus large, up to 15 cm diam, grey to brown-grey when dry, olive-green when wet, somewhat matt to shiny, smooth, not bullate, with ascending margins. Lower surface cream or light brown, with faint flattened veins and paler simple rhizines which usually have tufted tips. Apothecia usually abundant, red-brown, longer than broad, on the raised, curled, digitate lobe tips. Spores 3- to 7-septate, 65–80 x 4–5 µm.
Habitat: Very common, on rather acid soils often amongst short grass, also on sand, peat and damp mossy tree stumps and rocks.

P. lactucifolia x 3.

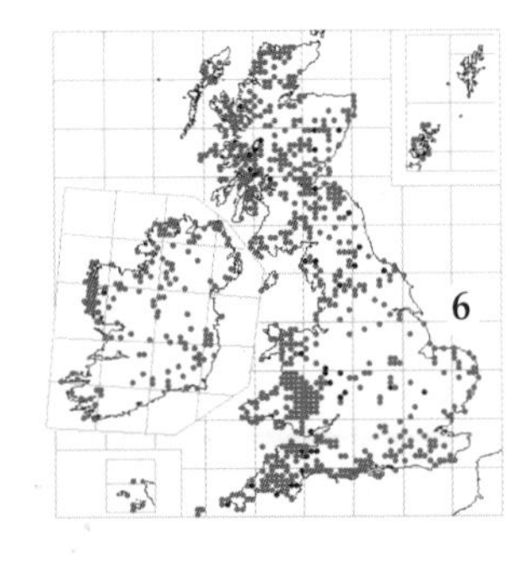

7. P. leucophlebia Thallus large, up to 20 cm diam, smooth, grey to brown when dry, bright green when wet, due to the green photobiont. Lobes large, to 4 cm wide, rounded, wavy edged. Distinctive dark, wart-like cephalodia that are not easily removed occur on the upper surface. Lower surface dark brown to black in the centre, lighter near the margin with distinct veins and usually dark rhizines. Apothecia rare in Britain. Spores 3- to 7-septate, 45–92 x 5–6 µm. It was at one time used as a supposed cure for thrush, due to the resemblance of the cephalodia to the appearance of the disease.
Habitat: Local on upland mossy ± calcareous rocks in ravines and coastal grass.

P. leucophlebia x 3.

8. P. membranacea Thallus large, up to 25 cm diam, thickly grey-white tomentose, grey when dry, brown when wet, broad rounded lobes, up to 3 cm wide, more or less bullate and reflecting the pattern of the veins, margins usually curled down (they do, however, sometimes curl upwards). Under-surface white to tan, usually with conspicuous veins and long, rather loose, fibrous-hairy to bottle-brush-shaped rhizines, discrete and not usually meeting at their base. Apothecia large, elliptical, red-brown. Spores 4- to 7-septate, 60–70 x 4–5 µm.
Habitat: Very common throughout Britain on mosses, trees and rocks. This and *P. lactucifolia* (6) are among the commonest large foliose lichens likely to be found in grass in open damp meadows or by roadsides.

P. membranacea x 4.

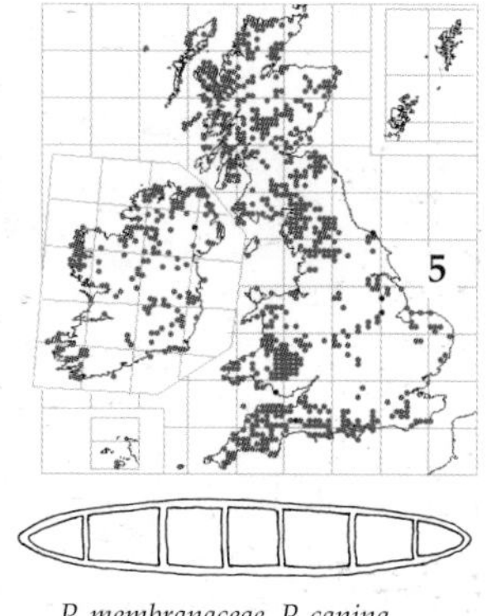

P. membranaceae, P. canina, P. rufescens. 3- to 7-septate.

9. P. neckeri Similar to *P. lactucifolia* (6) but often reduced to only scattered lobes. It has a glossy upper-surface, usually sparingly white-pruinose towards the margins of the lobes. Sharp, slash-like cracks exposing the medulla occur towards the centre of the thallus. Under-surface black towards the centre with dark veins, white interstices and a few weak rhizines. Apothecia common, with very dark red-brown, almost black, discs.
Habitat: Infrequent, on metal-rich soil and rocks, dunes and tennis courts.

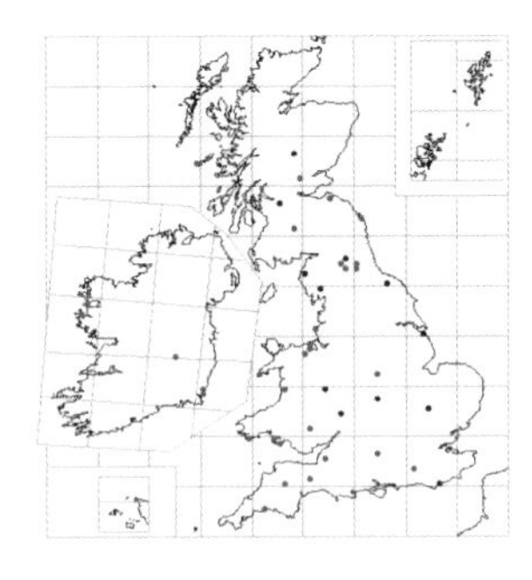

P. neckeri x 4.

10. P. praetextata Similar in appearance to *P. membranacea* (8). Large, with a grey-white tomentum and a bullate surface, but differing in having grey or brown, often dense, scale-like isidia along the margins and on any cracks on the thallus. The rhizines on the lower surface do not become bottle-brush-shaped. It is rarely fertile.
Habitat: Fairly common on moss-covered rocks, soil and trees, particularly in sheltered, damp sites in woods and heathland.

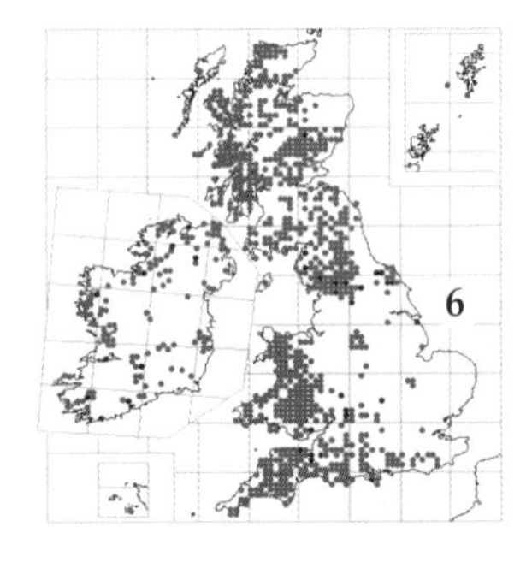

P. praetextata (wet) x 3.

11. P. rufescens Thallus often fragmented or rosette-shaped, grey to red-brown, grey-white-tomentose, sometimes sparingly bullate. Lobes mostly adpressed, only the margins curl upwards and are crisped and crinkled. The lower surface is usually darker towards the centre with flattened veins and dark, branched, fluffy rhizines that meet at the base. Frequently fertile with red-brown discs and crenulate margins. Spores 3- to 5-septate, 40–70 x 4–5 µm.
Habitat: Common, on drier, more basic, substrata than *P. membranacea*.

PERTUSARIA ('bored-through' – from the shape of the apothecia of the type species). **Thallus** crustose, often with a white prothallus. When sterile, some corticolous species may be recognised by the orbicular shape with concentric-zoned, marginal ridges. **Photobiont** chlorococcoid. **Apothecia** lecanorine, but in some species the disc does not expand and the apothecia are sunk within warts, often several in each wart. **Ascus** 1- to 8-spored, outer layer of ascus K/I+ blue. **Spores** simple, usually colourless, very large and thick-walled. Other genera with similar spores are *Ochrolechia* with thinner walls, and *Mycoblastus*. Some species were formerly used for dyeing but are more difficult to remove from the rock than the *Ochrolechia* dye species.

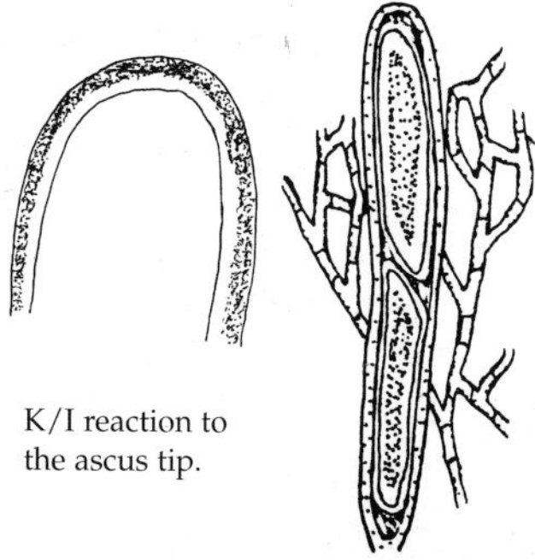

K/I reaction to the ascus tip.

P. coccodes x 200.

It should be noted that many corticolous species are occasionally found on rocks, and some saxicolous species are rarely found on trees.

1.	On bark	2
–	On rock	10
2.	Sorediate or isidiate	3
–	Not sorediate or isidiate	8
3.	Isidiate	4
–	Sorediate	5
4.	Thallus grey with grey-brown isidia, K+ orange to red	**4. P. coccodes**
–	Thallus grey with dull yellow isidiate crust, C+ orange	**8. P. flavida**
5.	Soralia grey, C+ red	**9. P. hemisphaerica**
–	Soralia white, C– and/or KC+ magenta	6
6.	Soralia widely spaced and covering apothecia, usually K+ dirty yellow, P+ orange	**13. P. multipuncta**
–	Soralia not covering apothecia, K–, P–	7
7.	White farinose soralia with bitter taste, KC+ magenta	**2. P. amara**
–	White farinose soralia (often sharply delimited), without bitter taste, KC–	**1. P. albescens**
8.	Apothecia conspicuous, open and ± lecanorine	**10. P. hymenea**
–	Apothecia, concealed in warts, opening only at the pore-like apex	9
9.	Apothecia grouped, several per wart. KC+ orange, P+ orange	**14. P. pertusa**
–	Apothecia usually single, with elliptical base, KC–, P–	**12. P. leioplaca**
10.	Not sorediate or isidiate	**14. P. pertusa**
–	Sorediate or isidiate	11

11.	Isidiate	12
–	Servediate	16
12.	Thallus dull sulphur-yellow, C+ orange	**7. P. flavicans**
–	Thallus cream to grey, C–	13
13.	Isidia globose to elongate. Usually on trees	**4. P. coccodes**
–	Isidia coralloid or short and stout. Usually on rock	14
14.	Thallus brownish grey, thick, K+y (turning red), P+y	**15. P. pseudocorallina**
–	Thallus grey, K+ yellow or orange, P+ orange	15
15.	Thallus grey, thin, K+ brown, P+ red (isidiate form very rare)	**3. P. aspergilla**
–	Thallus pure grey, thick, K+ yellow (persistent), P+ orange	**5. P. corallina**
16.	Soralia C+ orange or red	17
–	Soralia C–	18
17.	Thallus and soralia dull sulphur-yellow. C+ orange	**7. P. flavicans**
–	Thallus grey, soralia white to pale cream. C+ red	**11. P. lactea**
18.	White soredia with bitter taste	**2. P. amara**
–	White or yellowish soredia without bitter taste	19
19.	Thallus and/or soredia P+ orange or rust-red	20
–	Thallus P–	**1. P. albescens**
20.	Thallus P+ rust-red, K– or brown-red (no crystals)	**3. P. aspergilla**
–	Soredia P+ yellow, K+ yellow to red (crystals)	**6. P. excludens**

1. Pertusaria albescens Thallus grey to green-grey, thick, knobbly or cracked. Often difficult to separate visually from *P. amara*. The soralia, however, do not have a bitter taste and are always KC–. They are often much larger (1+ mm diam), more delimited, disc-like and more scattered. The margin of the thallus is usually more clearly zoned. *Ochrolechia turneri* is difficult to separate but has coarser soralia, often forming lines. In var. **corallina** the thallus is thickened in the centre and is ± covered by tightly packed, usually eroded, granular soredia.
Spot reactions: negative
Habitat: Common, on trees, often in light shade, rarer on mosses and acid rocks.

P. albescens x 6.

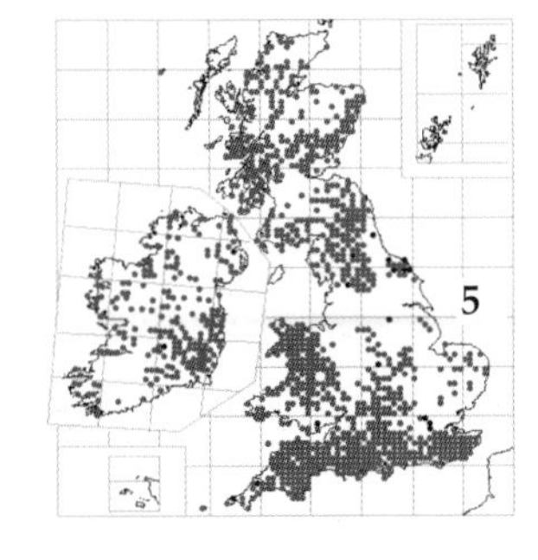

2. P. amara Thallus grey, thin to thick and delimited, sprinkled with punctiform soralia up to about 1 mm diam, containing white, coarsely farinose soredia. This species is most easily recognized by the very bitter, persistent taste of the soralia (moisten finger and rub on soralia, apply to tongue, wait a few seconds). Apothecia very rare, with 1-spored asci.
Soralia: KC+ magenta (not always clearly visible), sometimes P+ red.
Habitat: Very common on trees especially in the South, sometimes found overgrowing mosses on the ground or on rock. Due to its bitter taste it was at one time tried as a substitute for quinine.

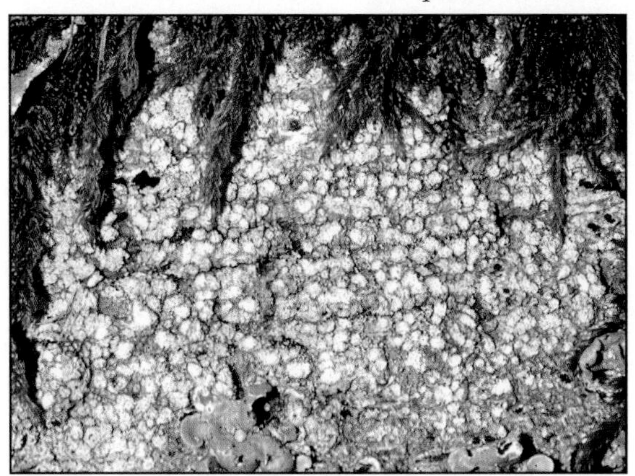

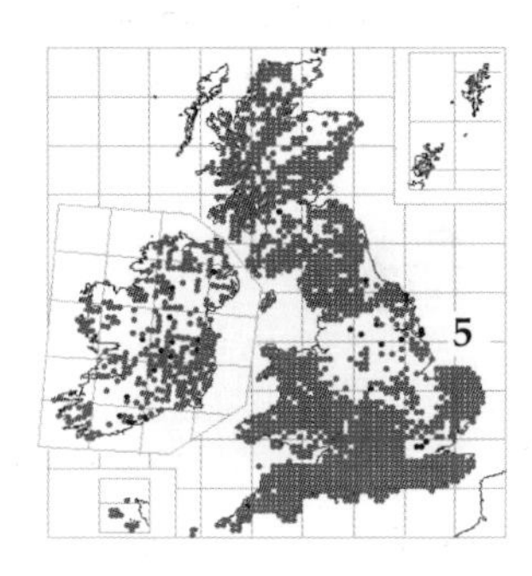

P. amara x 3.

3. P. aspergilla (P. dealbescens) Thallus thin, grey, cracked, sometimes with a pale grey to white prothallus. White punctiform soralia are ± evenly scattered over the surface. Very rarely with small isidia. Not known fertile.
K± brown-red, P+ rust-red, C– (*P. lactea* P–, C+ red), UV–.
Habitat: Common on acid rocks and walls in upland sites, very rarely on trees in old Scottish woods.

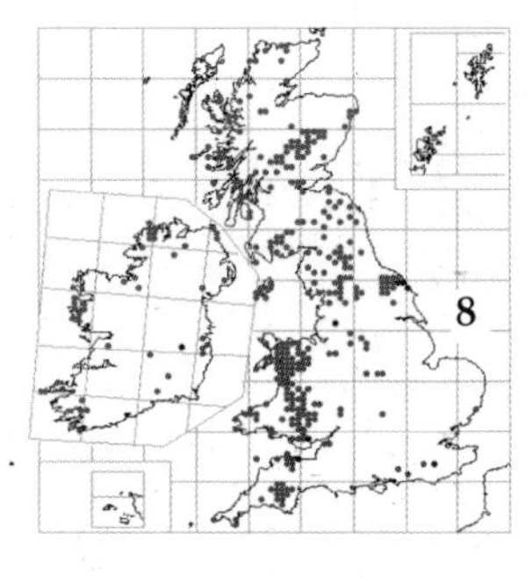

P. aspergilla x 8.

4. P. coccodes Thallus grey to yellow- or green-grey, prothallus pale or zoned at the margin, thick and cracked, normally with numerous small globose to elongate isidia that are concolorous or brown, sometimes on coralloid stalks. Apothecia very rare. Asci 2-spored. Sometimes parasitized by *Cyphelium sessile*.
Cortex: K+ yellow turning red, P+ orange, UV–.
Habitat: Mainly a south-eastern species found mostly on well-lit, old, rough-barked wayside trees but also, rarely, on siliceous rock.

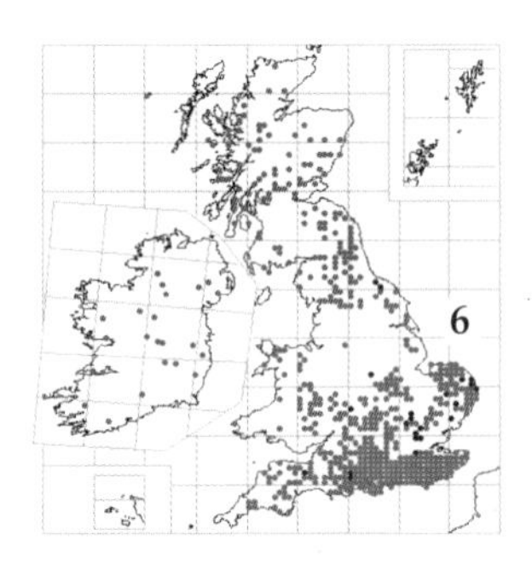

P. coccodes x 4.

5. P. corallina Thallus thick, white to pale grey, warted, usually with a white prothallus. The surface of the thallus becomes covered with isidia, which can be short and rounded but, when well developed are coralloid and up to 2 mm long (sometimes abraded). Apothecia rare, several in a wart. Asci 2- to 4-spored, spores 80–150 x 40–80 µm. See also *P. pseudocorallina*.
Thallus: K+ persistently yellow, P+ orange, KC+ yellow, UV–.
Habitat: Very common on exposed siliceous rocks in upland and coastal areas, rarely on bark.

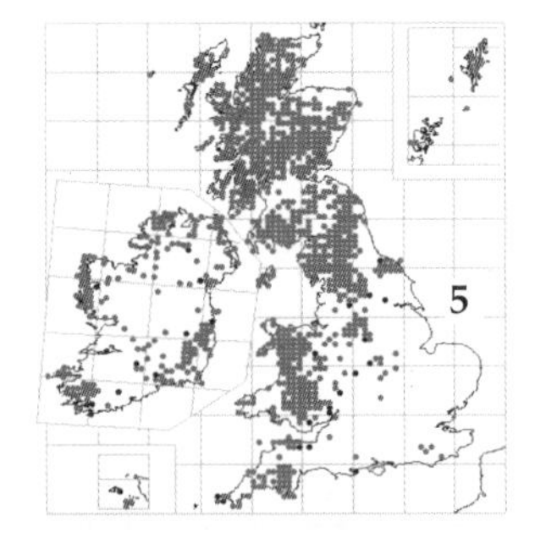

P. corallina x 7.

6. P. excludens Thallus pale grey, cracked and warted, prothallus pale or zoned. Soralia, up to 1 mm diam, are contained in warts . These contain coarse, white or yellowish soredia which may become confluent to cover the centre of the thallus.

Apothecia are rare and obscured by the soredia. They have not been recorded containing spores. However, a fertile counterpart occurs on coastal rocks in the West. This is **P. monogona** which lacks soralia but has fertile warts containing 1–4 apothecia, with dark grey, coarsely white-pruinose discs and 1-spored asci.
Soralia: K+ yellow turning red, P+ yellow, UV± yellowish grey.
Habitat: Fairly common, mostly on the coast in the West, on well-lit, often horizontal, siliceous rocks, especially frequent on granite.

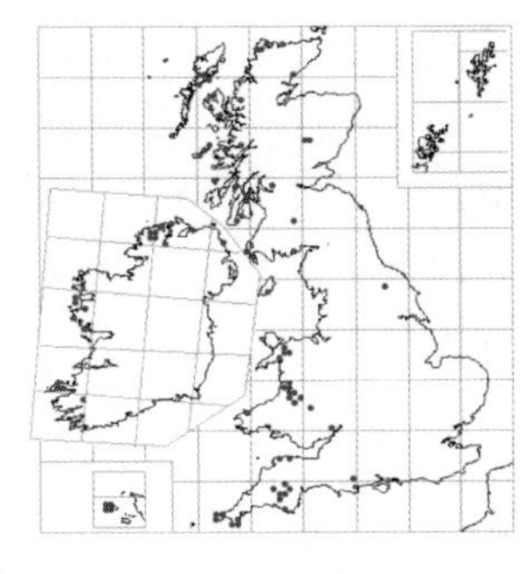

P. excludens x 4.

7. P. flavicans Thallus dull sulphur-yellow to greenish grey, thick and often areolate and warted. Soralia often arise around the margins of the areoles and contain yellowish, granular soredia which frequently become confluent. Apothecia rare with a thick margin. Asci 8-spored, spores 60–75 x 20–30 µm.
Soralia: C+ orange, UV+ bright orange.
Habitat: Locally frequent on well-lit siliceous rocks in the West and North.

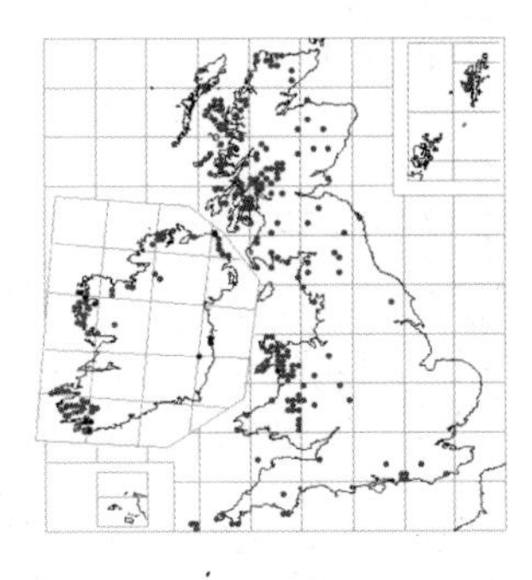

P. flavicans x 5.

8. P. flavida Thallus greenish yellow to yellowish brown, warted, rarely with a greyish prothallus. It is usually covered in a dense mass of short, dull yellow, rather globose isidia which can become coarsely sorediate. Apothecia extremely rare, up to 5 in a sorediate wart, small and punctiform, dark glossy brown with a thick thalline margin. Asci 8-spored, 60–100 x 24–40 µm.
C+ orange , KC+ orange, UV+ bright orange. *Ochrolecia inversa* and *Pyrrhospora quernea* which have the same spot reactions but are UV+ dull orange or UV–, are

never isidiate and have farinose soredia.
Habitat: Fairly common on well-lit, often rough-barked trees, in the South and East. It is often found on isolated trees in parkland.

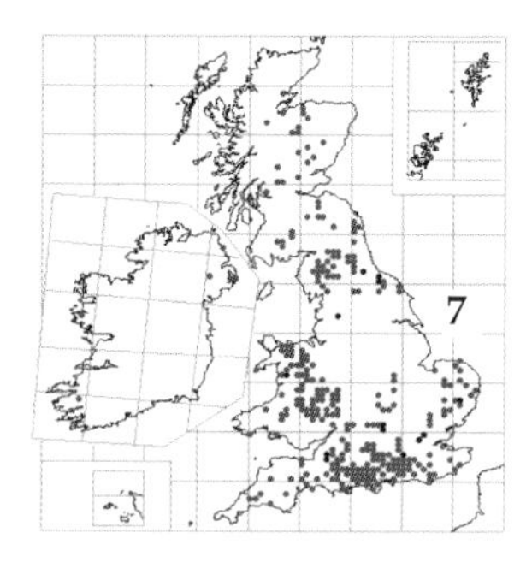

P. flavida x 4.

9. P. hemisphaerica Thallus thick, smooth to warted, blue-grey to yellow-grey usually with a wide white or, rarely, zoned prothallus. The soralia are up to 1.5 mm diam, pale greyish to concolorous with the thallus and markedly convex. It has never been found fertile.
Soralia: C+ red, KC+ red, UV+ blue-white.
Habitat: Locally common on rough-barked, mossy trees, particularly in the West and South, often in well-lit to slightly shaded sites, rarely on rocks.

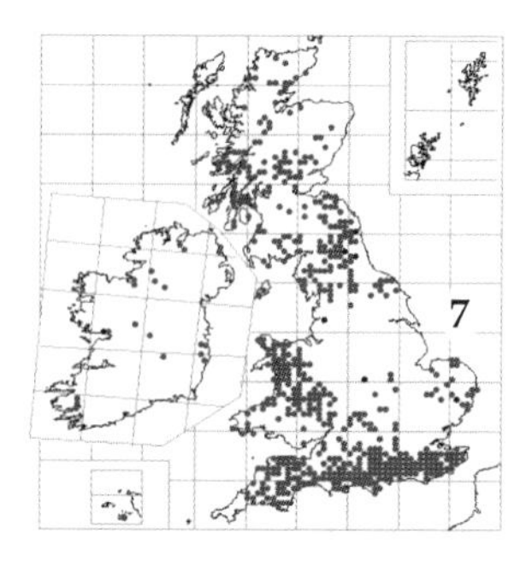

P. hemisphaerica x 6.

10. P. hymenea Thallus yellowish grey to greenish grey, thick, cracked and wrinkled, with a much less zoned margin than *P. pertusa*. Usually fertile. Apothecia often in small groups or covering the centre of the thallus. The discs are easily seen and much more open than in *P. pertusa* (in sunny sites the discs may be less open and it can be harder to separate the two species in the field). The margin is thick and crenulate. The disc is concolorous with the thallus to flesh pink and rarely thinly pruinose. Asci 8-spored, spores 60–110 x 25–50 µm.
C+ yellow, KC+ orange, UV+ orange.
Habitat: Common on trees, more frequently in shade, rarely also on rocks.

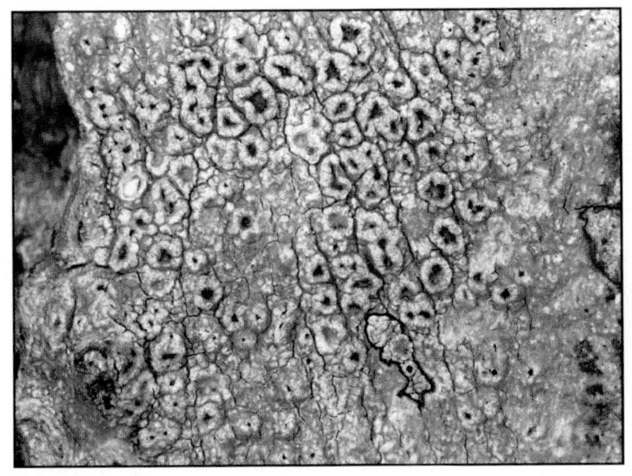

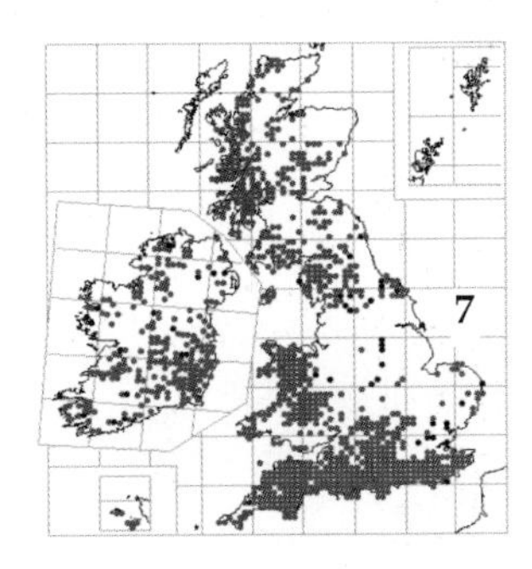

P. hymenea x 5.

11. P. lactea Thallus white to pale grey or ivory, thick, smooth, areolate or warted, often with a conspicuous white prothallus. Pale cream to pure white, delimited soralia, up to 1.5 mm diam, are scattered over the thallus. Very rarely fertile. Apothecia in warts, white-pruinose over a flesh-coloured disc and a sorediate margin. Asci 1-spored, spores 180–240 x 60–100 µm.
Thallus: C+ red, KC+ red, UV± faintly blue-white. Soralia: C+ pink-red.
Habitat: Frequent on well-lit, siliceous or slightly calcareous rocks in upland and coastal areas, more rarely overgrowing mosses on rocks.

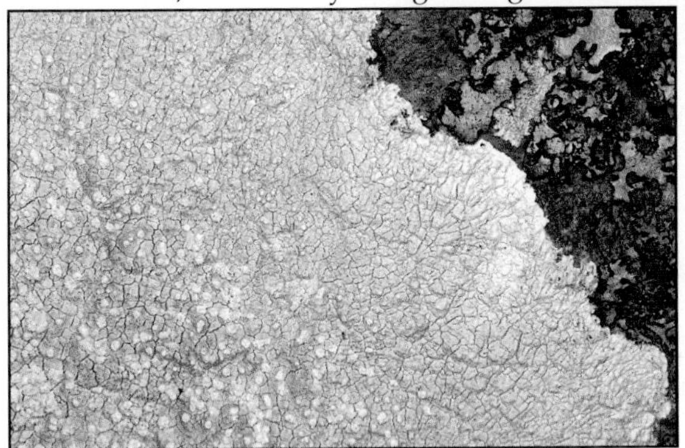

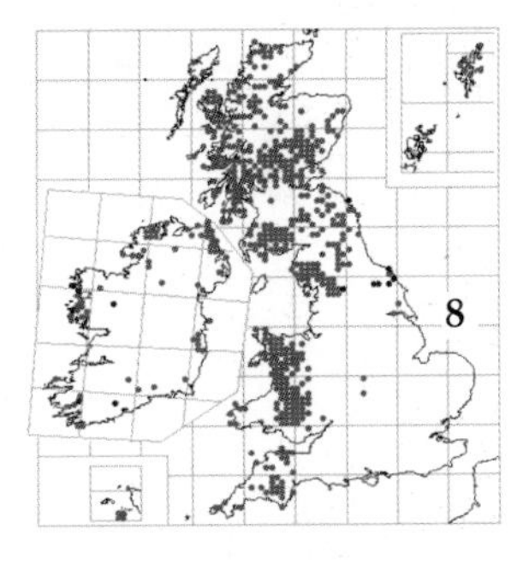

P. lactea x 7.

12. P. leioplaca Thallus creamy grey to green-grey, smooth and cracked or slightly warted, little zoned at the margin. The apothecia, up to 2 mm diam, are usually single but may be multiple arising in warts with a spreading, ± elliptical base and a flat top, appearing like bubbles rising to the surface of thick custard. Disc small and pore-like. Asci usually 4-spored, spores 50–100 x 25–40 µm.
K+ yellow, P+ deep orange or P–, KC+ yellow, UV± white to pale orange.
Habitat: Common on smooth-barked trees, mainly hazel or young oak, in shaded situations. Most frequent in the West and North.

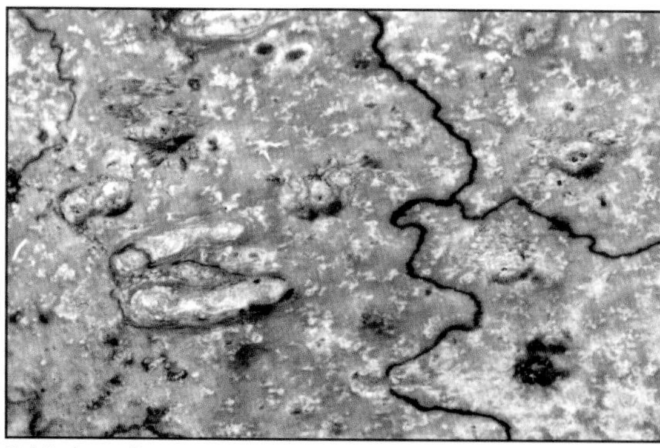

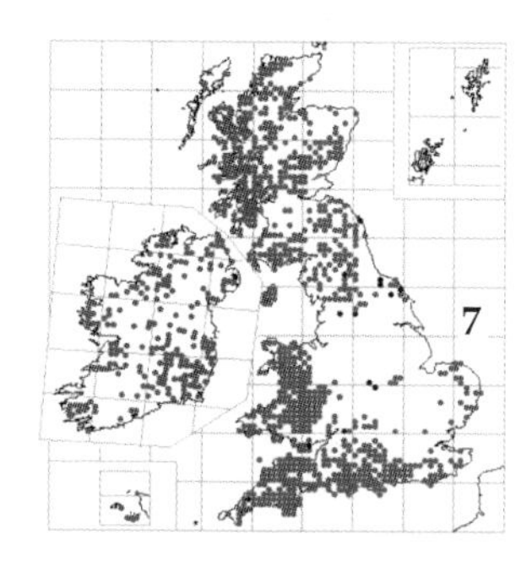

P. leioplaca x 5.

13. P. multipuncta Thallus grey, determinate, thick, smooth, cracked or wrinkled. The pure white soralia, up to 2 mm diam, are widely dispersed with rather flat tops and never form a sorediate crust as they cover the developing apothecia. The apothecia under the soredia are about 0.5 mm diam, usually 2 or 3 per wart. The asci each contain only a single large spore, 90–170 x 30– 70 µm. Thallus and soredia: K+ yellow, P+ deep orange, KC+ yellow, UV–.
Habitat: Common on smooth, acid-barked trees (especially young branches), particularly in the South and West, rarely on siliceous rocks.

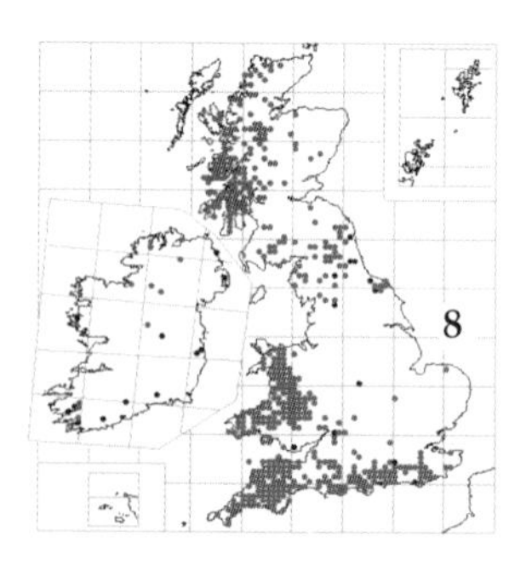

P. multipuncta x 5.

14. P. pertusa Thallus greenish grey to grey, thick and slightly cracked, often limited by a prothallus and with a concentrically zoned margin. Apothecia are produced in wart-like protuberances, 2–7 apothecia per wart, the discs are apparent as minute dark pits, sometimes slightly more open. Asci 2-spored (*P. hymenea* is 8-spored), spores 150–250 x 40–80 µm. The small, black, indian-club-shaped fruits of the parasitic *Sphinctrina turbinata* are sometimes found growing out of the thallus.
K+ yellow, KC+ yellow, P+ deep orange, UV+ orange.
Habitat: Very common on trees throughout most of Britain, but sometimes also on siliceous rocks, memorials and walls.

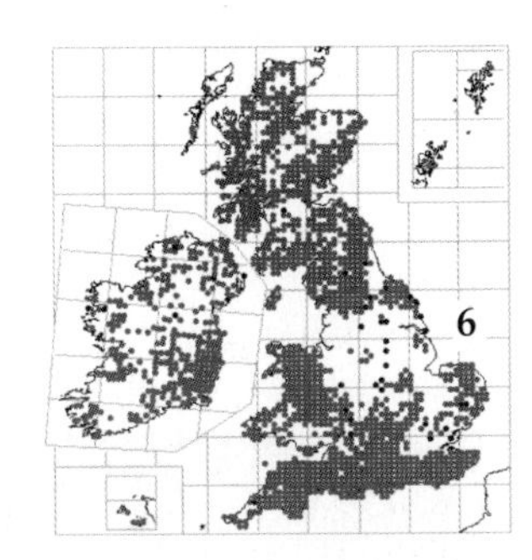

P. pertusa x 5.

15. P. pseudocorallina Thallus smooth or warted, similar to *P. corallina* but slightly darker grey with a slight yellow or cream tinge. Commonly with short, rather stout, little branched isidia, usually with brown tips. The isidia often break off to leave pale scars. Rather rare fertile, with several apothecia in each wart resembling *P. pertusa* growing on rock. Asci 2-spored, spores 120–200 x 50–80 µm.
Cortex: K+y (turning blood-red after about 30 seconds), P+ yellow, UV–.
Habitat: On well-lit siliceous rocks in similar habitats to, and often with, *P. corallina* but perhaps more common than that species in maritime regions.

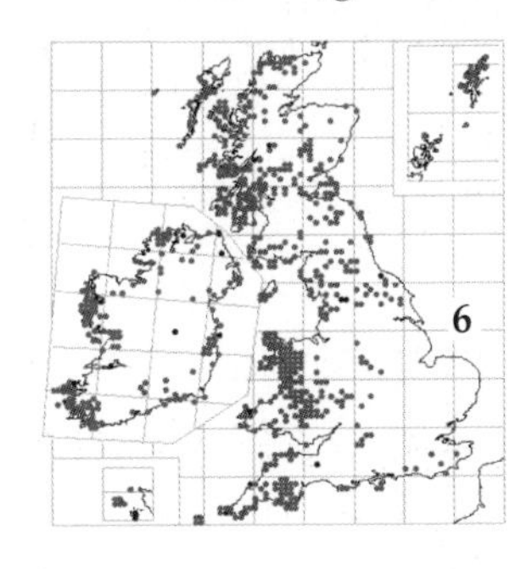

P. pseudocorallina x 5.

PETRACTIS ('ray-like on rocks' – from the appearance of the thalline apothecial cover) **Thallus** crustose. **Photobiont** *Scytonema*. **Apothecia** lecideine. Ascus 8-spored, K/I+ blue wall. **Spores** colourless, multi-septate, with a distinct perispore. There is only one British species. The furrowed thalline cover of the apothecia as well as containing *Scytonema*, not *Trentepohlia*, as the photobiont, differentiates it from *Gyalecta* and other genera of similar appearance.

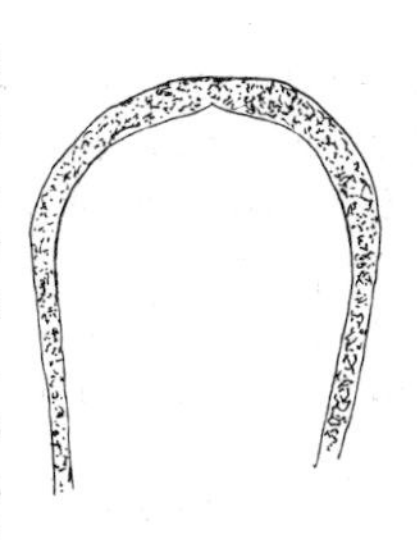

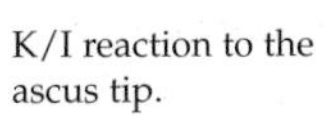
K/I reaction to the ascus tip.

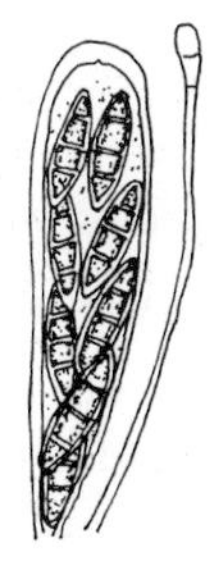

P.clausa x 500.

Petractis clausa Thallus scurfy or endolithic, light grey to yellowish. Apothecia about 0.5–0.8 mm diam, immersed at first and covered with a thin layer of cortex which splits open, to leave small, whitish, star-like teeth around the margin. The disc is concave, pale orange (brown when dry) and sunken. The apothecia leave shallow pits in the rock when they are shed. Spores 3-septate, 15–20 x 6–8 µm including the perispore.
Habitat: Locally abundant on hard, damp, limestone, including pebbles, in moderate shade.

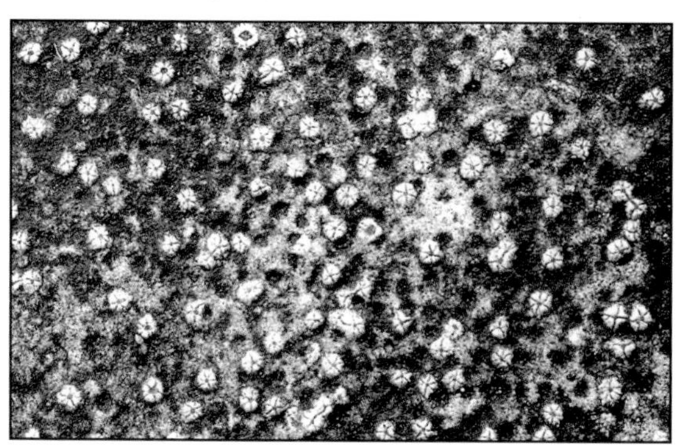

P. clausa x 5.

PHAEOGRAPHIS ('grey-brown writing' – from the shape and colour of the apothecia). **Thallus** crustose or immersed, the hyphae are I+ blue. **Photobiont** *Trentepohlia*. **Apothecia** lirellate, immersed, erumpent, or more rarely sessile. **Ascus** 8-spored, K/I –, *Graphis*-type. **Spores** multiseptate, cells thick-walled, lens-like, wider than long, brown (may be colourless when young), I+ purple.

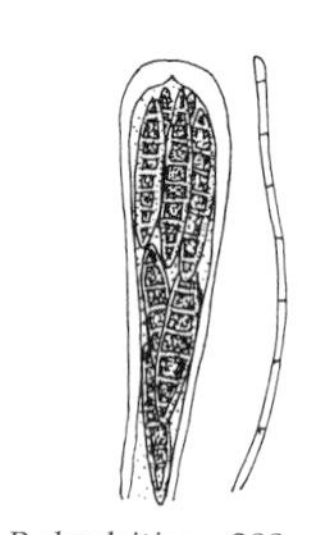

P. dendritica x 300.

The spores help separate this genus from the similar:

Graphis – spores multi-septate, colourless (rarely brown when over-mature), thin-walled, cells wider than long, lens-like (see p. 163).
Graphina – spores muriform, colourless, cells wider than long, lens-like.
Opegrapha – spores multi-septate, colourless, thick-walled, cells longer than wide, cuboid.

1. Thallus smooth, white to grey. Lirellae black or pruinose — 2
– Thallus oily, olivaceous brown. Lirellae brown and pruinose — **2. P. lyellii**

2. Lirellae much branched, carbonaceous margin extending under the apothecium — **1. P. dendritica**
– Lirellae little branched, carbonaceous margin not continued under the apothecium — **3. P. smithii**

1. Phaeographis dendritica Thallus light grey to creamy white, very variable, slightly granular, powdery or cracked-areolate. Apothecia numerous, very immersed, elongate or often stellate. Lirellae wide, often with a prominent pseudo-thalline margin and a relatively wide grey-brown pruinose disc. The dark carbonaceous margin continues under the hymenium (visible under a handlens in a roughly cut section). Spores (5-) 7- to 9-septate, 30–50 x 7–10 µm. K+ red (with crystals, visible in a squash), P+ yellowish orange, UV–.
Habitat: Fairly common on smooth patches of acid-barked, shaded trees, mainly in the South and West.

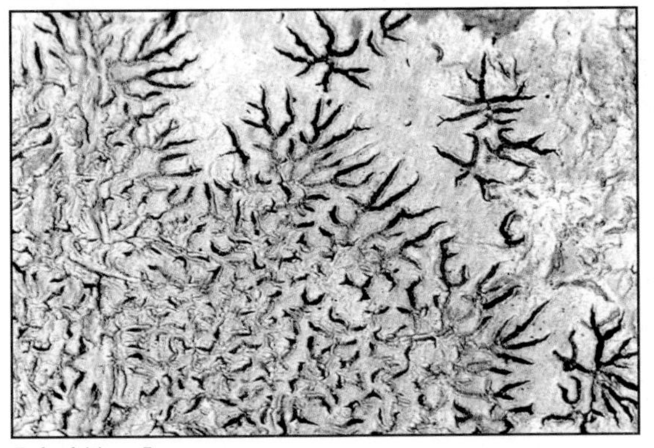

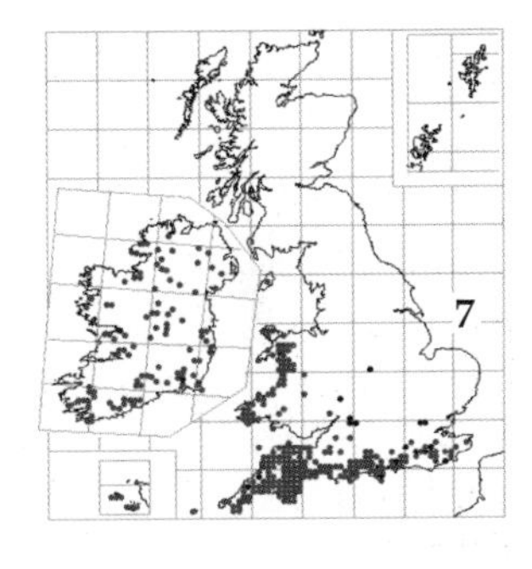

P. dendritica x 5.

2. P. lyellii Thallus olivaceous brown, smooth, waxy and glossy, often forming mosaics. Apothecia open, brown, ± pruinose, not very prominent, serpentine and having a thick, white-pruinose margin. The carbonaceous margin does not continue under the hymenium. Spores 5-septate, 22–35 x 7–9 µm.
Spot reactions and UV: all negative.
Habitat: Rare, on smooth-barked, often young, trees in damp shade in the south-west of Britain and Ireland.

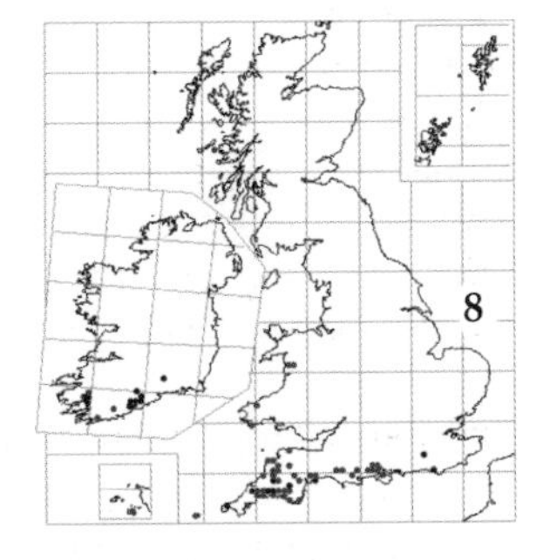

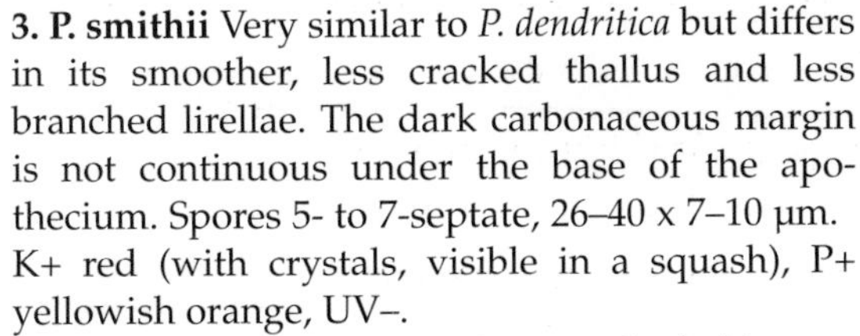

3. P. smithii Very similar to *P. dendritica* but differs in its smoother, less cracked thallus and less branched lirellae. The dark carbonaceous margin is not continuous under the base of the apothecium. Spores 5- to 7-septate, 26–40 x 7–10 µm.
K+ red (with crystals, visible in a squash), P+ yellowish orange, UV–.
Habitat: Rare or overlooked, in similar habitats to *P. dendritica*. Rarely found on the branches of conifers.

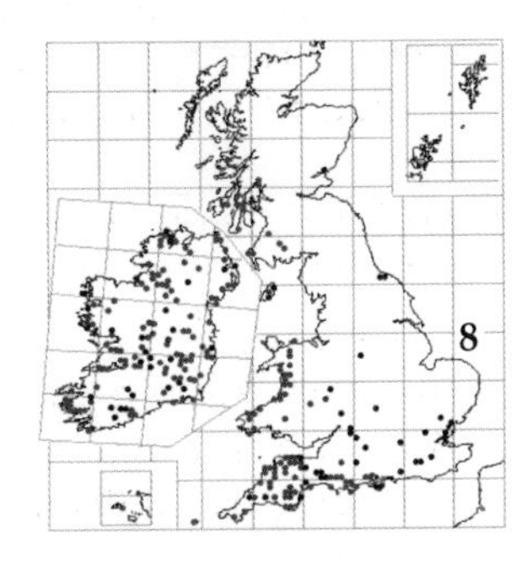

PHAEOPHYSCIA ('grey-brown and inflated' – from the thallus colour and the relationship with *Physcia*). **Thallus** foliose with simple rhizines. **Photobiont** trebouxioid. **Apothecia** lecanorine, sessile. Disc very dark brown to black. **Ascus** 8-spored, *Lecanora*-type. **Spores** brown, thick-walled, 1-septate. The habitat is base-rich, nutrient-rich rocks. It is a member of the *Physcia*-group but differs by the arrangement of the hyphae in the lower cortex.

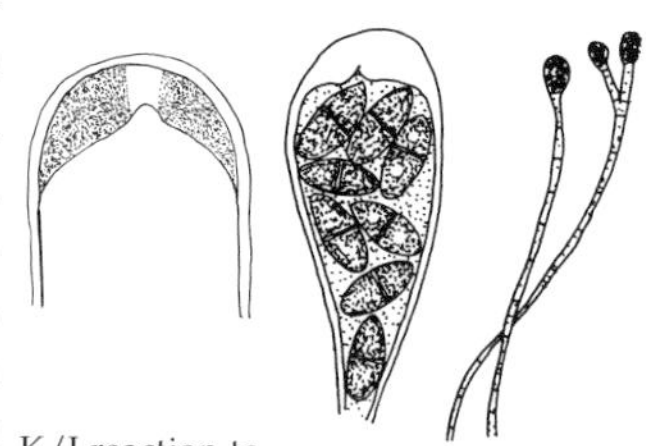
K/I reaction to the ascus tip. *P. orbicularis* x 250.

1. Lobes 0.2–1 mm wide, adpressed, lower surface black **1. P. orbicularis**
– Lobes to 0.2 mm wide, ascending, lower surface white to tan **2. P. nigricans**

1. Phaeophyscia orbicularis Thallus very variable in colour from pale brownish grey to brown or almost black. When wet, paler specimens become a vivid green. The thallus is orbicular, up to 3 cm diam or dispersed, irregular, and adpressed. Lobes long and becoming palmately divided at the tip, about 1 mm wide. Lower surface black with dark rhizines. The rhizines may protrude at the margins where they often have pale tips. Soralia laminal and marginal, white or cream to greenish, mottled blue to black, less globose, more marginal and smaller than in *Physcia caesia* which has a paler thallus and a K+ yellow medulla. Apothecia infrequent, up to 2 mm diam. Spores 17–26 x 7–11 µm. Pycnidia common. Conidia ellipsoid, 2–4 x 1–2 µm. Medulla: K– (rarely K± purple).
Habitat: Very common on nutrient-enriched bark, twigs and basic stones, especially common in urban areas on concrete.

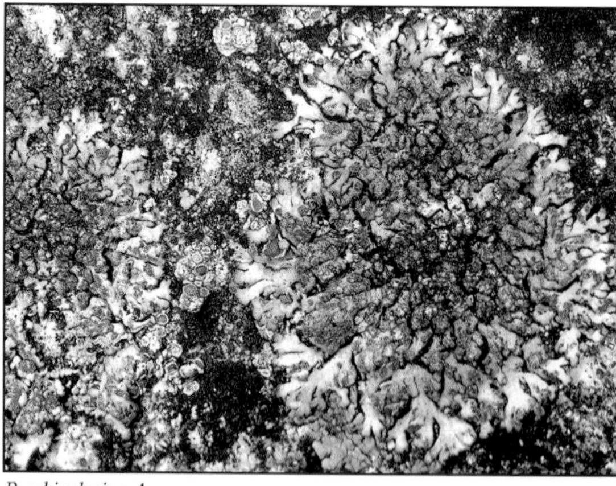
P. orbicularis x 4.

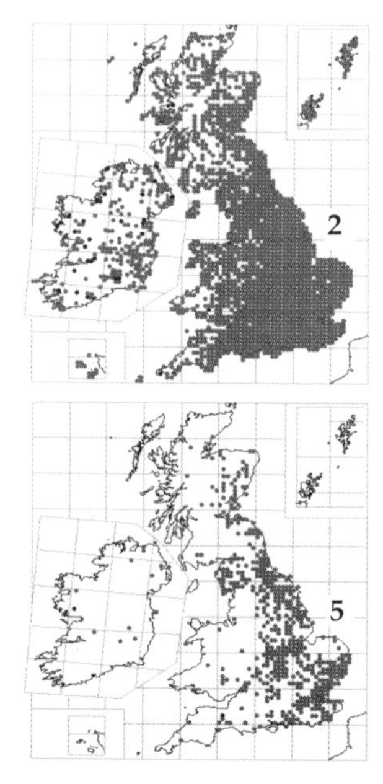

2. P. nigricans Thallus small, up to 1 cm diam, with narrow lobes about 0.2 mm wide, ascending towards the tips, shrubby, dark grey to brown, greenish when wet. Under-surface white to tan with pale rhizines. Isidia/soralia greenish to brown, along the margins of the lobes eventually spreading across the thallus, especially towards the centre. Apothecia are unknown in Britain.

Spot reactions: all negative.

Habitat: Common but overlooked, on bird-perching sites such as limestone gravestones, roofs. Rarely on the base of trees in open enriched situations.

PHLYCTIS ('ashen' – from the pale colour of the thallus). **Thallus** crustose. **Photobiont** chlorococcoid. **Apothecia** lecanorine, immersed, usually pruinose, often difficult to see. **Ascus** 1- to 2-spored, K/I+ blue outer sheath. **Spores**, colourless to pale brown, muriform in the British species, up to 150 µm long.

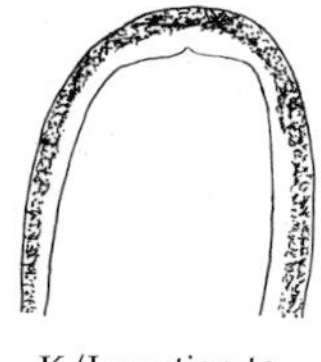

K/I reaction to the ascus tip.

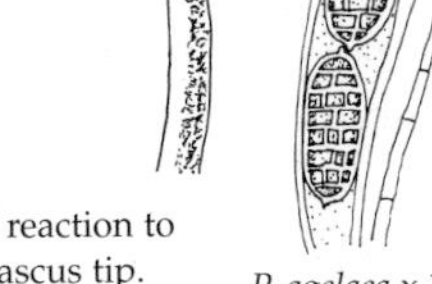

P. agelaea x 150.

1. Thallus sorediate. Very rarely fertile **2. P. argena**
– Thallus not sorediate. Apothecia in powdery depressions **1. P. agelaea**

1. Phlyctis agelaea Thallus whitish grey, with a pale margin, cracked or warted, without soralia, usually fertile. Apothecia 0.2–0.5 mm diam, in powdery warts through which small pink to dark red discs are often just visible. Ascus normally 2-spored. Spores 45–80 x 11–32 µm, colourless but becoming darker with age.

K+ yellow becoming red (crystals), P+ orange.

Habitat: Rare but overlooked and declining, on young smooth-barked trees, especially sycamore, rarely rocks, in sheltered, damp habitats.

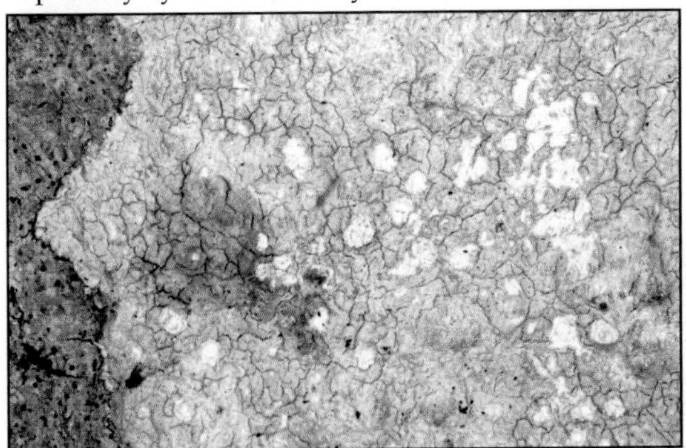

P. agelaea x 5 showing P+ orange reaction.

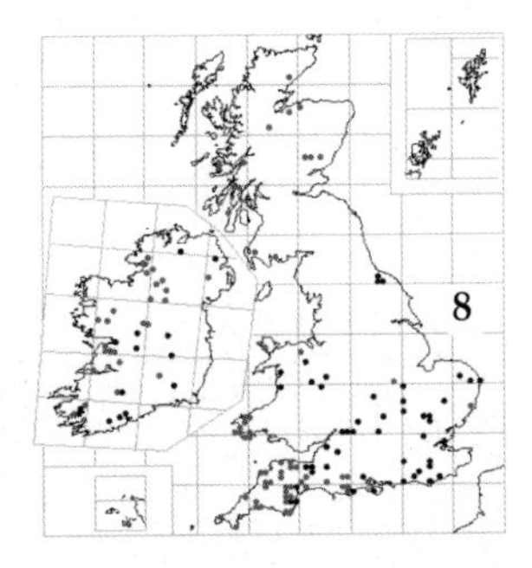

2. P. argena Thallus thin to thick, usually smooth and only slightly cracked, white to creamy grey, paler at the margin and sometimes covering extensive areas. White to greenish, granular to diffuse soralia form eroded lines (looking from a distance as if browsed by snails), later becoming confluent and then covering large areas of the thallus. The soralia arise from minute punctiform blisters, often surrounded by the raised edges of the torn cortex. Apothecia very rare, up to 0.5 mm diam, with a white-pruinose disc. Ascus 1-spored. Spores 100–140 x 25– 50 µm, very muriform.

Soralia and thallus: K+ yellow becoming red (crystals in a squash), P+ orange.

Habitat: Common throughout Britain on well-lit, nutrient-rich trees, shrubs and hedges. Rarely on mosses or on shaded, somewhat basic, walls of churches, etc.

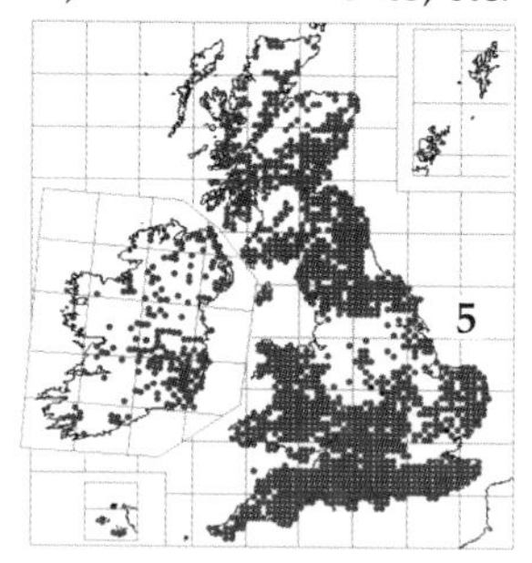

P. argena x 4.

PHYLLOPSORA ('scaly-leaf' – from the thallus structure and resemblance to *Psora*). **Thallus** squamulose to granular with a pale prothallus. **Photobiont** trebouxioid. **Apothecia** lecideine. **Paraphyses** surrounded in a gel-coat. **Ascus** 8-spored, *Bacidia*-type. **Spores** simple to septate, colourless. **Pycnidia** not known in Britain.

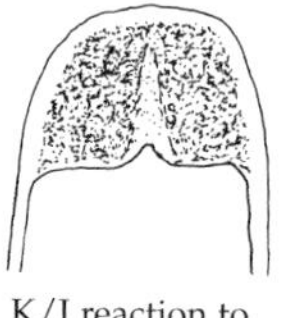

K/I reaction to the ascus tip.

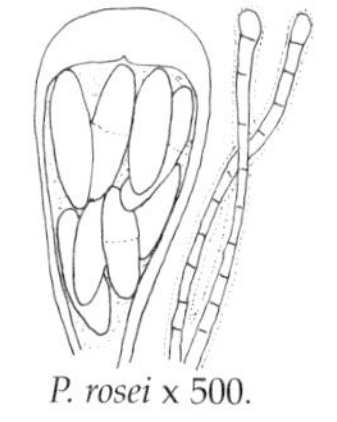

P. rosei x 500.

Phyllopsora rosei Thallus up to several cm wide, of grey to pale blue-grey, matt, flat, digitate squamules, up to 0.3 mm wide, frequently surrounded by a fluffy white prothallus. Apothecia not uncommon, up to 1.5 mm diam, orange to brown, convex and frequently clustered. Spores 10–14 x 2–3 µm.
K± pale yellow, P+ red.
Habitat: Not uncommon in ancient, damp, acid woodland, especially amongst mosses on old oaks.

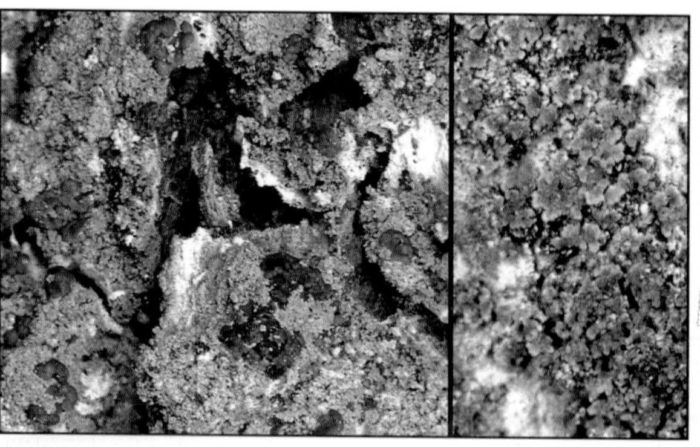

P. rosei x 4. *P. rosei* squamules x 10.

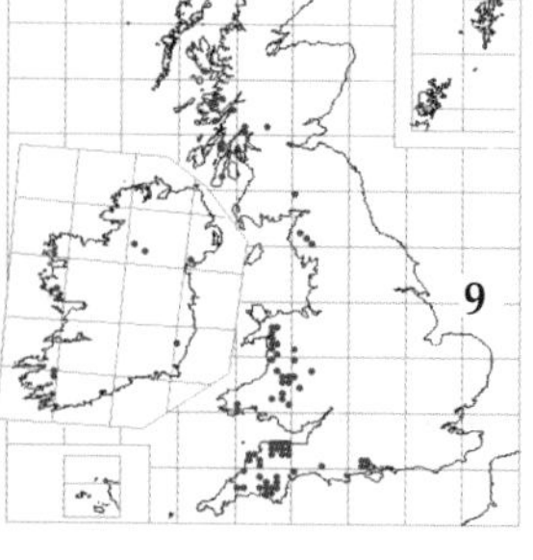

PHYSCIA ('inflated, sausage-like' – from the form of the type species). **Thallus** foliose with narrow lobes, sometimes closely adpressed. The upper surface of some species has minute pseudocyphellae. Under-surface pale and attached to the substratum by rhizines. **Photobiont** trebouxioid. **Apothecia** lecanorine, discs dark, sometimes pruinose and/or on short stalks. **Ascus** 8-spored, *Lecanora*-type. **Spores** brown, thick-walled appearing almost polarilocular. Similar broader-lobed, pruinose species belong in the genus *Physconia*. This and the very closely related genera *Phaeophyscia* and *Hyperphyscia* are also included in the following key. In performing K tests on the medulla care must be taken as the cortex of many species is K+y.

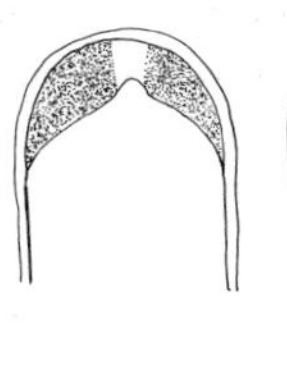

K/I reaction to the ascus tip.

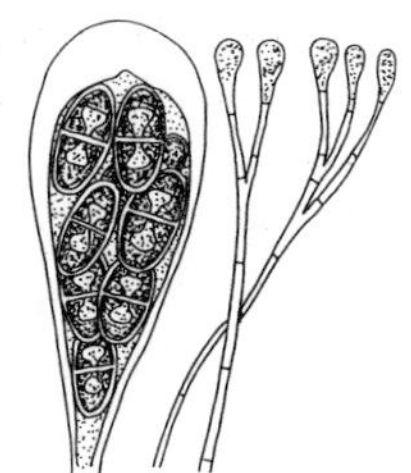

P. aipolia x 350.

Key to Hyperphyscia, Phaeophyscia, Physcia and Physconia

1. Thallus without soralia or isidia. Usually fertile — 2
– Thallus sorediate or isidiate. Rarely fertile — 5

2. Lobes to 2 mm wide, ascending. Long, pale marginal cilia — **6. P. leptalea**
– Lobes wider, adpressed. Without long, pale marginal cilia — 3

3. Lobes tips never pruinose. Thallus grey to blue-grey, ± unchanged when wet — 4
– Lobe tips pruinose. Thallus grey to grey-brown, greenish when wet — **Physconia distorta**

4. Thallus mottled with pale pseudocyphellae. Medulla K+y — **2. P. aipolia**
– Thallus without pseudocyphellae. Medulla K– — **7. P. stellaris**

5. Thallus pale to medium grey or bluish grey, ± unchanged when wet — 6
– Thallus pale brown-grey to dark brown, green to dark brown when wet — 13

6. Thallus with isidia — 7
– Thallus with soredia — 9

7. Lobes broad, white, brown or green, pruinose. Isidia coarse, granular, marginal becoming laminal — **Physconia grisea**
– Thallus pale grey, never pruinose — 8

8. Tufted. Lobe margins ± ascending with globular isidia — **9. P. tribacia**
– Lobes very narrow, adpressed, pale grey. Isidia fine and coralloid, initially central — **4. P. clementei**

9. Lobes ascending. Long concolorous marginal cilia (often with dark tips). Under-surface white — 10
– Lobes adpressed and/or lacking concolorous cilia, or under-surface brown to black — 11

10. Lobe tips inflated and splitting to expose soredia — **1. P. adscendens**
– Lobe tips not inflated, soredia on lower surface of lobe tip — **8. P. tenella**

11. Soralia ± laminal, convex, blue-flecked. Lobes with pale pseudocyphellae — **3. P. caesia**
– Soralia marginal or at lobe tips, ± concolorous, Lobes without pseudocyphellae — 12

12. Tufted. Lobe margins ± ascending with coarse granular soredia **9. P. tribacia**
– Radiating. Lobe tips sorediate on lower surface. Acid substrata **5. P. dubia**

13. Dry lobes brownish grey to black or greenish brown, not pruinose, often with dark cilia 14
– Dry lobes grey to brown, pruinose, cilia absent 16

14. Thallus green to greenish brown. Soralia laminal **Hyperphyscia adglutinata**
– Thallus pale brown-grey to almost black. Soralia marginal 15

15. Lobes uto 1 mm wide, adpressed **Phaeophyscia orbicularis**
– Lobes to 0.2 mm wide, at least lobe tips ascending **Phaeophyscia nigricans**

16 Medulla white. Rhizines simple **Physconia grisea**
– Medulla yellow. Rhizines squarrose **Physconia entroxantha**

1. Physcia adscendens Thallus pale grey, seldom more than 3 cm diam. Lobes up to 1 mm wide with, no to many, pseudocyphellae, lobe tips raised and with long marginal, darker-tipped cilia. Under-surface white with scattered darker tipped rhizines. The lobe ends become hood-shaped and inflated, bursting along the lower surface to expose an internal mass of cream to yellowish soredia contained within the inflated tip. When fertile, apothecia to 2 mm diam, on short stalks, the discs black and pruinose with tumid margins. Spores 16–23 x 7–10 µm. Pycnidia are often abundant. Conidia 4–6 x 1 µm.
Cortex: K+ yellow. Medulla: K–.
Habitat: Very common throughout Britain on well-lit calcareous rocks, tombstones, asbestos-cement, etc. Also frequent on nutrient-enriched tree bark.

P. adscendens x 6.

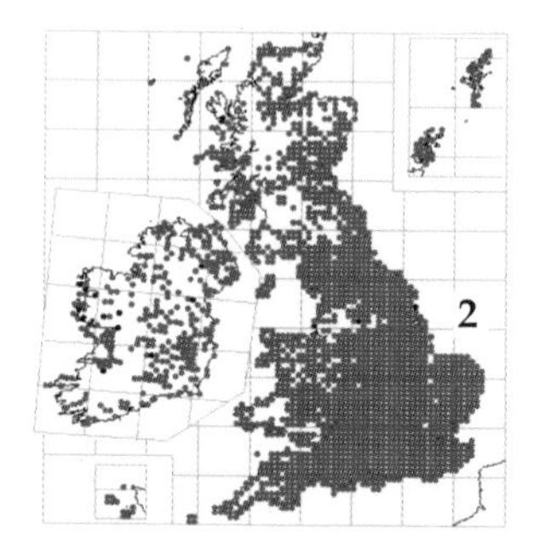

2. P. aipolia Thallus up to 6 cm diam, white, pale grey or blue-grey, lobes with distinct pale pseudocyphellae (best seen when wet, use hand lens). Lobes contiguous, becoming indistinct in the centre of the thallus. Under-surface with usually dark rhizines. Apothecia usually abundant, large (up to 3 mm), prominent with a thick thalline margin. Discs dark brown to black, becoming convex, sometimes white-pruinose. Spores 18–25 x 7–10 µm.

Cortex and medulla: K+ yellow.
Habitat: Common throughout Britain on well-lit, nutrient-rich trees, shrubs and hedges. Often on the rough nodes of twigs or branches. Rarely on nutrient-enriched walls and rocks. Now returning to many areas as pollution levels drop.

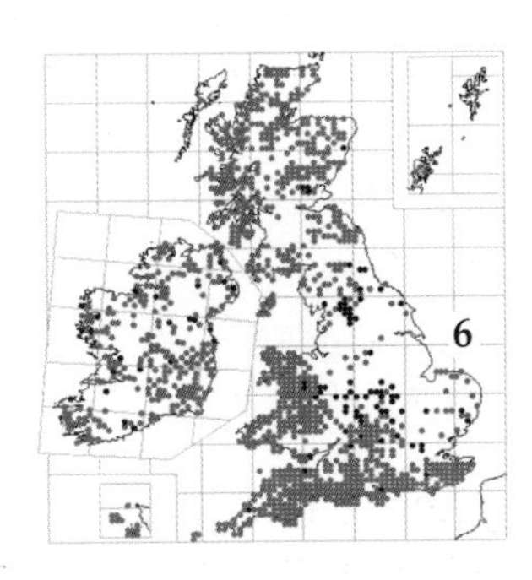

P. aipolia x 5.

3. P. caesia Thallus a characteristic bluish grey, matt, orbicular, very strongly adpressed. Lobes up to 1 mm wide, numerous minute pale pseudocyphellae, strongly convex, often overlapping and becoming less defined in the centre of the thallus. It may be recognized by the globular masses of granular to farinose soralia which are light grey, often with dirty blue flecks. Soralia laminal, especially in the centre of the thallus. Under-surface white to tan with scattered buff to black rhizines. Infrequently found fertile. Apothecia with black, grey-pruinose discs and prominent margins. Spores 18–25 x 6–10 µm. See *P. dubia* (5).
Cortex and medulla: K+ yellow.
Habitat: Very common throughout Britain on nutrient-enriched rocks, asbestos-cement, asphalt, tombstones and, more rarely, on dust-impregnated trees or wood.

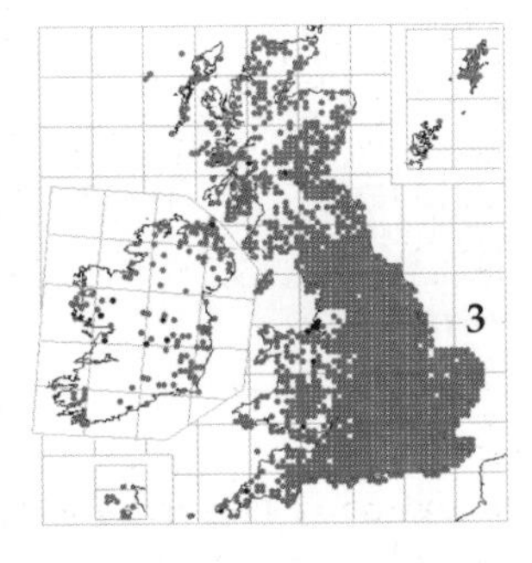

P. caesia x 5.

4. P. clementei Thallus light grey, closely adpressed, orbicular up to 3 cm diam but often joining to form larger colonies. Lobes narrow, about 0.2–0.8 mm wide, overlapping, widening at the tips and often rather wrinkled. Under-surface white with a few pale rhizines. The centre of the thallus is densely covered in short, granular isidia (which may break down to form coarse soredia). When fertile, the apothecia, to 1.5 mm diam, have thick, slightly crenulate margins and pruinose discs. Spores 15–20 x 8–10 µm.
Medulla and cortex: K+ yellow.
Habitat: Now very rare but still locally abundant in the SouthWest on nutrient-rich trees (sometimes wood), and often ± vertical walls and rocks.

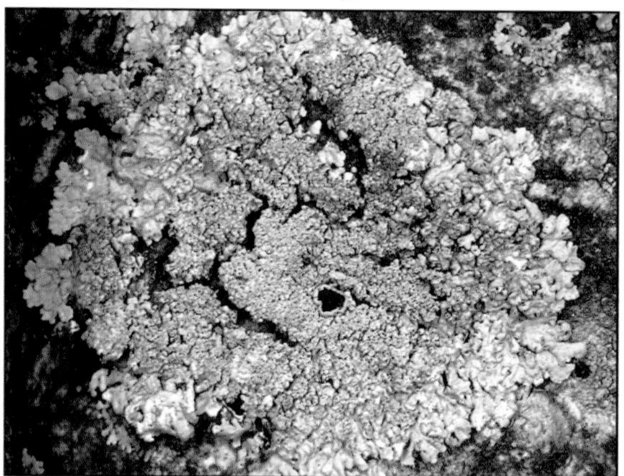

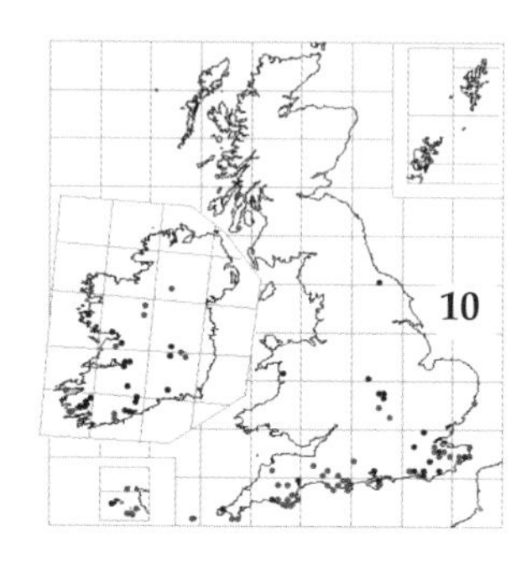

P. clementei x 6.

5. P. dubia Thallus up to 5 cm diam, light to dark grey with narrow (less than 1 mm wide) lobes that are clearly separated from each other and become palmate and ascending at the tips. Pseudocyphellae absent. The grey lip-shaped soralia are more apical than in *P. caesia* but may spread along the lobe margins and become confluent. The under-surface is white to cream with scattered rhizines. Apothecia not seen in Britain. Spores 16–25 x 7–11 µm.
Cortex: K+ yellow. Medulla: K– (*P. caesia* and *P. aipolia* are K+ yellow).
Habitat: Common on acid, well-lit, nutrient-enriched rocks, memorials and roofs. Often on sandstone.

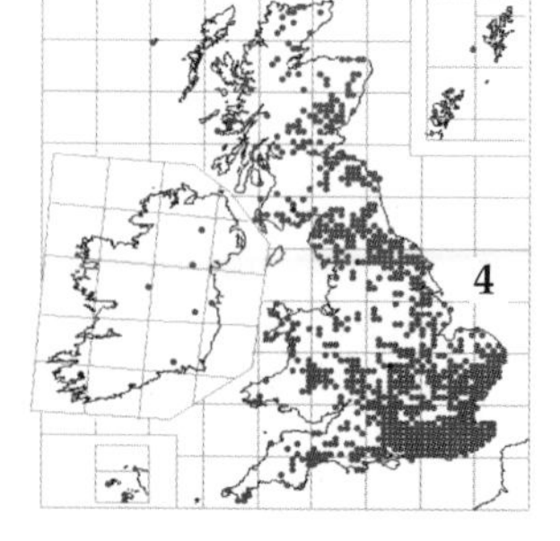

P. dubia x 5.

6. P. leptalea (P. semipinnata) Thallus light grey, lobes long and narrow (about 1–2 mm wide), mostly ascending, very pseudocyphellate, and bearing long marginal cilia, especially towards the lobe tips. Under-surface white with a few scattered rhizines. Often very fertile, the apothecia are up to 3 mm diam with tumid margins, discs frequently blue-grey pruinose. Young specimens of *P. adscendens* and *P. tenella* resemble this species but may be separated as they mature by the presence of soralia on the lobe tips or undersurface. *Anaptychia ciliaris* is much larger and K–. *P. aipolia* is closely adpressed and lacks long marginal cilia.
Cortex: K+ yellow.
Habitat: A rather local species. On nutrient-enriched trees and shrubs in well-lit situations, mainly in the South and West, exceptionally on rock.

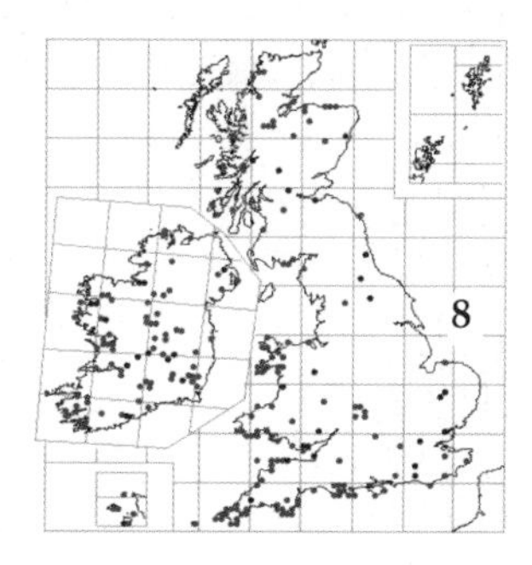

P. leptalea x 3.

7. P. stellaris This is very similar in appearance to *P. aipolia*, but often smaller, up to about 3 cm diam, the medulla lacks atranorin and is therefore K–. The lobes lack pale pseudocyphellae but may have small lobules which are also often found on the margins of the apothecia.
Cortex: K+ yellow. Medulla: K–.
Habitat: Mainly in North and West. On twigs and branches of well-lit or semi-shaded trees. Rarely on siliceous stone.

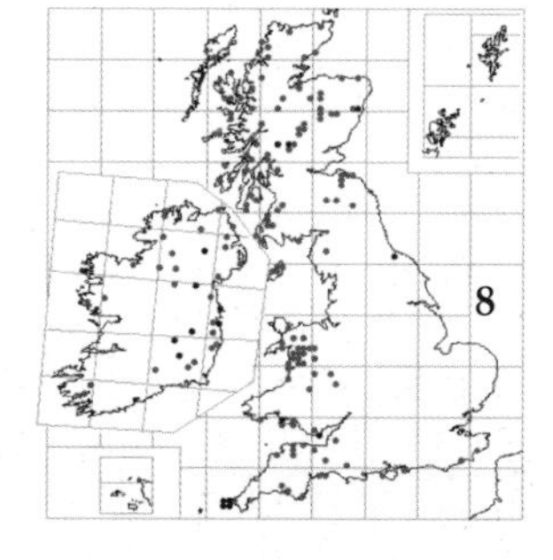

8. P. tenella Very similar to *P. adscendens* but with long, rather erect, lobes 0.4–1 mm wide and prominent marginal cilia. It differs in the lobe ends, which are not hood-shaped but split and turn back to reveal the rather coarse, cream-coloured soredia.
Thallus: K+ yellow. Medulla: K–.
Habitat: Similar to *P. adscendens* but usually found on trees and twigs.

P. tenella x 6.

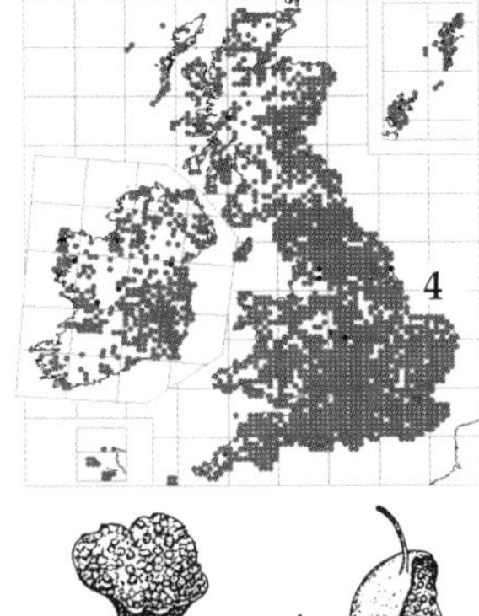

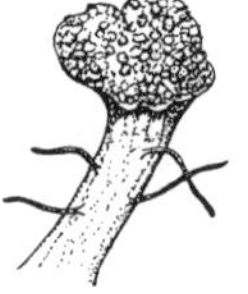

P. tenella P. adscendens

9. P. tribacia Thallus light grey, forming a mat of flat, incised lobes up to 1 mm (rarely 2 mm) wide with ascending tips, not pseudocyphellate. Laminal and apical, globular, erect, isidia-like lobules are present which break down to form granular soredia. Lower surface white to pale tan, with a few, light-coloured rhizines. Apothecia very rare. Spores 25–24 x 9–11 µm.
Cortex: K+ yellow. Medulla: K–.
Habitat: Not infrequent, mainly on rocks and trees in nutrient-enriched sites, particularly in the South and West.

P. tribacia x 8.

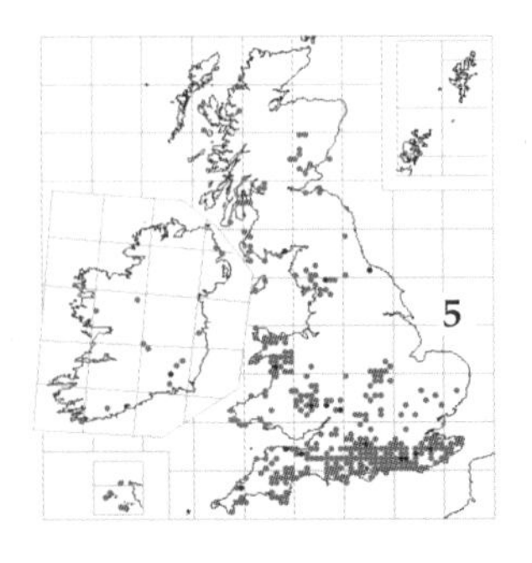

Typical spores.

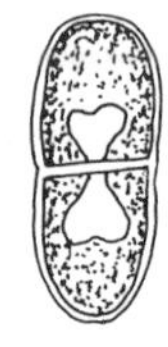

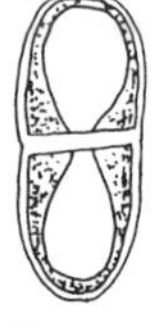

Physcia *Physconia*

PHYSCONIA (related to *Physcia*). **Thallus** foliose, lobes larger than in *Physcia* and usually pruinose (not visible when wet). No marginal cilia. **Photobiont** trebouxioid. **Apothecia** lecanorine with a dark brown disc that is usually pruinose. The margins are often lobulate. **Ascus** 8-spored, *Lecanora*-type. **Spores** thick-walled (without the thickened apex of *Physcia* but with a thickened septum), brown, 1-septate. **Pycnidia** immersed often in low warts. **Conidia** simple, colourless, bacilliform. **Chemical reactions** negative in British species except for *P. enteroxanta*.

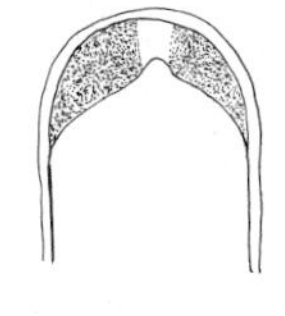
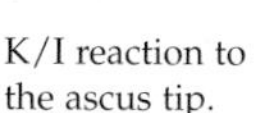
K/I reaction to the ascus tip.

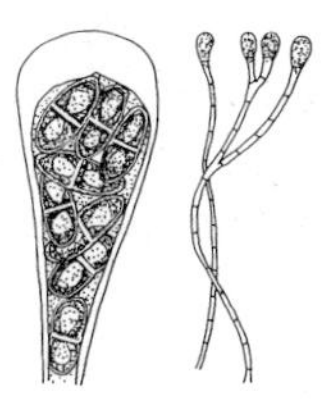
P. distorta x 150.

1.	Thallus without soralia or isidia	**1. P. distorta**
–	Thallus isidiate or sorediate	2
2.	Medulla white. K–. Rhizines simple or squarrose	3
–	Medulla yellowish. K+ yellow. Rhizines squarrose	**2. P. enteroxantha**
3.	Rhizines pale, simple	**3. P. grisea**
–	Rhizines dark, squarrose	**4. P. perisidiosa**

1. Physconia distorta (P. pulverulacea) Thallus grey to brown when dry, green when wet, orbicular, up to 10 cm across. Lobes rather palmate, overlapping, white-pruinose, especially at the tips. Often with many small lobules in the centre of the thallus. No pseudocyphellae. Lower surface light brown to black towards the centre with numerous squarrose rhizines. Apothecia very common and up to about 4 mm diam. Discs brown to dark brown and covered in a coarse pruina that looks like castor sugar. The thick thalline margin may become lobate. Spores 25–40 x 12–20 µm. This species is easily separated from *Physcia aipolia* by the pruina, the normally brown disc, the lack of pseudocyphellae and the K– reaction.
Habitat: Common, on well-lit, nutrient-rich bark and rock, often over mosses.

P. distorta x 3 .

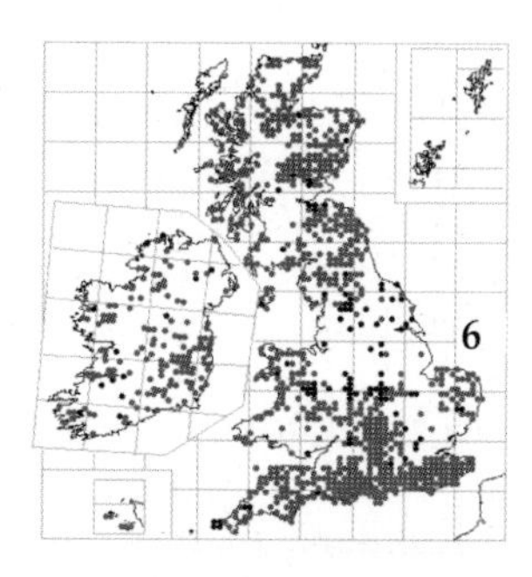

2. P. enteroxantha Similar to *P. grisea* but with a yellowish medulla, dark brown under-surface (pale at the margin) and with dark squarrose rhizines.
Medulla: K+ yellow.
Habitat: Infrequent in South, becoming commoner in the North. Found on well-lit, nutrient-enriched wayside trees, rarely on nutrient-enriched rocks and walls.

3. P. grisea Thallus white, grey or brown, green when wet, usually coarsely pruinose. Lobes up to 2 mm wide, short, overlapping and palmate at the tips. Parts of the lobe tips often turn upwards. Lower surface almost white with pale rhizines. Soralia are coarsely granular and often appear isidiate, initially on the margins of the lobes but may cover the centre of the thallus. It is the only *Physconia* species in Britain with simple rhizines. Apothecia rather rare with a sorediate margin and pruinose disc. Spores 22–34 x 12–17 µm.
Habitat: Common throughout Britain on nutrient-rich (often dust-impregnated) trees, tombstones, cement and rocks, often overgrowing mosses.

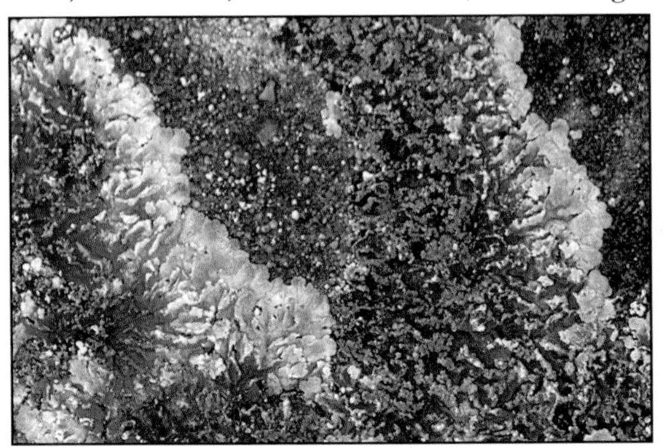

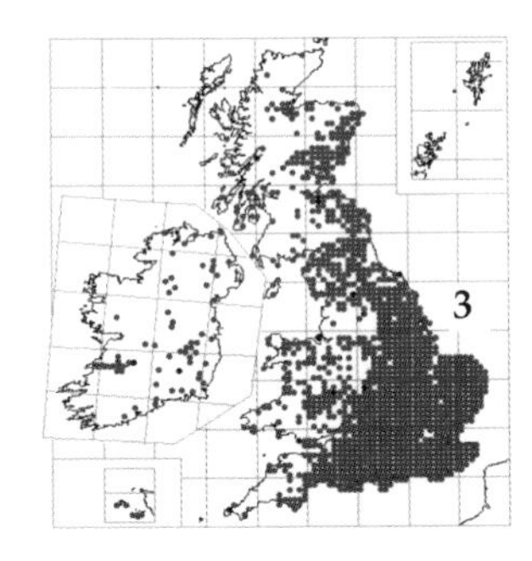

P. grisea x 4.

4. P. perisidiosa Thallus up to 3 cm diam, easily removed, green-brown to brown, often with a mauve tinge. Lobes short, overlapping, up to about 1 mm wide. The centre of the thallus is densely covered in coarse soredia/isidia. Medulla white, lower surface pale at the margin, dark at the centre. Rhizines squarrose, usually dark. Apothecia very rare, with sorediate margins. Spores 26–35 x 16–21 µm.
Habitat: Infrequent on well-lit to lightly shaded, basic-barked trees and overgrowing mosses on trees, walls and gravestones.

PILOPHORUS ('carrying a ball' – from the shape of the fruit bodies). **Primary thallus** crustose. **Secondary thallus** pseudopodetia. **Photobiont** *Trebouxia,* but cephalodia containing blue-green cyanobacteria (*Stigonema*) also present. **Apothecia** lecideine, on the tips of short coralloid pseudopodetia. **Ascus** 8-spored *Porpidia*-type. **Spores** simple, colourless. There is only one British species. It may be separated, when fertile, from similiar genera in Britain as follows:

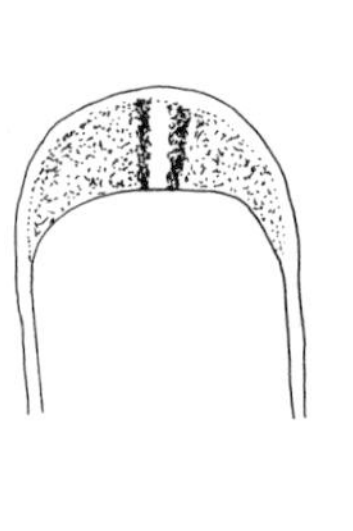

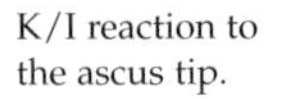

K/I reaction to the ascus tip.

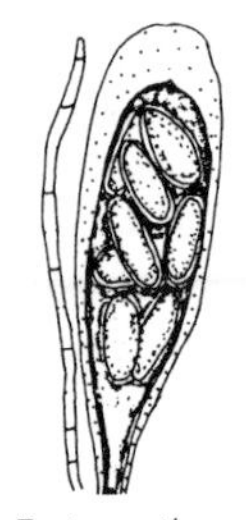

P. strumaticus x 300.

Cladonia – ± corticate, hollow true podetia, spores simple.
Baeomyces – no algae in pseudopodetia, spores multiseptate.
Stereocaulon – pseudopodetia usually more branched, spores multiseptate.

Pilophorus strumaticus Primary thallus white to grey, coarsely granular, almost squamulose, up to about 1 mm diam, but may become areolate. Usually with dark brown cephalodia, up to 1 mm diam, scattered over the surface. The rare, black, globose apothecia are borne on short, granular-corticate, pseudopodetia up to about 2 mm tall. Spores 15–20 x 6–10 µm.
K+ yellow.
Habitat: A local and rare species of damp shaded rocks in upland areas of the North and West.

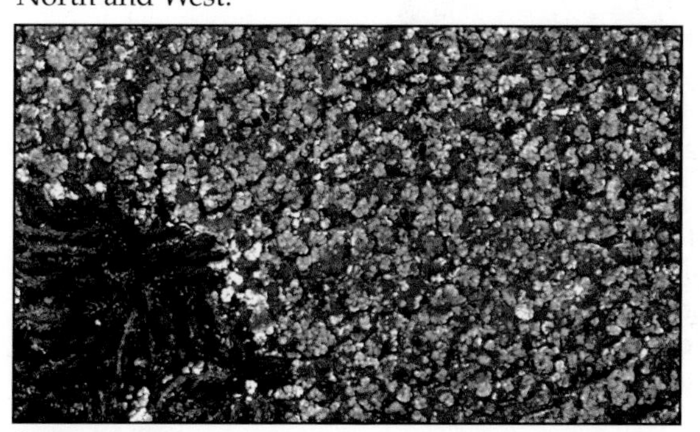

P. strumaticus x 6.

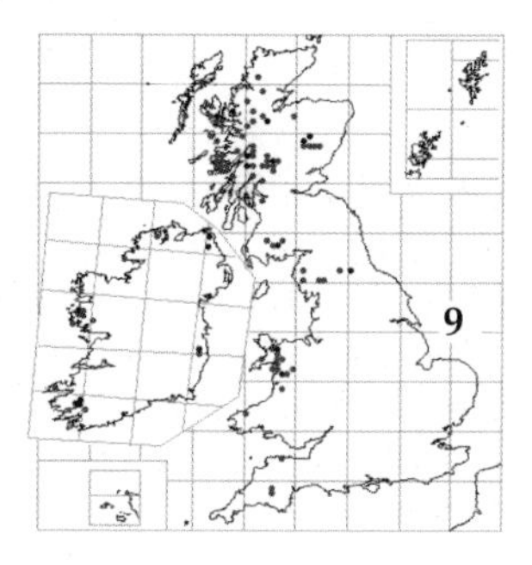

PLACOPSIS ('placodioid appearance' – from the thallus form). **Thallus** placodioid. **Photobiont** trebouxioid. **Cephalodia** containing blue-green cyanobacteria are usually present. **Paraphyses** branched with yellow granules on outer surface. **Apothecia** lecanorine. **Ascus** 8-spored, spores arranged in a single row, K/I+ blue tholus and internal dark blue cap. **Spores** simple, colourless to pale pink.

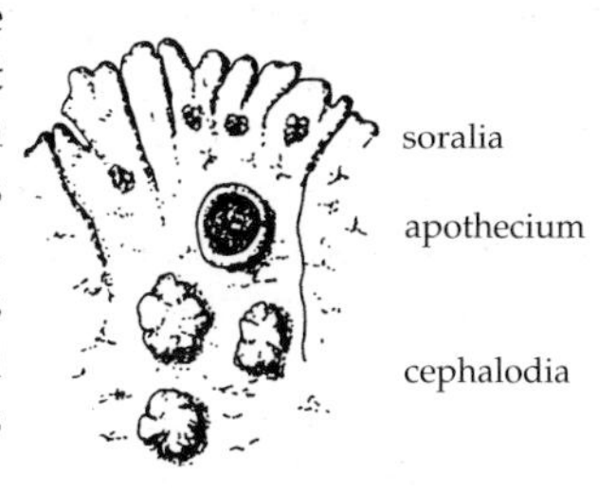

Placopsis gelida Thallus pinkish grey to cream-brown, adpressed, areolate centrally but becoming placodioid towards the margin. Lobes to 2 cm wide, convex. Conspicuous, pink to brown cephalodia are scattered over the surface and small delimited soralia which become abraded are also present. Apothecia to 1.5 mm diam are fairly common with a rather thick thalline margin and a pinkish to dark red-brown disc, often pruinose. Spores 12–18 x 6–9 µm.
C+ red.
Habitat: A rather local but often abundant species of upland regions on shaded or sometimes exposed, damp siliceous rocks by streams or water run-off, rarely on wall tops and fences. Often associated with heavy-metal mine sites. The

relationship with **P. lambii** is under investigation. Specimens without cephalodia and of irregular fragments are often allocated to this latter species.

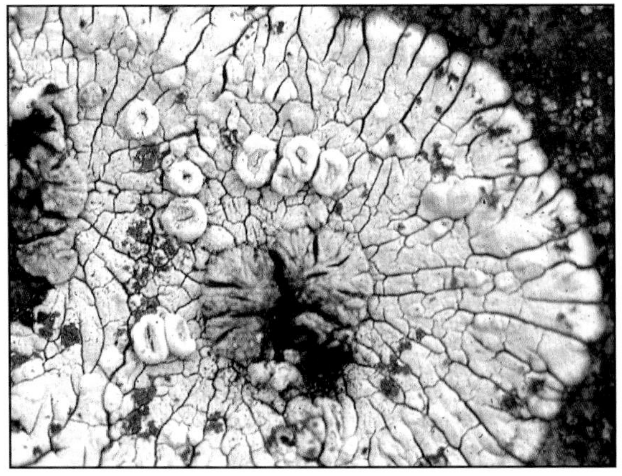

P. gelida x 6.

PLACYNTHIELLA (diminutive of *Placynthium* from the form of the thallus). **Thallus** crustose, of coralloid granules, becoming areolate. **Photobiont** green, possibly *Chlorella*. **Apothecia** lecideine, red-brown to black. **Paraphyses** of British species branched with a dark brown cap. **Ascus** 8-spored *Trapelia*-type. **Spores** simple, colourless, often containing oil droplets.

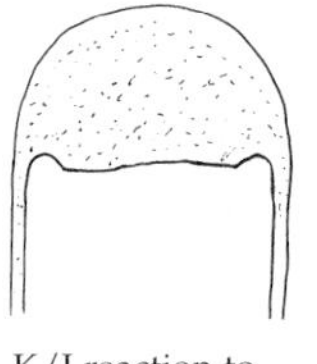

K/I reaction to the ascus tip.

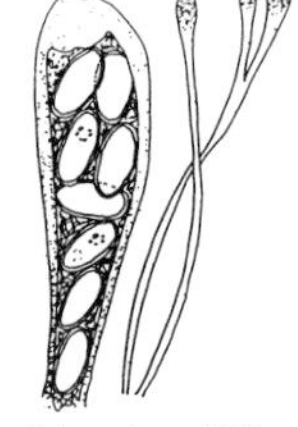

P. icmalea x 500.

1. Thallus C+ red. Granular/coralloid-isidiate **1. P. icmalea**
– Thallus C–. Granular, never coralloid-isidiate 2

2. Thallus of minute spherical granules, up to 0.04 mm diam **3. P. uliginosa**
– Thallus of almost squamulose granules, 0.1–0.3 mm diam **2. P. oligotropha**

1. Placynthiella icmalea Thallus of very small chocolate-brown coralloid granules/isidia, only up to 200 µm tall. Apothecia scattered, up to 0.5 mm diam, with a concolorous disc with a paler margin. Spores 8–12 x 4–5 µm.
C+ red, KC+ red (best seen in a squash).
Habitat: Common on tops of fence-posts, stumps of trees, etc., also commonly forming extensive crusts on soil in acid heathland.

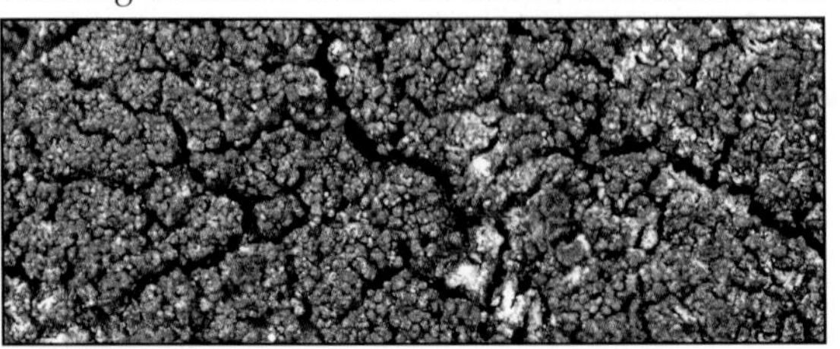

P. icmalea x 8.

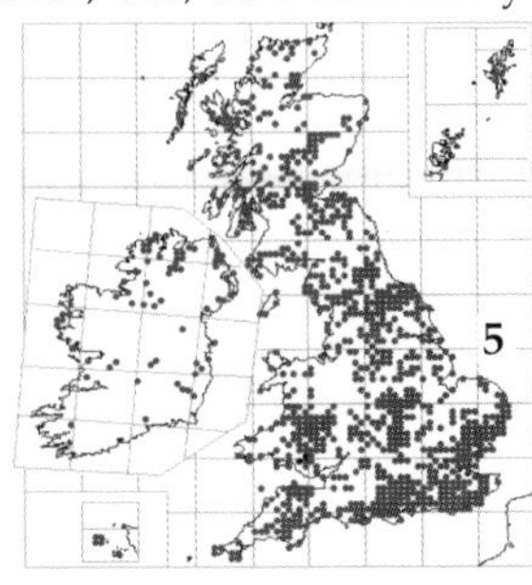

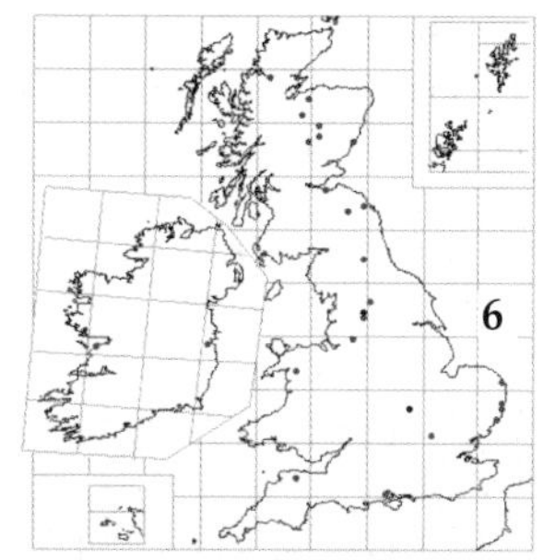

2. P. oligotropha Thallus of small (0.1–0.3 mm. diam), usually descrete, brownish granules that become yellowish green when wet. Apothecia to 0.4 mm diam, dark brown to black and often becoming convex and immarginate, rather *Bacidia*-like in appearance. Spores 10–14 x 5–6 µm.
Spot reactions: all negative.
Habitat: Infrequent, in open areas, on mildly acid heathland and on decomposing wood.

3. P. uliginosa Thallus forms a brown-black crust of contiguous, more or less spherical granules (up to 0.1 mm diam), slightly greener and more gelatinous when wet than *P. oligotropha*. Apothecia often clustered, gelatinous, up to 0.4 mm diam, chestnut to almost black with the margin becoming excluded as the apothecium becomes more convex. Spores 8–12 x 4–5 µm.
Spot reactions: all negative
Habitat: Fairly common in similar habitats to *P. oligotropha* but more common on soil and, unlike that species, sometimes occurs on dead bark.

P. uliginosa x 5.

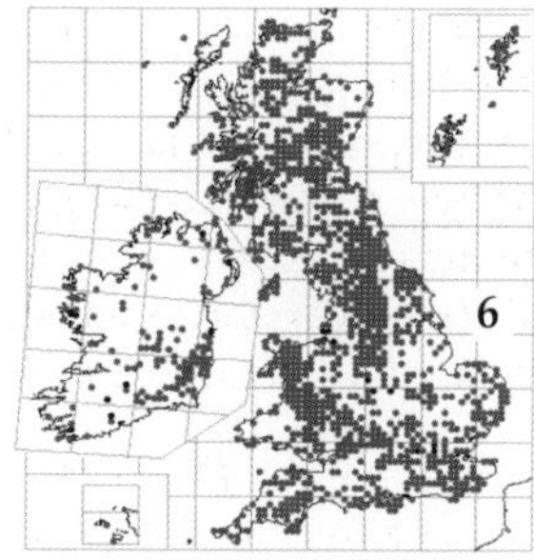

Probably over-recorded in the above map due to a change in the species concept.

PLACYNTHIUM ('stain from Kynthos' – a mountain in the Greek island Delos where the type species was found). **Thallus** crustose, placodioid or foliose, homoiomerous. **Photobiont** cyanobacteria. **Apothecia** lecideine, dark brown to black. **Ascus** normally 8-spored, *Peltigera*-type. **Spores** colourless, septate. **Pycnidia** immersed except for the dark ostiole. **Chemical reactions** negative.

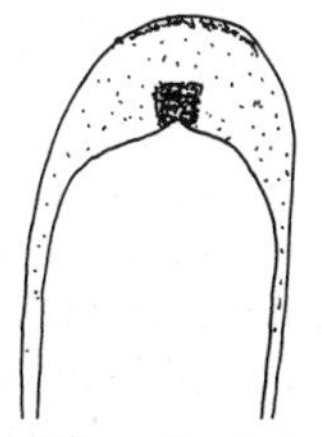

K/I reaction to the ascus tip.

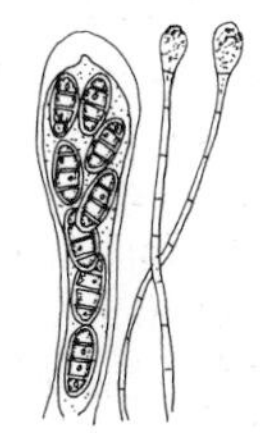

P. nigrum x 350.

1.	Thallus foliose. On acid rocks in or near streams	**1. P. flabellosum**
–	Thallus crustose. On calcareous substrates	**2. P. nigrum**

1. Placynthium flabellosum Thallus foliose, radiating, orbicular, brown to olive-green, with narrow lobes up to 0.5 mm wide and 3 mm long, the centre becoming crustose and covered in lobules. It resembles a *Phaeophyscia* species in its outline. It has not been found fertile in Britain.
Habitat: Infrequent but possibly overlooked when growing below the water surface. Occurs on very damp acid rocks in or near water.

2. P. nigrum Thallus dark brown or more usually black to blue-black, consisting of very small, granular to digitate squamules, often less than 0.3 mm wide and giving a coralloid appearance (use handlens), often gathered together in areolae, up to 2 mm diam, sometimes smoother and cracked, especially in polluted areas. The thallus is delimited by a wide, dark blue, felted prothallus. Apothecia, when present, less than 1 mm diam, black with a glossy disc and margin. Spores up to 3-septate, 9–18 x 3–6 µm.
Habitat: Very common, mainly on rather hard, often slow-drying, calcareous substrata. Often on tops of flat tombstones and cement.

P. nigrum x 8.

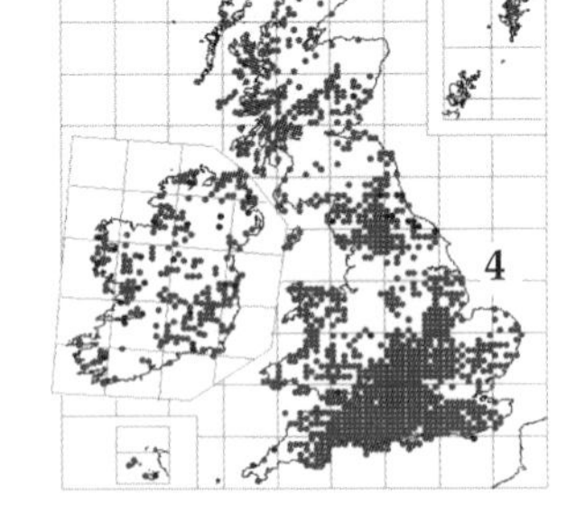

PLATISMATIA ('plate-like'). **Thallus** foliose, under-surface may have a few scattered rhizines. **Photobiont** trebouxioid. **Apothecia** lecanorine. **Ascus** 8-spored, *Lecanora*-type. **Spores** simple, colourless. **Pycnidia** marginal, immersed. It differs from *Cetraria* in the cells of the upper cortex and in the fact that atranorin predominates whilst in *Cetraria* it does not. It differs from *Parmelia* in having marginal apothecia and pycnidia (in *Parmelia* they are laminal). In addition to the chemistry and apothecial differences, the unswollen ends to the conidia separate *Platismatia* from *Cetrelia*.

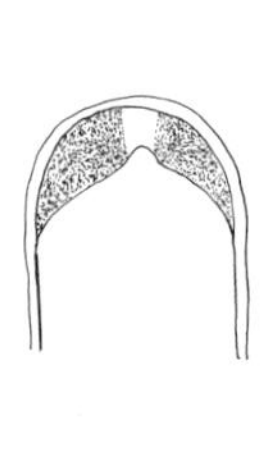

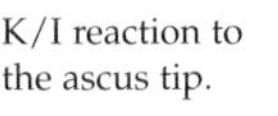

K/I reaction to the ascus tip.

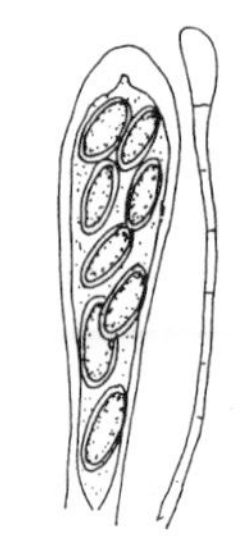

P. glauca x 600.

Platismatia glauca Thallus grey to brownish green, little changed when wet. Lobes up to 4 cm long and 1.5 cm wide, erect with crisped margins, often rather tufted. Upper surface somewhat shining and often slightly wrinkled. The incised lobe margins are frequently fringed with branched isidia or coarse soralia. Under-surface often white but becoming brown or black towards the centre. (The superficially similar but smaller *Cetraria chlorophylla* is K– and becomes greener when wet. It has a brown under-surface which frequently becomes paler towards the centre). Frequently without rhizines but sometimes with a few thick, divided rhizines towards the centre. Apothecia rare, disc red-brown with a thin, irregular margin. Spores 6–12 x 3–5 µm.
K+ yellow, UV–.
Habitat:. Very common, especially in upland areas, on acid-barked trees, frequently on the upper side of horizontal branches, sometimes on siliceous rocks. Particularly common in moderately polluted areas.

P. glauca x 2.

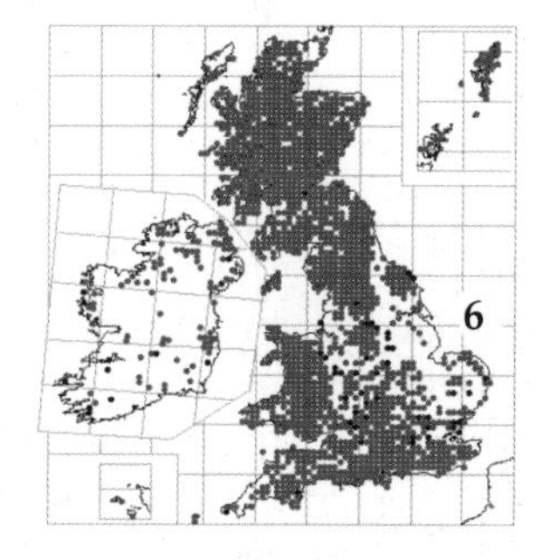

POLYBLASTIA ('many buds' – from the many spores in the type species). **Thallus** crustose or immersed in rocks, soil, or on mosses. **Photobiont** chlorococcoid. **Perithecia** single or multiple, superficial or immersed. With or without an involucrellum. **Paraphyses** absent at maturity. **Ascus** 2- to 8-spored, *Verrucaria*-type. **Spores** colourless or brown, muriform. **Chemical reactions** negative. None are very common.

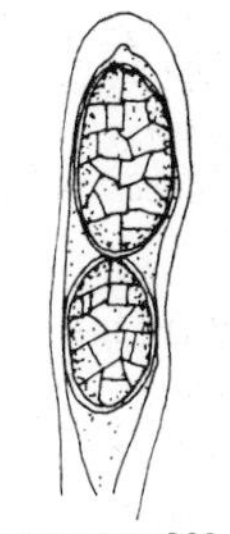

P. cruenta x 200.

It may be separated from some superficially similar genera that lack paraphyses and are found on rocks, as follows:

Verrucaria – simple, colourless spores.
Thelidium – 1- to 3-septate (sometimes appearing slightly muriform), colourless to brown spores.
Staurothele – muriform, colourless to brown spores, with algal cells in the hymenium.

Polyblastia – muriform, colourless to brown spores, without algal cell in the hymenium.

1. Perithecia in pits, up to 0.4 mm diam **1. P. albida**
– Perithecia superficial or less than half immersed, usually over 0.4 mm diam 2
2. Mature spores pale brown, 50–80 x 25–40 µm **2. P. cruenta**
– Mature spores colourless, 25–50 x 10–30 µm **3. P. cupularis**

1. Polyblastia albida Thallus white or light grey, rather scurfy, cracked or evanescent, usually limited by a black prothallus. Perithecia immersed in pits, very small (up to about 0.4 mm). Involucrellum absent. Spores colourless, 25–50 x 12–25 µm, 8 per ascus.
Habitat: Infrequent on hard limestone, often on exposed rocks in grazed grassland or on mortar in both lowland and upland Britain.

6

2. P. cruenta Thallus dark brownish green, cracked, thin or almost evanescent. Membranous, becoming gelatinous when wet. Perithecia up to 0.75 mm, appearing as prominent warts with a small dark protruding ostiole. Involucrellum dark on the outer surface, paler on the inner. Spores mainly pale brown, 50–80 x 25–40 µm, 8 per ascus.
Habitat: Rare, on siliceous rocks in streams in upland Britain.

P. cruenta x 6.

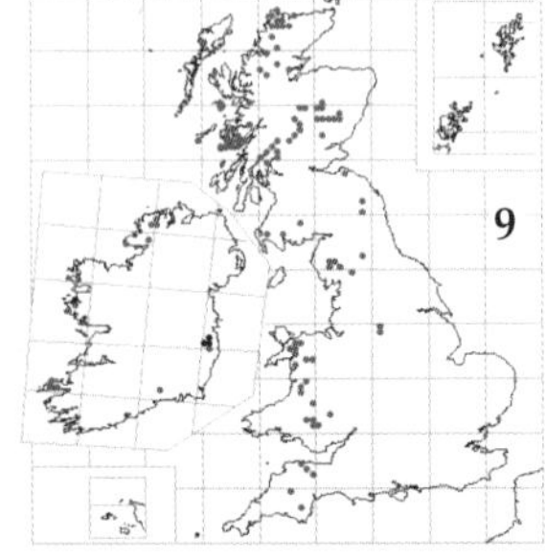

3. P. cupularis Thallus grey to brown, thin but with a narrow black prothallus. Apothecia about 0.5 mm diam, up to half immersed, often with a depressed ostiole. Involucrellum well-developed. Spores colourless, 20–50 x 10–30 µm, 8 per ascus.
Habitat: An infrequent species of damp, sheltered, upland, basic rocks and compacted chalky soils.

9

POLYSPORINA ('many-spored'). **Thallus** crustose. **Photobiont** chlorococcoid. **Apothecia** lecideine, brown to black, gyrose. **Paraphyses** anastomosing and richly branched (in *Sarcogyne* they are simple or slightly branched). **Ascus** 100+ spored, K/I+ blue outer coat. **Spores** very small, simple, narrowly ellipsoid, colourless. **Chemical reactions** negative.

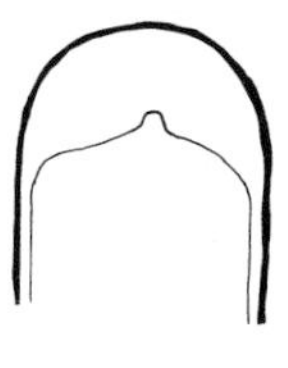
K/I reaction to the ascus tip.

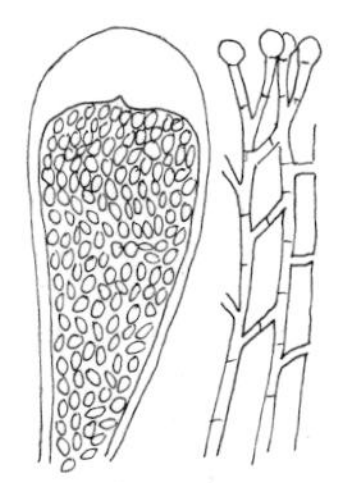
P. simplex x 400.

Polysporina simplex Thallus pale grey to greenish, frequently evanescent. Apothecia to 0.6 mm diam, often arranged along cracks in the substrate. Disc black or, when wet, dark red, not pruinose, margins black, wide, very crenulate and often arching over the umbonate disc giving a gyrose, knotted appearance. Spores 3–5 x 1–2 µm.
Habitat: Common on acid (especially rough granite and slate) to basic rocks, pebbles and mortar.

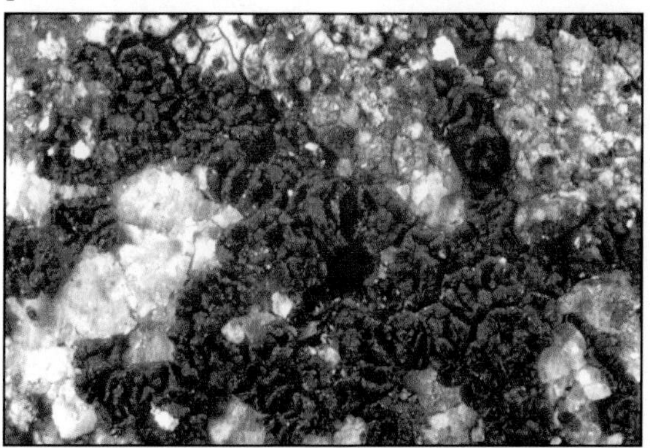
P. simplex x 8.

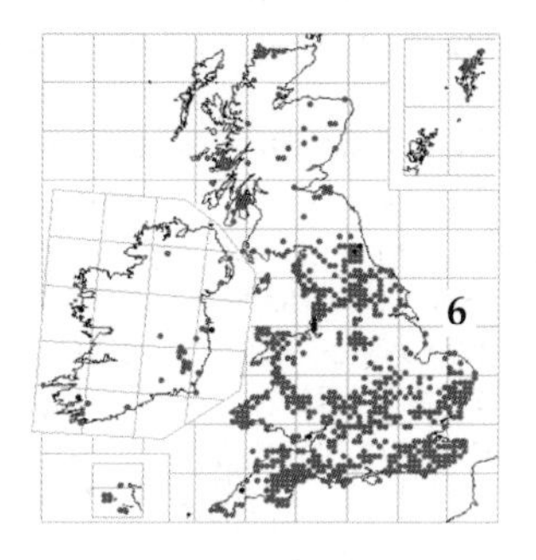

PORINA ('having a pore' – from the ostiole). **Thallus** crustose or immersed. **Photobiont** *Trentepohlia*. **Perithecia** emergent or immersed, often compound. **Paraphyses** thin and simple, only very rarely branched. **Ascus** 8-spored, K/I–. **Spores** colourless, 1- but usually 3- or more-, septate.

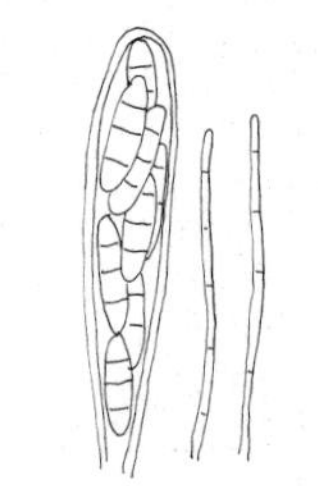
P. chlorotica x 450.

1.	Perithecia pink to orange-brown	2
–	Perithecia black	3
2.	Perithecia up to 0.3 mm. Mainly on deciduous trees	**4. P. leptalea**
–	Perithecia over 0.3 mm. Damp acid rocks, never trees	**3. P. lectissima**
3.	On limestone	**5. P. linearis**
–	On acid rocks	4

4. Thallus brown to green-brown, often with a black prothallus **2. P. chlorotica**
– Thallus reddish brown, often poorly delimited **1. P. aenea**

1. Porina aenea Thallus thin, dark reddish brown (greener in shade), often poorly delimited, lacking a prothallus. Perithecia very small (up to 0.3 mm but mainly 0.1 to 0.2 mm diam), with a glossy, black involucrellum and indistinct ostiole. Spores 3-septate, 14–20 x 5 µm.
Habitat: Common, mainly on young, lightly shaded, smooth-barked trees.

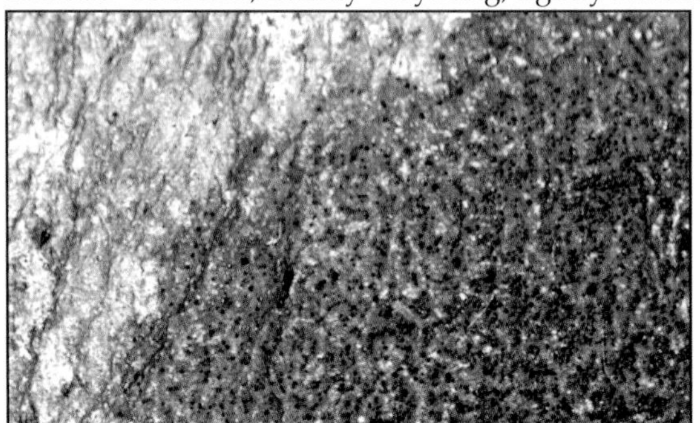

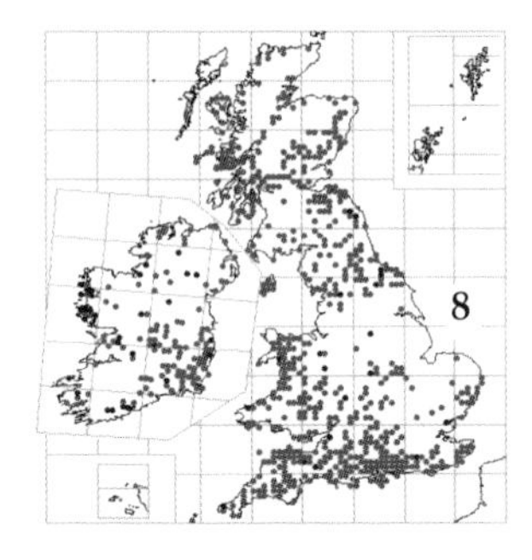

P. aenea x 8.

2. P. chlorotica Thallus brown to greenish black, thin, smooth or irregularly cracked, often with a black prothallus. Perithecia about 0.2–0.3 mm diam, prominent to partially immersed in thallus, often in pairs, involucrellum black, shiny, brown to black. Spores 3-septate, 15–25 x 4–6 µm.
Habitat: Common on damp, often vertical rocks or pebbles in upland regions, less common in the lowlands. Rarely found on smooth-barked trees.

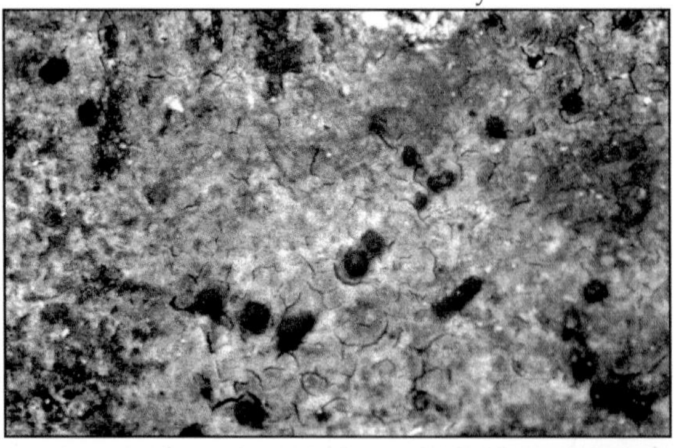

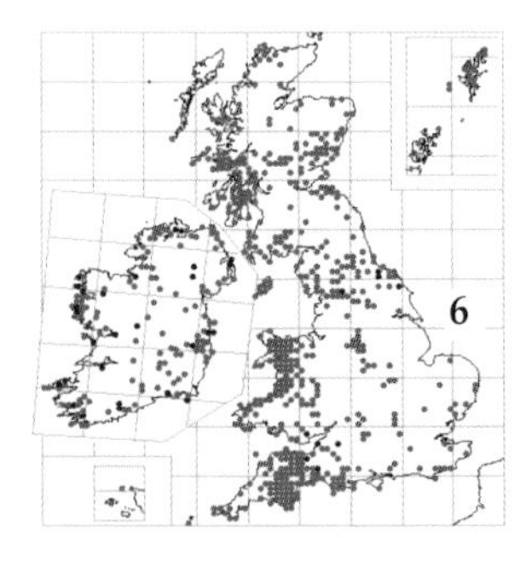

P. chlorotica x 8.

3. P. lectissima Thallus pale brown to brown-olive, usually more apparent than in many species of *Porina*. Perithecia 0.4–0.5 mm diam, conical and rather immersed, involucrellum pink to reddish brown. Spores 3-septate, 20–30 x 5–8 µm.
Habitat: Frequent on damp shaded rocks, often in the spray zone of streams.

4. P. leptalea Thallus grey to brown or evanescent but often thick, oily smooth and green when on rocks. Perithecia small (up to about 0.2 mm), wart-like, involucrellum pale pinkish brown to chestnut or darker, often irregular in outline. Spores 3-septate, 15–25 x 3–5 µm. Orange-pink pycnidia often common.
Habitat: An often overlooked species of deciduous trees, especially those with smooth bark in very damp areas, also on damp acid rocks.

P. leptalea x 8.

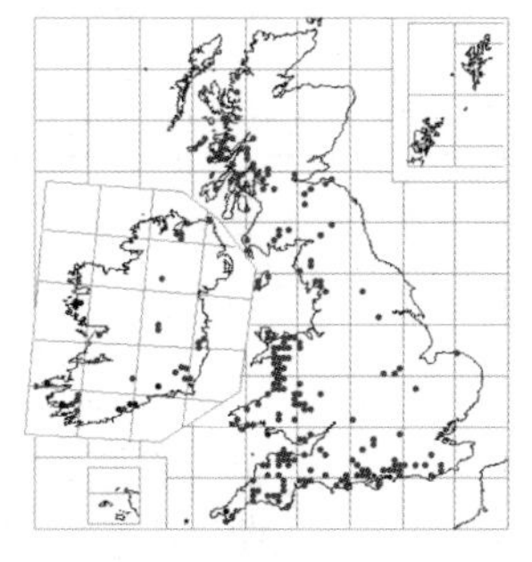

5. P. linearis Thallus thin or immersed, creamy grey to reddish brown. Perithecia 0.4 mm diam, black and often in pits. Involucrellum very dark violet. Spores 3-septate, sometimes slightly curved, 18–24 x 6–7 µm. Black pycnidia in pits are common.
Habitat: Frequent on hard, shaded limestone.

PORPIDIA ('ring-like' – as the apothecia are often arranged in rings, or from the white prothallus?). **Thallus** crustose. **Photobiont** chlorococcoid. **Apothecia** lecideine with a black or nearly black disc. **Paraphyses** anastomosing (in *Lecidea* they are simple to slightly branched). **Ascus** 8-spored, *Porpidia*-type. **Spores** colourless, simple. These species were formerly in *Huilia*. Identification at species level is often difficult unless using TLC.

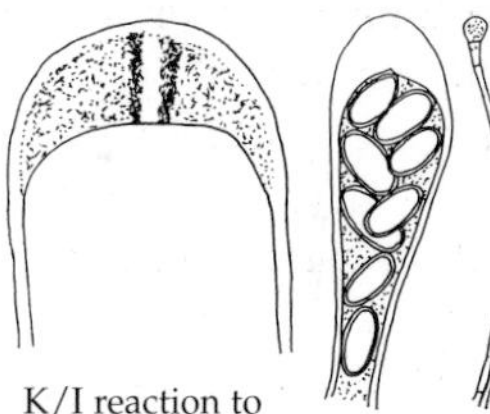

K/I reaction to the ascus tip. *P. cinereoatra* x 250.

1.	Sorediate	2
–	Not sorediate	3
2.	Thallus orange to orange-grey, medulla I–	**4. P. flavocaerulescens**
–	Thallus white to grey, medulla I+ blue	**9. P. tuberculosa**
3.	Thallus grey with greenish tinge. Epithecium bright, clear blue. On inundated acid rocks	**5. P. hydrophila**
–	Thallus white, grey or rusty. Epithecium not bright blue. Habitats various	4
4.	Apothecia up to 1.3 mm diam	5
–	Apothecia larger than 1.3 mm diam	7
5.	Apothecia about 0.5 mm diam, with a thalline collar	**8. P. speirea**
–	Apothecia about 1 mm diam, lacking a thalline collar	6

6. Thallus thin. Apothecia separate. Spores 10–17 mm long — **3. P. crustulata**
- Thallus areolate-cracked. Apothecia grouped. Spores 15–20 µm long — **2. P. contraponenda**

7 Exciple K+ yellow turning red (crystals in squash) — **7. P. platycarpoides**
- Exciple K– or K+ yellow not turning red — 8

8. Apothecia to 2 mm diam, pruinose — **1. P. cinereoatra**
- Apothecia to 3 mm diam, not pruinose — **6. P. macrocarpa**

1. Porpidia cineroatra (P. albocaerulescens, Huilia albocaerulescens) Thallus white to grey, cracked, sometimes warted, with a black prothallus between the areoles (only indistinct at the margin). Medulla I–. Apothecia very large (up to 2 mm diam), often in small groups, irregularly convex and often remaining partially immersed. Hymenium 90–110 µm tall. The apothecia differ from *P. macrocarpa* in having a blue-grey pruina. Spores 12–18 x 6–10 µm.
Spot reactions: negative.
Habitat: Common on exposed acid rocks. Upland and coastal areas.

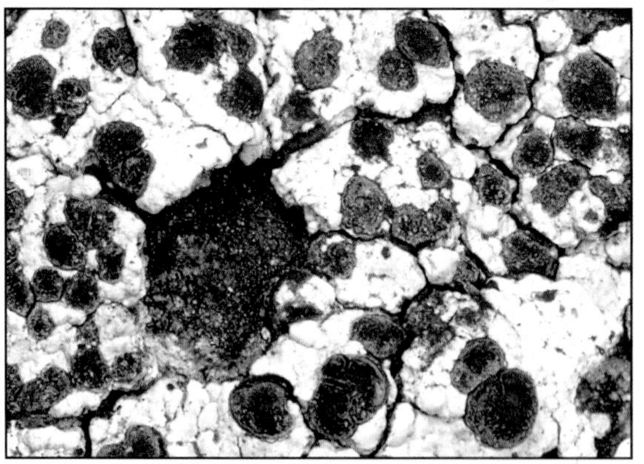

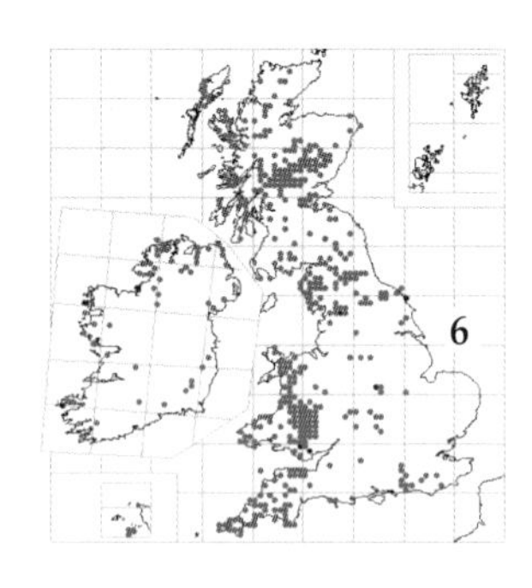

P. cineroatra x 4.

2. P. contraponenda Thallus white to creamy, light grey, thick, areolate, prothallus usually absent. Medulla I–. Apothecia up to 1 mm diam, pruinose, usually in small groups, immersed becoming sessile. Hymenium 75–100 µm tall.
Medulla: UV+ blue-white.
Habitat: Fairly common in the North and West in upland areas.

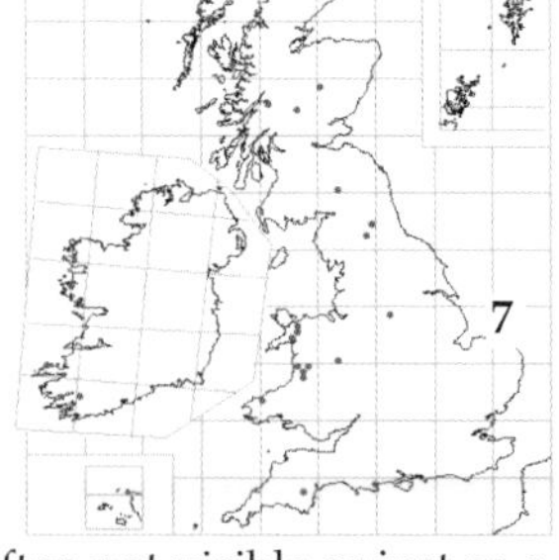

3. P. crustulata Thallus very thin, cream to pale grey, often not visible or just as a dark stain. Medulla I–. Hymenium 60–80 µm tall. Apothecia usually abundant, about 1 mm diam, black, becoming convex, sometimes slightly pruinose, often in groups or lines. Resembles a small version of *P. macrocarpa*. Spores 10–16 x 6–9 µm.
Habitat. Very common on acid rocks, small stones and rarely on old fences.

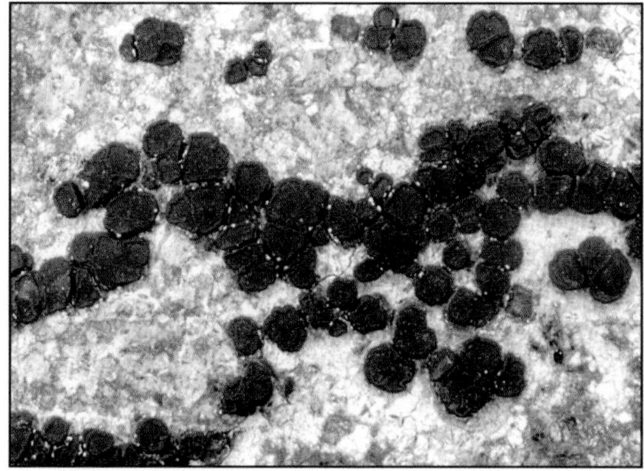

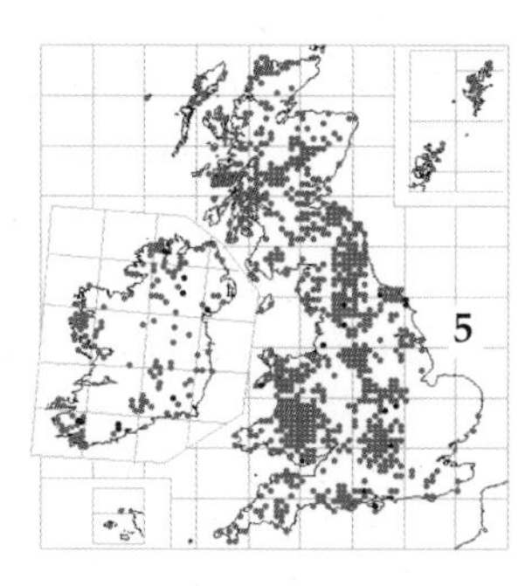

P. crustulata x 4.

4. P. flavocaerulescens Thallus orange-grey to rust-red, thick, areolate-cracked, prothallus black. Pale to dark grey-blue soralia are scattered or grouped over the thallus. Medulla I–. Apothecia common (soralia less abundant when fertile), up to 0.5 mm diam, solitary or in small groups, immersed but becoming sessile, often lightly pruinose. Hymenium 85–100 µm tall. Spores 9–15 x 4–8 µm. Medulla: K± yellow, P± orange.
Habitat: Local in upland areas, especially on metal-rich acid rock.

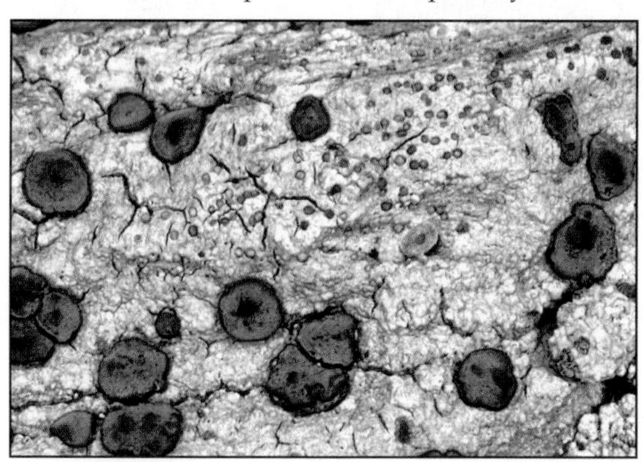

P. flavocaerulescens x 5.

5. P. hydrophila Thallus pale grey, often with a greenish or orange tinge, usually finely cracked and smooth, often in mosaics, surrounded by a pale or dark prothallus. Pycnidia black and numerous. Medulla I–. Apothecia up to 1.5 mm diam, becoming rough and convex when mature, sometimes pruinose. Epithecium bright, clear blue, 12–25 µm thick (only *P. cinereoatra* also has this character but its epithecim is only 6–12 µm thick and always more brownish). Hymenium 100–120 µm tall. Spores 17–23 x 6–9 µm.
Spot reactions: all negative.
Habitat: Local in and by streams and lakes on acid rocks in upland areas.

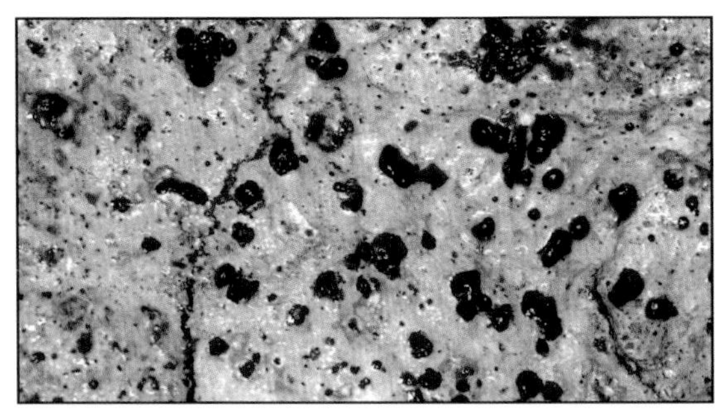

P. hydrophila x 6.

6. P. macrocarpa Thallus thin or cracked and warted, grey, greenish or often splashed rust-red. Often surrounded by a black prothallus. Medulla I–. Apothecia sessile, large (up to 3 mm diam), scattered or more rarely grouped. The margin becomes excluded and/or contorted, often appearing almost gyrose. Disc convex, rarely pruinose. Hymenium 80–100 µm tall. Spores 16–20 x 5–12 µm.
Medulla and apothecial margin: K± yellow, P± orange.
Habitat: Common on acid rocks, very rarely on old wood. Most frequent on exposed upland screes. It prefers drier conditions than *P. hydrophila.*

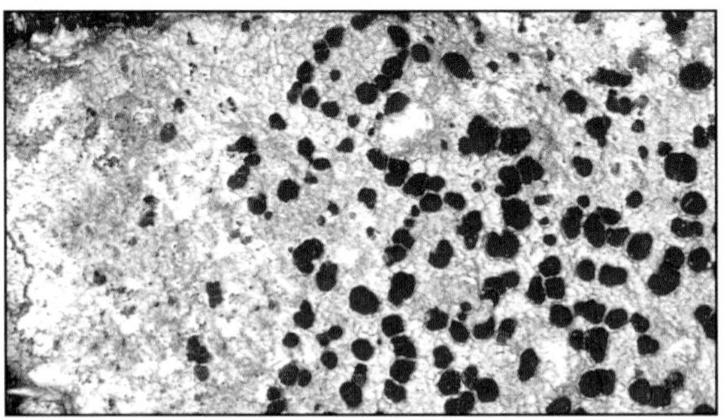

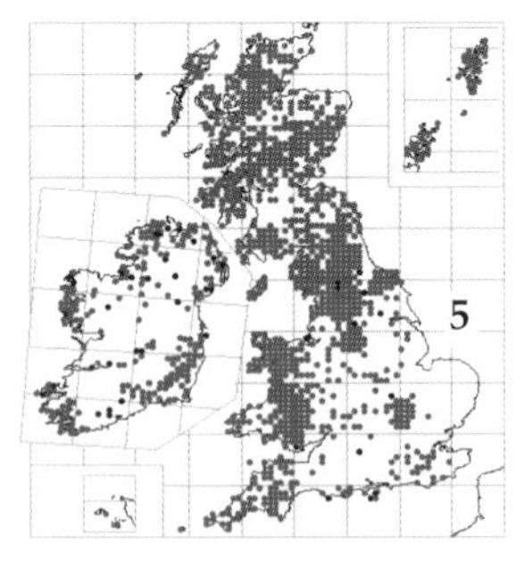

P. macrocarpa x 4.

7. P. platycarpoides Thallus white to grey, warted, areolate. Prothallus black or absent. Medulla I–. Apothecia up to 3 mm diam, separate, sometimes pruinose, sessile with a prominent, smooth, tumid margin. Hymenium 120–185 µm tall (*P. macrocarpa* is 80–100 µm tall and medulla is K± yellow). Spores 15–23 x 7–10 µm.
Apothecial margin: K+ yellow turning red (crystals in squash), P+ yellow.
Habitat: On well-lit, hard, acid rocks, especially coastal and on basalt.

P. platycarpoides x 6.

8. P. speirea Thallus white to grey and chalky or with a warted surface. Medulla I+ violet. Apothecia up to 0.8 mm diam, immersed, surrounded by a raised ring of thalline tissue often separated from thallus by a crack, pruinose when young, becoming convex and with a central plug when mature. Hymenium 75-100 μm. Spores 17–22 x 7–10 μm.
Spot reactions: all negative.
Habitat: Frequent on calcareous rocks in upland regions.

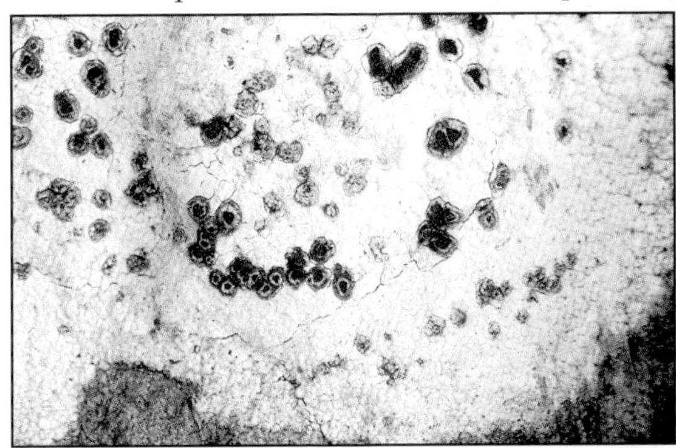

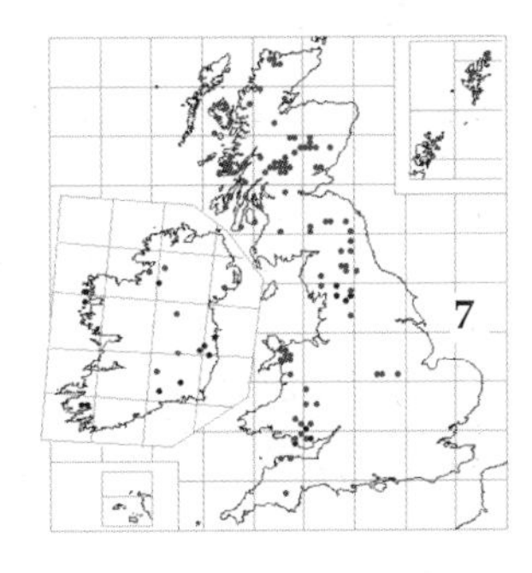

P. speirea x 6.

9. P. tuberculosa Thallus white to pale grey, continuous, cracked or warted areolate, sometimes surrounded by narrow dark prothallus. Medulla I+ violet. Bluish grey, punctiform soralia are scattered over the surface, becoming confluent. Apothecia rare, large (to 1.5 mm), becoming convex and sessile, black with white pruina. Spores 12–20 x 7–9 μm. The similar **P. soredizodes** has a thinner thallus, more oval-shaped soralia, I– medulla and soralia that are K+ yellow, P+ orange. **Lecanora panonica** is also similar but with indigo soralia.
Spot reactions: all negative.
Habitat: Common on exposed, acid rocks and pebbles, very rarely on fences. When fertile they may be separated from *P. cinereoatra* by the presence of soralia.

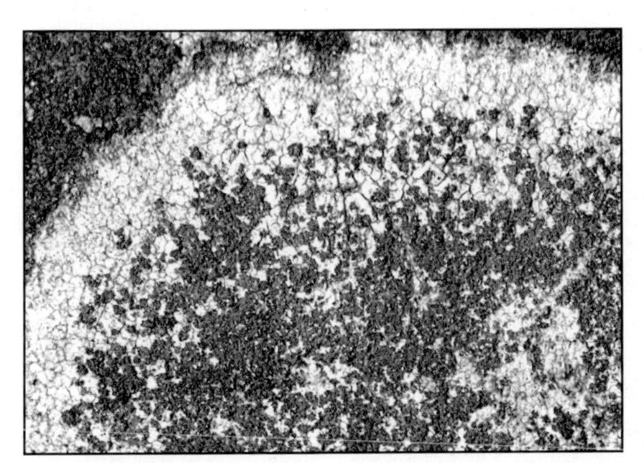

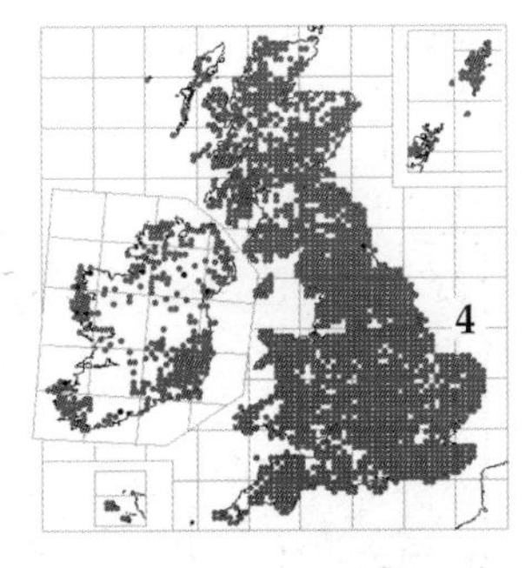

P. tuberculosa x 5.

PROTOBLASTENIA ('first budding' – referring to the early stage in development). **Thallus** crustose, saxicolous. **Photobiont** chlorococcoid. **Apothecia** lecideine, often orange or red and K+crimson. **Ascus** 8-spored, *Porpidia*-type. **Spores** simple, colourless. *Caloplaca* species differ in having polarilocular spores.

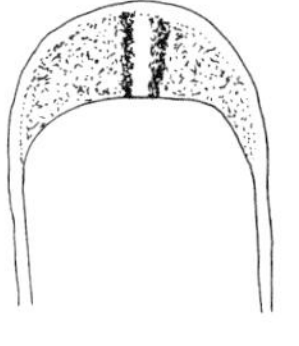

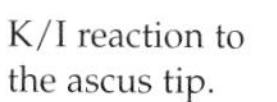

K/I reaction to the ascus tip.

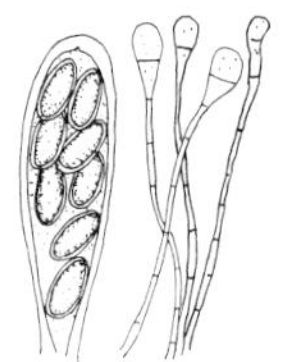

P. rupestris x 350.

1.	Apothecia in pits	**2. P. incrustans**
–	Apothecia not in pits	3
2.	Apothecia up to 1 mm	**3. P. rupestris**
–	Apothecia up to 1.5 mm	**1. P. calva**

1. Protoblastenia calva Thallus white to cream-grey, smooth and cracked but usually endolithic. Apothecia large (to 1.5 mm diam), deep orange, and almost hemispherical, in shallow pits. Spores ellipsoid, 8–15 x 5–10 µm.
Apothecia: K+ crimson.
Habitat: Fairly common on hard limestone.

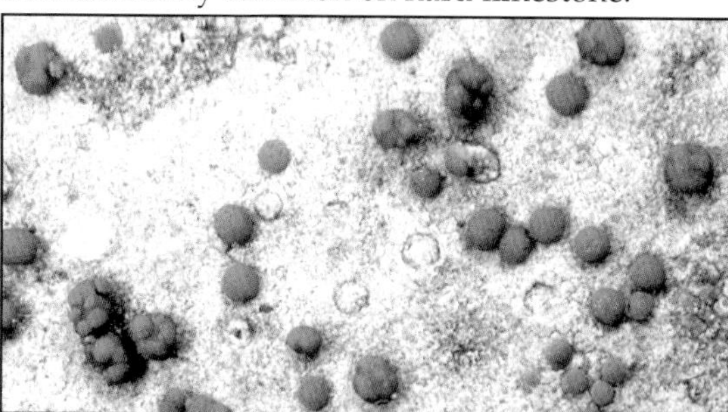

P. calva x 4.

7

2. P. incrustans Thallus pale yellowish grey, or endolithic. Apothecia less than 0.5 mm diam, clear yellow-orange, flat or slightly convex, in pits in the substratum when mature. Spores almost globose, 10–13 x 4–6 µm.
Apothecia: K+ crimson.
Habitat: Common on hard limestone.

P. incrustans x 6.

3. P. rupestris Thallus greenish brown to orange-grey (the thallus colour is best seen at a distance and helps to separate it from the grey to black thallus of *Caloplaca holocarpa*), scurfy, areolate or almost absent. Apothecia up to 0.7 mm diam, orange, often with a greenish tinge when wet, sessile, becoming very convex and distorted, not in pits. Spores ellipsoid, 8–17 x 5–8 µm.
Apothecia: K+ crimson.
Habitat: Common on mortar and other calcareous substrata. It is a good indicator of where the substratum is, or is becoming basic.

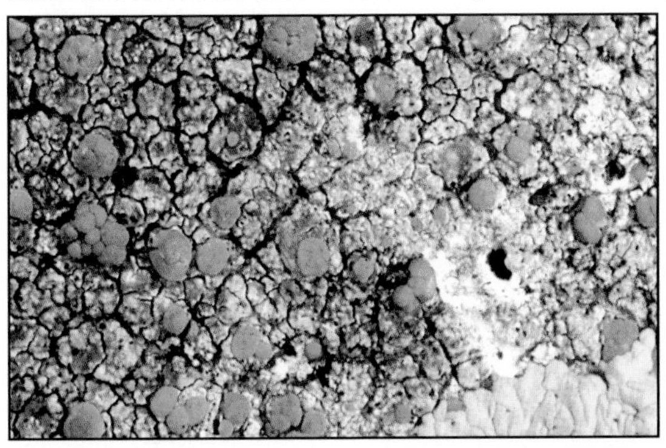

P. rupestris x 6.

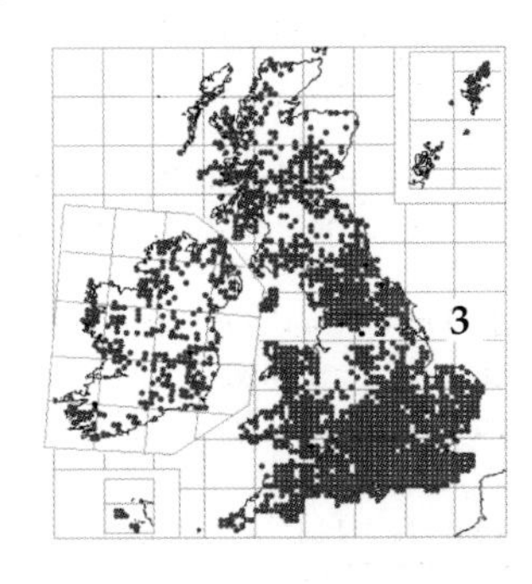

PROTOPARMELIA ('first *Parmelia*' – from the appearance of a well-developed thallus). **Thallus** crustose, brown. **Photobiont** trebouxioid. **Apothecia** lecanorine. Disc brown. **Ascus** 8-spored, *Lecanora*-type with a large apical cushion. **Spores** simple, colourless, narrowly ellipsoid (this shape and straight conidia separate it from *Lecanora*).

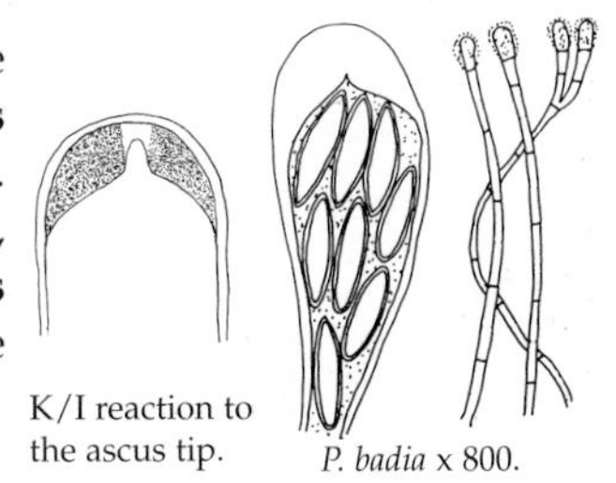

K/I reaction to the ascus tip. *P. badia* x 800.

Protoparmelia badia (Lecanora badia) Thallus thick, smooth or warted, pale greyish brown to dark chestnut and rather glossy. Apothecia usually abundant, up to 2 mm diam, with a glossy brown disc and usually paler, contorted or crenulate margins. Spores 8–14 x 3–5 µm.
Cortex: KC+ pink (in section). UV± white.
Habitat: Common in upland regions on well-lit, hard, acid rocks, also on walls, less frequently on coastal rocks.

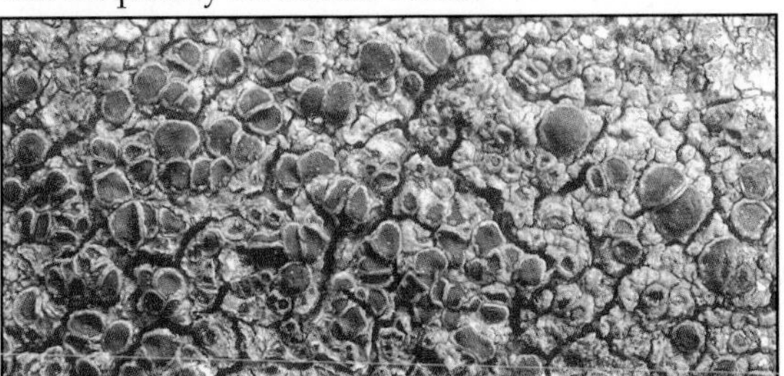

P. badia x 6.

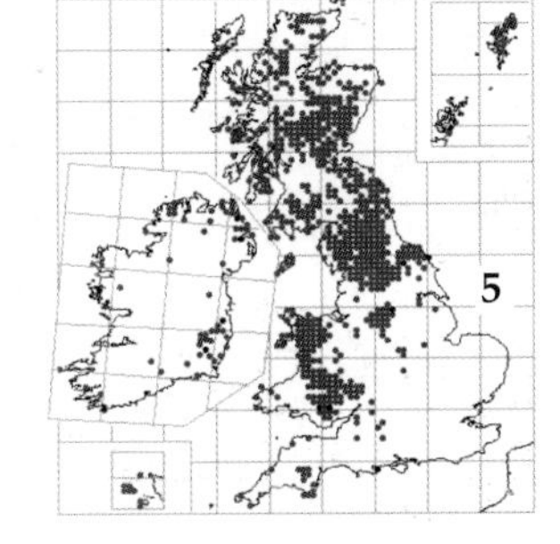

PSEUDEPHEBE ('false *Ephebe*' – from its similar appearance to *Ephebe*). **Thallus** fruticose, attached to the substratum by hapters. **Photobiont** trebouxiod. **Apothecia** lecanorine. **Ascus** 8-spored. **Spores** simple, colourless. Due to its appearance it is included in the lateral key to the *Alectoria* group. **Chemical reactions** all negative.

Pseudephebe pubescens Forms prostrate mats, usually radiating, rarely exceeding 1 cm in height, branching frequently from the base, attached to the substratum over almost the whole of the thallus area. Branches up to 0.2 mm diam. Dark brown to black, often glossy, wiry. Soralia absent. Apothecia are common, but mostly only found in specimens above about 600 metres. The discs are dark grey or brown, up to 5 mm diam, often with ciliate margins. Spores 7–12 x 6–8. Black pycnidia are usually present, especially at the axils of the branches. Conidia 5–7 x 1 µm.
Habitat: Frequent in mountainous regions on hard, siliceous rocks, especially granite.

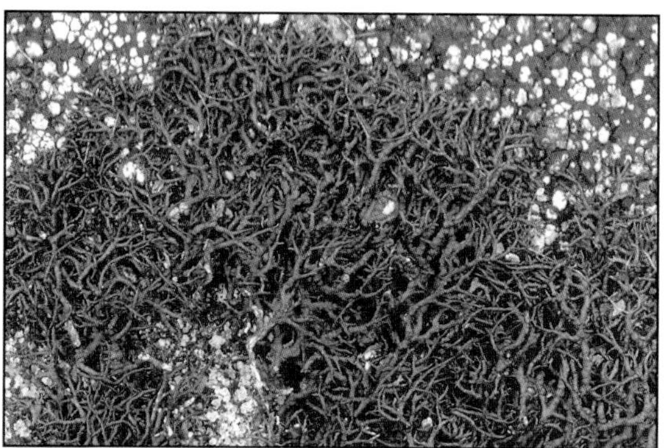

P. pubescens x 1.

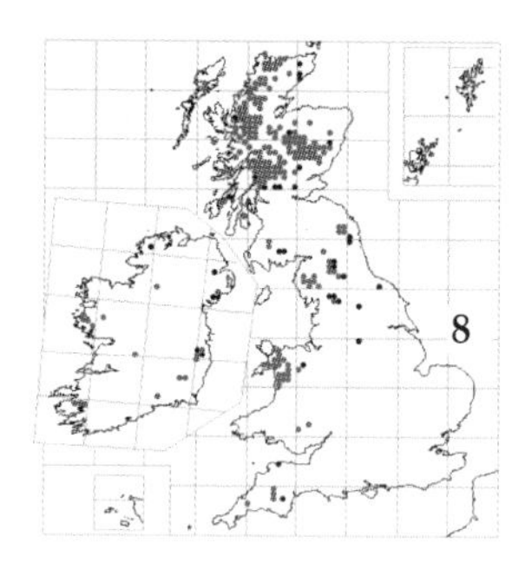

PSEUDEVERNIA ('false *Evernia*' – from the similar appearance to *Evernia*). **Thallus** foliose, strap-shaped, often ascending and attached at only one point so as to appear fruticose. **Photobiont** trebouxioid. **Apothecia** lecanorine, shortly stalked. **Ascus** 8-spored, *Lecanora*-type **Spores** simple, colourless. This genus was once included in *Parmelia* but is separated from it by the strap-like lobes attached at the base and the absence of rhizines.

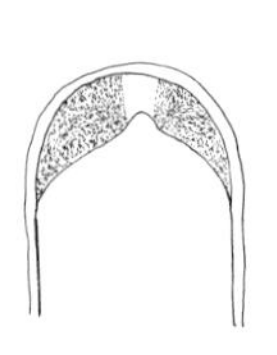

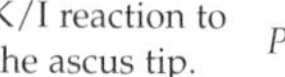

K/I reaction to the ascus tip.

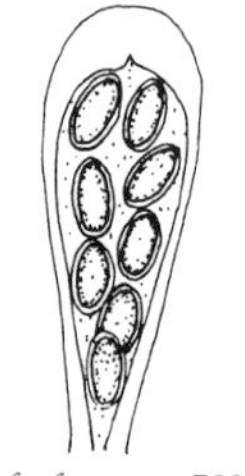

P. furfuracea x 500.

Pseudevernia furfuracea Thallus ascendent to pendent. Lobes to 4 mm wide. The upper surface grey with isidia or small lobules. The margins of the lobes curl under to almost cover the black (white to pinkish in the younger lobes) undersurface. Apothecia were not infrequent in British specimens in the nineteenth

century, but are very rare at the present. Apothecia up to 2 mm diam on short stalks. Spores 7–10 x 4–6 µm.
There are two chemical races :
Cortex: K+ yellow. Medulla: C–, KC+ rose-red [var. *furfuracea*].
Cortex: K+ yellow. Medulla: C+ rose-red , KC+ red [var. *ceratea*].
Habitat: Common on well-lit, siliceous rocks, acid-barked trees and fences in upland and northern areas. Rarer in lowland Britain (where it is usually on fences). At one time it was used to stop haemorrhageing, as a dye source, and by the ancient Egyptians for stuffing bodies in mummification.

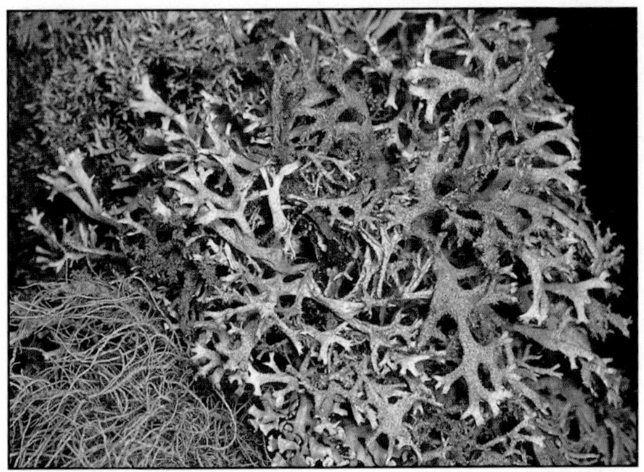

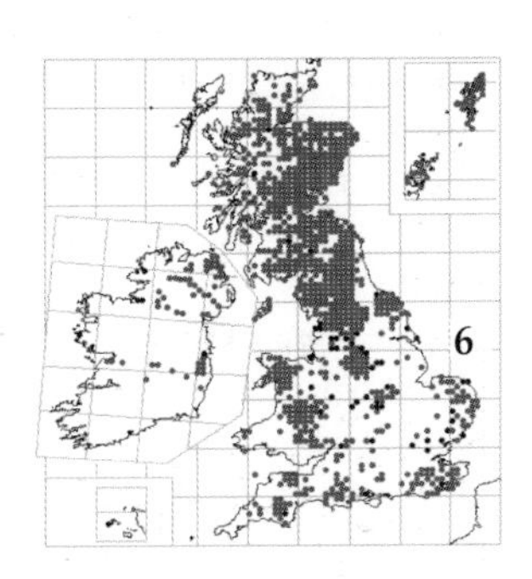

P. furfuracea x 2.

PSEUDOCYPHELLARIA (from the presence of pseudocyphellae) **Thallus** foliose, lower surface tomentose with pseudocyphellae, upper surface often sorediate. **Photobiont** green or, as in the species described below, blue-green *Nostoc*. Very rarely fertile in Britain. **Apothecia** lecanorine. **Ascus** 8-spored, *Peltigera*-type. **Spores** brown, up to 3-septate. This genus was once included in *Sticta* to which it is closely related; however, as the name suggests, the pores on the lower surface differ in structure; there are also differences in chemistry.

1.	Yellow pseudocyphellae, yellowish soralia	**1. P. crocata**
–	White pseudocyphellae, bluish grey soralia	2
2.	Medulla and soralia C–	**2. P. intricata**
–	Medulla and soralia C+	**3. P. norvegica**

1. Pseudocyphellaria crocata Thallus grey-brown to reddish, greener when wet. Lobes to 15 mm wide, smooth at first but developing coarse ridges. From these, puntiform soralia develop with coarse yellow soredia which may become confluent. Lower surface pale brown, darker towards the centre, with yellow pseudocyphellae. Apothecia very rare. Spores 1-septate, 20–30 x 5–10 µm.
May be separated from the other species by the conspicuous yellow pseudo-cyphellae underneath and soralia above.
Medulla and soralia: K+ yellow, P+ orange, UV+ dull orange.

Habitat: Found mainly in the West in damp, boggy, sheltered sites. On mossy trees and rocks, especially near the coast.

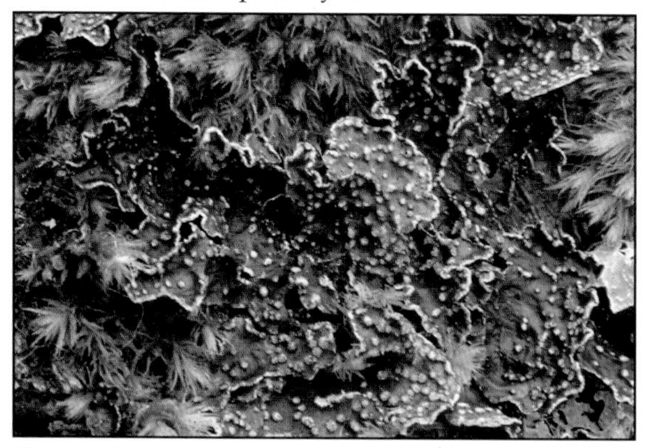

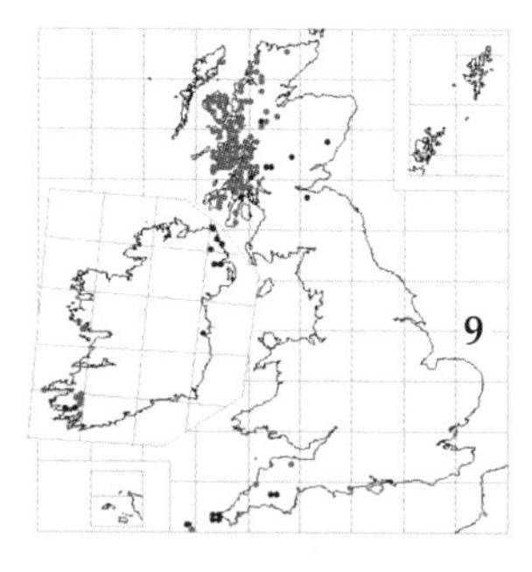

P. crocata x 3.

2. P. intricata Thallus brown, grey-brown to grey when dry, lobes up to 1 cm wide, incised but with rounded tips, sometimes weakly ridged. Margins with bluish grey soralia which sometimes spread over the surface of the lobe. Under-surface tomentose, brown, darker towards the centre, with small white, circular pseudocyphellae, which may be difficult to detect.
Medulla and soredia: K+ yellow, KC–, UV+ glaucous white.
Habitat: Very rare on moss-covered trees, rocks and heather stems in western Scotland and south-west Ireland.

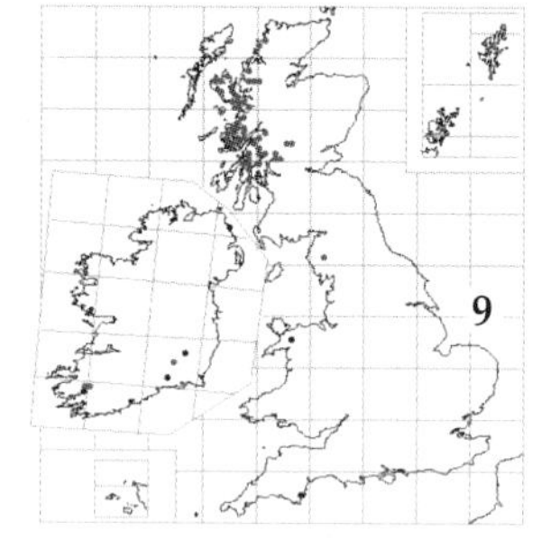

3. P. norvegica Very similar to *P. intricata* but differs in its chemistry. It also has wider (to 1.5 cm), more rounded lobes. The soralia become laminal in younger lobes. Fresh soredia have a distinctive lilac tinge.
Medulla and soredia: KC+ orange, C+ red, UV+ bright glaucous white.
Habitat: Rare, in similar sites to the previous two species.

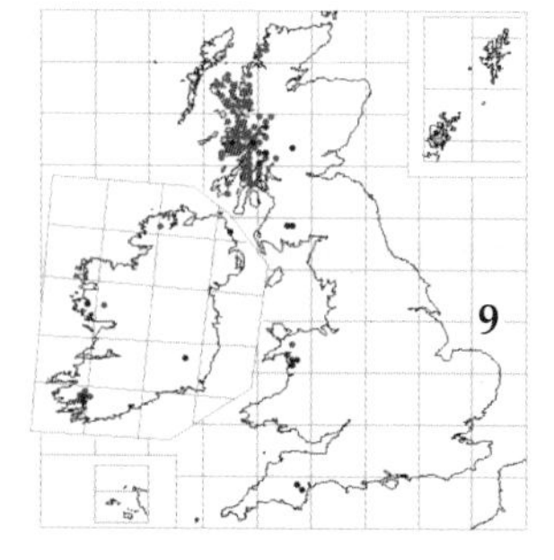

P. norvegica x 3.

PSILOLECHIA ('naked plates' – from the form of the thallus). **Thallus** crustose, becoming leprose, and consisting of goniocysts. **Photobiont** trebouxioid. **Apothecia** lecideine. **Ascus** 8-spored, *Porpidia*-like but with a dark blue outer layer. **Spores** simple, colourless, narrowly ellipsoid or clavate.

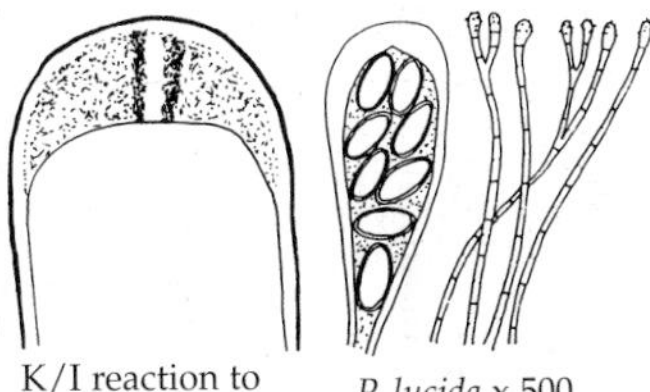
K/I reaction to the ascus tip.
P. lucida x 500.

1. Thallus sulphur-yellow, C– **2. P. lucida**
– Thallus white to grey or pale brown, sometimes pinkish, C+ red **1. P. leprosa**

1. Psilolechia leprosa Thallus granular or rather leprose, white to pale brownish or greenish grey, often covering wide areas. Apothecia often present, especially where sheltered under window sills and in crevices, etc., 0.2–0.5 mm diam, pale pink, convex, immarginate and often irregular. These features give it the appearance of a grey *Lepraria* with *Bacidia*-like fruits. Spores simple or 1-septate, clavate, 5–7 x 1–2 µm.
C+ red, UV–.
Habitat: Widespread but much overlooked. On rocks and buildings and frequently associated with metal run-off, especially copper from lightning conductors, window grilles, etc.

P. leprosa x 8.

2. P. lucida Thallus bright sulphurous yellow, finely granular-leprose. Its English name is 'sulphur lichen'. The granules may form an areolate crust. Apothecia rare, ± hidden amongst the granules. Up to 0.5 mm diam, with yellow to pale orange discs. Paraphyses with minute yellow granules at the tips. Spores rather oblong, simple, 4–7 x 1–2 µm.
Spot reactions: negative, UV+ orange.
Habitat: Very common on sheltered, shaded rocks and bricks especially where it is damp. Very rarely found on trees. Its distinctive colour is such that it can be recognized at a distance. It is, however difficult to separate from sterile *Chaenotheca furfuracea*, which occurs on trees and soil in more shaded situations. It also has the oval-shaped cells of *Stichococcus* as the photobiont.

P. lucida x 3.

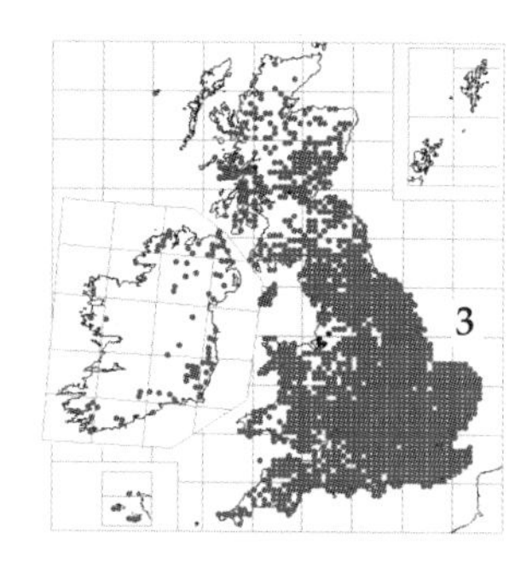

PSORA ('scurfy' – from the form of the thallus). **Thallus** squamulose. **Photobiont** mainly trebouxioid. **Apothecia** lecideine with dark brown to black discs. **Ascus** 8-spored, K/I+ apical dome with a darker blue tube. No ocular chamber, *Porpidia*-like. **Paraphyses** have dark tips, stick together and are difficult to separate. **Spores** colourless, simple.

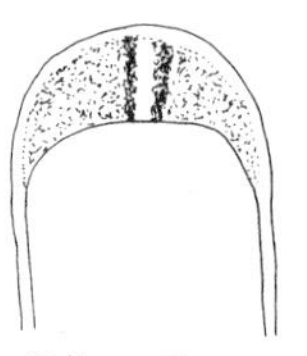

K/I reaction to the ascus tip.

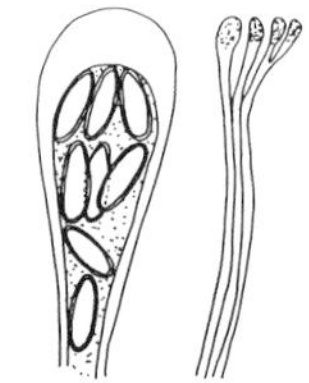

P. decipiens x 350.

1. Squamules pink with white margins **1. P. decipiens**
– Squamules brown without white margins **2. P. lurida**

1. Psora decipiens Thallus of pale pink or sometimes brown squamules with conspicuous white-pruinose, often upturned margins. Lower surface white, attached by a hyphal net penetrating into substratum. Squamules scattered or overlapping, circular or contorted, up to about 4 mm wide. Apothecia up to 1.5 mm, black, convex with a paler, sometimes pruinose, margin that becomes excluded. The apothecia are usually only one per squamule and situated towards the margin. Hymenium I–. Spores 10–18 x 6–8 µm.
Habitat: A distinctive species of well-lit, base-rich soils, shell-sand and calcareous soils.

P. decipiens x 5.

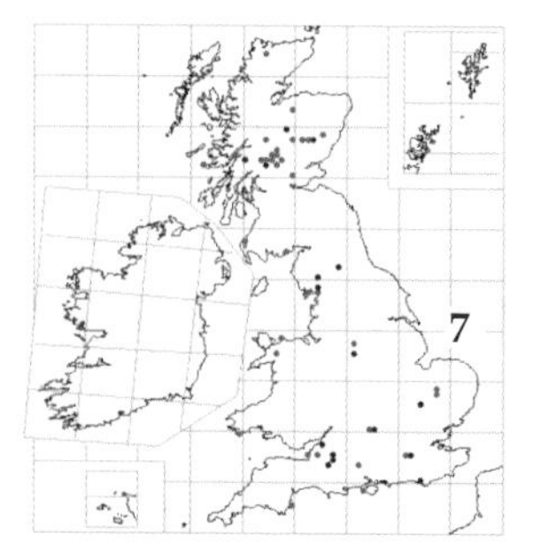

2. P. lurida Thallus green to coffee- or dark chestnut-brown, under-surface often dark and attached to the substratum by a pale hyphal net. Squamules imbricate, to 5 mm wide, convex and contorted, often forming a thick crust. Apothecia up to about 1 mm, crowded, black or dark brown with the margins becoming excluded. Hymenium I+ blue. Spores 13–15 x 5–7 µm. Often confused with *Catapyrenium* species which have immersed perithecia. The coastal species *Solenopsora holophaea* may be separated by its 1-septate spores.
Habitat: Frequent in humus-filled crevices in hard limestone or on calcareous soils and rocks.

P. lurida x 5.

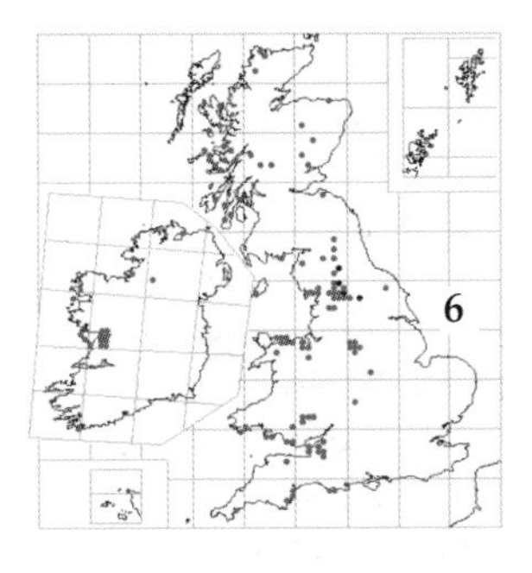

PSOROMA (similar to *Psora*). **Thallus** squamulose or lobate. **Photobiont** *Myrmecia.* External cepalodia containing *Nostoc* are usually present. **Apothecia** lecanorine with a persistant thalline margin. **Ascus** 8-spored, K/I+ blue apical dome containing a darker blue tube. **Spores** colourless, simple, usually containing one or two oil droplets. There is only one British species. This genus is related to *Pannaria*.

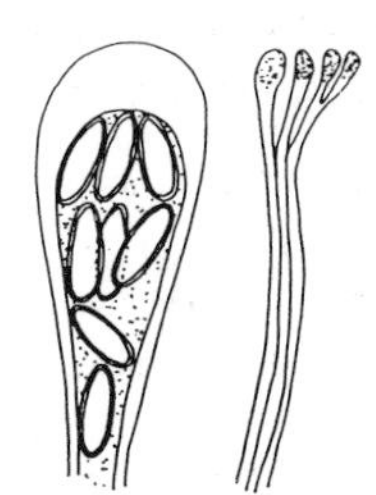

P. hypnorum x 250.

Psoroma hypnorum Thallus green to orange-brown, of small (up to 0.5 mm) squamules, sometimes almost granular. Fixed by a tomentum of fine, dark hairs. Cephalodia are usually scattered across the surface. These are similar in appearance to the thallus but darker. Apothecia, one to a lobe, brown to red-brown, up to 3 mm diam, concave, becoming plane, underside covered with pale hairs (hairs absent on *Pannaria pezizoides*). Thalline margin wide, often knobbly lobate. The apothecia when mature may almost cover a squamule. Spores 20–35 x 8–12 µm, surrounded by a thick, warted epispore.
Habitat: Not common, on mossy, damp shaded trees, rocks and soil.

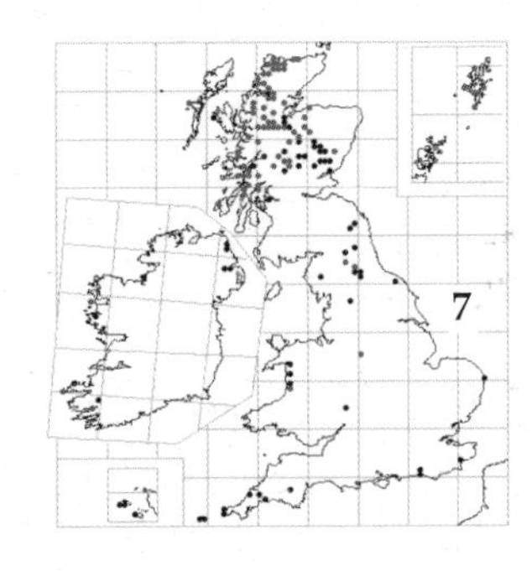

PYCNOTHELIA ('thick nipple' – from the shape of the secondary thallus). **Primary thallus** crustose. **Podetia** short, digitate and hollow. **Photobiont** trebouxioid. **Apothecia** lecideine, rare on the tips of the podetia. **Ascus** 8-spored, *Cladonia*-type. **Spores** colourless, simple, rarely becoming 1-septate. There is only one species.

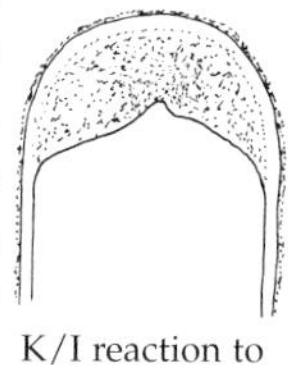

K/I reaction to the ascus tip.

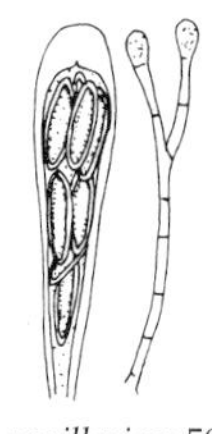

P. papillaria x 500.

Pycnothelia papillaria Primary thallus white or grey, of persistent, crustose granules. Podetia arise from the primary thallus; these are cylindrical, hollow, simple or branched, white to pale purplish brown and often densely packed, up to 1.5 cm high but usually less. Often tipped with brown apothecia or, more commonly, dark pycnidia. Spores 10–15 x 4–5 µm.
K+ yellow, UV+ blue-white.
Habitat: Common on old and wet peat moors and acid soils in the North and West, rarer elsewhere.

P. papillaria (with *Cladonia diversa*) x 3.

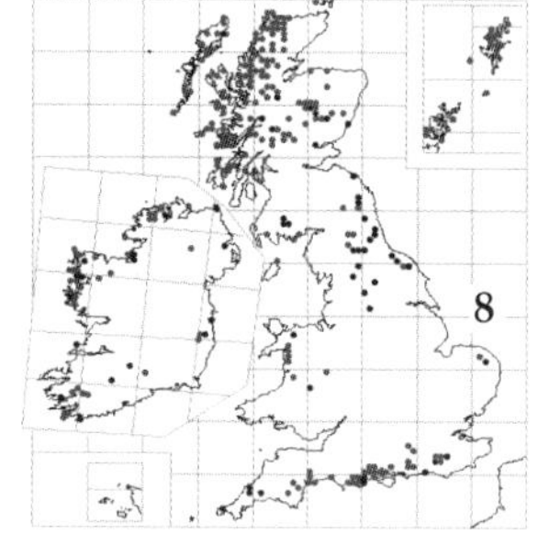

PYRENOCOLLEMA ('*Collema* with a hard fruit'). **Thallus** crustose or immersed. **Photobiont** cyanobacterial. **Perithecia** black. **Ascus** 8-spored, K/I–. **Spores** colourless, 1-septate, clavate. It differs from *Arthopyrenia* in the structure of the wall of the perithecia, the absence of an involucrellum, the anastomosed paraphyses, and in having cyanobacteria as the photobiont.

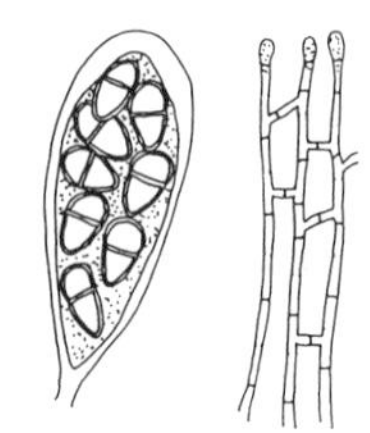

P. halodytes x 300.

Pyrenocollema halodytes (Arthopyrenia halodytes) Thallus thin and dirty yellow-brown and rather gelatinous when on acid rocks. It more commonly occurs endolithically on barnacles and limpets or limestone. Perithecia about 0.25 mm in pits when on shells or limestone, sessile with a dark ring around the ostiole when on acid rocks. Spores 12–25 x 5–7 µm, one cell wider and shorter. **P. sublitoralis** is a similar species sometimes found growing with *P. halodytes* on chalky rock, has a white thallus and larger perithecia, up to 1.5 mm diam.
Habitat: Common around the coast around high-water mark. Very many barnacles, limpets and mussels act as hosts to this species.

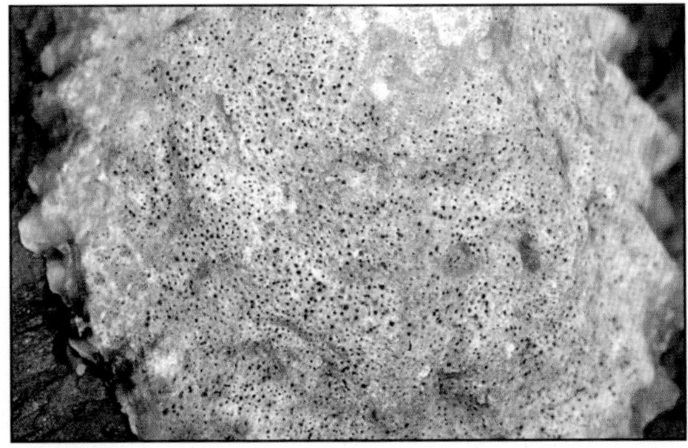

P. halodytes x 3.

PYRENULA ('small nut-like fruits'). **Thallus** crustose, sometimes immersed, found on smooth-barked trees. **Photobiont** *Trentepohlia*. **Perithecia** volcano-shaped to globular (K+ red-purple in a squash in many species). **Ascus** 8-spored, K/I–. **Spores** brown, to 5-septate with distinctive locules and and a common outer wall surrounding the wall of the individual cells (distoseptate).

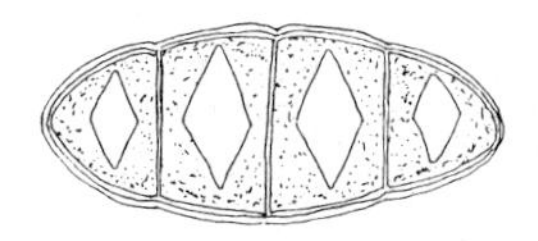

P. macrospora x 1000.

1.	Thallus whitish or yellow-brown with orange flecks. No pseudocyphellae	2
–	Thallus pale tan to olive-green. White pseudocyphellae present	3
2.	Thallus white to cream. UV–	**2. P. laevigata**
–	Thallus yellowish brown with orange flecks. UV+ yellow	**4. P. occidentalis**
3.	Perithecia about 1 mm diam	**3. P. macrospora**
–	Perithecia up to 0.3 mm diam	**1. P. chlorospila**

1. Pyrenula chlorospila Thallus light tan to olive-green flecked, with white pseudocyphellae resembling small cracks in wax. Perithecia about 0.3 mm diam. No K+ purplish crystals present inside the perithecial wall. Spores 3-septate with angular locules in each cell, 26–32 x 10–13 µm.
K+ yellow, P± yellowish, UV–.
Habitat: Common on smooth-barked trees in shaded woodland. Together with *P. macrospora* it often forming extensive mosaics, intersected by the dark prothallus.

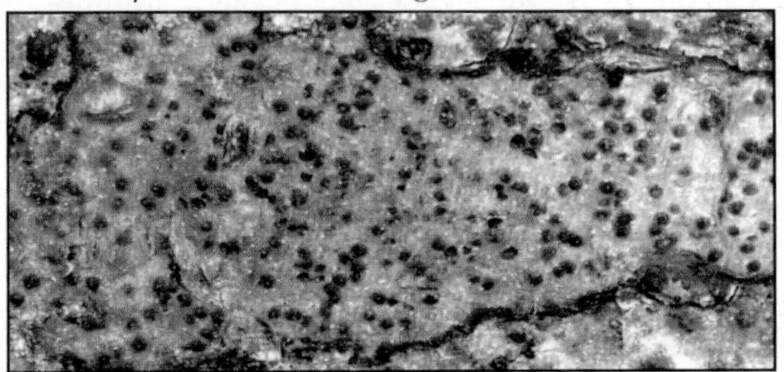

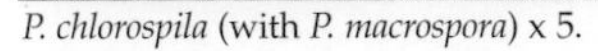

P. chlorospila (with *P. macrospora*) x 5.

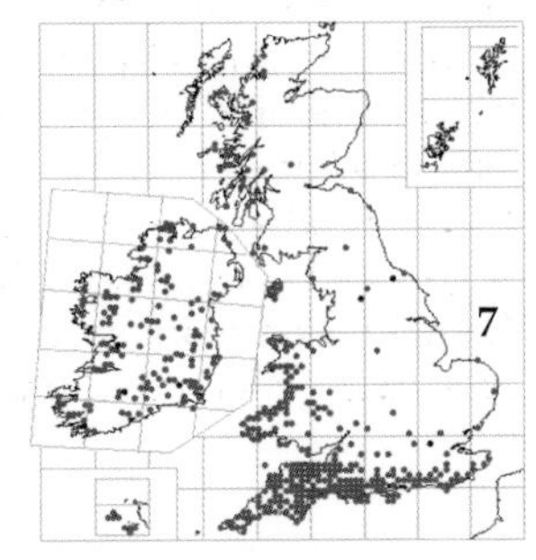

2. P. laevigata Thallus white to cream, differing from *P. chlorospila* and *P. macrospora* in the lack of pseudocyphellae, prothallus rarely present. Perithecia about 0.3 mm diam. No K+ purple crystals in perithecial walls. Spores, brown, 3-septate, 17–22 x 8–10 µm. Black, globose pycnidia often common.
K+ yellow, P± yellowish, UV–.
Habitat: A rare oceanic species of smooth-barked trees, especially hazel.

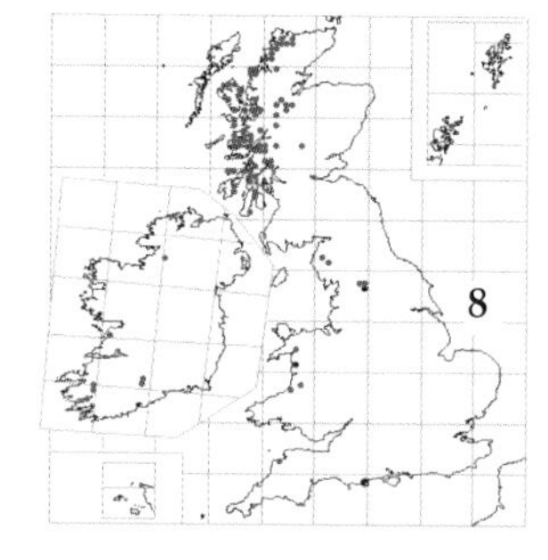

3. P. macrospora Thallus waxy, creamy yellow to greenish brown, small, with white flecks scattered over the thallus (use hand-lens). It often forms mosaics, individual thalli being separated by a pronounced black prothallus. Perithecia up to 1 mm across, globose, becoming prominent when mature with a clearly visible ostiole (use hand-lens). K– crystals inside the perithecial wall. Spores brown, 3-septate , 25–35 x 8–12 µm.
K+ yellow, P± yellowish, UV ± yellow or orange.
Habitat: Very common on shaded, smooth-barked trees, especially in the South and West, decreasing northwards.

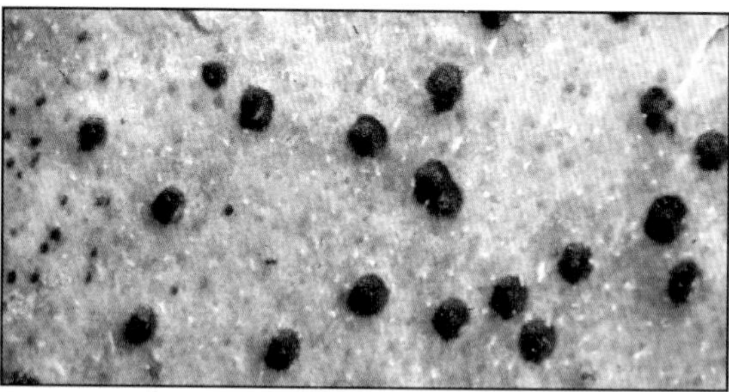

P. macrospora x 6.

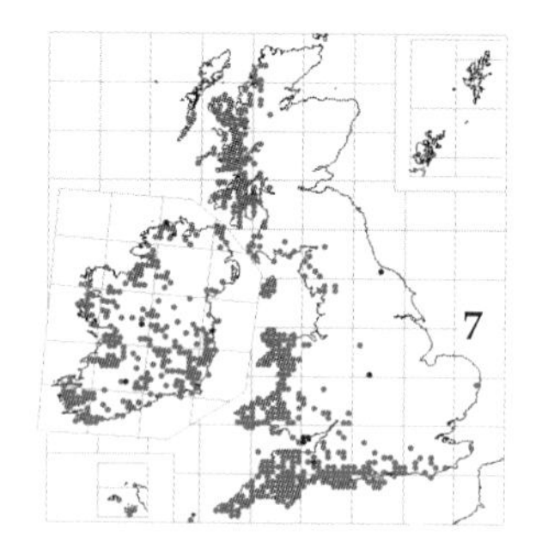

4. P. occidentalis Thallus creamy orange to yellowish brown usually with brownish orange flecks. No pseudocyphellae. Perithecia up to 0.6 mm diam. No K+ purplish crystals in perithecial wall but the surface of the perithecia may be K+ purple. Spores 18–22 x 8–11 µm. Globose pycnidia are common.
K+ yellowish and purplish in parts, P+ orange, UV+ yellow.
Habitat: Very local, on smooth-barked trees in damp, very sheltered sites.

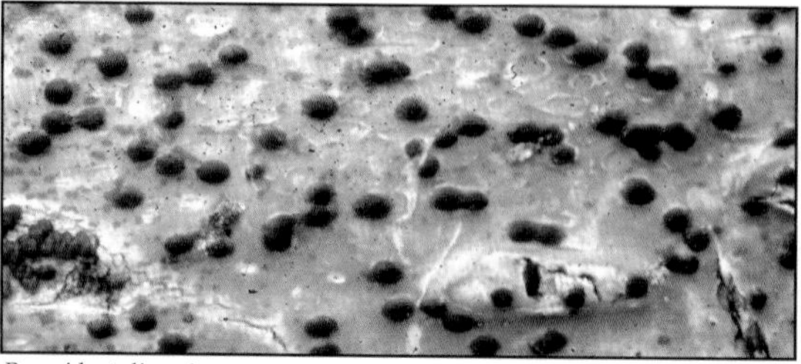

P. occidentalis x 6.

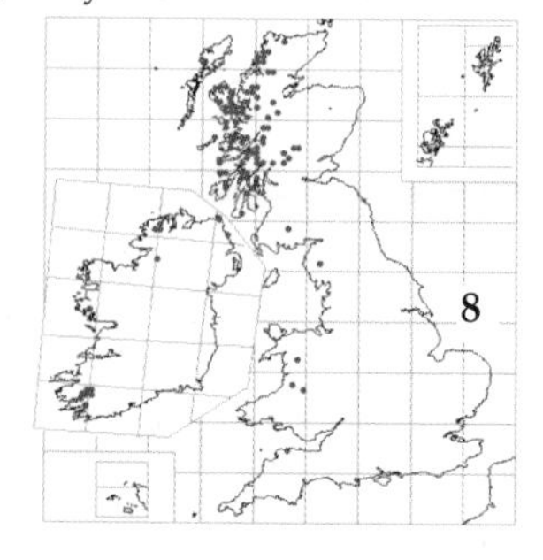

PYRRHOSPORA ('fire-red spores' – from the colour of the apothecia). **Thallus** crustose. **Photobiont** trebouxioid. **Apothecia** lecanorine, but appearing superficially to be lecideine. **Paraphyses** often slightly branched and not having swollen tips. **Ascus** 8-spored, *Lecanora*-type. **Spores** simple, colourless, but pale brown when over-mature. There is only one British species.

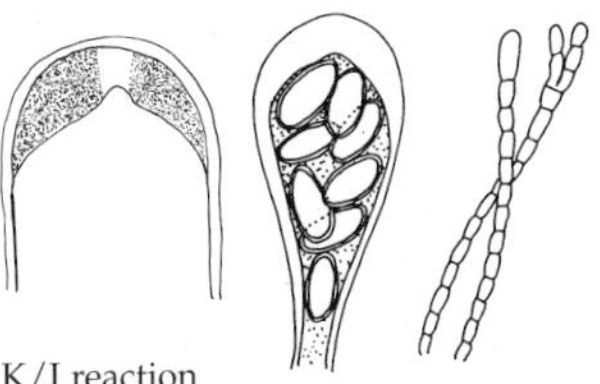

K/I reaction to the ascus tip.

P. quernea x 400.

Pyrrhospora quernea Thallus ochre to yellow-grey consisting of very finely farinose soredia on a faintly areolate thallus. It is frequently surrounded by a black prothallus. Usually infertile or with numerous small (up to about 1 mm wide), purplish to red-brown, irregular-shaped, very convex apothecia which darken with age and appear almost as if they are melting. Spores 8–12 x 5–7 µm. When infertile it may be confused with *Lecanora expallens* but that species has coarser, less buff, more green-yellow soralia without a black prothallus.
KC+ orange, C+ orange, UV–.
Habitat: Frequent on well-lit to lightly shaded, rather nutrient-rich, rough-barked trees, especially oaks, in 'old forest' situations. It becomes rarer in the North.

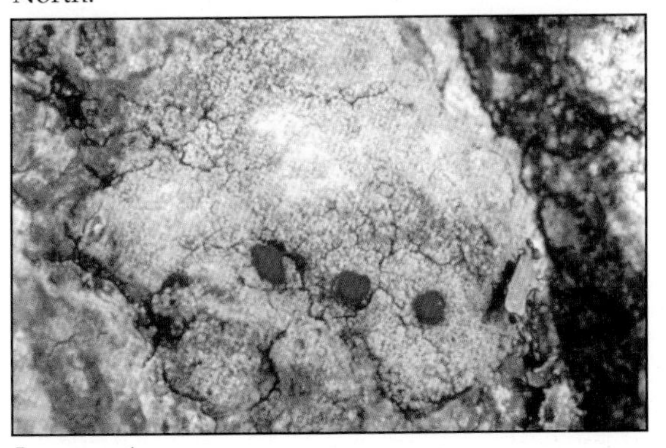

P. quernea x 4.

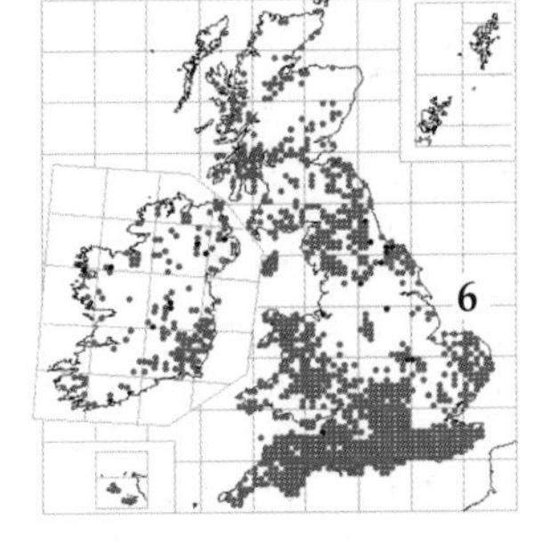

RACODIUM ('disorganized' from the random form of the thallus). **Thallus** consisting of a mat of filamentous strands, each composed of an algal filament (*Trentepohlia*) surrounded by dark fungal hyphae. These hyphae are arranged parallel to the algal filament and, in this, it differs from *Cystocoleus* where the hyphae are irregularly arranged to give an uneven, wavy appearance in a squash preparation under the microscope. There is only one British species.

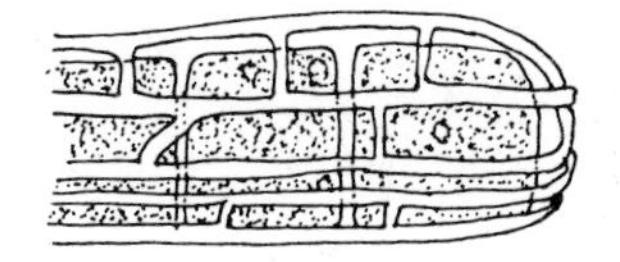

R. rupestre x 200.

Racodium rupestre Thallus dark brown to black, felted. The fungal hyphae surrounding the algal cells are straight and more or less parallel. Frequently found growing with *Cystocoleus ebeneus* and *Lepraria* species.
Habitat: Common, especially in the North and West, on more or less vertical, shaded, damp, siliceous rocks where it is sheltered from direct rain.

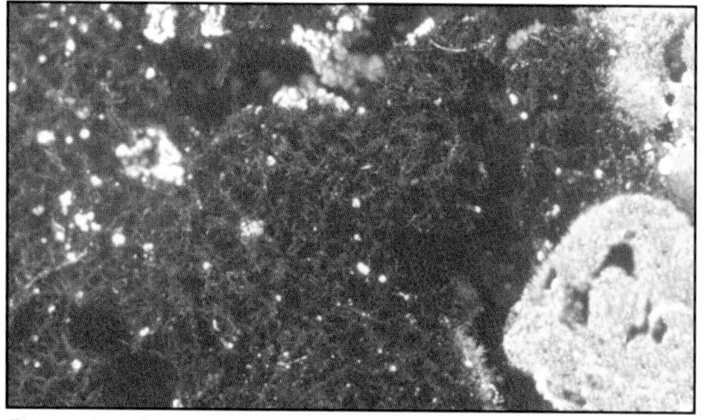

R. rupestre x 8.

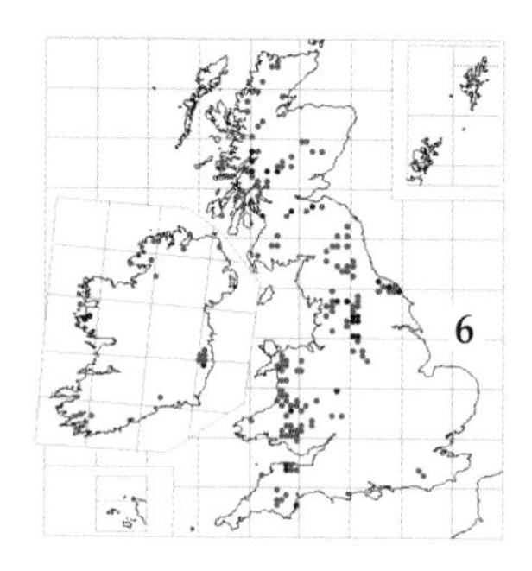

RAMALINA ('branch or twig' – from the shape of the thallus). **Thallus** fruticose, greenish grey to yellowish grey, more or less flattened, upper and lower surfaces similar, tufted, pendent. **Photobiont** trebouxioid. **Apothecia** lecanorine, fawn-coloured and usually on short stalks. **Ascus** 8-spored, *Bacidia*-type. **Spores** colourless, 1-septate. **Pycnidia** immersed with dark or pale ostioles. All species contain some usnic acid (sometimes difficult to detect). They have been used for a number of purposes including being ground up to make a hair powder.

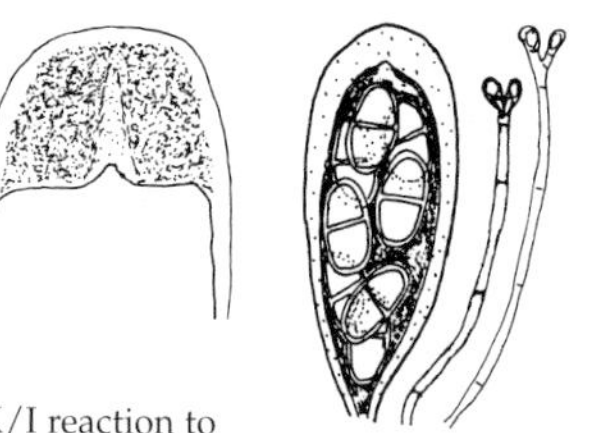

K/I reaction to the ascus tip.

R. calicaris x 500.

1.	Sorediate, normally infertile	2
–	Lacking soredia, normally fertile	5
2.	Soralia marginal or laminal, not in inflated lobe tips	3
–	Lobe tips inflated and split to reveal contained soredia	**2. R. canariensis**
3.	Soralia oval, marginal and delimited	4
–	Soralia irregular, laminal and marginal	**7. R. lacera**
4.	Medulla and soralia usually K–. Single holdfast	**4. R. farinacea**
–	Medulla and soralia K+ yellow to red. Multiple holdfasts	**9. R. subfarinacea**
5.	Corticolous, not very hard and brittle when dry	6
–	Saxicolous, hard and brittle when dry	8
6.	Lobes strap-shaped, erect or pendent. Apothecia laminal, marginal as well as at lobe tips	7

–	Lobes short and bushy, usually covered with apothecia at tips	**5. R. fastigiata**
7.	Lobes narrow with channels (canaliculate)	**1. R. calicaris**
–	Lobes widen from the base, wrinkled but not canaliculate	**6. R. fraxinea**
8.	Thallus erect or slightly pendent, pitted, not blackened at base. Pycnidia with light-coloured tips	**8. R. siliquosa**
–	Thallus pendent, more or less smooth, usually blackened at base. Pycnidia with black tips	**3. R. cuspidata**

1. Ramalina calicaris Thallus grey-green, shiny, up to about 8 cm long with narrow, divided branches with edges turned-up to give a deep single channel (canaliculate). Usually fertile. Apothecia fawn-coloured, on or near the tips of the branches. Spores straight, 10–16 x 5–7 µm.
Spot reaction: all negative
Habitat: Occasional on well-lit to lightly shaded, nutrient-rich, rather basic bark such as that of willow, especially near the coast. A declining species.

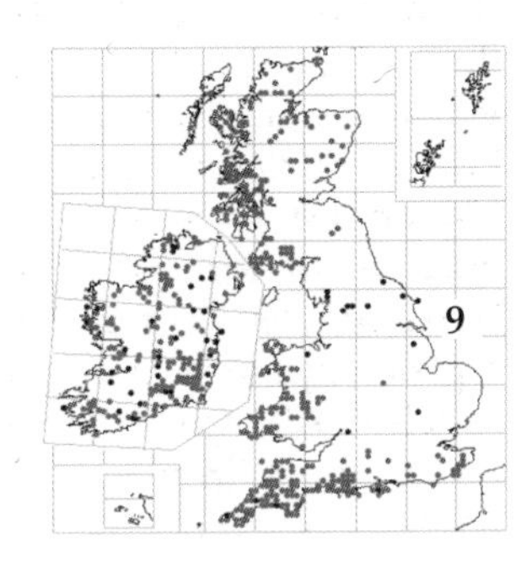

R. calicaris x 2.

2. R. canariensis (R. baltica) Thallus grey-green, matt, only slightly branched with wrinkled lobes up to 1 cm wide. The lobe tips become inflated and split open to reveal the farinose soredia inside. Apothecia very rare. Spores 15–21 x 6 µm.
Spot reactions: negative. Medulla and soralia: UV+ blue-white.
Habitat: Common on well-lit basic bark, rock underhangs and church walls.

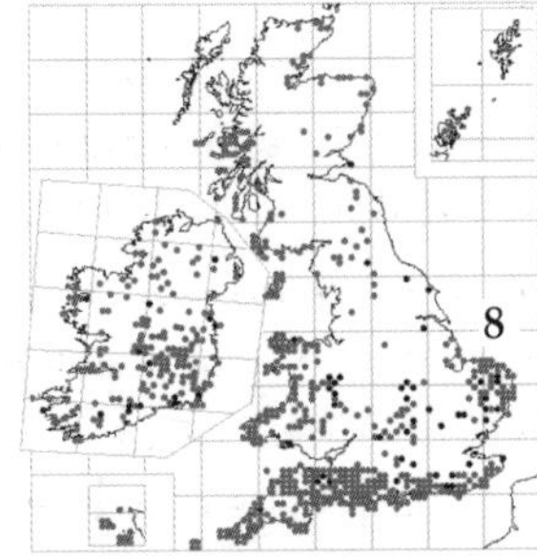

R. canariensis x 3.

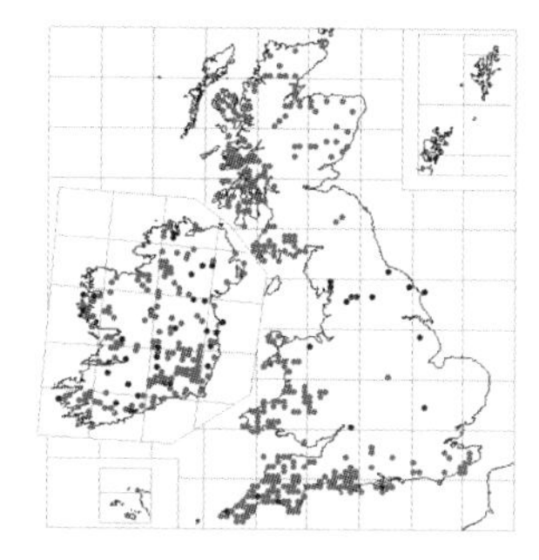

3. R. cuspidata Thallus shiny, cream to yellow-green, pendent, up to 15 cm long, more or less terete (up to 3 mm diam). Similar to *R. siliquosa* but more distinctly pendent and terete, more yellowish in colour and usually blackened at the base. Pycnidial ostioles black (beware ingrained dirt).
Several chemotypes: P± yellow-orange, K± yellow-orange or yellow-red, UV–.
Habitat: As *R. siliquosa* but often lower on the shore and in more sheltered positions. Rarely on fences.

4. R. farinacea Thallus variable, consisting of pale grey-green to yellow-green, flattened, rather narrow (up to about 3 mm wide) branches, often weakly canaliculate, to about 5 cm long, arising from a compact holdfast. Farinose soredia are found along the margins of the branches in disc-like or oval soralia. Very seldom fertile. Apothecia marginal or laminal. Spores 8–15 x 5–7 µm.
Medulla and soralia: nomally K–. A rare chemical race is K+ yellow turning red.
Habitat: The commonest of the British species of *Ramalina* and the most tolerant to air pollution. Usually found on nutrient-rich bark, sometimes on rocks.

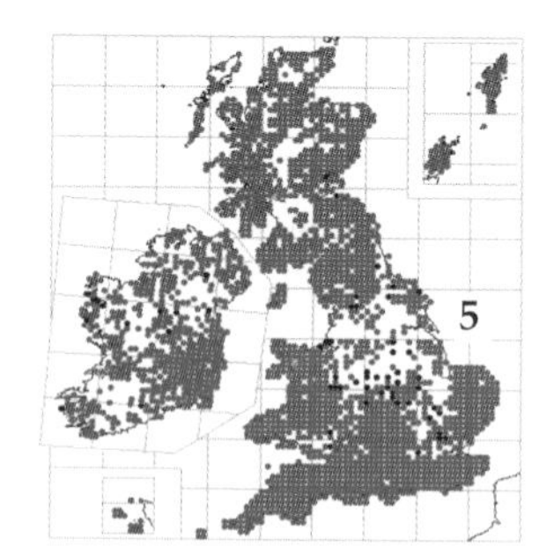

R. farinacea x 3.

5. R. fastigiata Thallus more or less erect and tufted, up to 5 cm long. Lobes much branched, wrinkled, rounded or flattened, often swollen, bearing many apical apothecia that may almost conceal the thallus. Spores kidney-shaped, 10–17 x 5–7 µm.
Spot reactions: all negative.
Habitat: Common on well-lit, nutrient-rich bark, rarely on soft basic rock.

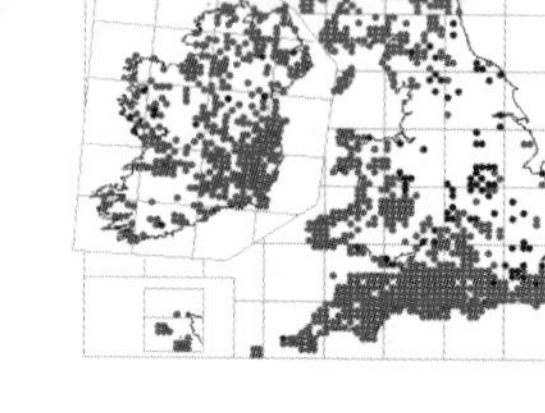

R. fastigiata x 3.

6. R. fraxinea Thallus normally to 7 cm long, rarely much longer, grey-green to brown-black in very exposed sites. Most branches usually widen from the base, are up to 4 cm wide and not canaliculate. Well-developed specimens have coarsely wrinkled branches with marginal, laminal and apical apothecia. Discs pale fawn. Spores kidney-shaped, 10–12 x 5–7 µm. Poorly developed specimens resemble *R. fastigiata* but that species has abundant apothecia confined to the lobe tips.
Spot reactions: all negative.
Habitat: Locally frequent on nutrient-rich bark, now rare in many areas, very sensitive to SO_2 pollution and eutrophication.

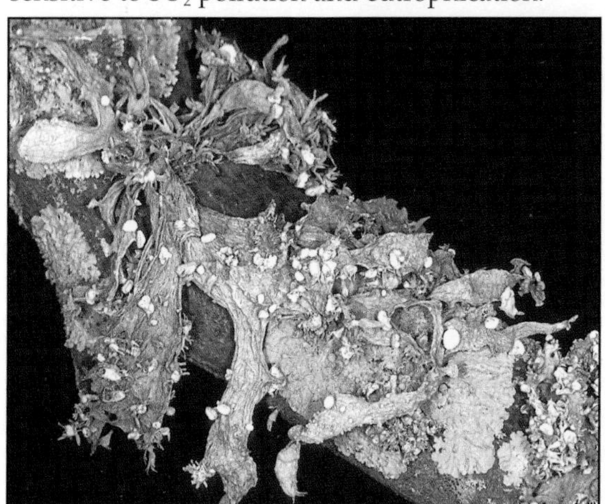

R. fraxinea x 3.

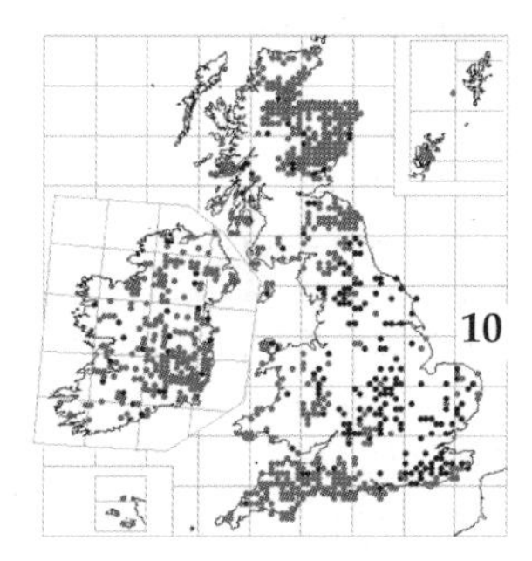

7. R. lacera Thallus variable, having one to many branches, grey-green to yellowish grey, to 5 cm long, flattened, sometimes ridged with a matt and often peeling cortex. Irregularly shaped soralia are both marginal and laminal. It has not been found fertile. *R. canariensis* has apical, pustulate soralia. **R. pollinaria** is a rare, but similar species with much divided, thin, flattened or slightly rounded, shiny lobes with numerous nodules. The soralia are laminal, ulcer-like, lip-shaped and swollen on the apices. It is found in similar habitats.
R. lacera: spot reactions and UV: all negative. *R. polinaria* and *R. canariensis*: medulla UV+ white.
Habitat: Nutrient-rich trees, rocks and stone walls, especially in pastures and farms. It is also frequent on sheltered rocks and church walls near the coast.

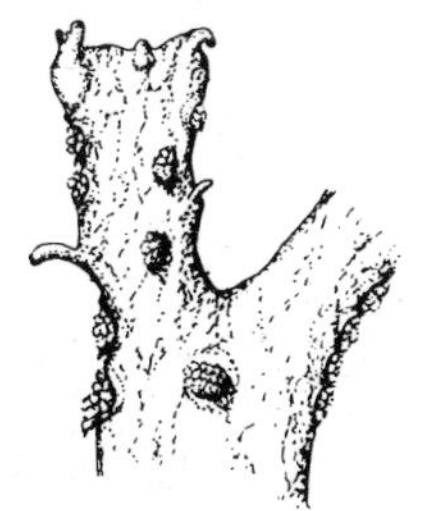

Lobe tip of *R. lacera.*

Lobe tip of *R. canariensis.*

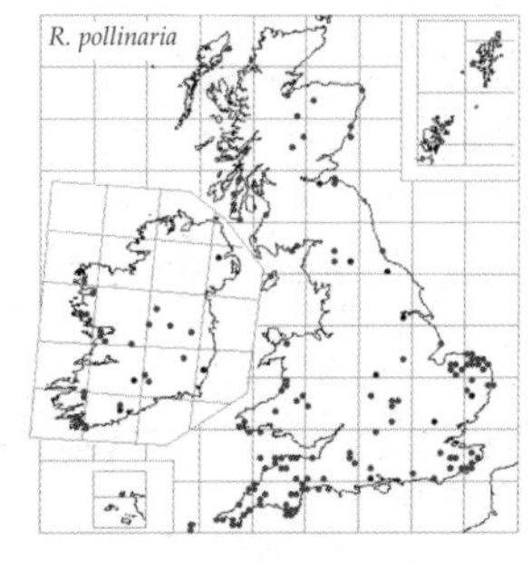

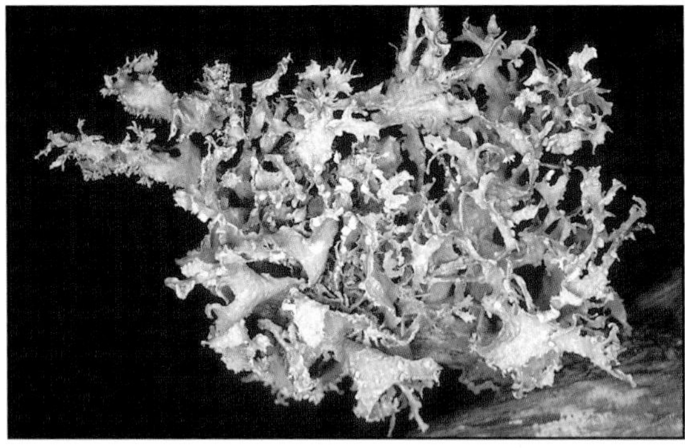

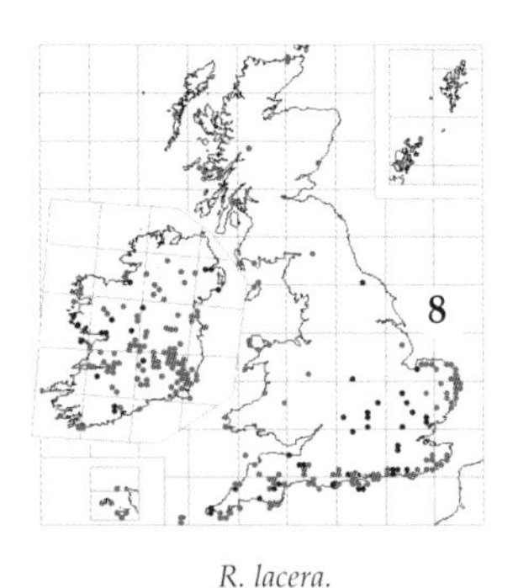

R. lacera.

R. lacera x 3.

8. R. siliquosa Thallus erect or pendent, very variable. Glossy, or warted and wrinkled, pale yellow-grey to greenish grey, branches often scimitar-shaped, brittle and little divided above the base. Often fertile, with pale fawn discs. Pycnidial tips pale or concolorous. Not normally blackened at the base (beware of dirt). Known locally as 'sea ivory'; it is eaten by sheep in Shetland and N. Wales. There are four chemical races with a range of reactions.
Habitat: Very common on hard siliceous rocks in maritime districts above high-water mark and inland in exposed sites in regions subject to maritime influence.

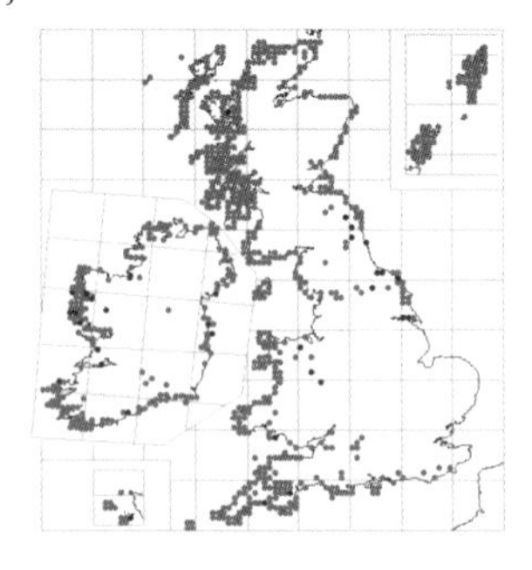

R. siliquosa x 0.5.

9. R. subfarinacea Similar to *R. farinacea* but usually smaller, with much-divided branches and a diffuse, spreading holdfast, giving it a bushy appearance. It frequently forms a dense sward. It is more yellow and has more excavate soralia.
Medulla and soralia: Usually K+ yellow turning red.
Habitat: Mainly on nutrient-enriched, exposed rocks in maritime sites.

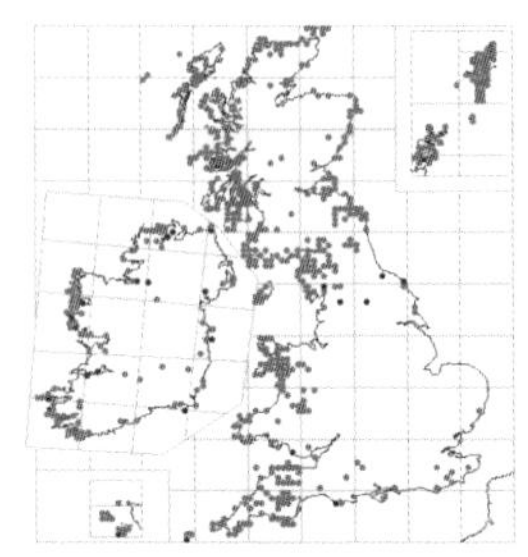

R. subfarinacea x 3.

RHIZOCARPON ('fruits with roots' – derivation unclear). **Thallus** crustose, saxicolous, usually with a distinct prothallus. **Photobiont** trebouxioid. **Apothecia** dark brown to black, lecideine, usually immersed in the thallus but may become convex, often on the edges of the areoles or growing from the prothallus, especially when on flints and pebbles. **Paraphyses** conglutinate and anastomosing (simple in *Buellia*). **Ascus** 1- to 8-spored, *Rhizocarpon*-type. **Spores** sometimes colourless but often green-brown to brown when mature, usually ± muriform but 1-septate to multi-septate in a few species. Several species are parasitic on other lichens.

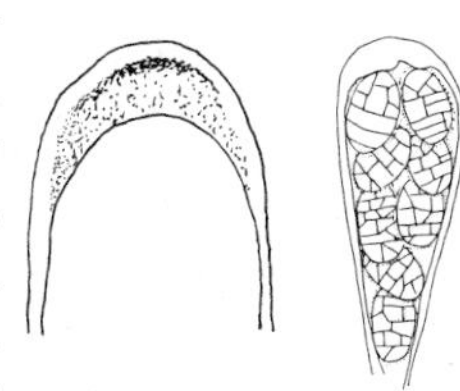
K/I reaction to the ascus tip. *R. reductum* x 250.

1.	Thallus rust-coloured. Apotheca convoluted, gyrose	**7. R. oederi**
–	Thallus grey, brown, white or yellow. Apothecia smooth	2
2.	Thallus yellow-green or white	3
–	Thallus grey, brown or pale ochre	7
3.	Thallus yellow to yellow-green	4
–	Thallus white	6
4.	Parasitic on other lichens. Usually with a weak prothallus	**11. R. viridiatrum**
–	Not parasitic. Strong black prothallus	5
5.	Crust with angular areoles	**3. R. geographicum**
–	Mainly individual, cresent-shaped areoles	**6. R. lecanorinum**
6.	On slightly basic rock. Apothecia often in concentric rings	**1. R. concentricum**
–	On pure limestone. Apothecia not in concentric rings	**10. R. umbilicatum**
7.	Thallus brown with purple tinge, cortex C± red (maritime)	**9. R. richardii**
–	Thallus grey, pale ochre or brown-grey, cortex C–	8
8.	Mature spores 1-septate, margins of apothecia narrow or excluded	**4. R. hochstetteri**
–	Mature spores muriform, margins of apothecia distinct	9
9.	Epithecium green-brown, K–	10
–	Epithecium brown, K+ crimson	**2. R. distinctum**
10.	Proper margin thick. Spores 30–40 x 14-18 µm. On acid rock where periodically inundated	**5. R. lavatum**
–	Proper margin thin. Spores 20–32 x 9–15 µm. On acid rocks and monuments, where not inundated	**8. R. reductum**

1. Rhizocarpon concentricum Thallus chalky white, matt, cracked, areolate in the centre, up to about 5 cm diam. Prothallus, weak, dark. Apothecia up to 1 mm diam, innate, irregular in shape, often arranged in concentric rings. Disc black, not pruinose, roughened, with a slightly paler or white-pruinose margin. Epithecium green-brown. Spores colourless, muriform, 20–50 x 12–24 µm.
Medulla: K+ yellow, P+ yellow-orange.
Habitat: Widely distributed on slightly basic rocks, or acid rocks with mortar.

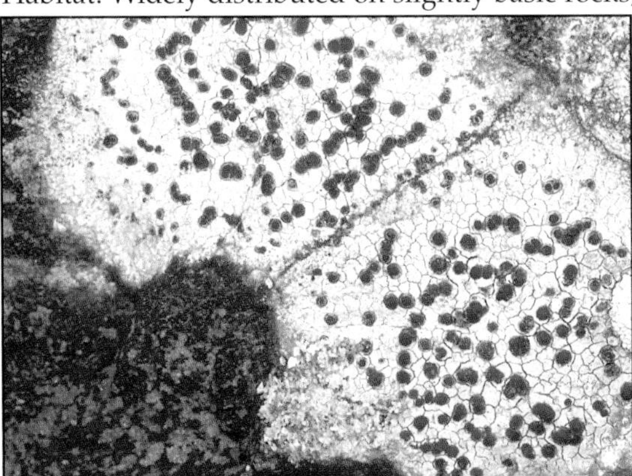

R. concentricum x 3.

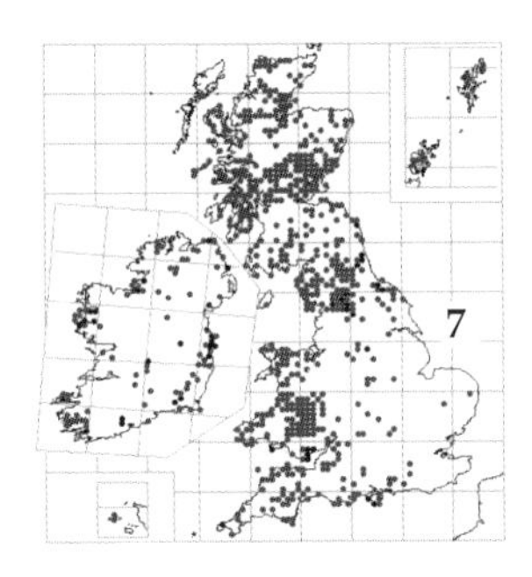

2. R. distinctum Thallus grey to dark brown, of flat or convex areoles (when wet resembling *Toninia aromatica*), usually surrounded by a black prothallus. Medulla I+ blue. Apothecia up to 0.5 mm diam, with a persistent, darker margin. Epithecium brown, K+ crimson. Spores colourless when young, becoming greenish brown, 3-septate to muriform, 15–25 x 8–13 µm.
Medulla: K+ yellow, P+ yellow.
Habitat: On siliceous tombstones, walls and rocks, more common in the North.

3. R. geographicum Thallus bright yellow-green to almost yellow, glossy with a pronounced black hypothallus showing between the areoles and limiting the thallus. Often mosaic-forming. Medulla I+ blue. Apothecia black, innate, usually irregular in shape, up to 1.5 mm diam. Epithecium variable in colour from chestnut and K+ crimson (the usual form) to dark green with a weaker K reaction. Spores brown, muriform when mature, 20–40 x 10–20 µm. Sometimes parasitized by *Lecidea insularis* and other lichen fungi.
Medulla: P± yellowish orange, C± red, UV+ bright orange.
Habitat: Very common, on hard siliceous rocks, sometimes transported to new sites on roof slates. Its distinctive colouration enables it to be recognized at a distance. Due to the strong pattern of lines formed by the black hypothallus running between the areoles and the black apothecia it is often known as the 'map lichen'.

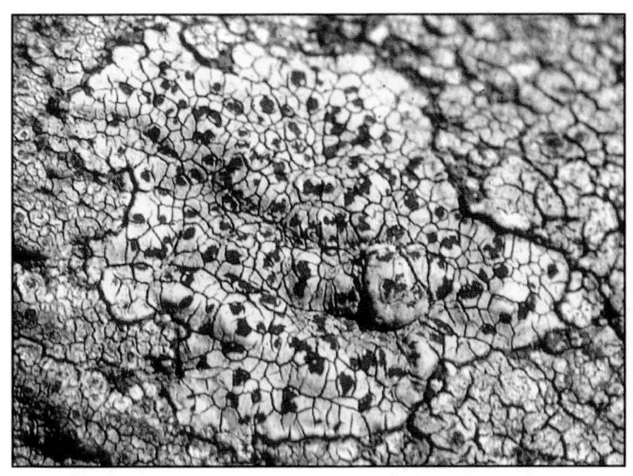

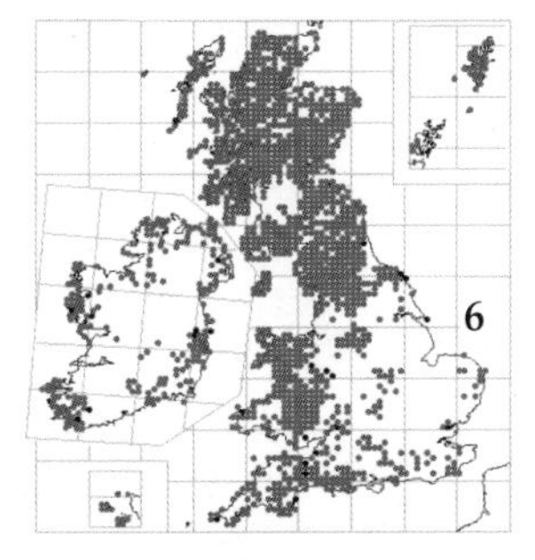

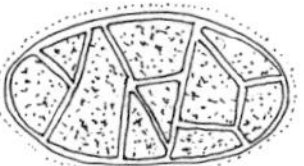

R. geographicum x 5.

R. geographicum spore.

4. R. hochstetteri Thallus brown-grey to very dark brown, cracked into angular plates, smooth, usually with a brown-black prothallus. Apothecia black, about 1 mm diam, flat, innate with a thin proper margin that may become excluded. Epithecium dark chestnut. Paraphyses have a dark brown cap. Spores colourless, 1-septate, 25–36 x 12–17 µm.
Spot reactions: negative or very rarely K+ yellow, P+ yellow.
Habitat: Occasional in upland regions of Britain on slightly basic, damp, siliceous rocks, sometimes on bare rocks in woodland, rare in maritime regions.

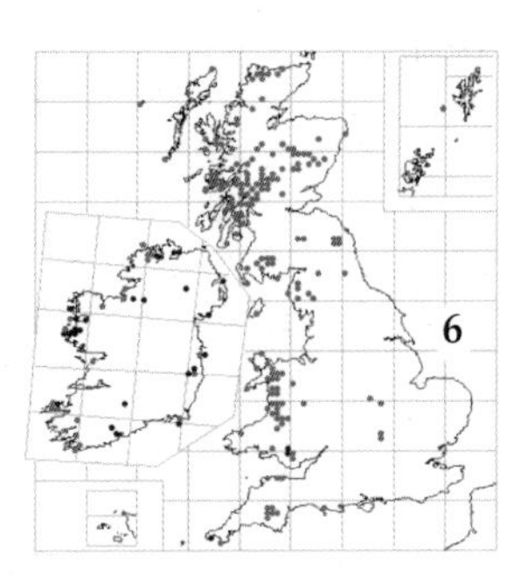

R. hochstetteri x 8.

5. R. lavatum Thallus pale grey to light ochre (greener when wet or in shade), smooth or cracked with a weak or no prothallus. Apothecia to 1.5 mm diam, black, more or less flat with a thick, paler, persistent margin. The centre of the disc is sometimes umbonate. Epithecium brown-green. Spores colourless, only becoming slightly darker with age, muriform, 30–40 x 14–18 µm.
Spot reactions: all negative.
Habitat: Frequent, on siliceous rocks near unpolluted streams and lake sides where it is subject to frequent inundation. Its pale colour with dark fruits makes it a distinctive species in this habitat. Mainly an upland species.

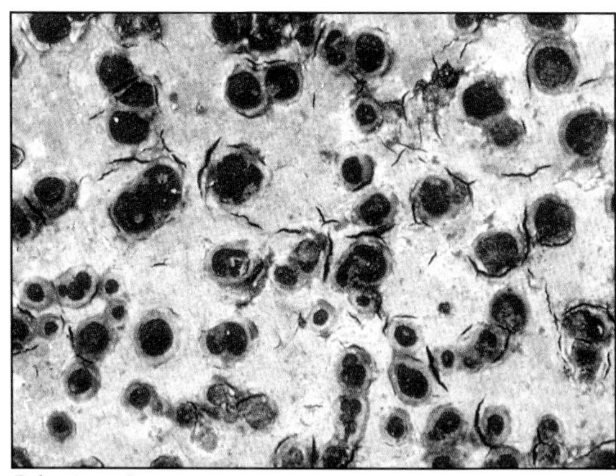

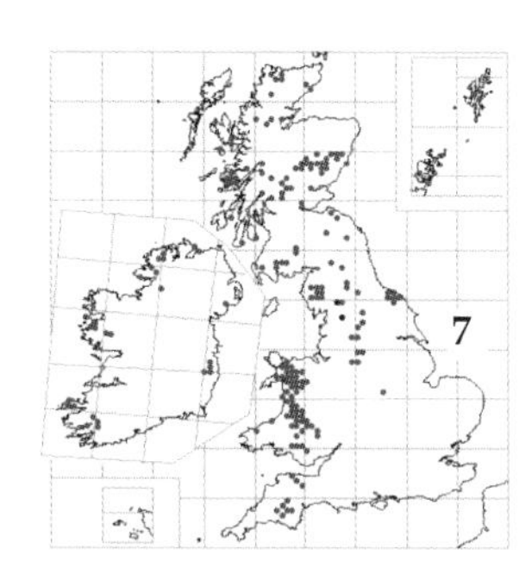

R. lavatum x 8.

6. R. lecanorinum Thallus bright yellow to slightly greenish, matt, of separate areoles surrounded by a pronounced black prothallus. The areoles form arcs around the areoles, which distinguishes this species from *R. geographicum*. Apothecia about 1 mm diam, one or sometimes more per areole, often occupying much of the areole. Epithecium pale green-brown, K–. Spores muriform, brown, 30–45 x 12–20 µm.
Medulla: K+ yellow, P+ orange.
Habitat: On siliceous rocks and walls and roofs, especially if metal-rich. In upland areas especially in the North.

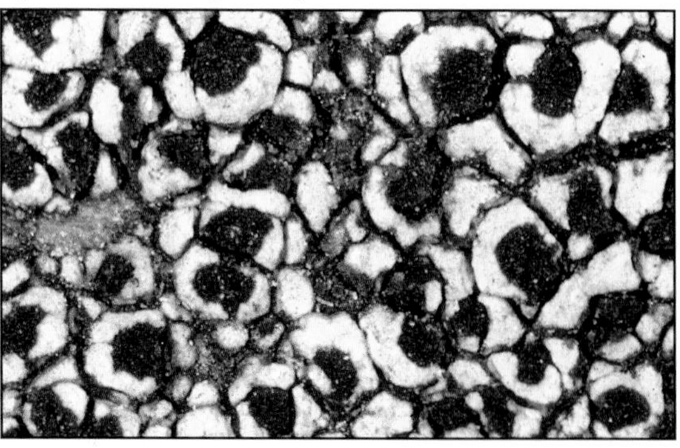

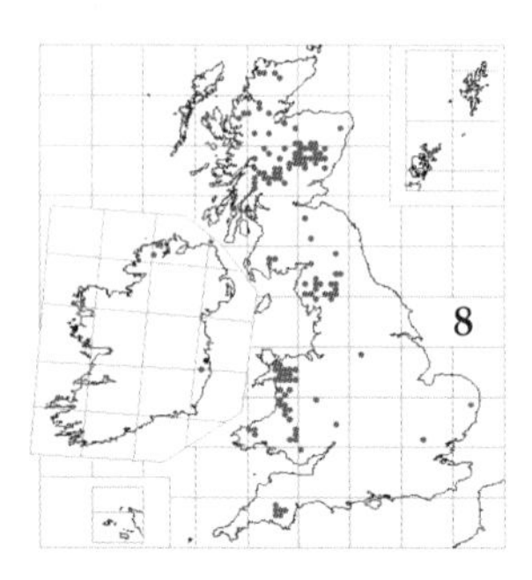

R. lecanorinum x 6.

7. R. oederi Thallus rust-coloured, cracked to regularly angular-areolate, with a sometimes indistinct, black prothallus. Apothecia less than 0.6 mm diam, concave, the proper margin becoming convoluted, serpentine, umbonate or almost gyrose when mature. Epithecium very dark green, K–. Spores colourless becoming pale brown, 3-septate, 12–20 x 3–8 µm.
Spot reactions: all negative.
Habitat: Common on iron-rich, siliceous rocks in upland areas. *Tremolechia atrata* occurring on similar rocks also has a rust-red thallus. It may be separated by its simple spores and smooth, concave, non-gyrose disc.

R. oederi x 6.

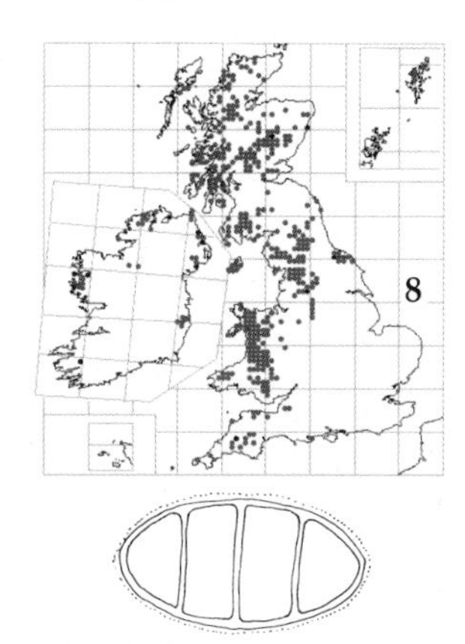

R. oederi spore.

8. R. reductum (R. obscuratum) Thallus grey to mouse-brown, cracked-areolate, often with a thin black prothallus. Apothecia innate becoming sessile, black, almost flat, about 1 mm diam, with a persistent, thick, proper margin. This is often paler on the inner side. Epithecium dark green to green-brown, K–. May be confused with *Fuscidea cyathoides* from which it differs in having colourless ellipsoid, muriform spores (20–40 x 10–16 µm), a P– medulla, less regularly areolate thallus, and apothecia which are less distinctly marginate and often convex. Small specimens can resemble the *Buellia aethalea* group which have brown, 1-septate spores and are mostly K+ yellow or red.
Spot reactions: all negative.
Habitat: Very common on smooth siliceous rocks and tombstones; if on pebbles the thallus is often thin consisting mainly of a black, web-like prothallus.

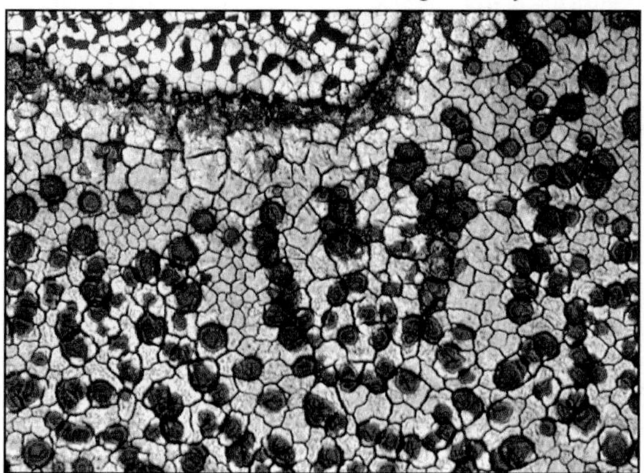

R. reductum x 6.

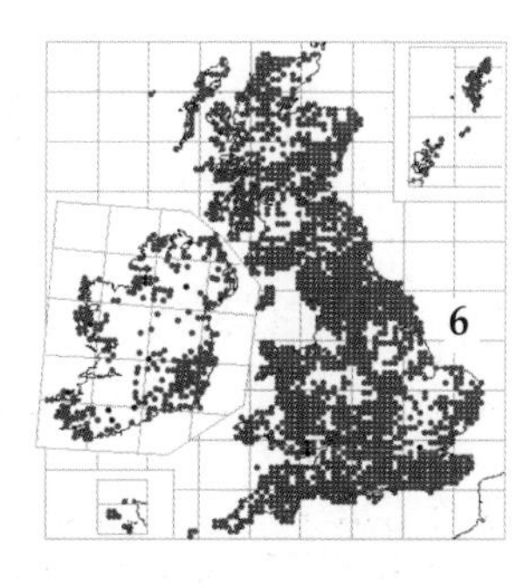

9. R. richardii (R. constrictum) Thallus chocolate-brown to brownish grey with a purplish tinge, areolate-cracked, often with a fimbriate brown-black prothallus. Medulla I+ blue. Apothecia about 1 mm diam, innate, flat, black, with a thin proper margin that may be paler on the inner edge. Epithecium dark green to

grey, K–. Spores 1-septate, but, one or both cells may have faint muriform septa, colourless becoming slightly brown when mature, 21–30 x 10–16 µm.
Cortex: C+ red (very rarely C–). This reaction helps separate it from the superficially similar *R. hochstetteri* and *R. reductum*.
Habitat: Very common on siliceous rocks and pebbles in maritime areas.

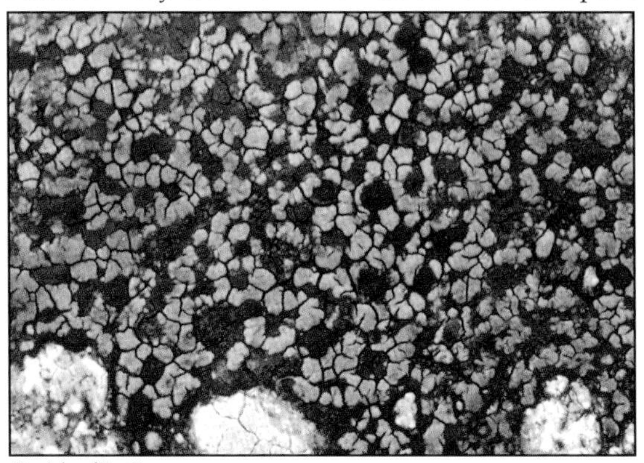

R. richardii x 5.

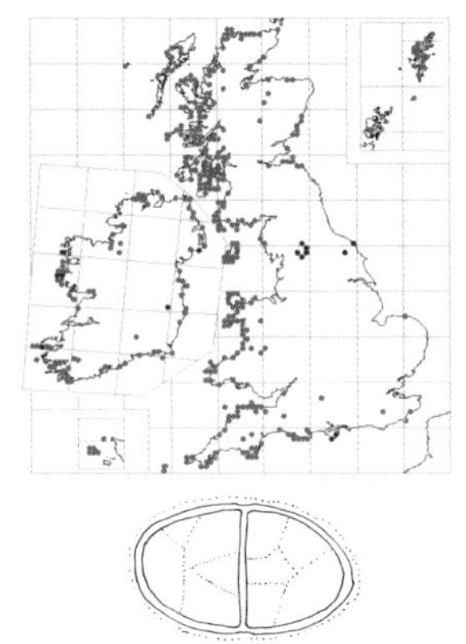

R. richardii spore

10. R. umbilicatum Thallus white, thick, smooth or somewhat cracked, often with a black but white-pruinose prothallus. Apothecia large, up to 1.5 mm, black with a persistent margin that is often white-pruinose. Epithecium dark green-brown. Spores colourless, muriform, 20–30 x 10–18 µm.
Medulla: K+ yellow, P+ yellow.
Habitat: Infrequent, mainly on hard limestone.

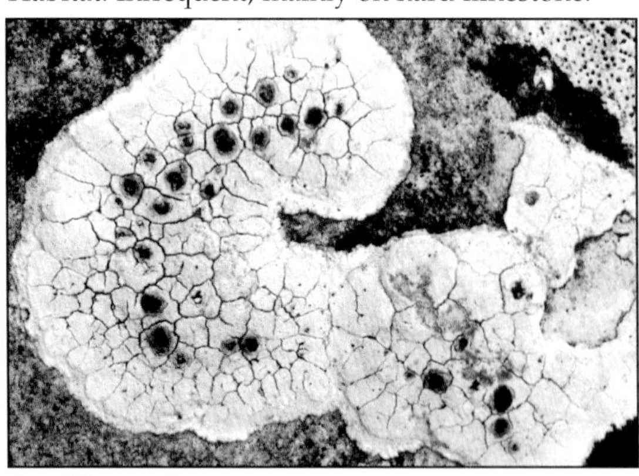

R. umbilicatum x 5.

11. R. viridiatrum Thallus parasitic, mainly on *Aspicilia caesiocinerea,* later spreading directly onto the rock. Green-yellow, smooth, areolate. Prothallus less pronounced than in other yellow *Rhizocarpon* species. Apothecia about 1 mm diam, the margin becoming excluded. Epithecium dark brown, K+ purple. Spores brown, muriform, 12–25 x 8–12 µm. Spot reactions: negative.
Habitat: Local, associated with siliceous to rather calcareous rocks in upland areas.

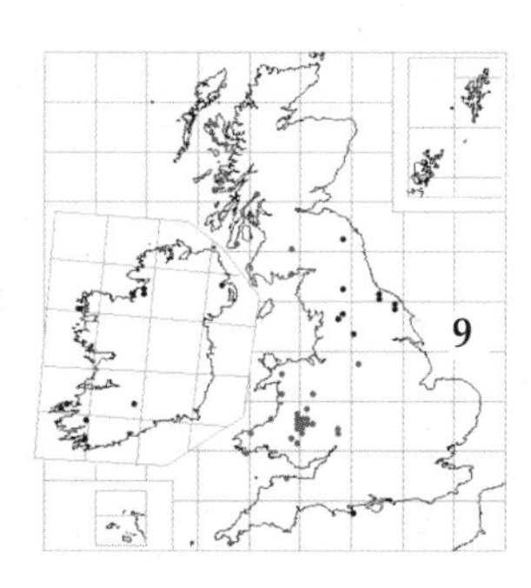

R. viridiatrum on *Aspicilia caesiocinerea* x 6.

RINODINA ('dish-like' – from the shape of the apothecia). **Thallus** crustose, often limited by a dark prothallus. **Photobiont** *Trebouxia*. **Apothecia** lecanorine with black discs. **Epithecium** brown. **Hymenium** Colourless, I+ blue. **Ascus** 8-spored, *Lecanora*-type. **Spore**s brown, thick-walled, 1- to 3-septate. **Pycnidia** rarely abundant.

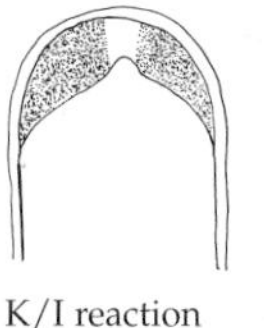

K/I reaction to the ascus tip.

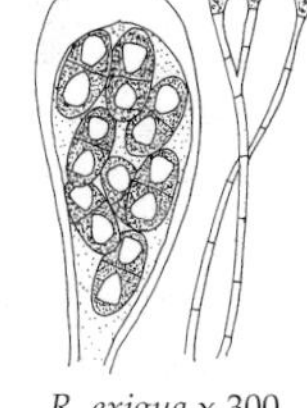

R. exigua x 300.

1.	Corticolous	2
–	Saxicolous	5
2.	P+ red. Not fertile. Sorediate	**4. R. efflorescens**
–	P–. Usually fertile. Not sorediate	3
3.	Mature apothecia up to 0.6 mm diam	**5. R. exigua**
–	Mature apothecia 1 mm diam or larger	4
4.	On rough bark. K+ yellow. Spores thick-walled	**8. R. roboris**
–	On twigs and smooth bark. K–. Spores thin-walled (if thick-walled see *R. teichophila*)	**9. R. sophodes**
5.	Cortex K+ yellow	6
–	Cortex K–	9
6.	C+ red	**1. R. atrocinerea**
–	C–	7
7.	P–	8
–	P+ yellow	**3. R. confragosa**
8.	Thallus pale blue-grey to green-grey. Sheltered maritime sites	**2. R. beccariana**
–	Thallus dark grey, black or brown. Various exposed sites	**10. R. teichophila**
9.	C+ orange	**7. R. luridescens**
–	C–	10

10. Apothecia up to 0.5 mm **6. R. gennarii**
– Apothecia larger, up to 1.25 mm 11

11. Thallus pale blue-grey to green-grey. Sheltered maritime sites **2. R. beccariana**
– Thallus dark grey, black or brown. Exposed inland sites **10. R. teichophila**

1. Rinodina atrocinerea Thallus light grey, sometimes yellowish, with a conspicuous black prothallus, very angular-areolate. Apothecia up to 1 mm across, becoming sessile. Thalline margin even, thin. Disc dark brown, becoming black. Spores thick-walled, 1-septate, locules not angular, 16–21 x 9–14 µm. Pycnidia often abundant. Resembles *R. gennarii* but on acid stone.
K+ yellow, C+ red, P+ yellow.
Habitat: Frequent on rough acid rocks, particularly granite on or near the coast.

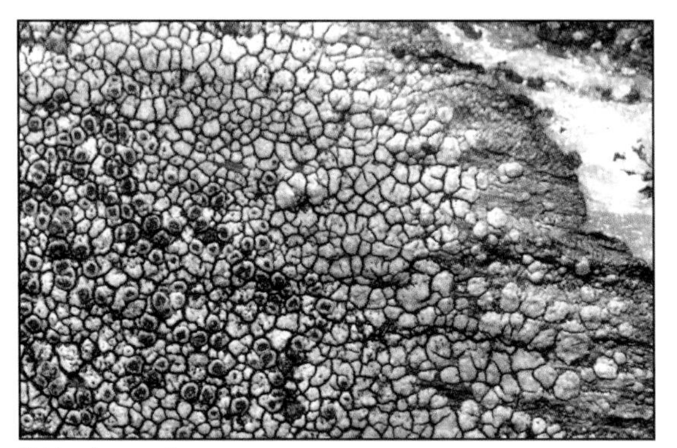
R. atrocinerea x 5.

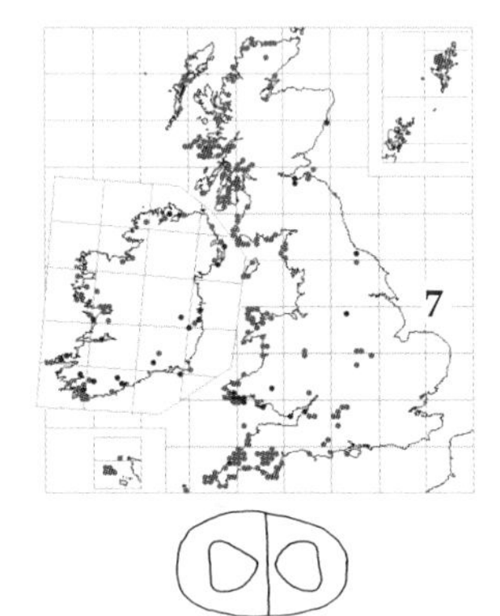

R. atrocinerea spore.

2. R. beccariana (R. subglaucescens) Thallus light grey, often with a greenish tinge, often coarsely granular, usually continuous and cracked. Rarely with a black prothallus. Apothecia up to 1.25 mm diam, with a flat, black disc and a persistent, wide margin that may become crenulate. Spores very thick-walled with an indistinct septum, 17–23 x 9–14 µm. It often resembles *Lecanora gangaleoides* but that species has simple spores. *R. confragosa* differs in having thinner-walled spores with a definite septum and is P+ yellow.
K± yellow.
Habitat: A locally frequent species of sheltered, coastal rocks and soil. Mainly in the South and West.

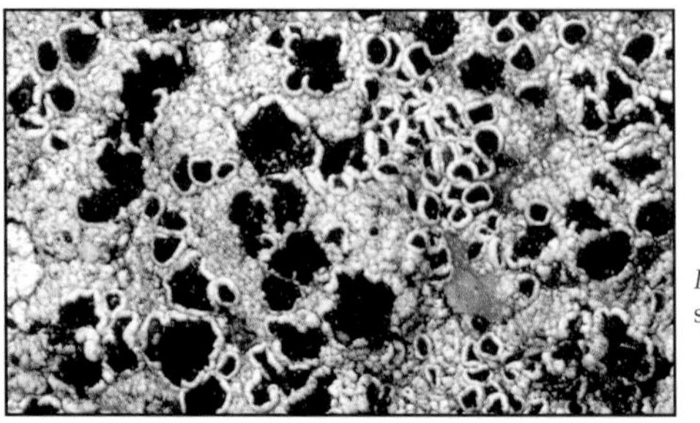
R. beccariana x 5.

R. beccariana spore.

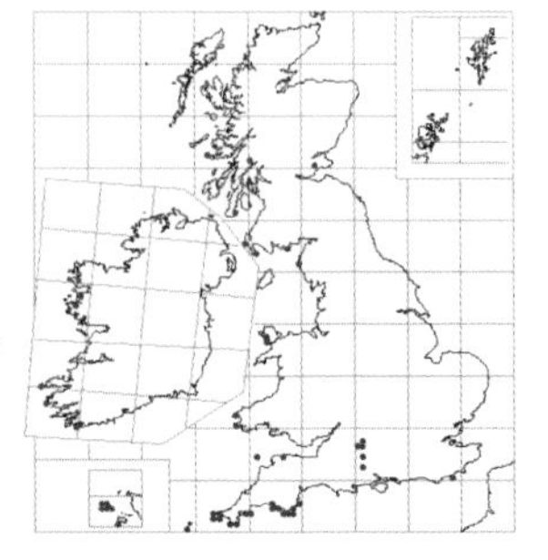

3. R. confragosa Thallus pale grey to cream, cracked or warted with ± flexuose edges. Prothallus indistinct. Apothecia up to 0.5 mm diam with a wide, persistant margin. Disc black, flat. Spores angular with thick walls towards the ends, 17–27 x 8–13 µm. Resembles *Tephromela atra* but that species has larger apothecia and simple spores.
K+ yellow, P+ yellow.
Habitat: On sheltered acid rocks often by the sea.

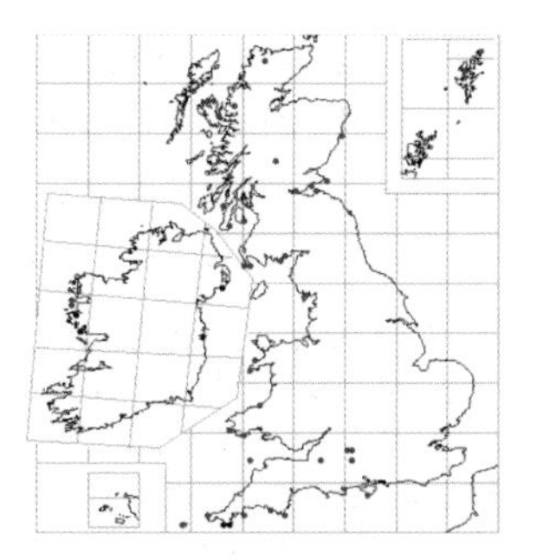

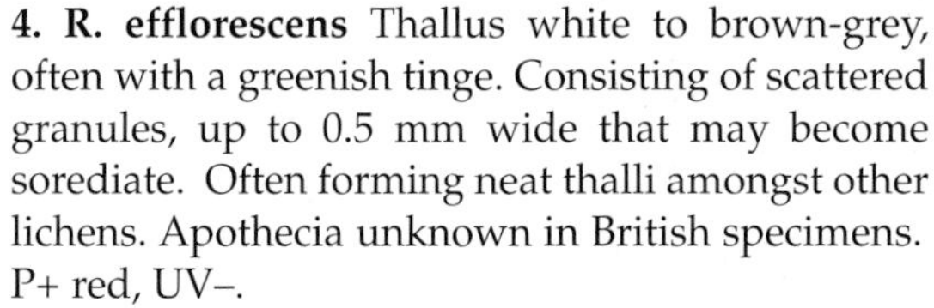

4. R. efflorescens Thallus white to brown-grey, often with a greenish tinge. Consisting of scattered granules, up to 0.5 mm wide that may become sorediate. Often forming neat thalli amongst other lichens. Apothecia unknown in British specimens.
P+ red, UV–.
Habitat: Frequent, but overlooked in damp woodlands. Often on more or less horizontal branches of trees. It resembles a pale *Fuscidea lightfootii* but that species is frequently fertile and is P– and UV+ blue-white.

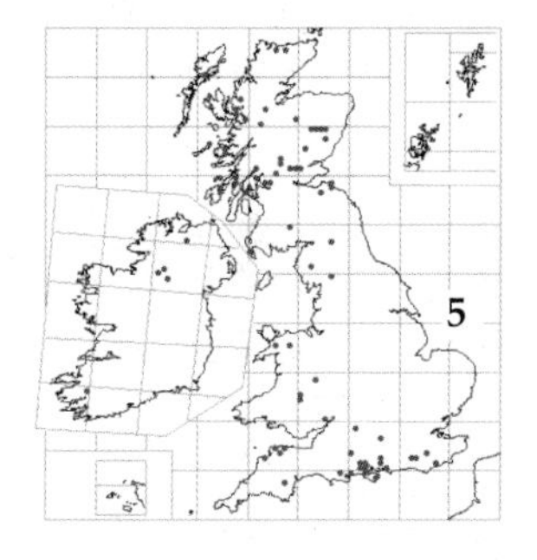

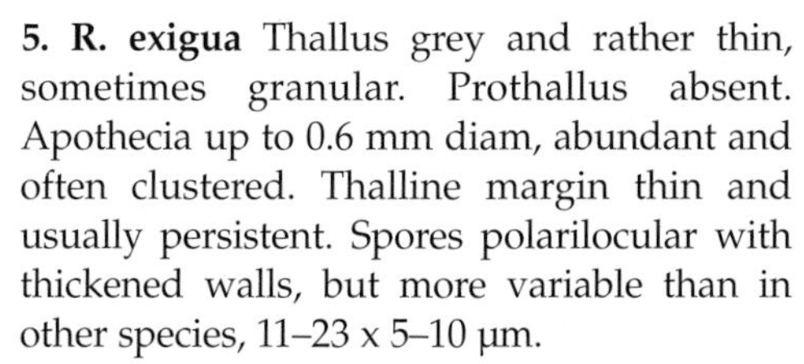

5. R. exigua Thallus grey and rather thin, sometimes granular. Prothallus absent. Apothecia up to 0.6 mm diam, abundant and often clustered. Thalline margin thin and usually persistent. Spores polarilocular with thickened walls, but more variable than in other species, 11–23 x 5–10 µm.
Sometimes K+ yellow.
Habitat. Fairly common on the rough bark of tree boles. *R. sophodes* is usually found on thin branches or twigs, is olive-brownish, and has thin-walled spores.

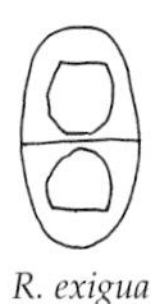
R. exigua spore.

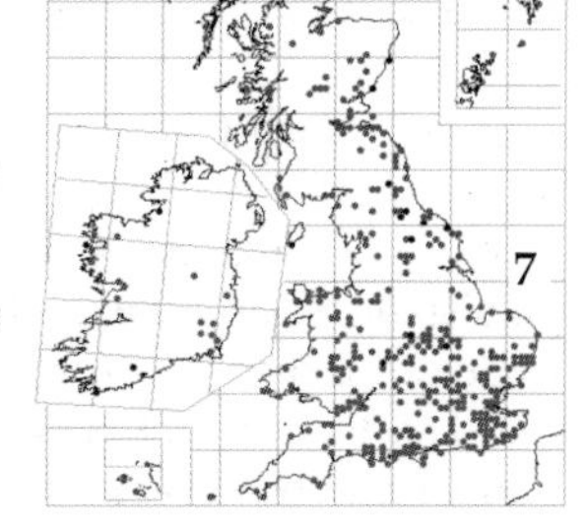

6. R. gennarii Thallus dull greenish grey to dark brown-grey, granular, cracked or, frequently, almost absent. Prothallus weak or absent. Apothecia usally abundant, about 0.5 mm diam, sessile with brown-black discs and a thick, pale, thalline margin in young fruits which may become excluded with age. Spores polarilocular, 11–20 x 7–11 µm.
Thallus: K–. Hymenium: K+ blue.
Habitat: Common on mainly well-lit, calcareous or other basic or nutrient-enriched rocks, walls, mortar, bricks or asbestos-cement. Common in urban and coastal sites. *R. atrocinerea* has a similar appearance but has angular areoles, is K+ yellow, C+ red and is found on acid rocks.

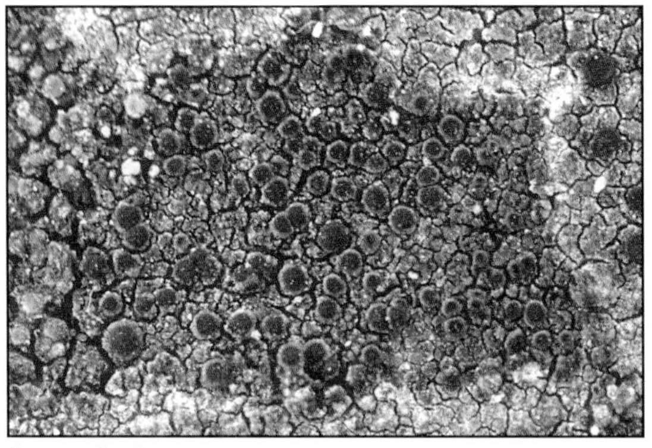

R. *gennarii* x 6.

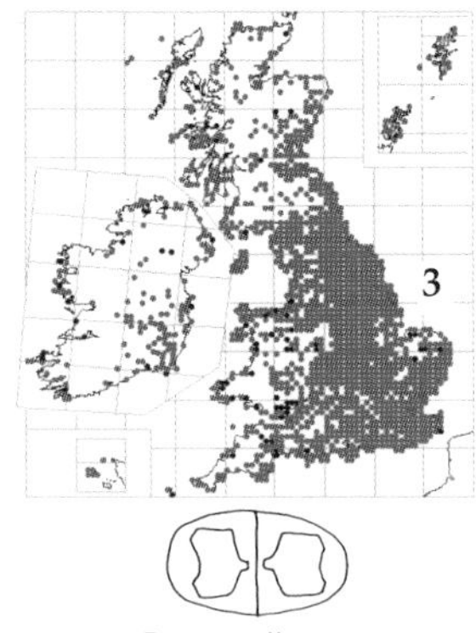

R. gennarii spore.

7. R. luridescens Thallus dark grey to dark brown with a distinct purple tinge, thick, cracked, often slightly warted. Limited by a dark prothallus. Normally fertile with scattered, immersed apothecia, up to 1 mm diam. The thin, slightly darker margin soon becomes excluded. Spores thick-walled with a wide septum, 15–23 x 7–12 µm.
C+ deep orange.
Habitat: Common, on well-lit, acid rocks in the maritime grey zone.

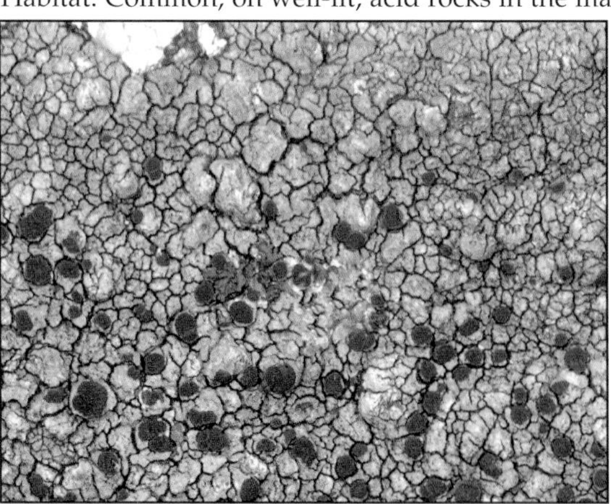

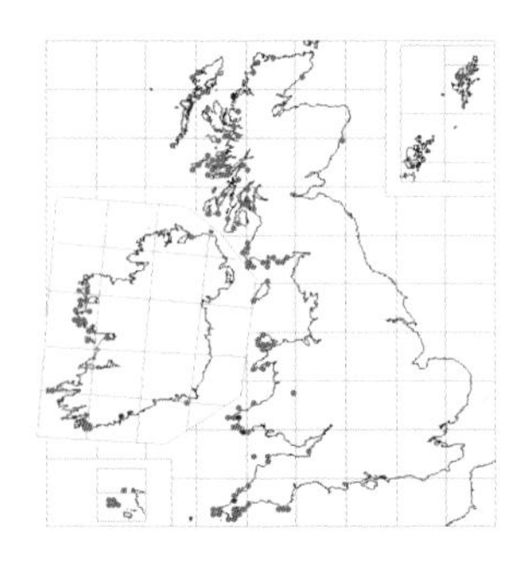

R. luridescens x 5.

8. R. roboris Thallus grey, usually with a distinctive greenish tinge (best visible at a distance), cracked or granular, thick. There is rarely any prothallus. Usually abundantly fertile. Apothecia up to 1.5 mm diam, sessile, with a thick, often crenulate, thalline margin. Discs dark brown to black, roughened. Spores thick-walled with rounded locules, 1-septate, 14–22 x 8–12 µm. *R. sophodes* mainly occurs on smooth-barked twigs and is K–.
K+ yellow.
Habitat: Common, on well-lit, deciduous, mainly rough-barked trees in the South, becoming less common northwards.

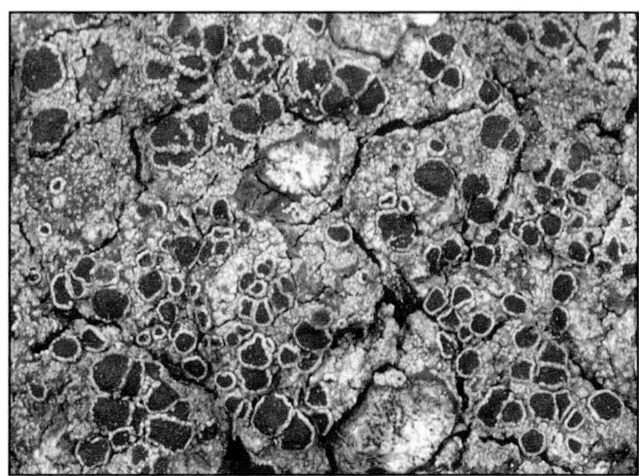

R. roboris x 6.

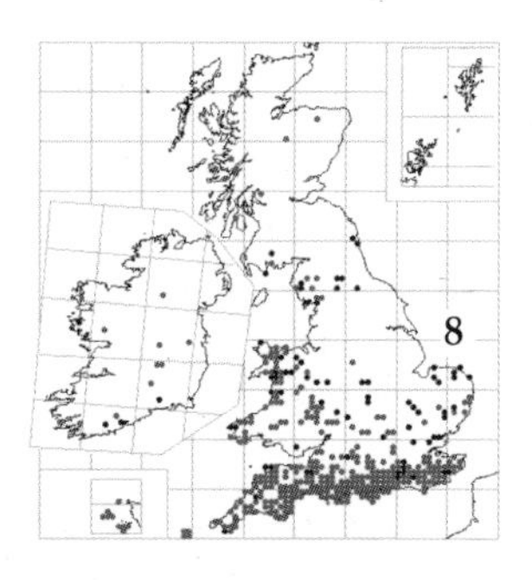

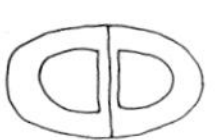

R. roboris spore. *R. sophodes* spore.

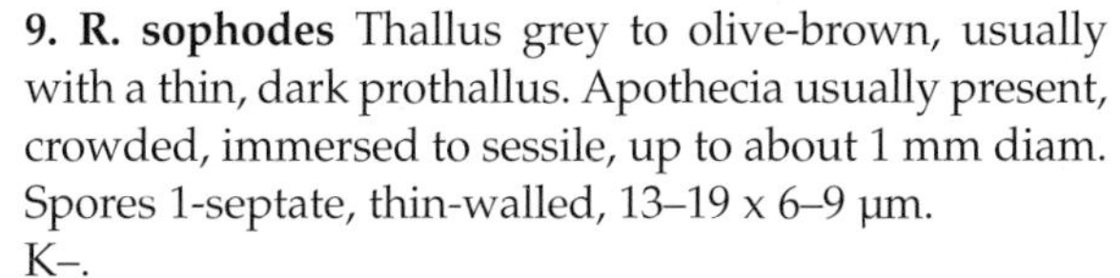

9. R. sophodes Thallus grey to olive-brown, usually with a thin, dark prothallus. Apothecia usually present, crowded, immersed to sessile, up to about 1 mm diam. Spores 1-septate, thin-walled, 13–19 x 6–9 µm.
K–.
Habitat: Common on smooth-barked trees, especially ash, often on rough areas of thin branches. Most common in upland regions. Very rare in the South and East. A pioneer species of twigs.

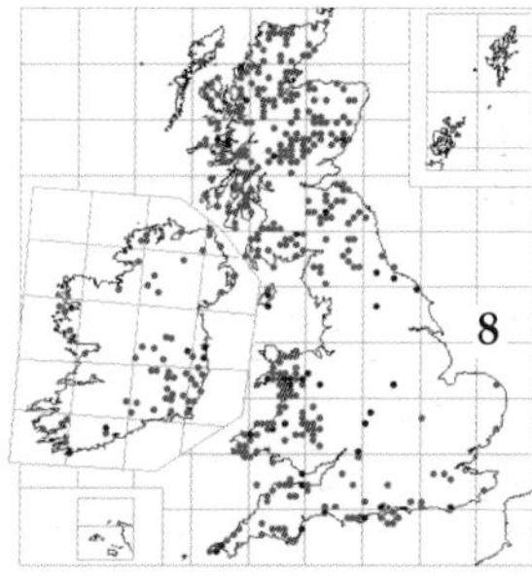

10. R. teichophila Thallus usually dark grey or chocolate-brown, lighter or greyish in shade. Thick, cracked or slightly granular with no, or a weak prothallus. The apothecia are more innate than in most other species of *Rinodina*, up to 1.25 mm diam, with a persistent margin and a dark brown to black disc. Spores very thick-walled with rounded locules and an indistinct septum, 20–32 x 11–20 µm.
K– or rarely K+ yellow..
Habitat: Frequent, on nutrient-enriched rocks, especially ironstone, also stone walls, rarely on trees.

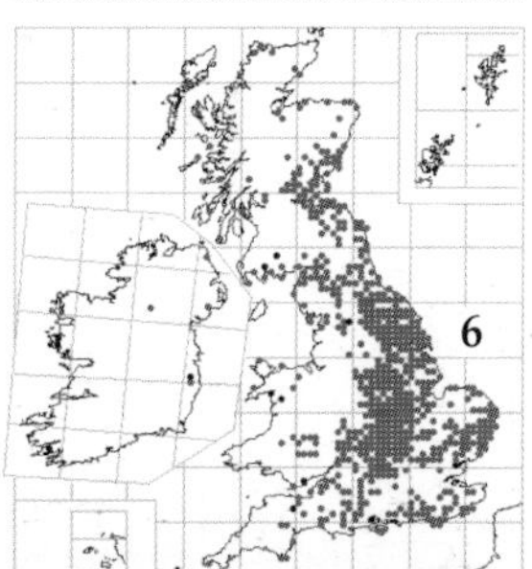

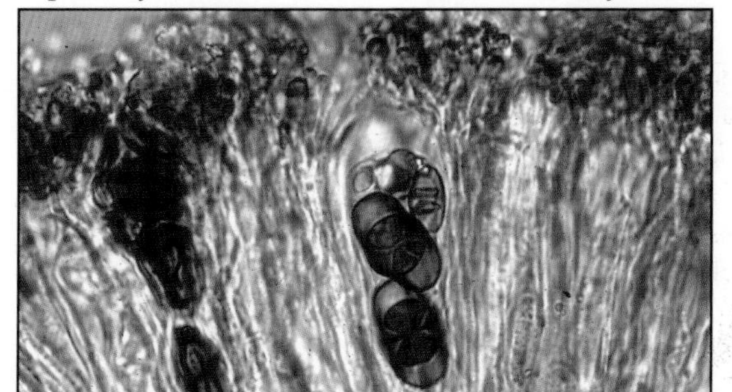

R. teichophila section through hymenium x 2000.

R. teichophila x 6.

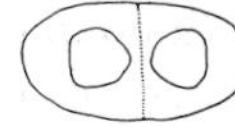

R. teichophila spore.

ROCCELLA (from the Florentine trading family Orcellaria who in the 15c. first used the species for dying). **Thallus** fruticose, pale fawn to bluish-grey, cylindrical or strap-shaped, attached by a holdfast. **Photobiont** *Trentepohlia*. **Apothecia** extremely rare in British species. Discs black. **Ascus** 8-spored, K/I+ small blue ring. **Spores** colourless, elongate-ellipsoid, multi-septate. This is a large genus widely distributed in warmer latitudes, but only two species are found as far north as Britain. *Roccella* species (but not the British ones) are used to produce litmus and the purple dye orchil, the best known species for this purpose being *R. tinctoria* and *R. montagnei*. British species may be separated from *Ramalina siliquosa*, with which they can grow, by the thallus colour and the C+ red reaction. Both the British species are rare and should not be collected.

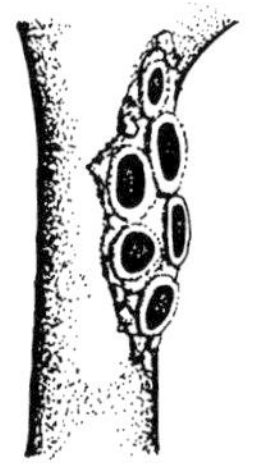
Apothecia of *R. fuciformis*.

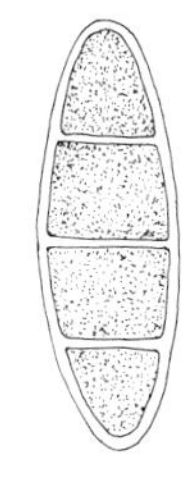
R. phycopsis x 1500.

1. Thallus pendent, flattened. Medulla C–, soralia C+ red **1. R. fuciformis**
– Thallus erect or slightly pendent, terete. Medulla C+ red, soralia C– **2. R. phycopsis**

1. Roccella fuciformis Thallus pendulous, up to 20 cm long, pale mauve-grey, irregularly branched, lobes flattened, strap-shaped, up to 1.5 cm wide. Small lobules are frequently found on the lobe margins. Convex glaucous or brownish-white soralia occur in dense clusters. Medulla white within the holdfast. Apothecia very rare in Britain. Spores 3-septate, 20–30 x 4–6 µm.
Cortex and medulla: C–. Soralia: C+ bright red, UV+ blue-white.
Habitat: A rare species of dry sheltered recesses in supralittoral rocks, very rarely on trees, in the extreme SouthWest. Frequently occurs with *R. phycopsis*.

R. fuciformis x 2.

2. R. phycopsis Thallus tufted, pale mauve-grey, not or scarcely pendent, usually not exceeding 5 cm in length, branches round or slightly flattened, up to 5 mm diam. Soralia abundant, large and coarse, soredia whitish. Medulla orange within the holdfast. Very rarely fertile. Spores 18–21 x 4–6 µm. Cortex: C+ rose-red. Soralia and medulla: C–, UV+ blue-white.
Habitat: As *R. fuciformis*, but somewhat more frequent: it also occurs on tombstones and walls.

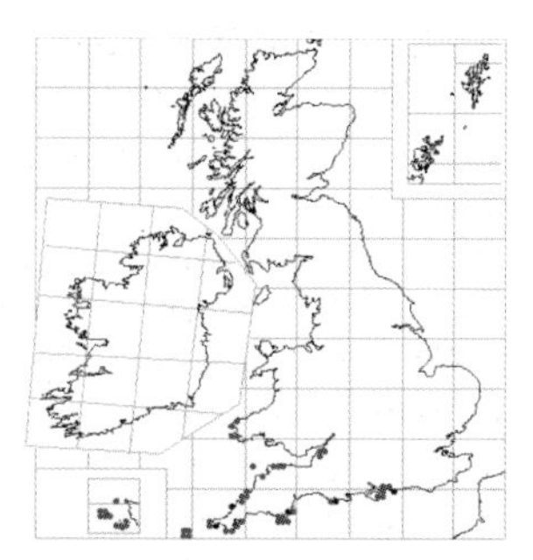

R. phycopsis x 2.

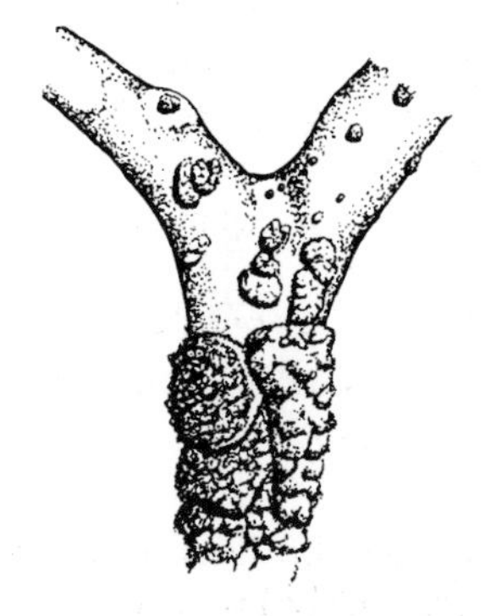

Soralia on *R. phycopis*

SARCOGYNE ('female flesh' – from the flesh colour of the apothecia in the type species). **Thallus** crustose, evanescent or endolithic. **Photobiont** *Myrmercia*. **Apothecia** lecideine, with a thin proper margin. **Paraphyses** simple or only slightly branched (in *Polysporina* they are anastomosed). **Ascus** multi-spored (100+), K/I– except for a blue outer coat. **Spores** colourless, simple, small. **Chemical reactions** negative.

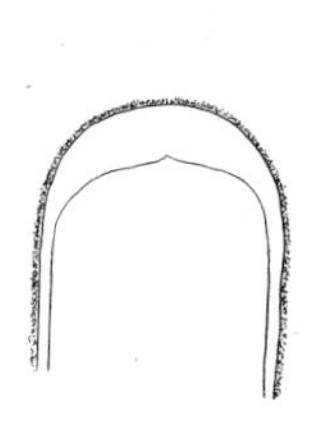

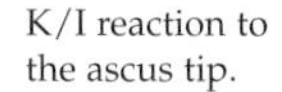

K/I reaction to the ascus tip.

S. regularis x 450.

1.	Calcareous substrates, apothecia often pruinose	**S. regularis**
–	Siliceous substrates, apothecia not pruinose	2
2.	Margin not crenulate, disc smooth	**S. privigna**
–	Margins very crenulate, almost gyrose, knot-like	**Polysporina simplex**

1. Sarcogyne privigna Thallus grey, thin and gelatinous or endolithic. Apothecia to 1 mm diam. Disc almost black, becoming much more red-brown when wet, not pruinose. Proper margin persistent, often distorted by the pressure of adjacent apothecia. Spores 3–4 x 1 µm.
Habitat: Rare on damp, hard, acid rocks, especially granite.

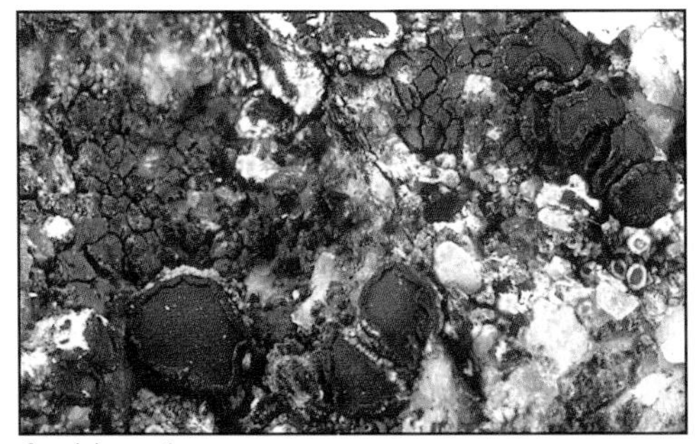

S. privigna x 8.

2. S. regularis Thallus pale grey, frequently evanescent. Apothecia up to 1.5 mm diam, often in depressions in the substratum. Disc black or, when wet, chestnut to dark red, usually bluish-pruinose, margin becoming excluded. Spores 3–5 x 2 µm. Habitat: Common, on calcareous substrata throughout Britain, but epecially in lowland regions.

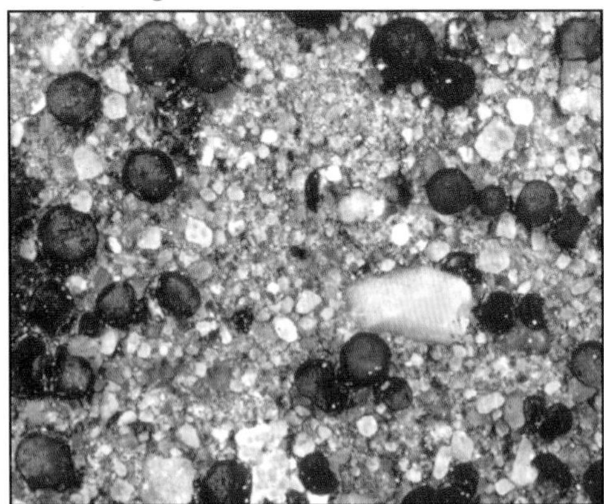

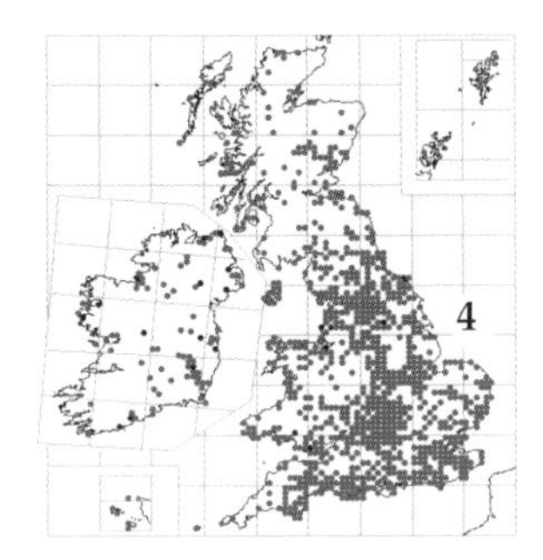

S. regularis x 5.

SARCOPYRENIA ('flesh nut' – from the thick, soft, nut-like perithecia). **Thallus** crustose, usually immersed, rarely with a pale prothallus. **Photobiont** chlorococcoid. **Perithecia** simple, lacking an involucrellum but with an inner and outer wall separated by a paler region. **Ascus** 8-spored *Verrucaria*-type, rather cylindrical, thin-walled and breaking down early in development. **Spores** simple, colourless, with swollen ends giving them a distinctive propeller-like shape. **Chemical reactions** negative.

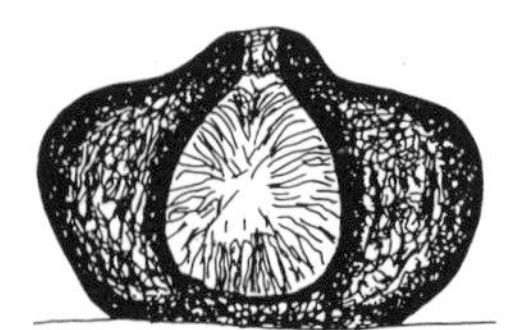

Section through a perithecium of *S. gibba*.

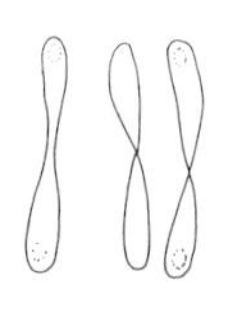

Spores of *S. gibba* x 700.

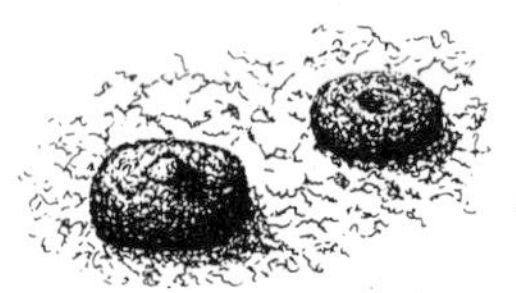

Perithecia of *S. gibba*.

Sarcopyrenia gibba Thallus thin, warm grey but usually endolithic. The species can often be recognized at a distance from the clear area on the substratum where there are no other lichens, algae or mosses. Rarely with a pale prothallus. The globose black perithecia are clearly visible on the clean surface. Perithecia about 0.5 mm diam with a minute papillate ostiole which later becomes sunken and volcano-like. They have a double wall that is visible in vertical section. If cut when wet they have the consistency of an unbaked loaf. Spores 30–40 x 3–4 µm, with swollen ends which are often twisted at the centre like a propeller. Paraphyses and asci break down early in the development of the perithecium.
Habitat: Probably frequent but is easily overlooked. On well-lit calcareous rocks, especially the tops of chest-tombs where it is often occurs towards the corners and outer edges. It is initially parasitic on crustose lichens.

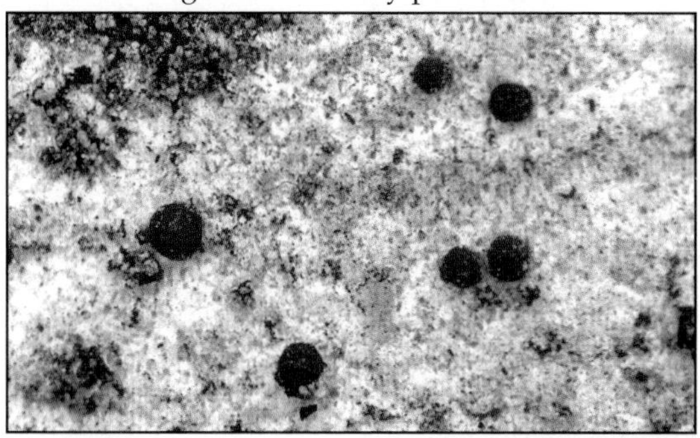

S. *gibba* x 6.

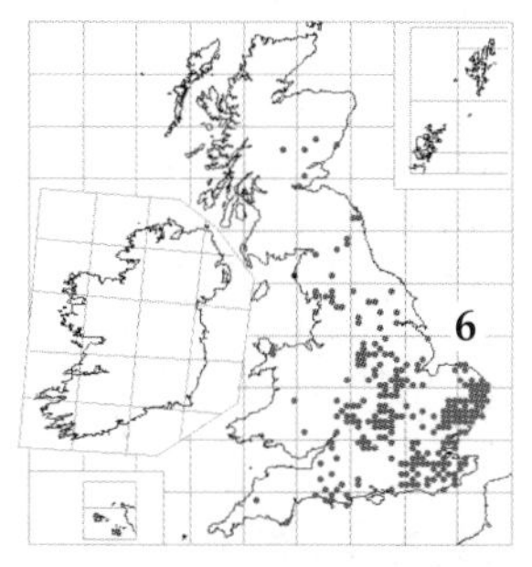

SCHAERERIA (after the Swiss lichenologist Ludwig Emanuel Schaerer, 1785–1853). **Thallus** crustose and areolate or squamulose. **Photobiont** *Trebouxia*. **Apothecia** lecideine, black. **Hypothecium** mid-brown to almost black. **Ascus** 8-spored, *Schaereria*-type, faint K/I+ outer coat. **Spores** simple, colourless. Separated from *Lecidea* on accout of the thin-walled, cylindrical asci.

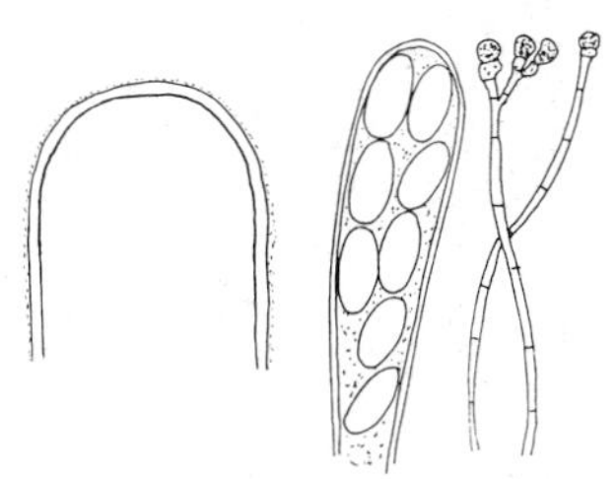

K/I reaction to the ascus tip. S. *fuscocinerea* x 350.

1. Thallus squamulose. Spores globose **1. S. cinerorufa**
– Thallus areolate. Spores ellipsoid **2. S. fuscocinerea**

1. S. cinerorufa Thallus grey to red-brown . Squamules, up to 2.5 mm wide and 1.5 mm thick, slightly warted, usually surrounded by a pronounced black prothallus. Looking like an *Acarospora* but with an 8-spored ascus. Apothecia frequent, up to about 1 mm diam, innate, becoming sessile, black, flat with a persistent margin. Spores globose, uniseriately arranged in the ascus, 7–9 µm diam.
C+ pinkish red.
Habitat: Frequent in upland areas on hard, acid rocks and schists, sometimes overgrowing mosses.

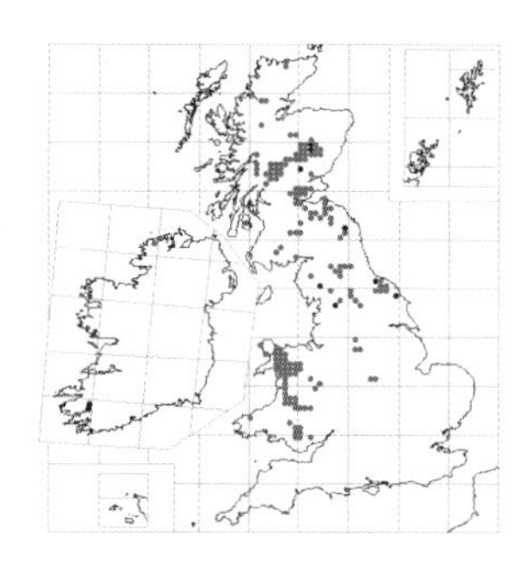

S. cinerorufa (orange due to iron-rich substratum) x 4.

2. S. fuscocinerea (S. tenebrosa) Thallus smooth with sharply angled, convex areoles, brown-grey to very dark brown but mainly a milk-chocolate colour. Apothecia are immersed in the areoles, irregular in shape and almost appear to have a thalline margin, becoming convex when the proper margin is excluded. Rarely with dark soralia. Hypothecium K+ blue-green or sometimes mauve. Spores mainly arranged in the ascus in two rows, 10–16 x 5–8 µm.
C+ pinkish red (often hard to obtain).
Habitat: Common on hard, acid, well-lit rocks, flat tombstones, etc.

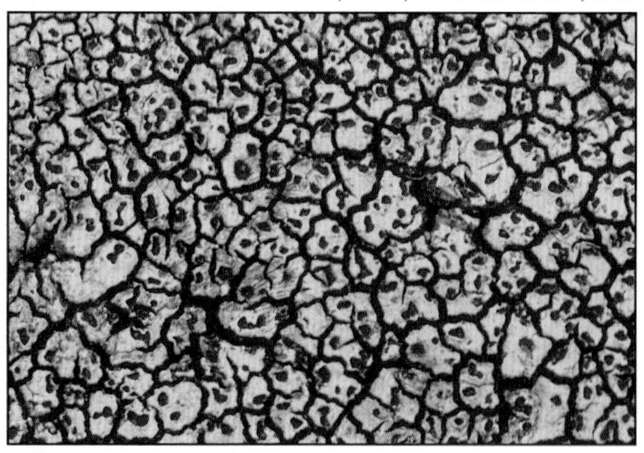

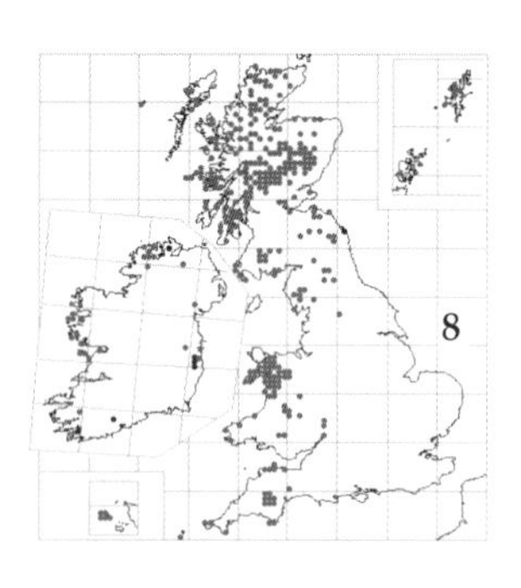

S. fucocinerea x 5.

SCHISMATOMMA ('split eye' – from the often split apothecia). **Thallus** crustose. Frequently with a poorly defined, dark prothallus. **Photobiont** *Trentepohlia*. **Apothecia** lecanorine, not seen in Britain in the common species described below. **Ascus** 8-spored, K/I+ blue ring. Thallus usually shows orange when a fresh specimen is scratched. A mainly tropical species.

1. Thallus pure white, K+ golden yellow — **1. S. cretaceum**
– Thallus pink-grey to brown or mauve-grey, K– — 2
2. Thallus mauve-grey, P– — **2. S. decolorans**
– Thallus grey or brown grey, P+ orange — 3

3. Thallus pinkish to pale grey, P+ yellow-orange. Confluent soralia **3. S. niveum**
– Thallus pale brown-grey, P+ red-orange. Discrete soralia **4. S. quercicola**

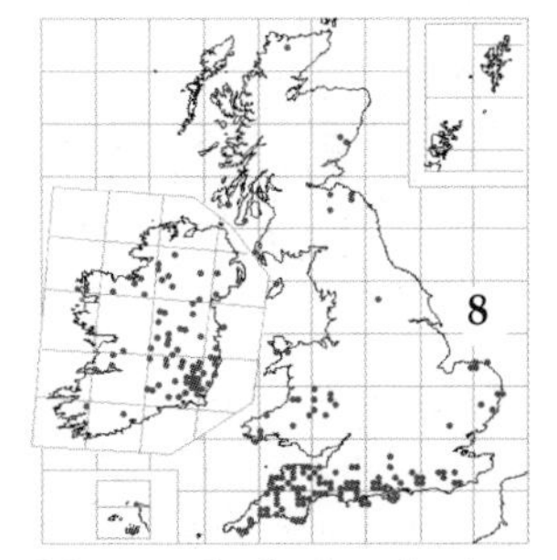

1. Schismatomma cretaceum (S. virgineum) Thallus thick and powdery, very pale grey but usually seen as a pure white thallus due to the soralia that almost entirely cover the surface.
K+ pale golden yellow, C–, P–, UV orangish grey.
Habitat: Occasional on well-lit, ancient, slightly nutrient-enriched trees, out of direct rain, less common in the North.

2. S. decolorans Thallus mauve-grey to brown-grey, thin, cracked, developing concolorous or slightly paler sorediate patches which combine to cover the whole surface of mature thalli giving a leprose appearance.
K–, C–, P–, UV– or UV+ white.
Habitat: Common in the South and West on dry bark, most commonly in sheltered and shaded recesses of old rough-barked deciduous trees, often forming extensive patches. Rarely occurring on rocks.

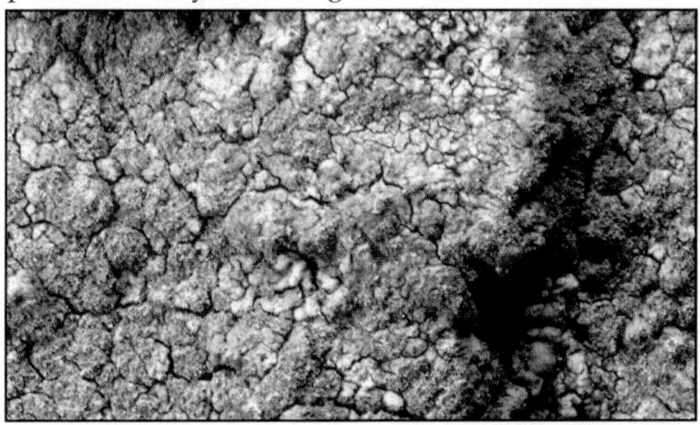

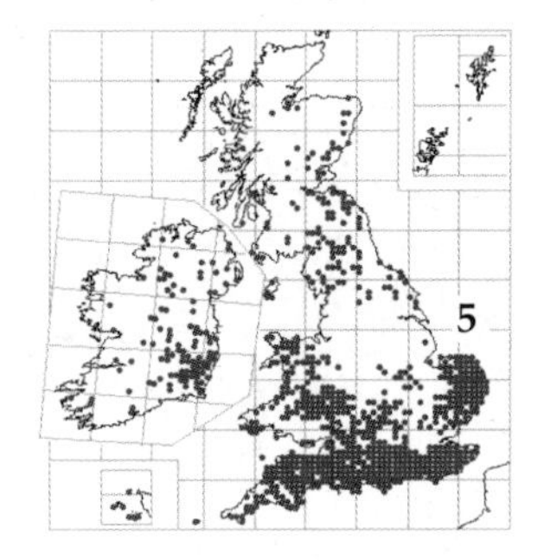

S. decolorans x 5.

3. S. niveum Thallus pale grey, often tinged pink. Thicker than the previous species. Concolorous or slightly paler punctiform soralia, up to 1 mm diam, often spreading to cover the entire thallus.
K– (or very pale yellow), C–, P+ yellow-orange, UV± orange grey.
Habitat: Local, occurs in the South in similar habitats to *S. decolorans*, especially on ancient oak trees.

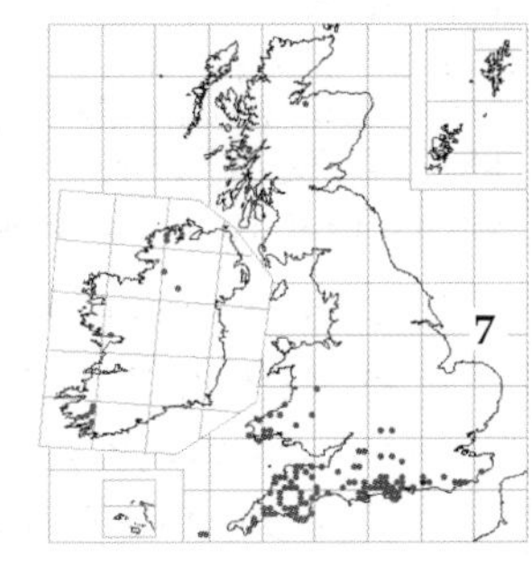

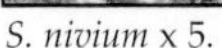

S. nivium x 5.

4. S. quercicola Thallus warm grey (but often greenish from overgrowing alien algae), slightly warted with discrete pinkish grey soralia which seldom become confluent. Many specimens, called *Lecidea cinnabarina* in the past by British authors, are this species.
K–, C–, P+ orange.
Habitat: Occasional, on old deciduous trees, especially oak and beech. More common in the South and West.

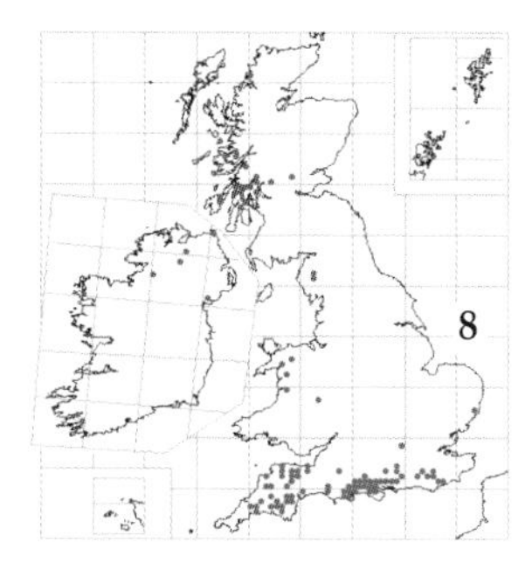

SCLEROPHYTON ('dry, hard plant' – from the hard thallus or habitat preference). **Thallus** crustose, areolate with a dark prothallus. **Photobiont** *Trentepohlia*. **Apothecia** lecideine, immersed, very small, dot-like usually arranged in lines. **Ascus** 8-spored **Spores** brown, 5- to 7-septate. This is a mainly tropical genus and is represented in Britain by only two species.

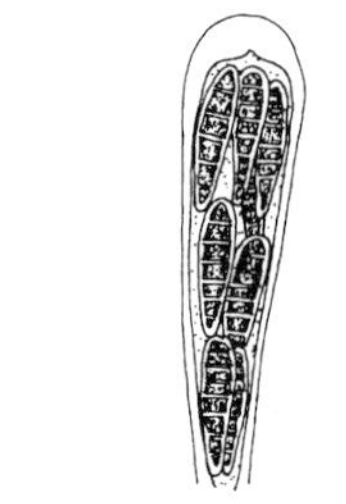

S. circumscriptum x 500.

Sclerophyton circumscriptum Thallus white, thin and scurfy or very thick and soft, areolate, the side faces of the thick areoles often appear fluted. Thallus limited by a dark prothallus, often forming mosaics. The orange photobiont can be seen if the thallus of a fresh specimen is scratched. Apothecia very small, 0.1 mm diam, immersed, pruinose, often arranged in lines in the areoles. Spores brown, 5- to 7-septate, clavate and slightly constricted at each septum, 15–25 x 5–6 µm.
P+ orange, UV–.
Habitat: Locally common in the West on dry, sheltered, maritime, acid rocks, especially under overhangs, avoiding direct wetting from the rain.

S. circumscriptum x 5.

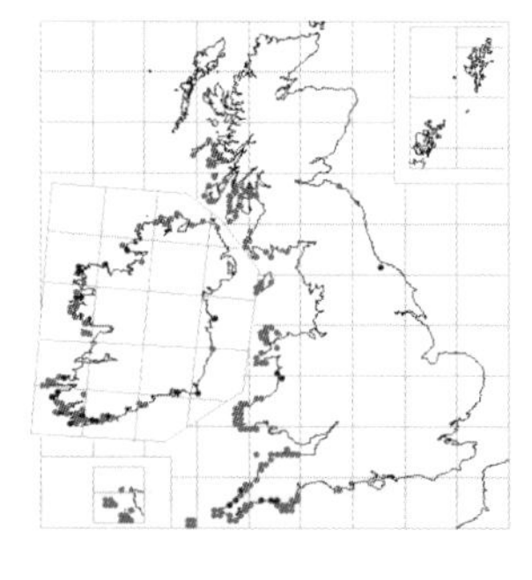

SCOLICIOSPORUM ('spiral-shaped or worm-like spores'). **Thallus** crustose granular to powdery. No prothallus. **Photobiont** chlorococcoid. **Apothecia** lecideine. **Ascus** 8-spored, *Lecanora*-type. **Spores** straight, curved or twisted, colourless, multi-septate but with thin septa and often difficult to observe.

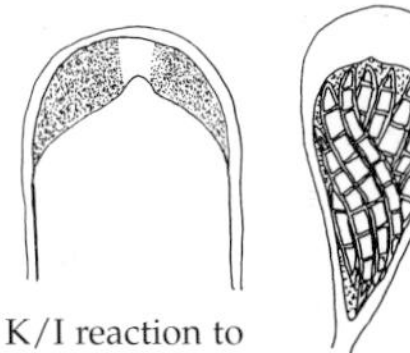

K/I reaction to the ascus tip. *S. umbrinum* x 300.

1. Thallus green to black-green. Apothecia up to 0.3 mm **1. S. chlorococcum**
– Thallus green-brown to black. Apothecia up to 0.75 mm **2. S. umbrinum**

1. Scoliciosporum chlorococcum Thallus green to black-green, granular. Apothecia often absent, up to 0.3 mm diam, glossy black, brown when wet, it may be difficult to separate from the common green alga *Desmococcus viridis*. Spores 7-septate, clavate, straight or curved, 20–40 x 4–5 µm.
Habitat: Common but overlooked. Found on the damper side of nutrient-enriched deciduous trees. It is extremely pollution-tolerant and often grows with *Lecanora conizaeoides*.

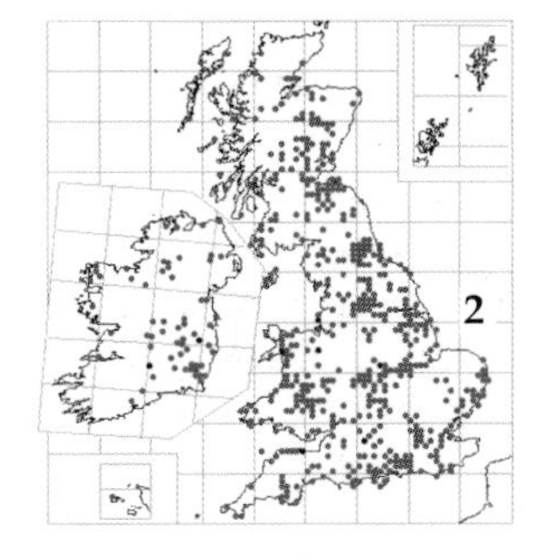

2. S. umbrinum Thallus green-brown to black, areolate or frequently drying out as thin scattered flakes. Apothecia up to 0.75 mm diam, very dark brown to black, becoming very convex. Spores 3- to 7-septate, twisted, 20–35 x 2–3 µm.
Habitat: Common on a wide range of substrata (especially if metal-rich), mainly acidic, sometimes on trees, especially common on the tops of table-tombs.

S. umbrinum x 5.

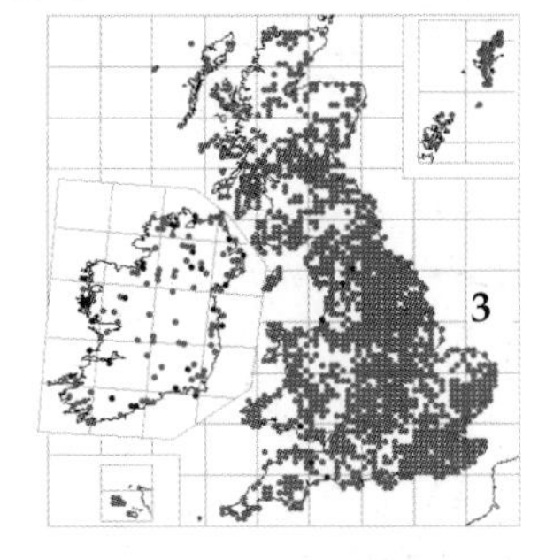

SOLENOPSORA ('tube-like *Psora*' – from the resemblance to the genus). **Thallus** placodioid or squamulose. **Photobiont** chlorococcoid. **Apothecia** lecanorine. **Ascus** 8–spored, *Catillaria*-type. **Spores** colourless, 1-septate. **Pycnidia** immersed. **Conidia** simple, colourless. 3–4 x 1 µm.

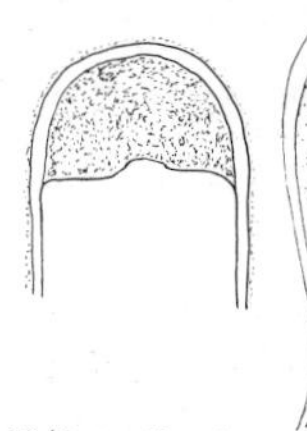

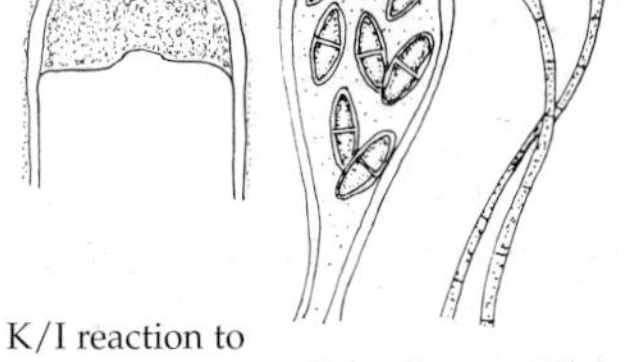

K/I reaction to the ascus tip. *S. candicans* x 350.

1.	Thallus white, placodioid, on well-lit rocks	**1. S. candicans**
–	Thallus pale green-grey or brown, squamulose, on sheltered rocks	2
2.	Thallus of brown overlapping, non-sorediate squamules	**2. S. holophaea**
–	Thallus of pale green-grey, often sorediate squamules	**3. S. vulturiensis**

1. Solenopsora candicans Thallus chalky white, placodioid. The lobes widening towards the tips, slightly convex, very pruinose. Thallus up to about 5 cm diam, crustose, cracked in the centre. Usually fertile, apothecia about 1 mm diam with a thick thalline margin which often becomes excluded. Discs black but usually pruinose. Spores 12–20 x 3–4 µm. Can be confused with *Diploicia canescens*, but that species is sorediate, more blue-tinged, K+ yellow and seldom fertile (except in the South).
P+ orange, UV+ greyish white.
Habitat: Locally abundant on well-lit, hard calcareous rocks, especially on monuments.

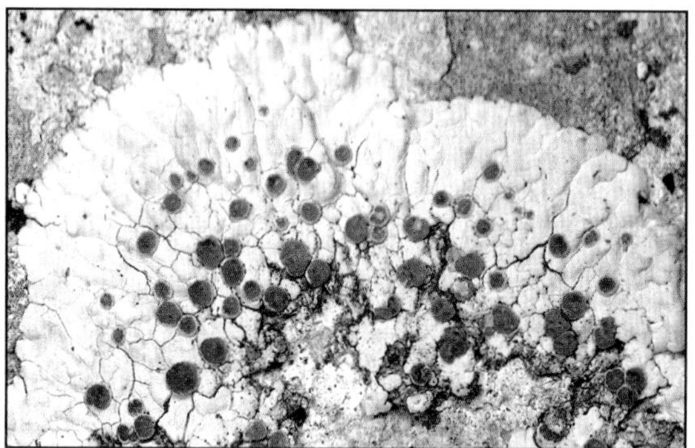

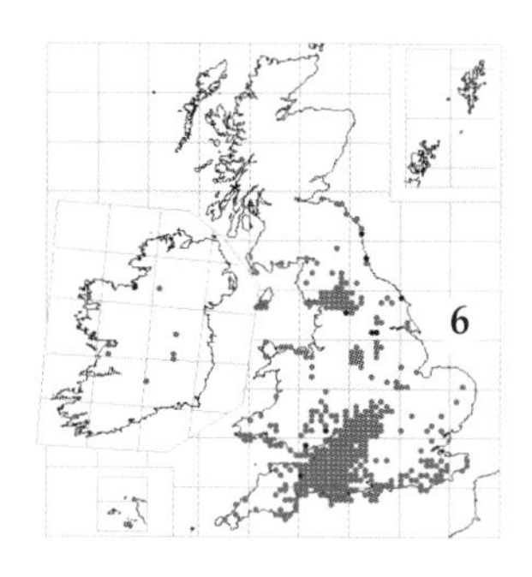

S. candicans x 4.

2. S. holophaea Thallus of overlapping brown (green when wet) squamules about 2 mm wide with raised edges. Lower surface tan with pale rhizines. Apothecia usually present, sessile, chestnut to almost black, not pruinose, soon becoming convex, the margin may sometimes be excluded. Spores 12–18 x 4–5 µm. The somewhat similar *Psora lurida* has simple spores.
Spot reactions: all negative.
Habitat: Frequent on vertical, damp, shaded, often soft rocks and in shallow crevices, on or near the coast.

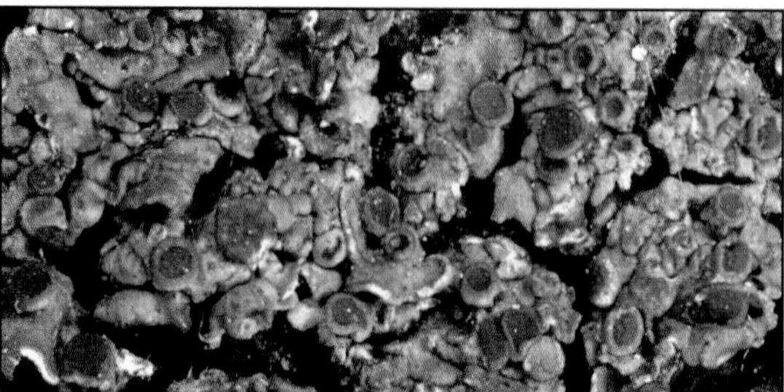

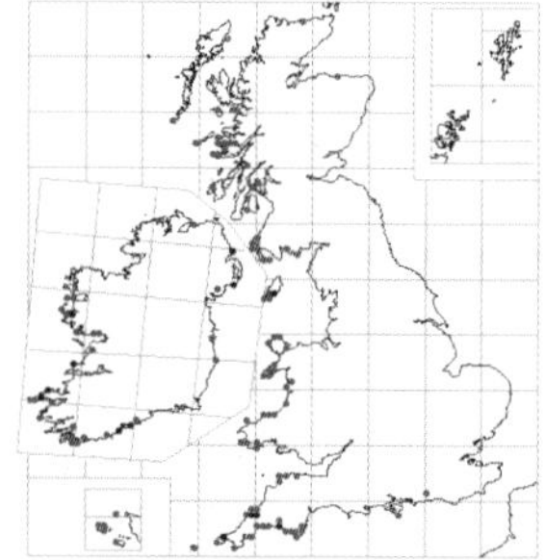

S. holophaea x 5.

3. S. vulturiensis Thallus pale graucous grey becoming green when wet, of scattered or overlapping, small (up to 0.5 mm wide), often granular, contorted, pruinose squamules which usually become sorediate in the swollen tips. Apothecia rare, about 0.5 mm diam, rather globose. Disc pale brown, often with a pinkish tinge. Spores simple when young, becoming 1-septate, 9–12 x 4–5 µm. KC+ pale yellow.
Habitat: Frequent in the extreme SouthWest on shaded rocks and damp, nutrient-enriched soil pockets from just above the high-water mark. Often on the edges of seepage tracks. Much less common on other coasts in Britain. It is sometimes found inland especially on church walls in the SouthWest.

S. vulturiensis x 8.

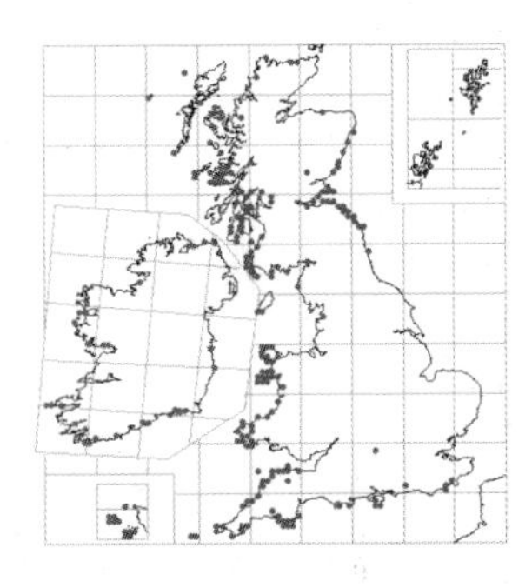

SOLORINA ('ground-plate' – from the form of the thallus). **Thallus** foliose, thin, lower surface tomentose with rhizines. **Photobiont** *Coccomyxa*, often with *Nostoc* contained in internal or external cephalodia. **Apothecia** lecideine, sunken in the surface of the thallus, giving it the English name of 'socket lichen'. **Ascus** up to 8-spored, *Peltigera*-type. **Spores** brown, 1-septate, warted in some species. **Pycnidia** not known.

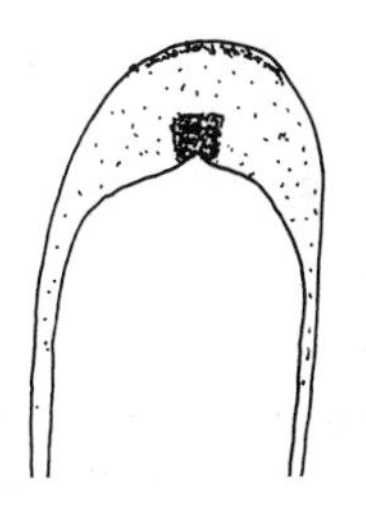

K/I reaction to the ascus tip.

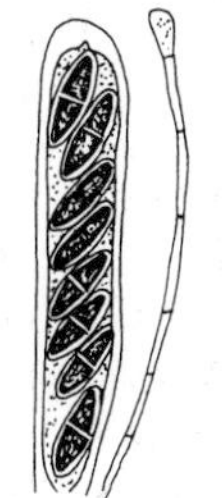

S. crocea x 200.

1. Thallus grey-brown (dark green when wet), lower surface and medulla bright orange. K+ purple. Acid sites — **1. S. crocea**
– Thallus grey (bright green when wet), lower surface and medulla white. K–. Calcareous sites — 2
2. Internal cephalodia (seen as dark areas through the cortex). Thallus extensive — **2. S. saccata**
– External cephalodia. Thallus just a collar around apothecia — **3. S. spongiosa**

1. Solorina crocea Thallus brown to grey-brown becoming dark green when wet. Lobes with rounded tips. Lower surface and medulla bright orange-red

with net-like raised ribs. Apothecia innate, large (up to 1.5 cm), chestnut, flat or slightly convex. Spores brown, 1-septate, bacilliform, 35–45 x 10–12 µm, mainly 8-spored. It differs from other British lichens in having a bright green algal layer, below which is a similar blue-green layer of *Nostoc*.
Medulla and lower surface: K+ purple.
Habitat: An arctic-alpine species of acid soils. Locally common above 900 metres in the Scottish Highlands, especially associated with areas of late snow lie or with permanent snow patches.

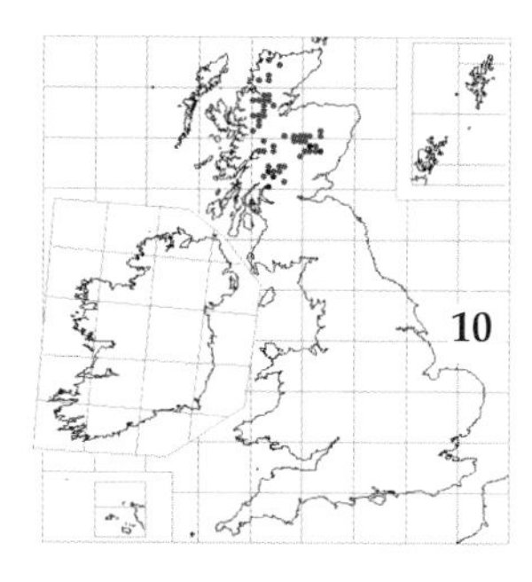

2. S. saccata Thallus brownish green to grey, often pruinose, bright green when wet. Lobes rounded with wavy edges. Lower surface white or buff, often with darker spots where the internal cephalodia are just visible. Very tomentose with only indistinct veins and, rarely, a few rhizines. Apothecia common up to about 5 mm diam, sunk into the thallus. Ascus 4-spored. Spores 1-septate, reddish brown with a pitted epispore, 30–50 x 18–27 µm.
Spot reactions: negative.
Habitat: locally common, on upland limestones and calcareous grassland.

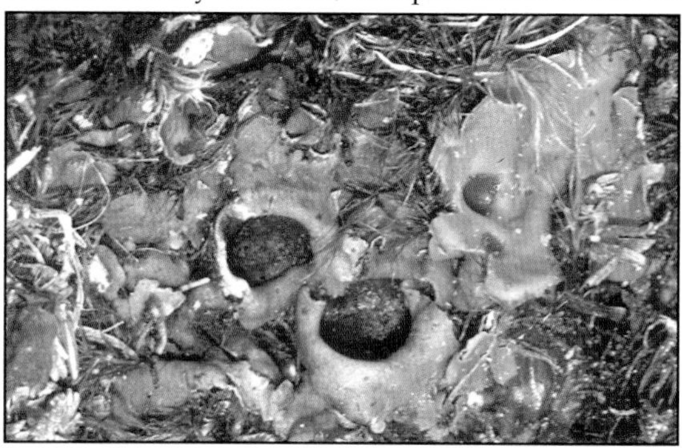

S. saccata x 5.

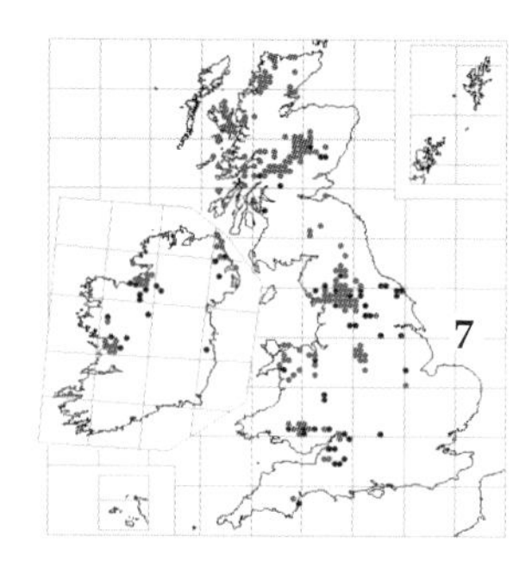

3. S. spongiosa. Thallus reduced to a green collar surrounding the apothecia. Outside this collar are the partially buried, external cephalodia forming a dark warted to coralloid mass, gelatinous when wet. Apothecia common, up to 5 mm diam, sunken, developing below the upper cortex which then splits to reveal the dark red-brown, flat disc of the apothecium. Spores brown, with a warted, furrowed surface, 1-septate, ascus 4-spored, 32–50 x 18–27 µm.
Spot reactions: negative.
Habitat: Locally abundant, especially in the North, in short turf, amongst mosses or in crevices in hard calcareous rocks. A rare but similar species, **S. bispora,** has internal cephalodia and 1- or 2-spored asci. Spore size helps distinguish 3 varieties: var. **bispora**, 1-septate, 70–100 x 30–50 µm; var. **monospora**, ascus 1-spored, spores 2-septate, 95–165 x 33–45 µm; var. **macrospora**, 1-septate, 100–120 x 45–60 µm.

S. spongiosa x 3.

SPHAEROPHORUS ('wearing balls' – from the shape of the fruit bodies). **Thallus** fruticose, bushy, branches solid, smooth, not sorediate. **Photobiont** *Cystococcus* or trebouxioid. **Apothecia** arise from inside swollen tips of the branches. **Ascus** 8-spored, the ascus breaks down early to liberate the spores, forming a powdery mazaedium. **Spores** brown, globose, simple, with a granular epispore. There are three British species.

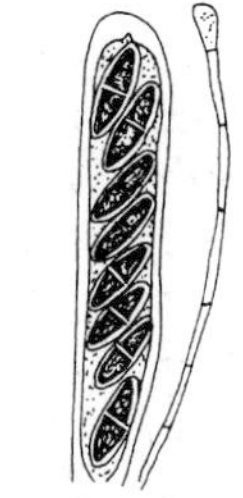

S. globosus x 500.

1. Main branches distinctly flattened. Medulla K+y, P+o **3. S. melanocarpus**
– Main branches more or less terete. Medulla K–, P– 2

2. Thallus to 6 cm high, branches unequal in diameter. Medulla I+ blue **2. S. globosus**
– Thallus to 3 cm high, all almost branches equal in diameter. Medulla I– **1. S. fragilis**

Sphaerophorus branching patterns

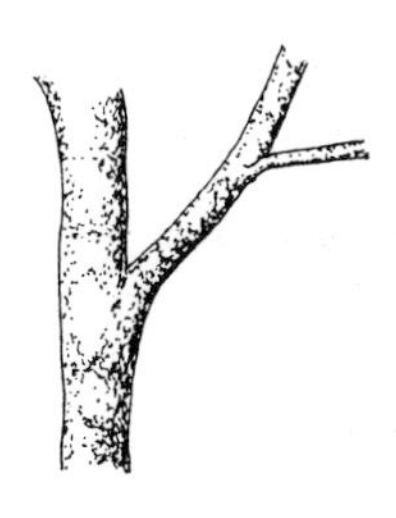

S. globosus
Dichotomous, unequal

S. fragilis
Dichotomous, more or less equal

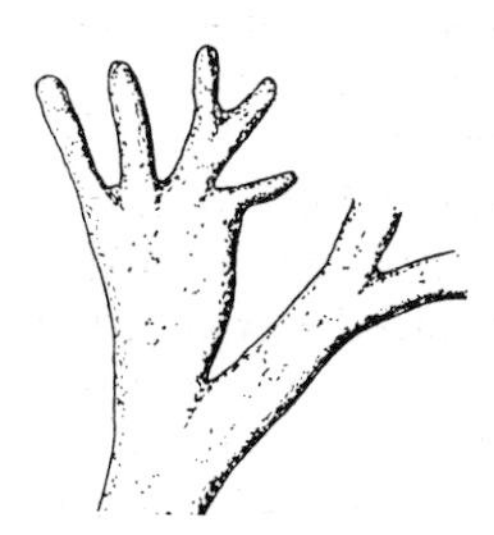

S.melanocarpus
Palmate

1. Sphaerophorus fragilis Thallus up to about 4 cm high, bushy, forming more even and compact cushions and with fewer distinct main branches than *S. globosus*. Greenish grey and only rarely with a pinkish tinge. The branchlets tend to grow all to the same height so that it often appears as though it has been mown. More doubtful specimens may be separated from *S. globosus* by the iodine test and the branching pattern. Only very rarely fertile. Spores blue-black, 8–10 µm diam.
Medulla: K–, P–, I– (test in slide preparation).
Habitat: Rocks and screes, often at higher altitudes than *S. globosus*.

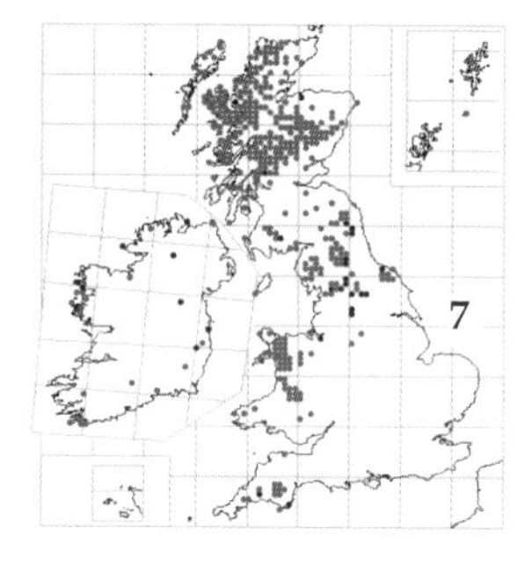

S. fragilis x 3.

2. S. globosus Thallus bushy, up to 5 cm high, green-grey to brown, often with a pink tinge, usually brown towards the base. Many short, narrower, digitate branchlets arise in clusters right up the main stem. Apothecia develop in globose swellings in the branch tips, these swellings split open to liberate the spores which are brown-black, globose, 9–15 µm diam.
Medulla: K–, P–, I+ blue (test in slide preparation).
Habitat: Very common in upland regions on peaty soil, rocks or mossy trees.

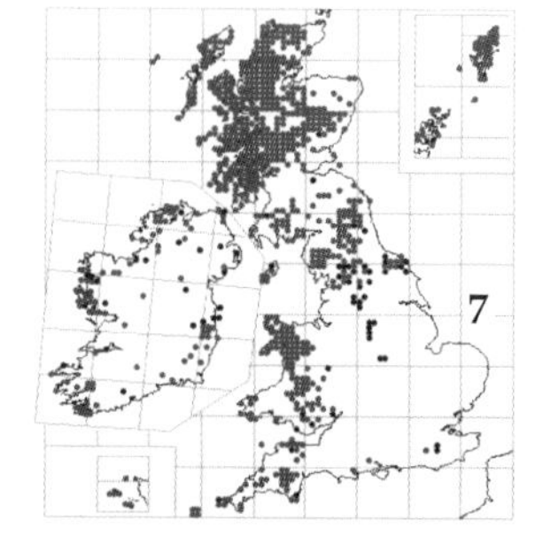

S. globosus x 3. *S. globosus* apothecia x 8.

3. S. melanocarpus Thallus up to 4 cm high, often decumbent, less erect than the previous species, green-grey to olive-green, often reddish brown towards the base, lower surface often almost white. Main branches very distinct and flattened, up to 3 mm wide. Short, rather flat branchlets arise from the edges of

the main branches. Very rarely fertile in Britain. Apothecia formed on the lower surface near the tips of the branches. Spores globose, grey-black, 7–12 µm.
Medulla: K+ yellow, P+ orange, I–.
Habitat: Common in north-west Scotland, rarer elsewhere, usually amongst mosses on acid rocks (especially in woodlands). In more sheltered sites than the previous two species.

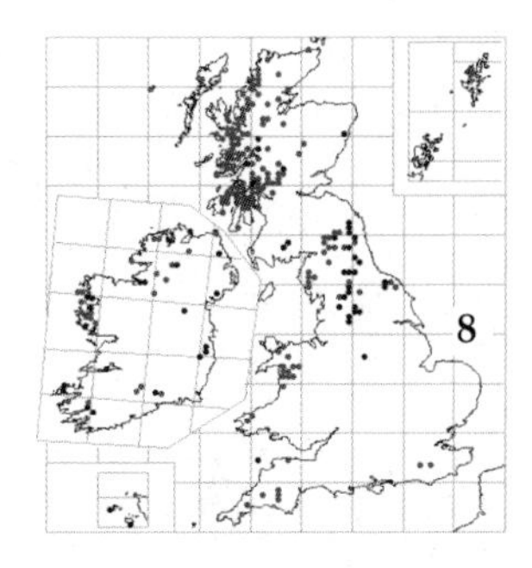

S. melanocarpus x 3.

SQUAMARINA ('scale-like' – from the squamulose thallus). **Thallus** squamulose, usually pruinose. **Photobiont** chlorococcoid. **Apothecia** lecanorine, more or less sessile when mature. **Ascus** 8-spored, *Bacidia*-type. **Spores** colourless, simple. There are two British species.

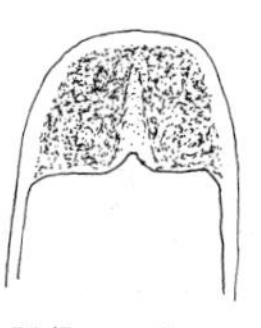

K/I reaction to the ascus tip.

S. cartilaginea x 400.

1. Thallus greenish yellow to brown-green. Lower surface dark **1. S. cartilaginea**
– Thallus grey-brown. Lower surface pale **2. S. lentigera**

1. Squamarina cartilaginea Thallus light greenish yellow to brown-green, consisting of overlapping, white-pruinose squamules, the pruina most clearly seen on the margins of the squamules. Lower surface dark. Apothecia up to about 3 mm diam. Thalline margin pronounced but may become excluded. Discs light brown to dark red-brown. Spores 11–16 x 4–6 µm.
Medulla: P+ yellow or P– (there are two chemical races in Britain).
Habitat: A species of crevices in calcareous rocks or on stony calcareous soils.

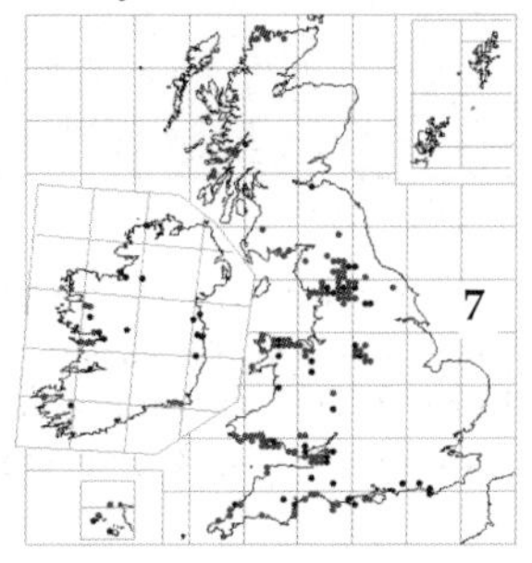

S. cartilaginea x 3.

2. S. lentigera Thallus rosette-forming, grey-brown, densely white-pruinose, squamules with distinctive upturned edges. The pale-coloured under-surface shows as white margins to the squamules. Spores slightly smaller than in *S. cartilaginea*, 9–12 x 4–5 µm.
Medulla: P–.
Habitat: A very rare and declining species of highly calcareous sandy soils and is especially characteristic of a few sites in Breckland heaths.

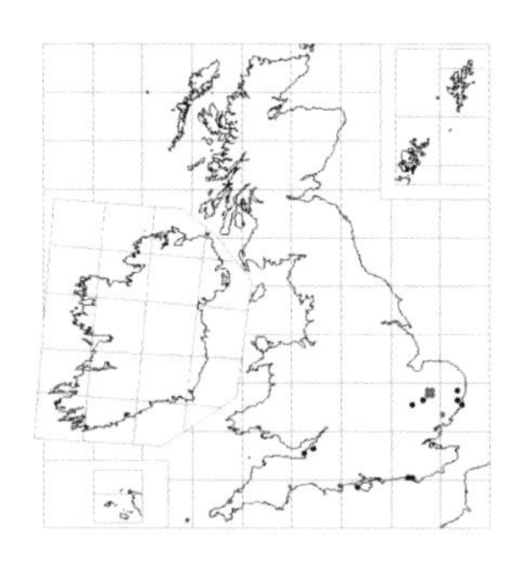

STAUROTHELE ('nipple with a cross' – from the form of the young perithecia in the type species). **Thallus** crustose, saxicolous, sometimes immersed. **Photobiont** *Stichococcus*. **Perithecia** simple or compound. **Ascus** 2- to 8-spored. **Spores** colourless or becoming brown, muriform. **Chemical reactions** negative. This genus may be separated from the superficially similar *Thelidium* and *Porina* species by the presence of minute rather cube-shaped or elongate algal cells in the hymenium. *Endocarpon* also has this feature but has a squamulose thallus.

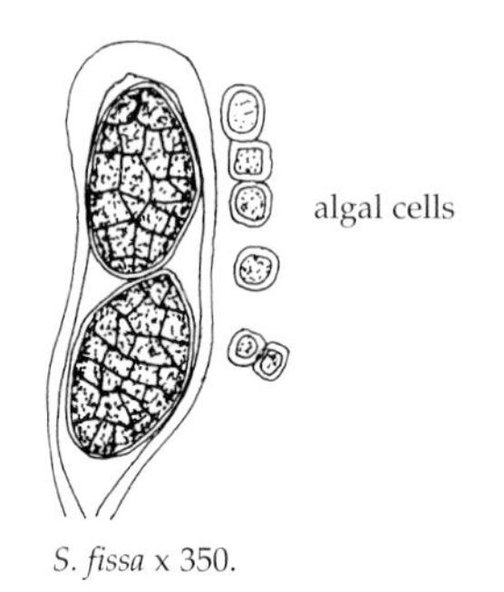

S. fissa x 350.

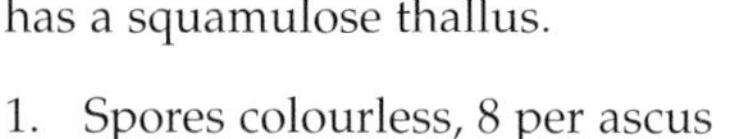

1.	Spores colourless, 8 per ascus	**2. S. hymenogonia**
–	Spores brown, 2–4 per ascus	2
2.	Spores 2 per ascus. Thallus green-grey to brown, epilithic	**1. S. fissa**
–	Spores 4 per ascus. Thallus steel- to brownish grey, usually endolithic	**3. S. rupifraga**

1. Staurothele fissa Thallus green-grey to brown, thin to thick, smooth, cracked or areolate or becoming slightly squamulose. Perithecia prominent, arising in warts, singly (about 0.5 mm diam) or in groups of two or three. The involucrellum dark brown, surrounded by a raised belt of the lighter thallus. Ascus 2-spored. Spores 35–50 x 15–25 µm, brown and muriform. The paraphyses break down early in the development of the perithecia. Hymenial alga 2–3 µm diam, cube-shaped to rounded, often in pairs.
Habitat: Fairly common but overlooked. On inundated acid rocks by streams. Often occurs with *Hymenelia lacustris*.

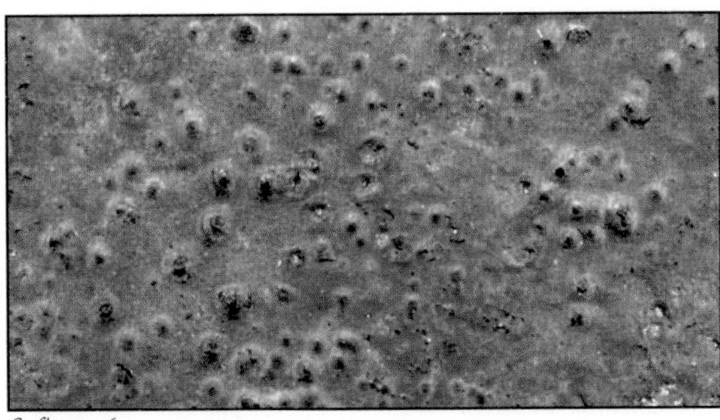

S. fissa x 6.

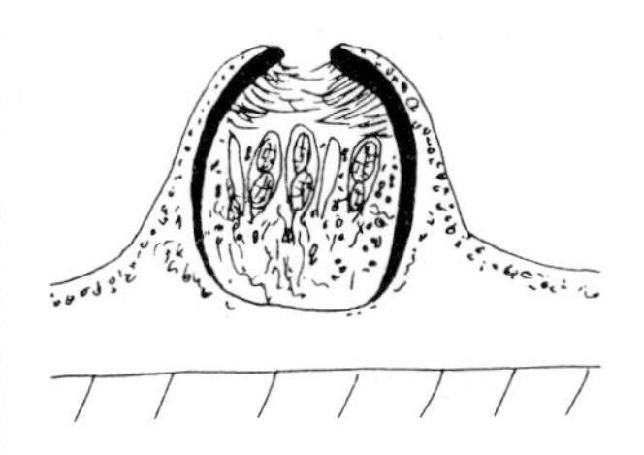

Section through a perithecium of *S. fissa*.

2. S. hymenogonia Thallus pale grey, usually endolithic. Perithecia 0.5–0.7 mm diam, partially immersed in shallow pits, often compound and usually pruinose. Ascus 8-spored. Spores colourless, 1-septate, soon becoming muriform, 25–32 x 15–20 µm. Hymenial algae 3–10 x 2–3 µm.
Habitat: The commonest species of *Staurothele* in the South and West but less frequent in the rest of Britain. On calcareous rocks, chalk pebbles and mortar.

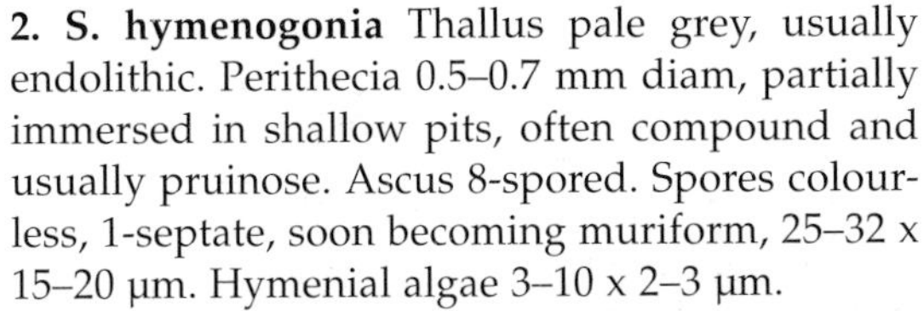

3. S. rupifraga Thallus pale steel-grey to brownish grey, thin and scurfy, more usually endolithic. Perithecia only 0.2–0.4 mm diam, immersed in pits. No involucrellum. The only British *Staurothele* species that has 4-spored asci and brown, muriform spores. Spores 30–50 x 18–25 µm. Hymenial algae rounded, 2–3.5 µm.
Habitat: Frequent on well-lit hard limestone.

STENOCYBE ('narrow cube' – from the shape of the apothecial head). This species lacks a photobiont and, therefore, a true thallus and is non-lichenized. It is, however, included here due to the many references relating to this genus in lichen texts. **Apothecia** on the ends of short, black stalks. **Ascus** 8-spored, breaking down when the spores mature. **Spores** brown, 3- to 7-septate. **Chemical reactions** negative.

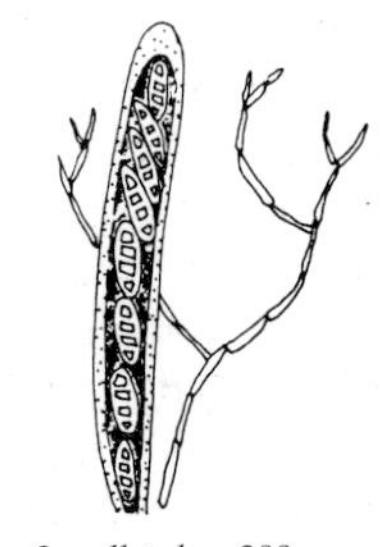

S. pullatula x 300.

1. Fruiting bodies to 2 mm high. Mainly on holly **2. S. septata**
– Fruiting bodies to 1 mm high. Mainly on alder **1. S. pullatula**

1. Stenocybe pullatula (S. byssacea) Similar to *S. septata* but with rather broader apothecia, which, together with the stalk, are only up to 1 mm tall. Spores greyish brown, simple, becoming up to 3-septate, 12–20 x 4–5 µm.
Habitat: Occasional, on alder twigs, often where these overhang water. Due to its small size, it is most easily viewed by looking at the top edge of the twigs against the light. Often with *Scoliciosporum chlorococcum*.

2. S. septata Apothecia dark brown, sometimes in small groups, borne on the end of dark brown stalks. The whole is Indian club-shaped, shiny, up to 2 mm tall, rarely more. Spores become dark reddish brown, mostly 3-septate, 40–70 x 14–20 µm.
Habitat: Not uncommon on old shaded holly trees, exceptionally on other trees.

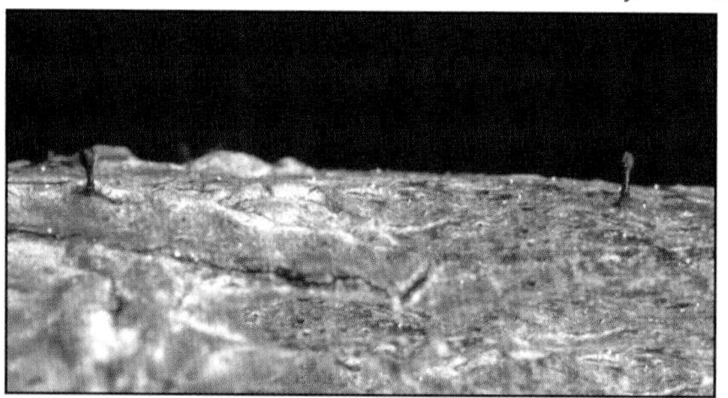

S. septata x 10.

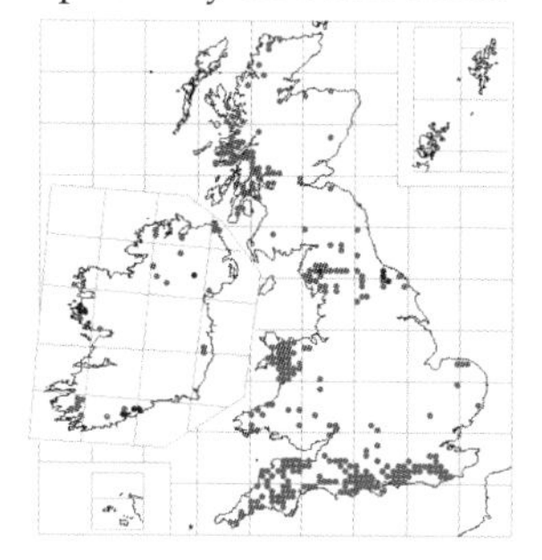

STEREOCAULON ('with a sturdy stalk' – from the shape of the pseudopodetia). **Primary thallus** squamulose or granulose, often evanescent. **Secondary thallus** of erect, tufted, solid pseudopodetia, bearing ± flattened phyllocladia. **Photobiont** *Trebouxia*. The pseudopodetia often have cephalodia containing cyanobacteria (*Nostoc* or *Stigonema*). **Apothecia** are not common in Britain, terminal on the pseudopodetia, lecideine. **Ascus** 8-spored, *Porpidia*-like with a thin blue outer coat. **Spores** colourless, multi-septate. **Chemical reactions** all species are K+ yellow.

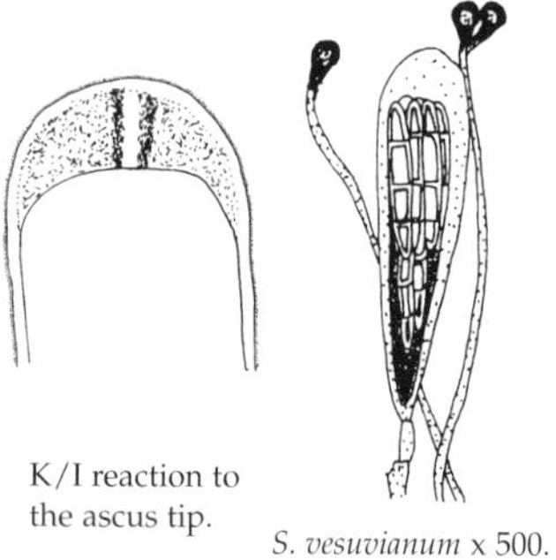

K/I reaction to the ascus tip.

S. vesuvianum x 500.

May be separated from *Cladonia* which has hollow true podetia and from *Sphaeophorus* which has digitate, rounded, branchlets and simple spores in globose apothecia. *Stereocaulon* species are frequently found on metal-rich rocks, e.g. lead, when other conditions are suitable.

1. Sorediate — 2
- Not sorediate — 5

2. Greenish grey to grey. K+ yellow — 3
- Yellowish green with concolorous soralia. K– **Leprocaulon microscopicum**

3. Primary thallus evanescent, pseudopodetia over 7 mm tall **5. S. vesuvianum**
- Primary thallus persistent, pseudopodetia less than 7 mm tall — 4

4. Primary thallus of flattened phyllocladia, sorediate below **3. S. nanodes**
- Primary thallus of granular phyllocladia, soredia on tips of pseudopodetia **4. S. pileatum**

5. Phyllocladia button-shaped with dark centres **5. S. vesuvianum**
- Phyllocladia without dark centres and/or terete — 6

6. Phyllocladia flattened, incised and palmate. P± yellow. Cephalodia rare **2. S. evolutum**
- Phyllocladia terete, becoming densely coralloid. P+ orange. Cephalodia common **1. S. dactylophyllum**

1. Stereocaulon dactylophyllum Primary thallus soon disappearing. Pseudopodetia yellowish white or pale grey, rather stout, up to about 4 cm tall, rarely bearing brown, wrinkled clusters of cephalodia. Phyllocladia numerous, terete and becoming densely coralloid when mature. Apothecia fairly common, brown, convex when mature.
K+ yellow, P+ orange.
Habitat: Frequent on acid rocks, sometimes in lowland areas. It often forms extensive mats.

S. dactylophyllum x 5.

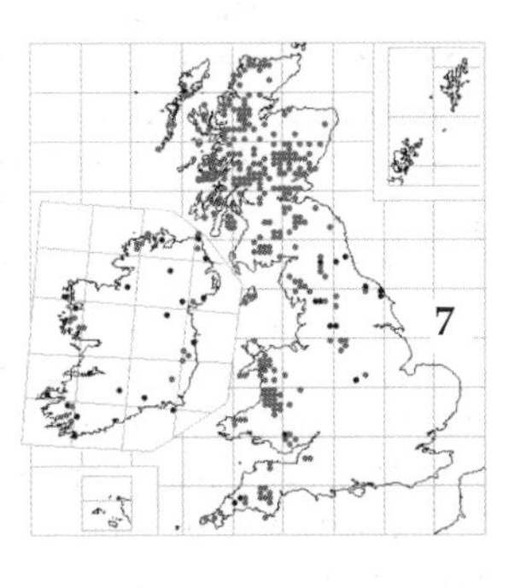

2. S. evolutum Primary thallus soon disappearing. Pseudopodetia to 3 cm tall, usually bending over towards the tips. Similar to *S. vesuvianum* but often more spreading, branching more from the base with somewhat flattened, spreading

pseudopodetia. Many of the phyllocladia are wider than the pseudopodetia and are flattened, almost digitate. Except for the paler, digitate extremities the phyllocladia are not darker in the centre. Apothecia not common, brown with a paler margin, becoming darker and the margin excluded. Spores 3-septate.
K+ yellow, P± yellow, KC+ violet (perform test on filter paper).
Habitat: Fairly common in acid, upland regions on rocks or moss.

S. *evolutum* x 5.

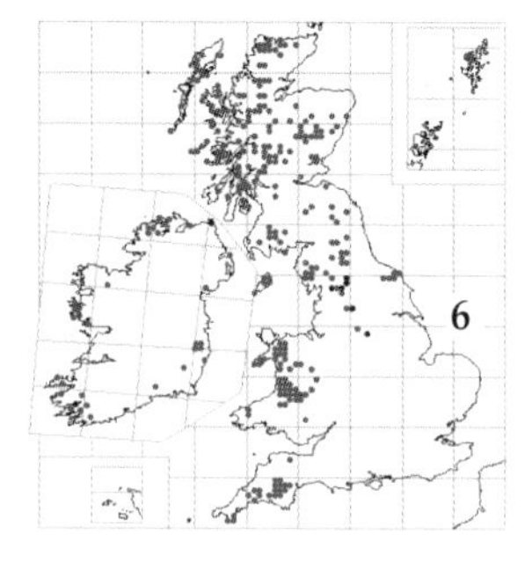

3. S. nanodes Primary thallus persistent consisting of vertical, flattened phyllocladia up to 5 mm tall with a sorediate lower surface. The pseudopodetia are infrequent, up to 1 cm tall, becoming sorediate. Grey cephalodia sometimes occur scattered over the thallus. Apothecia are very rare.
K+ yellow, P± yellow KC+ violet (perform test on filter paper).
Habitat: An increasing species of damp metal-rich rocks and walls. Frequently found by roads in urban areas.

S. *nanodes* x 10.

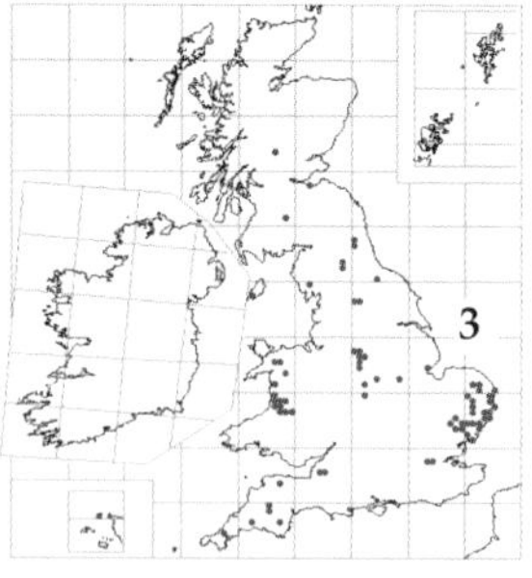

4. S. pileatum Primary thallus persistent, consisting of grey, rather granular phyllocladia up to 2.5 mm high. Pseudopodetia greenish grey, less than 5 mm tall, mainly unbranched, erect, often packed into a compact, globose mass, giving a crustose appearance. Phyllocladia indistinct, small, white and granular, except at the apices which are grey and have green-grey globose soralia. Grey to brown cephalodia are sometimes present. Apothecia rather rare, brown, convex. Spores 3-septate, 18–30 x 4–5 µm. Differs from *S. nanodes* in the granular, rather than flattened and sorediate, under-surface of the primary thallus.
K+ yellow, P± weak yellow, KC+ violet (perform test on filter paper).
Habitat: An increasing species in damp, man-made habitats rich in heavy metals, e.g. mine-spoil tips and lead-impregnated roadside walls (will it decline with lead-free petrol?), rather rare on natural damp, acid rocks.

5. S. vesuvianum Primary thallus soon disappearing. Pseudopodetia white to grey, up to about 3 cm high, very variable in form. Rarely with globose soralia at the tips. It is most easily distinguished by the button-shaped phyllocladia which have indented margins, are narrower than the pseudopodetia and a darker grey in the centre when mature. Cephalodia containing *Stigonema* sometimes present, very dark brown, rough and brain-like in appearance. This species is sometimes found fertile. Apothecia dark brown, concave at first becoming convex. Spores 3- to 7-septate, 26–46 x 3–4 µm.
K+ yellow, P+ orange.
Habitat: Very common in upland regions on well-lit, siliceous rocks, especially if metal-rich, often forming dense mats; also on man-made substrata.

S. vesuvianum x 4.

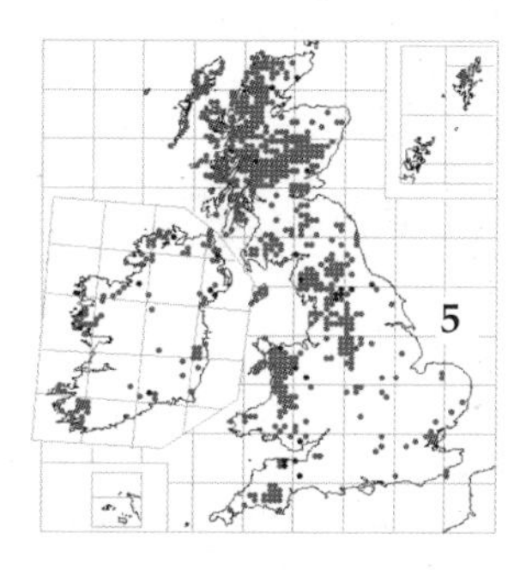

STICTA ('pierced' – from the pale cyphellae on the lower surface). **Thallus** foliose, loosely attached. The tomentose lower surface characteristically has pale circular cyphellae, although these may be indistinct in some species. Photobiont *Nostoc* in all the British species (except the rare, green morph of *S. canariensis*). **Apothecia** lecanorine. Not normally fertile in Britain. **Ascus** 8-spored, *Peltigera*-type. **Spores** colourless, 1- to 3-septate. **Chemical reations** negative. A number of species contain trimethylamine which gives wet thalli a fishy smell. Some species are indicators of an 'old forest' habitat; all are very sensitive to air pollution.

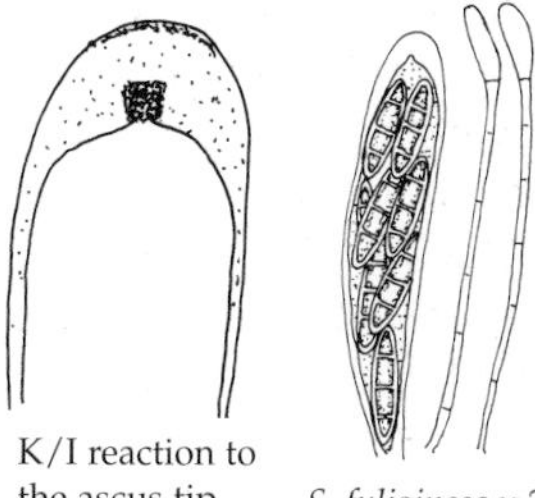

K/I reaction to the ascus tip. *S. fuliginosa* x 300.

1. Thallus bright green when wet **1b. (green algal morph) S. canariensis**
– Thallus grey-brown to dark brown when wet 2

2. Lobe margins with dense blue-grey soredia **3. S. limbata**
– Thallus isidiate, not sorediate 3

3. Lobe margins and surface with lobules and flattened isidia **1a. ('blue-green' cyanobacterial morph) S. canariensis**
– Lobes with coralloid isidia 4

4. Lobes deeply incised so as to appear many lobed, isidia clustered especially on ridges **4. S. sylvatica**
– Lobes little incised often appearing single-lobed, isidia scattered **2. S. fuliginosa**

1a. Sticta canariensis (S. dufourii s.str.) ***Blue-green morph.*** Thallus pale greenish or bluish grey to grey-brown. Lobes to 2 cm wide, rounded, incised, margins bearing small lobules and flattened isidia that become laminal in mature specimens. Lower surface pale brown with net-like ridges, a thin tomentum and large irregular cyphellae. It has a strong fishy smell when wet. Not known fertile.
Habitat: Local in the West on mossy trees and rocks in very damp, sheltered situations.
1b. S. canariensis (S. canariensis s.str.) ***Green morph.*** Thallus grey-green, bright green when wet, smooth. Lobes to 1 cm wide, rounded, lacking the isidia found in the blue-green morph. Lower surface pale, usually dark brown tomentose towards the centre. Apothecia rare, to 5 mm diam. Disc red-brown. Spores 1-septate, 23–30 x 6–7 µm.
Habitat: A very rare morph found on damp trees and rocks. Blue-green morphs with attached leaflets of the green morph are more frequent.

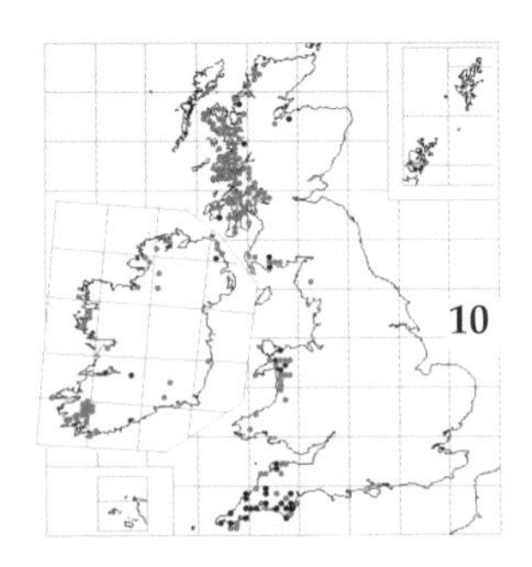

S. canariensis (bue-green morph) x 3.

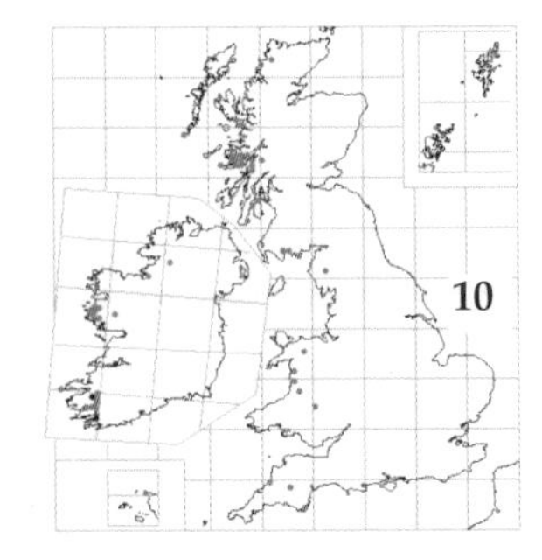

S. canariensis (green morph attached to blue-green morph) x 3.

2. S. fuliginosa Thallus brown-grey to dark brown. Lobes rounded, to 3 cm wide, often almost single-lobed, isidia scattered in clusters over the surface and margins. Lower surface pale brown, tomentose. It has a strong fishy smell when damp. Very rarely fertile Apothecia to 4 mm diam with a crenulate, tomentose, rarely ciliate, margin. Spores 1-septate, 30–33 x 5–9 µm. It is difficult to separate from *S. sylvatica* when young.
Habitat: Local, mainly in old oceanic woods on damp, mossy trees and rocks.

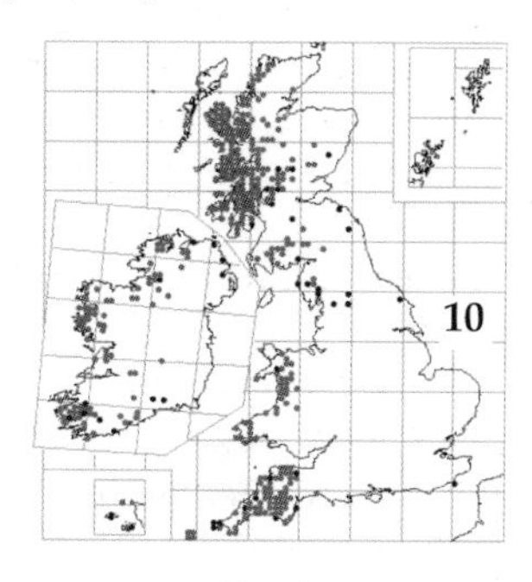

S. fuliginosa x 3.

3. S. limbata Thallus pale grey to dark brown. Lobes up to 3 cm wide, few in number, rounded, only slightly incised. The margins of the lobes are generally upturned and edged with dense, bluish grey, granular soredia. The soredia may spread towards the centre of the thallus. Under-surface tan with a thick, paler tomentum, which often makes the cyphellae indistinct. This is the only sorediate *Sticta* in Britain. It may be separated from *Peltigera collina* and *Nephroma parile* by the presence of pale cyphellae on the lower surface.
Habitat. Infrequent, mainly in the West on mossy trees and rocks. It can tolerate more basic substrata than *S. fuliginosa* and *S. sylvatica.*

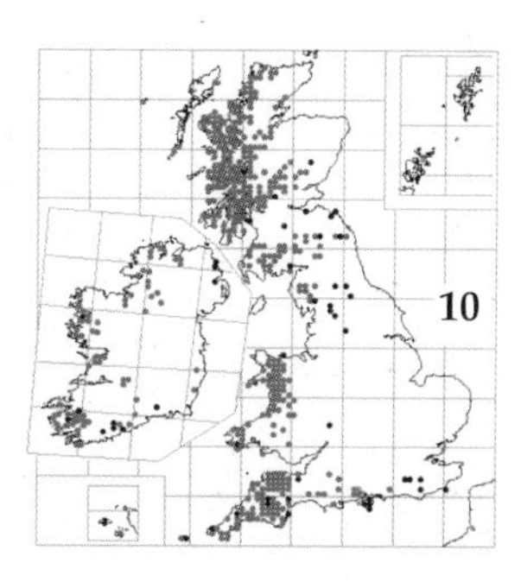

S. limbata x 4.

4. Sticta sylvatica Thallus large (up to 8 cm across), dark brown, often with greyish brown areas, usually multi-lobed. Lobes deeply incised with ascending margins and faint, net-like ridging over the upper surface. Darker brown

coralloid isidia are scattered over the surface of the lobes, especially along the ridges. Lower surface dark brown, becoming buff at the margins of the lobes. The pale, rather regular cyphellae stand out against the dark lower surface. When damp it emits a strong smell of fish.
Habitat: Not common in the West and decreasing elsewhere. On damp, mossy trees and rocks.

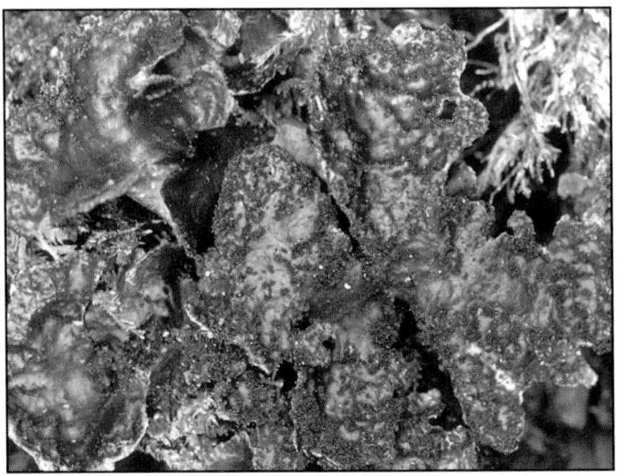

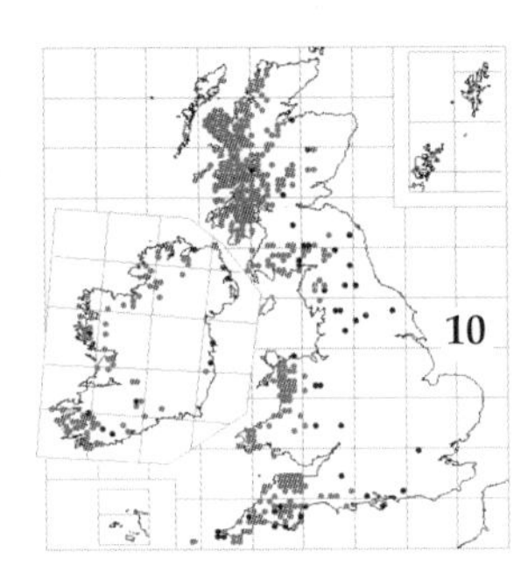

S. sylvatica x 4.

TELOSCHISTES ('split ends' – from the form of the thallus). **Thallus** fruticose. Greenish or grey-orange to bright orange. Attached by a basal holdfast. **Photobiont** trebouxioid. **Apothecia** lecanorine, thalline margin often ciliate. **Ascus** 8-spored, *Teloschistes*-type. **Spores** colourless, polari-locular. **Chemistry** all British species contain physcion. Britain is at the northern end of the range of this mainly Mediterranean to sub-tropical genus.

K/I reaction to the ascus tip.

T. flavicans spore x 3000.

1.	Apothecia absent. Soredia present	**2. T. flavicans**
–	Apothecia normally present. Soredia absent	**1. T. chrysopthalmus**

1. Teloschistes chrysophthalmus Thallus forming tufts up to 1 cm high, yellowish orange to grey-orange, paler on the lower surface. Lobes to about 2 mm wide with abundant spinules. Usually very fertile, Apothecia up to 5 mm diam, on short stalks. The narrow thalline margin has numerous spinulose extensions so that it resembles a diminutive, orange, *Usnea florida*.. Spores 10–15 x 5–8 µm. Pycnidia common, about 100 µm diam, located within small orange warts.
K+ purple.
Habitat: Occurs on well-lit, nutrient-enriched twigs. Only one recent, but now extinct site known on the mainland (Cornwall), also recorded from the Scilly and Channel Islands but now extinct at these sites.

T. chrysophthalmus x 4.

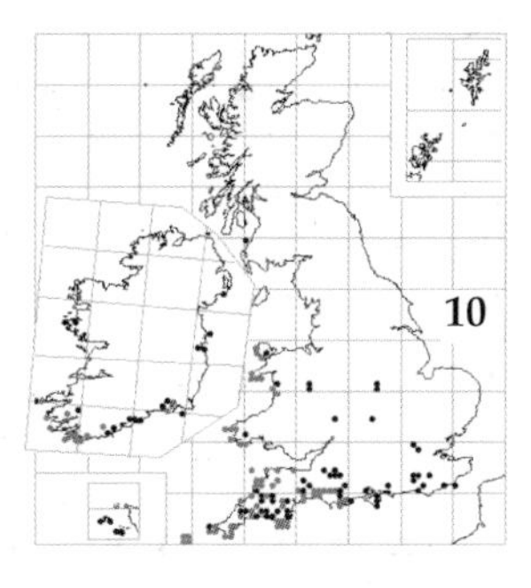

Now probably extinct at all these sites.

2. T. flavicans Thallus erect or slightly pendent, green-orange to deep orange. The lobes are up to 4 cm long and rather flattened and richly branched, with claw-shaped, long spinules. The margins bear yellowish farinose soredia which may rub off leaving scattered pits in the cortex. Apothecia very rare in Britain (no recent records). Discs orange with a thin margin. Pycnidia are often present in small warts. On supralittoral rocks the thallus is bright orange, more terete, glossy and less branched forming a decumbent mat.
K+ purple.
Habitat: Formerly widespread on trees and rocks in southern Britain. Now a rare and decreasing species, mainly on well-lit, nutrient-enriched bark and misty, windy maritime rocks, especially on offshore islands. Not to be collected.

T. flavicans x 5.

10

TEPHROMELA ('ashy-black' – from the colour of the apothecial disc). **Thallus** crustose. Saxicolous. **Photobiont** chlorococcoid. **Apothecia** lecanorine with black discs. Thalline margin sometimes present. **Ascus** 8-spored, *Bacidia*-type. **Spores** simple, colourless. It is closely related to the genus

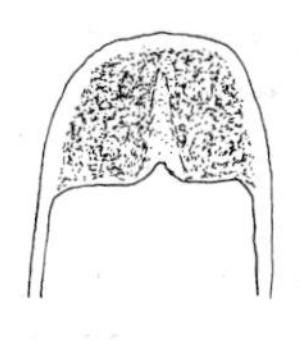

K/I reaction to the ascus tip.

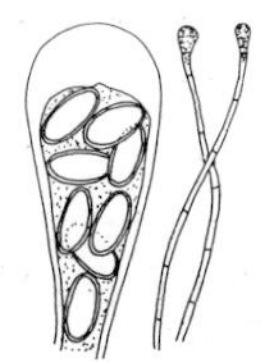

T. atra x 400.

Lecanora but differences include the ascus structure, conidia which are formed in chains and paraphyses which have a gelatinous coat and unswollen apices.

1. Apothecia normally present. Soredia absent **1. T. atra**
– Apothecia rare. Soredia present **2. T. grumosa**

1. Tephromela atra Thallus light to medium grey, smooth or warted, often with a thin dark prothallus. Usually fertile, mainly with the apothecia in the more central part of the thallus. Apothecia large, up to 3 mm diam, immersed becoming sessile, disc black with a thick margin. When mature the disc is flat with a grey contorted and crenulate margin. Hymenium opaque, purple-red in section. Spores 10–15 x 6–8 µm. It resembles *Lecanora gangaleoides* but that species has neater apothecia with smoother margins and if cut open the thecium is colourless to greenish brown and the medulla does not fluoresce under UV light.
K+ yellow, UV+ ice-blue.
Habitat: Very common throughout Britain on well-lit siliceous rocks and walls, often where there is slightly basic from run-off from adjacent mortar, etc.; rarely found on trees.

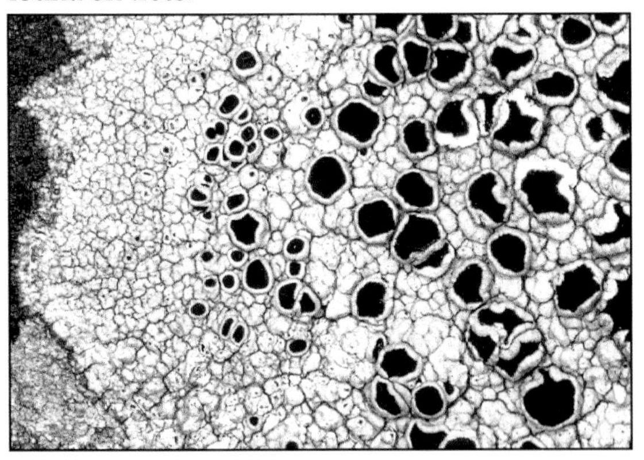

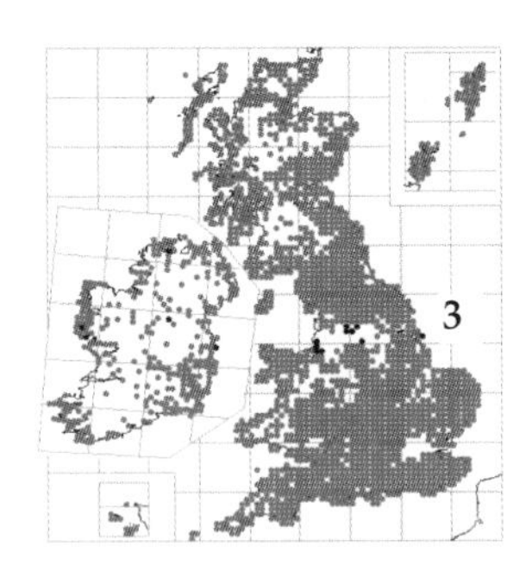

T. atra x 4.

2. T. grumosa Similar to *T. atra* but differs in the dense covering of deep blue-grey, granular soredia (see also *Porpidia tuberculosa)*. Rarely fertile. Thalline margin sorediate.
K± yellow, UV–.
Habitat: An upland species of well-lit siliceous rocks, rarely on wood.

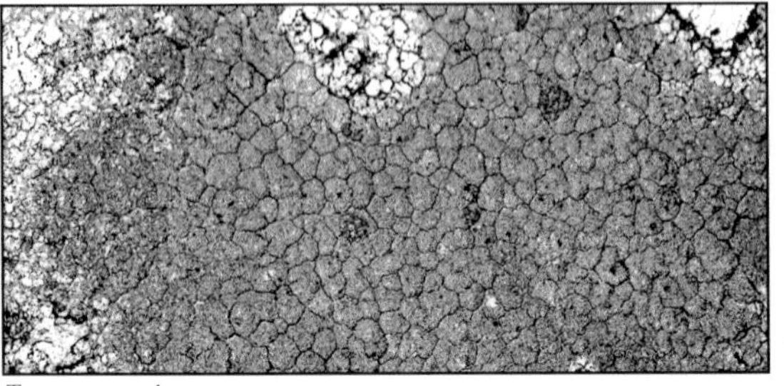

T. grumosa x 4.

THAMNOLIA ('bushy, shrub-like' – from the form of the thallus). **Thallus** fruticose, consisting of simple or sparsely branched hollow tubes. **Photobiont** trebouxioid. Never reported with apothecia, it also lacks soredia or isidia and is presumed to be dispersed by fragmentation. It is found throughout the world in arctic-alpine habitats above about 2000 feet, but down to sea level in Canada, Greenland, etc. It is especially common in these high latitudes. There is only a single species in the genus.

Thamnolia vermicularis Thallus macaroni-like, consisting of sinuate, prostrate, hollow tubes, pure white to yellowish-white, slightly wrinkled, up to 5 cm long and 1–2 mm wide, narrowing to a point, sometimes flattened and fluted, unbranched or slightly branched. Forming loose mats, or more commonly, scattered amongst mosses and dwarf shrubs.
K+ yellow, P+ yellow, UV+ white or dull orange. (var. **subuliformis**; the var. **vermicularis** differs chemically and is not known in the British Isles).
Habitat: Common in arctic-alpine situations, above 2000 feet but down to the coast in northern Scotland, especially in lichen-rich mature heath with dwarf shrubs.

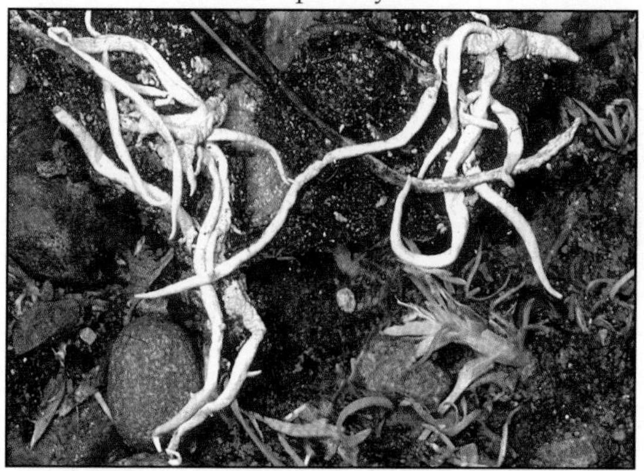

T. vermicularis x 4.

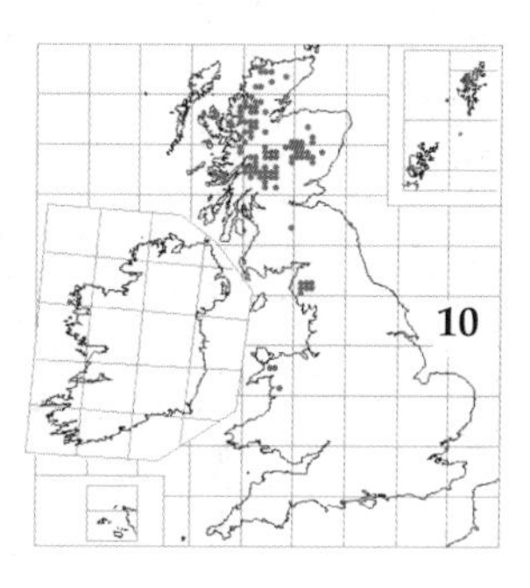

THELIDIUM ('nipple-shaped' – from the form of the perithecia). **Thallus** crustose, often endolithic or thin, sometimes appearing as if sprinkled with pepper. **Photobiont** chlorococcoid. **Perithecia** may be compound. The hymenium reacts I+ red. **Ascus** 8-spored, I–. **Spores** 1- to 3-septate, often clavate and sometimes also with a few longitudinal septa. **Chemical reactions** all negative. In the field, it is difficult to separate some species from the closely related *Verrucaria*, but that genus has simple spores.

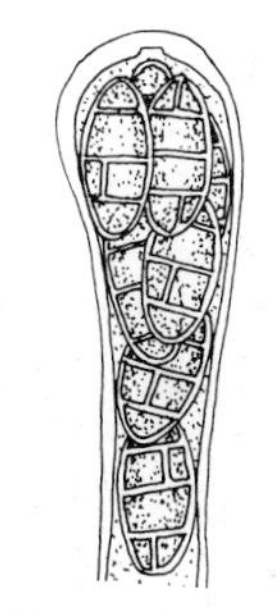

T. incavatum x 300.

1.	Perithecia to 0.75 mm wide, hemispherical, superficial	2
–	Perithecia to 0.5 mm wide, more or less immersed	3

2.	Spores 1-septate	**5. T. pyrenophorum**
–	Spores 3-septate	**4. T. papulare**
3.	Spores 1-septate. Many substrates	4
–	Spores 3-septate. Hard limestone	**2. T. incavatum**
4	Perithecia to 0.5 mm wide. Hard calcareous rocks	**1. T. decipiens**
–	Perithecia to 0.25 mm wide. Various substrates	**3. T. minutulum**

1. Thelidium decipiens Thallus green-white, pale brown-grey or endolithic. Perithecia brown, rather widely spaced, flat-topped, immersed in pits, 0.2–0.5 mm diam with a prominent ostiole and sometimes slightly pruinose. The perithecia are separated from the thallus or substratum by a narrow gap and leave empty pits when they fall out. Spores 1-septate, clavate, 20–37 x 10–16 µm.
Habitat: A frequent species of hard calcareous rocks.

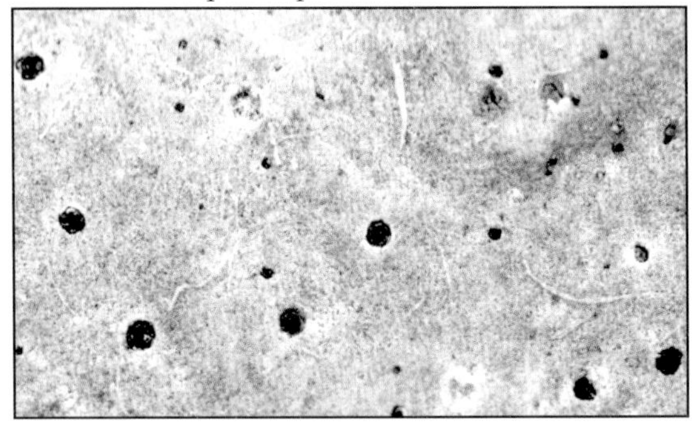

T. decipiens x 6.

2. T. incavatum Thallus white or pale cream-grey, thin or endolithic. Perithecia small, about 0.25–0.5 mm, surrounded by a narrow gap, more or less immersed with only the ostiole showing, leaving pits when the perithecia fall out. Spores 3-septate or rarely slightly muriform, 33–50 x 11–17 µm.
Habitat: An infrequent species of hard limestone.

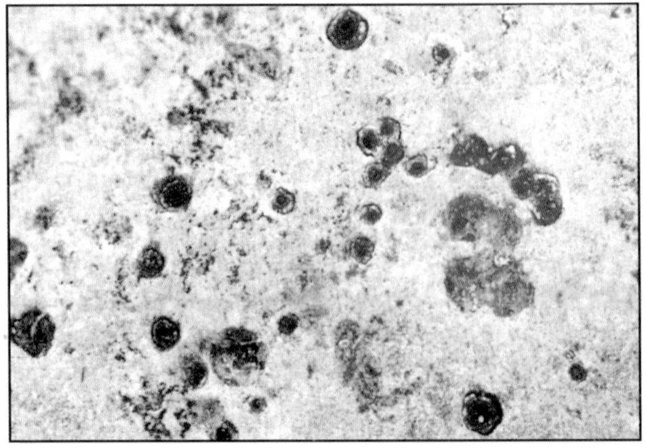

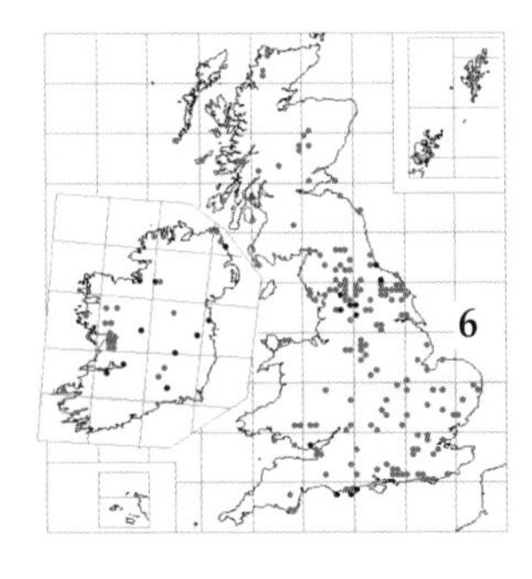

T. incavatum x 6.

3. T. minutulum Thallus light greenish grey to brown, with prominent globose perithecia which may more rarely be partially immersed in the thallus. Perithecia only about 0.25 mm wide with an indistinct ostiole. Spores 1-septate, 15–30 x 6–12 µm.
Habitat: Local, on shaded calcareous rocks and pebbles, frequently on mortar.

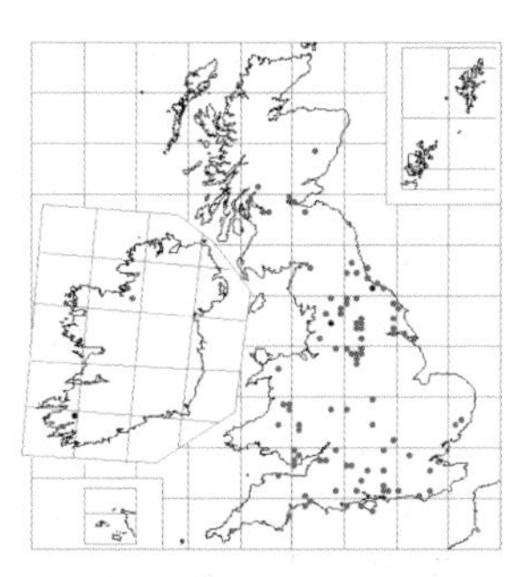

4. T. papulare Thallus light grey to purplish grey, thin, sometimes cracked. Perithecia about 0.75 mm diam, hemispherical with a smooth depression in the centre around the often paler ostiole. Involucrellum conspicuous. Spores 3-septate or slightly muriform, 30–55 x 12–20 µm.
Habitat: An infrequent species of damp calcareous or slightly acidic rocks.

T. papulare x 20.

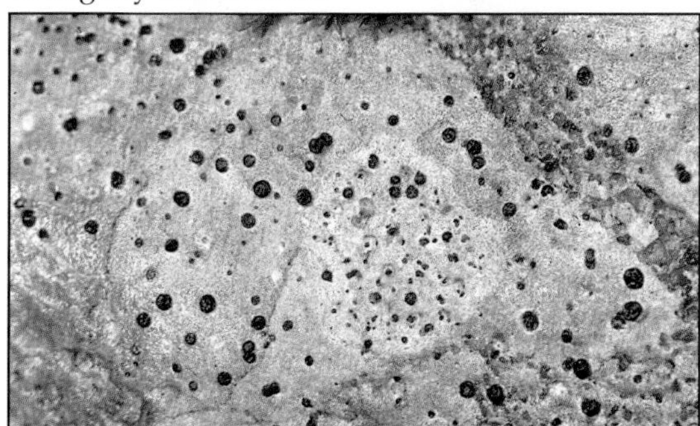

T. papulare x 5.

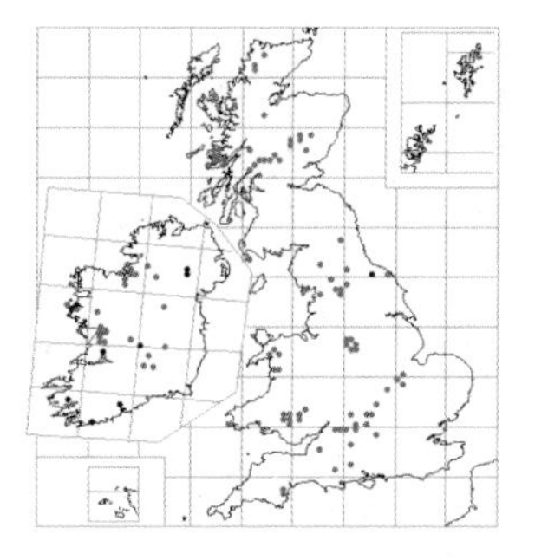

5. T. pyrenophorum Thallus immersed, thin or cracked, brownish-grey. Perithecia prominent, 0.3–0.7 mm diam, usually with a depressed ostiole. Involucrellum conspicuous. Spores 1-septate, 18–30 x 9–15 µm.
Habitat: On hard limestone and mica-schist. Mainly in the North.

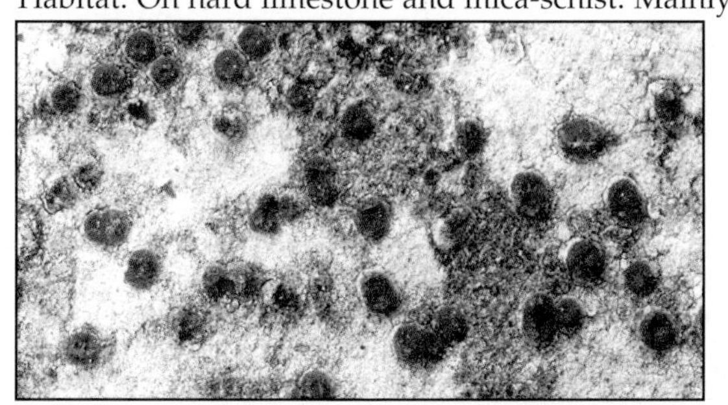

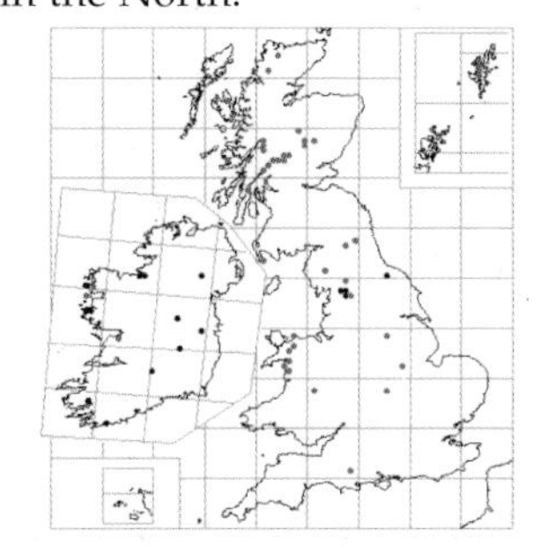

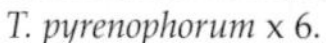

T. pyrenophorum x 6.

THELOPSIS ('nipple-like' – from the shape of the perithecia). **Thallus** crustose. **Photobiont** *Trentepohlia*. **Perithecia** sessile or slightly immersed, tough but somewhat gelatinous. **Ascus** 100- or more- spored, K/I–. Spores colourless, 1- to 4-septate. **Chemical reactions** all negative.

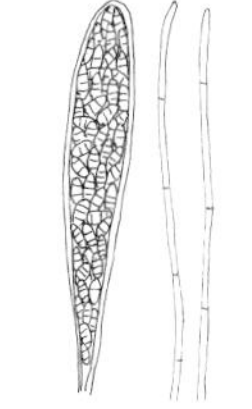

T. rubella x 500.

Thelopsis rubella Thallus thin, grey-green to brownish, waxy. Perithecia 0.3–1 mm diam, initially immersed, becoming somewhat sessile but retaining a ring of thallus around the base of the perithecium, red-brown, orange and almost gelatinous when wet. Ascus 100- to 150-spored. Spores 12–16 x 4–8 µm, mainly 3-septate.
Habitat: Indicator species of 'old woodland'. Occurs on bark of old trees especially in shallow cracks and rain tracks.

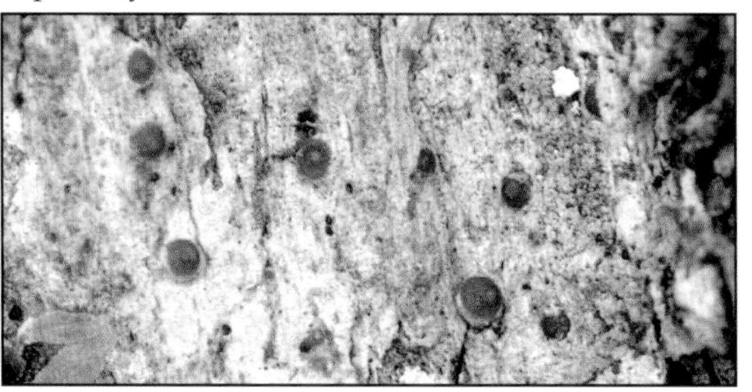

T. rubella x 5.

9

THELOTREMA ('perforated nipple' – from the form of the apothecia). **Thallus** crustose. **Photobiont** *Trentepohlia*. **Apothecia** with a detached, enclosing, thalline margin and an inner fused proper margin, giving a double appearance. **Ascus** 1- to 8-spored, K/I–. **Spores** colourless or brown, multi-septate or muriform, spore wall often laminated, I+ purplish. Mainly a tropical genus.

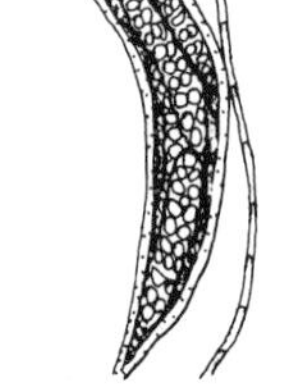

T. lepadinum x 150.

1. Apothecia prominent. Spores 60–140 µm long **1. T. lepadinum**
– Apothecia flattened. Spores 35–50 µm long **2. T. petractoides**

1. Thelotrema lepadinum Thallus creamy white to grey, thin, or thick and ridged. Apothecia to 2 mm diam, in warts with a large central opening, mature fruits shaped like a ring doughnut. The thin proper margin visible inside the thalline margin, giving the apothecium the appearance of a barnacle. Spores colourless, elongate, fusiform, 10- to 18-septate with a few transverse septa, usually 2–4 per ascus, 60–140 x 12–28 µm.
Habitat: Common in sheltered situations, mainly on smooth areas of bark on deciduous trees, more rarely on acid rocks.

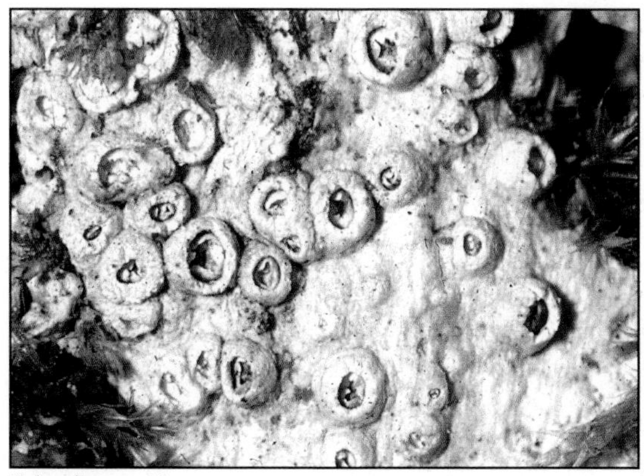

T. lepadinum x 10.

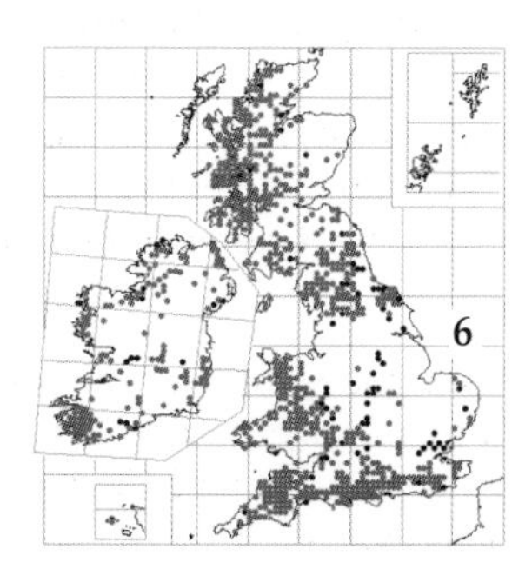

2. T. petractoides (T. subtile) Thallus cream to pale tan. Apothecia much less prominent than in the previous species, almost level with the thallus surface, with a striate, inner proper margin and a pruinose disc. Spores colourless, 8- to 12- septate, not becoming muriform, usually 8 per ascus, 35–50 x 8–10 µm. Habitat: Frequent in the NorthWest in damp shaded woods. On smooth bark, especially hazel.

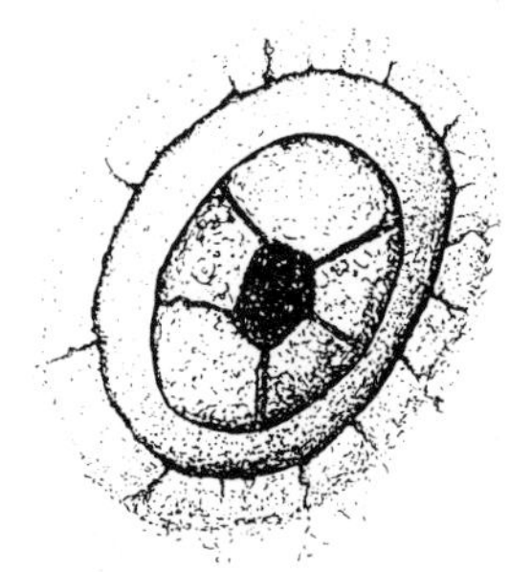

Apothecium of *T. petractoides*x 25.

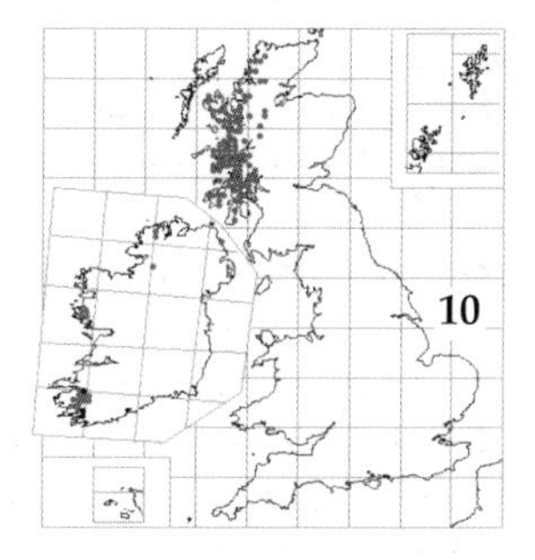

TOMASELLIA (after the 18th century botanist Abbate G. Tomaselli). **Thallus** crustose, thin or endophloeodal. **Photobiont** Probably not lichenized. **Apothecia** flask-shaped and grouped together in a cushion-like stroma, only separated from each other by thin walls. **Ascus** 8-spored, K/I–. **Spores** colourless becoming brown, up to 3-septate, clavate and constricted at the septa. **Chemical reactions** all negative. *Mycoporum* has a similar stroma but submuriform spores.

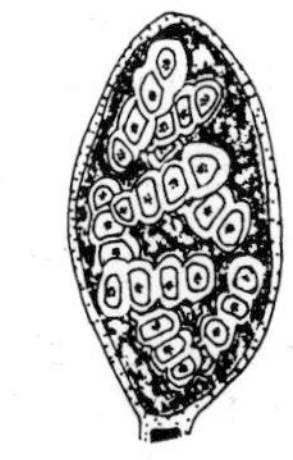

T. gelatinosa x 400.

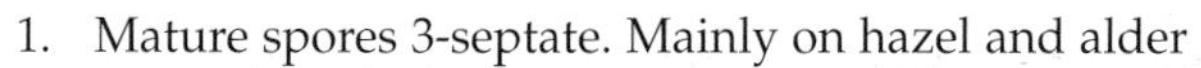

1. Mature spores 3-septate. Mainly on hazel and alder **1. T. gelatinosa**

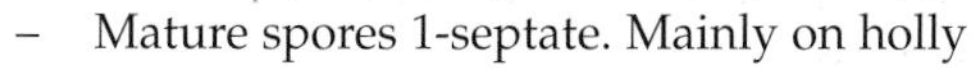

– Mature spores 1-septate. Mainly on holly **2. T. lactea**

1. Tomasellia gelatinosa Thallus buff-grey or not apparent. Perithecia grouped together in a rather flat, black, compound fruit, up to 2 mm diam. Up to 12 ostioles are visibleon the top of each fruit (use hand-lens). Spores colourless to pale brown, 3-septate when mature, 20–25 x 5–7 µm.
Habitat: Rather common on smooth-barked trees (almost always hazel, rarely alder), especially in the West. (Microscopic examination is essential to separate this species from similar-looking fungi.)

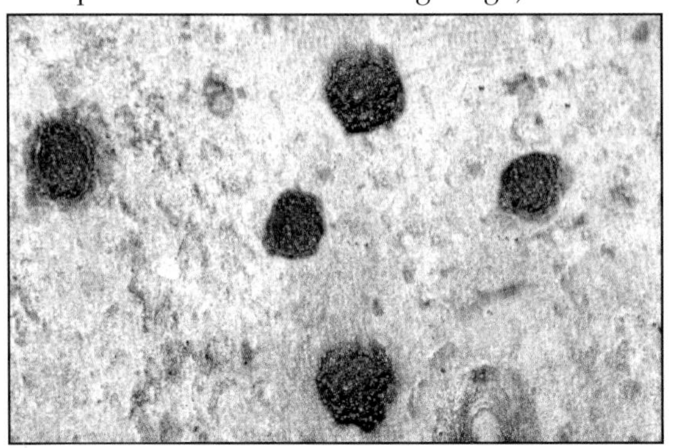

T. gelatinosa x 15.

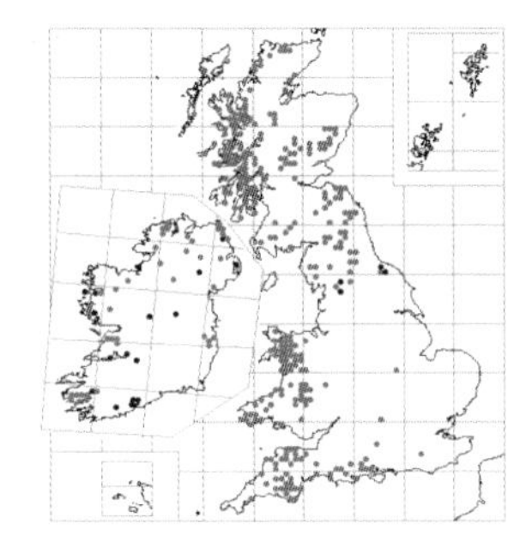

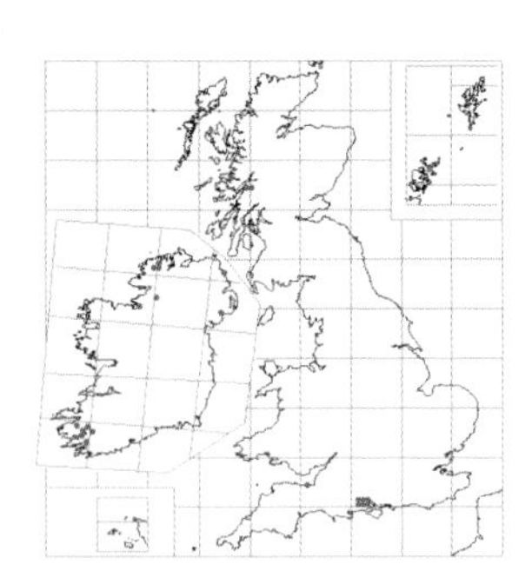

2. T. lactea Thallus forming white patches. Perithecia in the stroma sometimes die in the centre forming a ring with a pale centre. Spores 1-septate, colourless (a few over-mature spores may darken and become 3-septate), 18–25 x 5–8 µm.
Habitat: Rare, low down on the trunks of holly.

TONINIA (after Carlo Toninia, friend of A. Massalongo) **Thallus** areolate or squamulose (usually with deep-rooting hyphae). **Photobiont** trebouxioid in the species described. **Apothecia** lecideine, black, large, flat to globose. **Hymenium** K/I+ blue. **Ascus** 8-spored, K/I+ blue outer coat, tholus and darker central tube. **Spores** colourless, 1- to 3-septate. Many species are associated with cyanobacteria, especially when young.

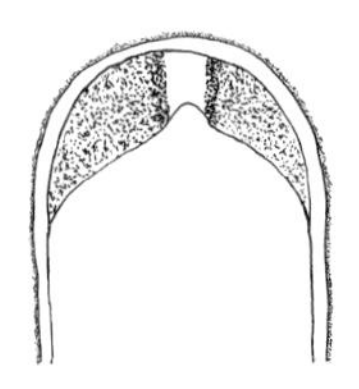

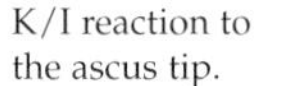

K/I reaction to the ascus tip.

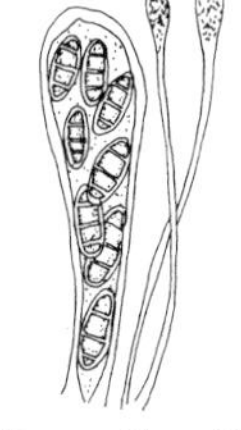

T. aromatica x 450.

1. On maritime rocks. Areolate — **2. T. mesoidea**
– On calcareous soils, rocks and mortar. Squamulose — 2
2. Squamules warted and contorted, not pruinose. Spores 3-septate — **1. T. aromatica**
– Squamules smooth, involute, glaucous-pruinose. Spores 1-septate — **3. T. sedifolia**

1. Toninia aromatica Thallus light to dark grey, often tinged brown or green. Squamules warted, rounded and contorted with paler spots or ridges towards the centre of the squamules. Apothecia usually numerous, black, often faintly pruinose, flat to slightly convex, up to 2 mm across, often angular in shape from compression, proper margin persistent. Epithecium green, K–. Spores 3-septate, 14–20 x 4–6 µm.
Habitat: Common on soft calcareous rocks and mortar. Often in seepage cracks and on consolidated soil.

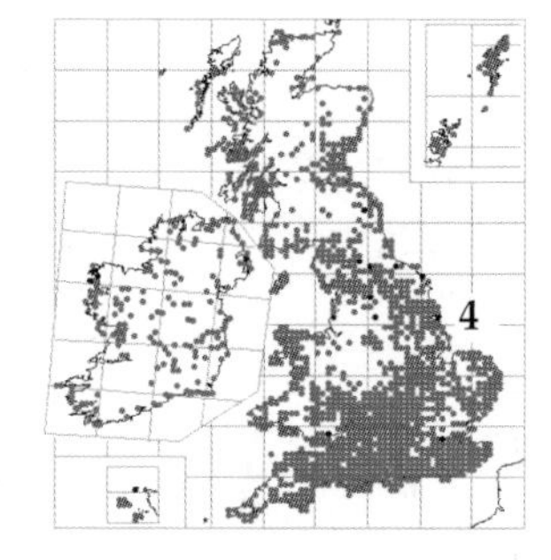

T. aromatica x 4.

2. T. mesoidea Thallus crustose, never squamulose, olive-brown to dark grey. No pale spots on the areoles. Apothecia up to 1 mm diam, black, flat becoming convex. Proper margin becoming excluded. Epithecium K–. Spores 3-septate, 14–20 x 4–6 µm.
Habitat: Infrequent, in crevices on ± basic coastal rocks in the West. It is common on serpentine but does not occur on pure limestone.

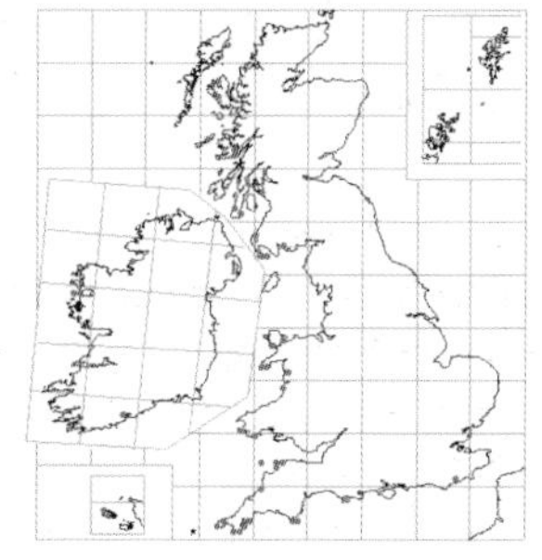

3. T. sedifolia (T. caeruleonigricans) Thallus pale grey to brown-grey, very white- to glaucous-pruinose. Squamules to 3 mm diam, smooth, convex and rounded, no pale spots, under-surface pale. Apothecia black, flat to slightly convex, up to 3 mm diam, often angular in outline. The young apothecia are pruinose with a thick black margin. Epithecium greyish, K+ violet. Spores 1-septate, but oil globules can give a multi-septate appearance, 15–28 x 2–4 µm.
Habitat: Locally abundant on calcareous soils, crevices in limestone and basic sand dunes.

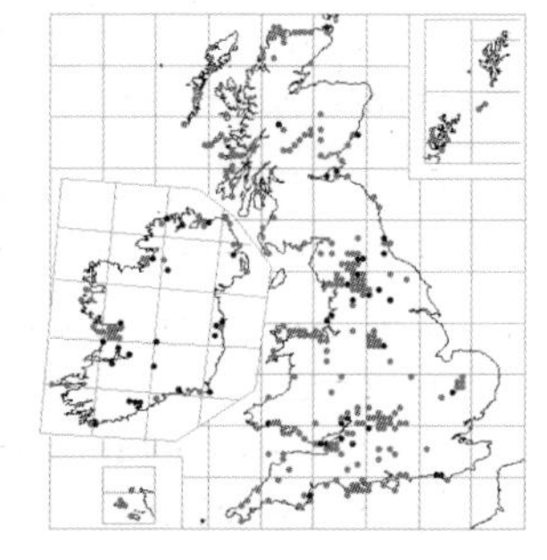

T. sedifolia x 5.

TRAPELIA ('angular table' – from the angular shape of the apothecia when compressed together). **Thallus** crustose or subsquamulose. **Photobiont** chlorococcoid. **Apothecia** lecideine. **Ascus** 8-spored, K/I+ pale blue throughout or K–. **Spores** simple, colourless. It is very closely related to *Trapeliopsis,* indeed some authors unite them; the following key includes both genera.

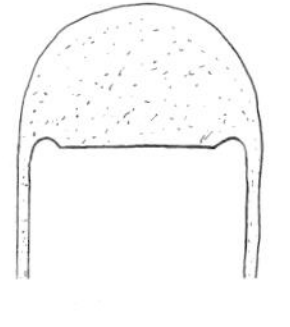
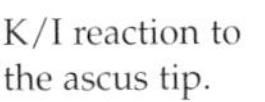
K/I reaction to the ascus tip.

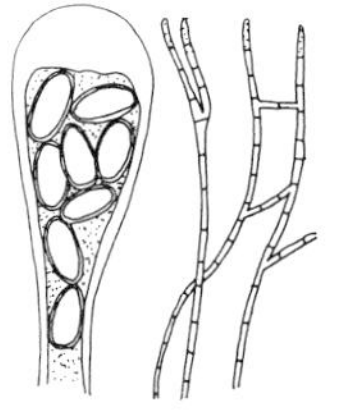
T. coarctata x 300.

T = *Trapelia*; **Ts** = *Trapeliopsis*

1.	Sorediate	2
–	Not sorediate	7
2.	Soredia buff to mottled orange	3
–	Soredia white, yellow or greenish	4
3.	Soredia buff, dot-like. On deciduous trees in high rainfall areas	**2. T. corticola**
–	Soredia with orange patches. On soil or plant debris	**3. Ts. pseudogranulosa**
4.	Thallus bluish green to grey with green soredia	**1. Ts. flexuosa**
–	Thallus colour various. Soredia cream to yellow or yellow-green	5
5.	Thallus subsquamulose. With punctiform soralia	**4. T. placodioides**
–	Thallus not subsquamulose. With globose soralia	6
6.	Soredia uniformly pale yellow-green. Often fertile	**2. Ts. granulosa**
–	Soredia yellow-green with orange patches. Sterile	**3. Ts. pseudogranulosa**
7.	Squamules with coarse knobbly isidia. On coastal soils	**4. Ts. wallrothii**
–	Squamules without isidia. On acid rocks and walls	8
8.	Thallus subsquamulose. Not usually fertile	**3. T. involuta**
–	Thallus crustose, areolate. Often fertile with red-brown disc	**1. T. coarctata**

1. Trapelia coarctata Thallus variable, thin, or thick and cracked, never with subsquamulose margins, white, grey or sometimes, especially on exposed rocks, distinctly pink, sometimes with a white prothallus. Apothecia up to 0.8 mm diam, disc dark red-brown (brighter red-brown or pinkish when wet), often with a white halo where it has erupted through the thallus. Spores 15–25 x 7–15 µm. C+ red.

Habitat: Very common, on well-lit, siliceous rocks, pebbles, and often on brick walls.

T. coarctata x 3.

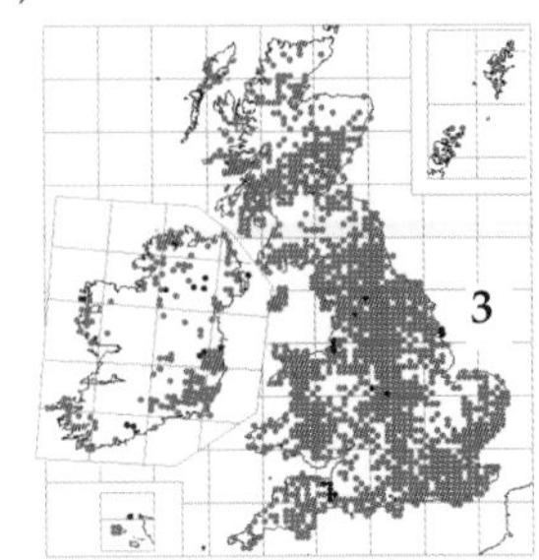

2. T. corticola Thallus dark greenish brown, inconspicuous, consisting of scattered granules, to 0.2 mm diam. The most conspicuous feature is the dot-like, buff-coloured, fluffy balls of fine soredia scattered over the surface, rarely becoming confluent. Apothecia very rare, about 0.2 mm diam, with a brown disc.
Soralia C+ red.
Habitat: Uncommon, on deciduous trees by water in high rainfall areas.

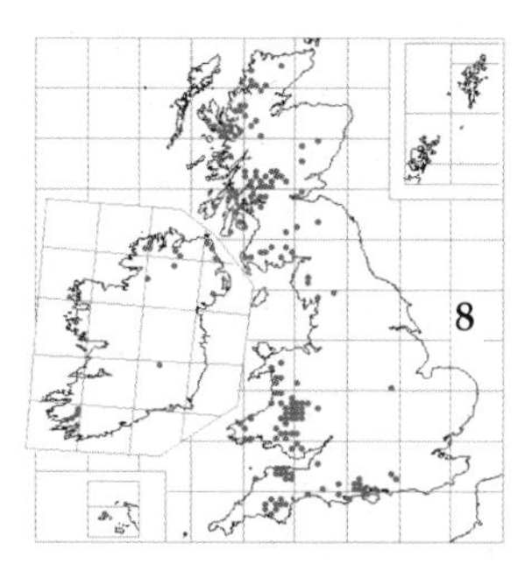

3. T. involuta is similar *T. coarctata* but consisting of scattered, glossy, squamule-like areoles that may grow together to form a continuous, uneven overlapping crust. Margin of thallus subsquamulose. Often infertile. Apothecia as in *T. coarctata*.
C+ red.
Habitat: As *T. coarctata*, also on fibrous soil, especially common near the coast.

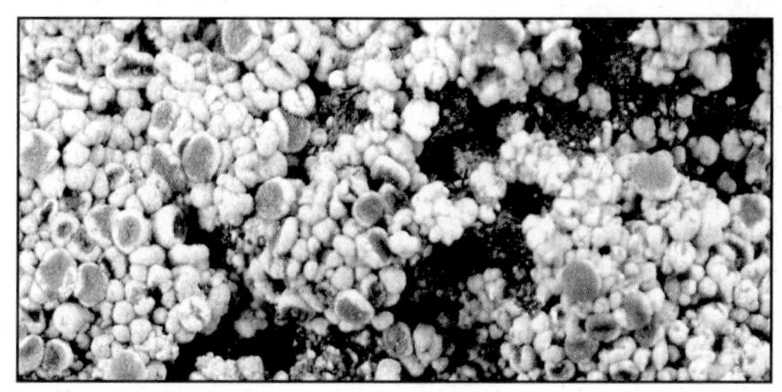

T. involuta x 5.

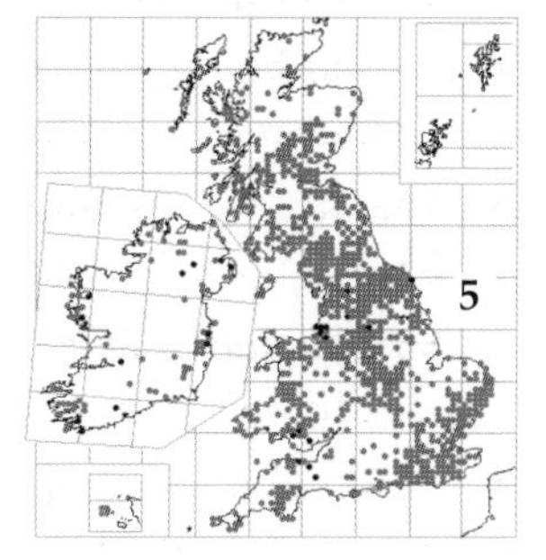

4. T. placodioides Thallus creamy white to pinkish white, often continuous, forming patches, cracked in the centre and almost placodioid at the margin. Yellow-green to cream soralia erupt from the edges of the areoles, these may coalesce to form lines of soredia. Apothecia similar to *T. coarctata* are very rare.
Thallus and soredia: C+ red.
Habitat: Common on acid rocks and walls, especially on metal-rich rocks, in the North and in upland areas.

T. placodioides x 5.

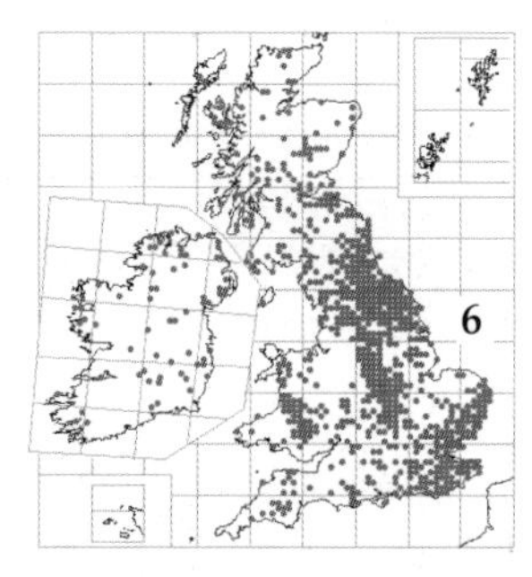

TRAPELIOPSIS ('resembles *Trapelia*'). The genus is very closely related to *Trapelia* and the two genera should possibly be recombined. It often has larger apothecia and usually, smaller spores. The following species are included in the '*Trapelia*' key (page 382).

1. Trapeliopsis flexuosa Thallus bluish green to pale or bluish grey, rather granular. Bluish green soredia may become confluent, covering the surface of the thallus. Apothecia rather rare, up to 0.7 mm diam, with green-black discs (paler in shade). Spores 7–10 x 3–4 µm.
C+ red.
Habitat: Common, on old fences, tree stumps, etc., sometimes on bark in polluted areas. It occurs rarely on sandstone.

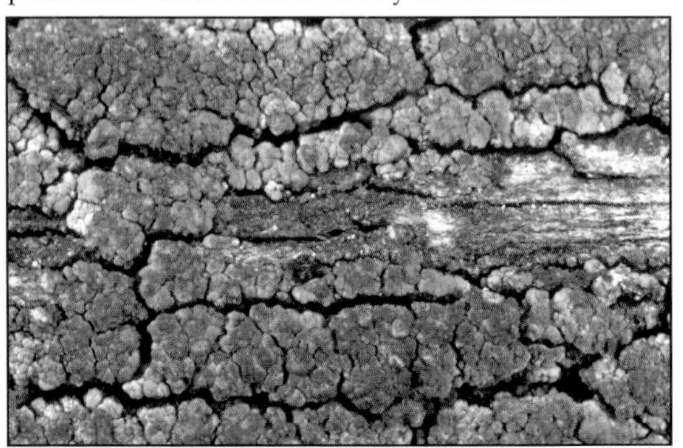

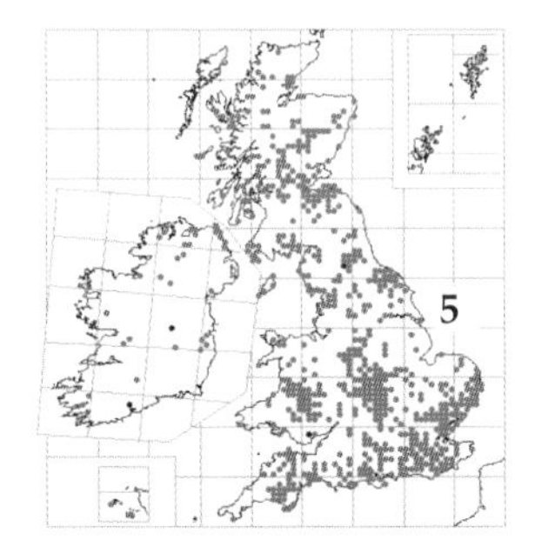

T. flexuosa x 6.

2. T. granulosa Thallus very pale grey to greenish grey, sometimes with pinkish areas, usually granular but may be areolate and warted. Large soralia (up to 0.5 mm) containing pale yellowish soredia are usually present. Often fertile with large (up to 1.5 mm diam) convex apothecia. Disc pale pink to dark brown or greenish or piebald. Spores 9–14 x 4–6 µm. Rarely some spores 1-septate.
C+ red.

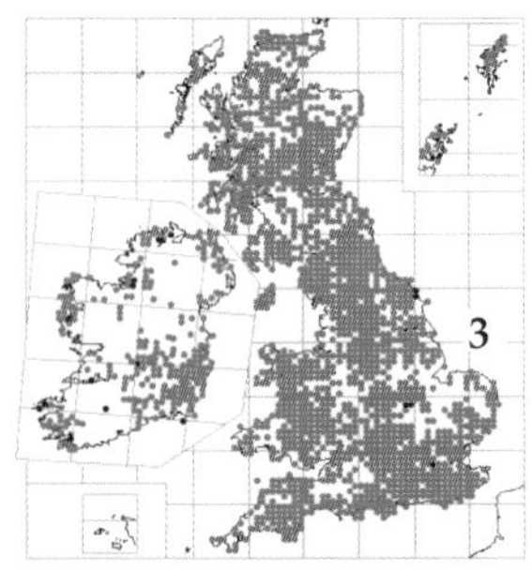

Habitat: Very common on moorland soils and decaying plants, rarely on shaded rocks. A primary, and often short-lived, colonizer of heathland soils, especially after burning. Frequently occurs in these sites with *Placynthiella* species.

3. T. pseudogranulosa Thallus greenish grey usually with bright orange patches. Granular but soon forming an extensive crust. Scattered, large soralia with pale greenish soredia, with orange patches, may eventually cover the surface. Apothecia very rare, about 1 mm diam, flat, with a greenish grey disc with a paler, flexuose margin. Spores 10–13 x 4–6 µm.
Thallus and soralia: C+ red, UV–. Orange patches: K+ purple, UV orange-red.
Habitat: Common in damp, more shaded, habitats than *T. granulosa,* such as old woods and heaths. More especially on dead and decaying plant debris, wet peat and rotting wood.

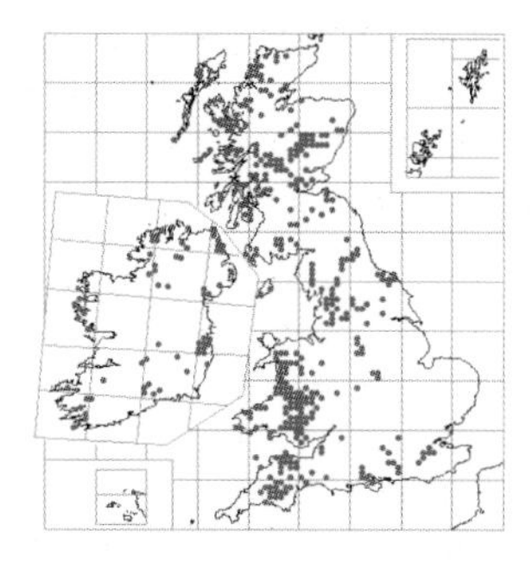

T. pseudogranulosa x 3.

4. T. wallrothii Thallus white or pale grey, sometimes pruinose, thick and warted in the centre, appearing squamulose at the margins. Large coarse, isidia-like warts are scattered over the surface, become detached leaving distinctive circular scars. Apothecia often crowded, up to 2 mm diam. Disc pinkish brown, slightly pruinose with a paler, flexuose margin. Spores 8–14 x 4–5 µm.
C+ red.
Habitat: Local on sheltered soil under rocks and on walls, in ± base-rich coastal sites.

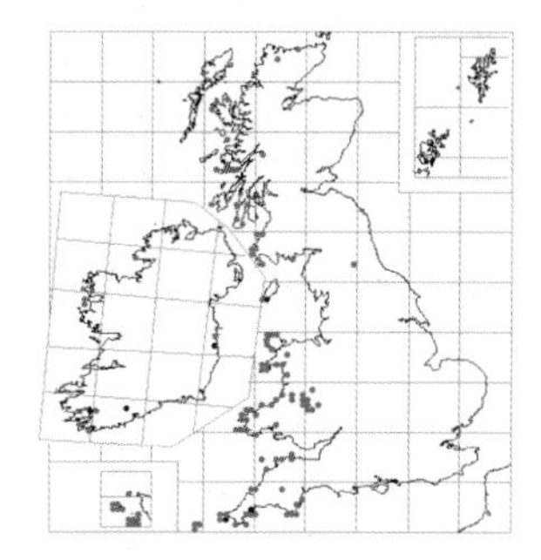

T. wallrothii x 4.

TREMOLECIA ('little discs with a hole' – the significance is unclear). **Thallus** crustose. **Photobiont** trebouxioid. **Apothecia** lecideine, immersed. **Ascus** 8-spored, *Tremolecia*-type, tholus K/I+ pale blue or K/I– . **Spores** simple, colourless. **Chemical reactions** all negative. There is only one species known in this genus.

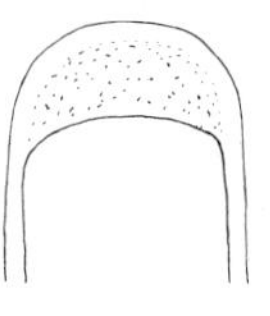

K/I reaction to the ascus tip.

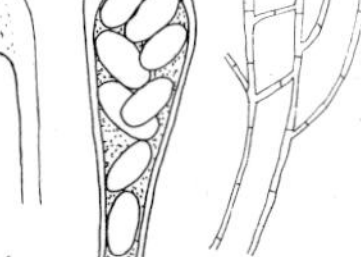

T. atrata x 300.

Tremolecia atrata Thallus cracked-areolate, bright rust colour, almost black in very well-lit situations. Limited by a black prothallus. Apothecia immersed, about 0.5 mm diam, black, smooth and slightly concave. Spores 10–16 x 5–9 µm.
Habitat: Common in upland areas on hard, metal-rich rocks. It can be confused with *Rhizocarpon oederi* with which it frequently grows. That species, however, has knot-loke, gyrose apothecia and septate to muriform spores.

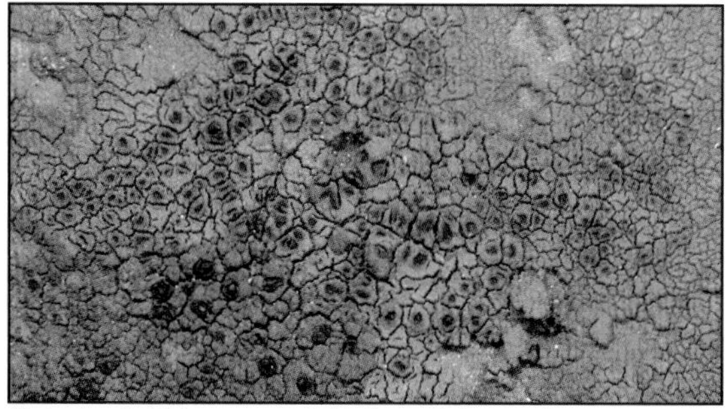

T. atrata x 4 (*Rhizocarpon oederi* in lower left corner).

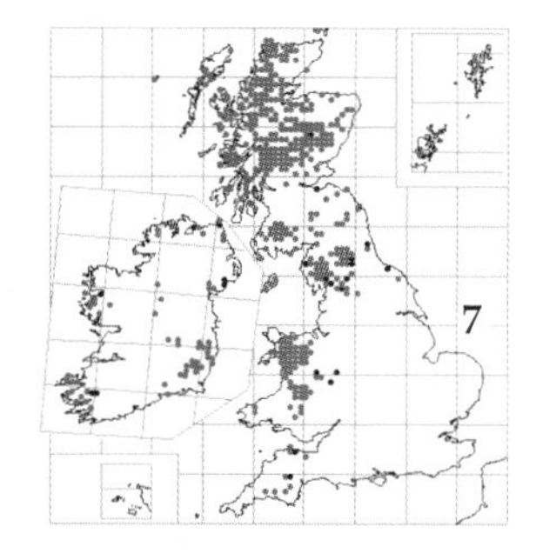

UMBILICARIA ('with a navel'). **Thallus** foliose, attached only at a central point (umbilicate). **Photobiont** trebouxioid. **Apothecia** lecideine, disc often gyrose. **Ascus** 8-spored, K/I+ blue apical dome. **Spores** colourless or brown, simple (muriform in some species not in this book). Members of this genus have been used as a survival food in the Arctic ('rock tripe'). One species, *U. esculenta*, is eaten as a delicacy in Korea and Japan. The British species are brittle when dry, becoming pliable and greenish or brownish when wet. *Lasallia* differs in its 2-spored ascus and pustulate surface.

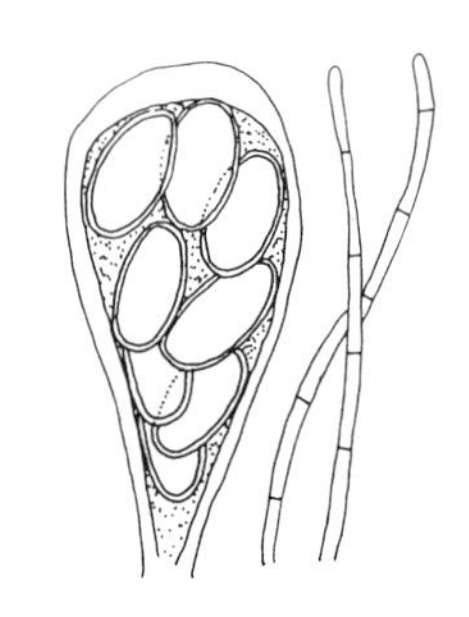

U. torrefacta x 700.

1. Thallus pruinose, brown and pustulate or grey, often with stiff marginal fibrils or with reticulate ridges in the centre — 2
– Thallus mid- to dark brown, not pruinose, not pustulate or with marginal fibrils — 4
2. Thallus with reticulate ridges at the centre — **4. U. proboscidea**
– Thallus pustulate or with marginal fibrils — 3
3. Thallus brown, coarsely pustulate Medulla C+ red — **Lasallia pustulata**
– Thallus pale grey with few to many stiff, dark fibrils on the lobe margins. Medulla C– — **1. U. cylindrica**
4. Thallus becoming tessellated, margins perforated — **5. U. torrefacta**
– Thallus smooth, margins entire or lobulate — 5
5. Lobes dark brown, distorted and appearing multi-lobed, thin and papery, under-surface lacks rhizines — **2. U. polyphylla**
– Lobes copper-brown, robust and rounded, under-surface with a dense, felt-like mass of black rhizines — **3. U. polyrrhiza**

1. Umbilicaria cylindrica Thallus pale to dark grey, often brownish, pruinose, up to 4 cm wide. The lobe margins wavy, curling upwards, usually fringed with stiff dark fibrils, to 5 mm long. Lower surface buff or pale grey, darker towards the centre, with few to many rhizines and often trabeculate. Frequently fertile with gyrose, black, superficial apothecia. Spores colourless, simple, 10–14 x 6–8 µm.
Medulla: K+ red or –, C–, P+ orange or P–, UV–.
Habitat: Locally abundant on well-lit, coarse-grained, acid rocks, mainly in upland regions.

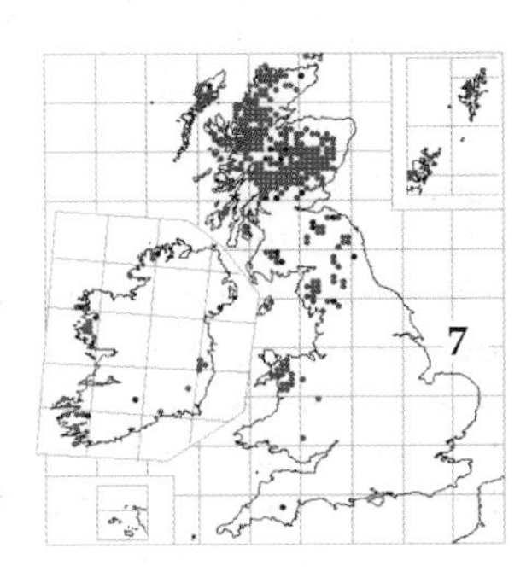

U. cylindrica x 2.

2. U. polyphylla Thallus dark brown to almost black, smooth, slightly shiny, not pruinose, ascending, much contorted so as to appear multi-lobed, brittle and thin, difficult to remove intact from the substrate. Under-surface black, more or less smooth. It differs from *U. polyrrhiza* in the often more divided lobes and complete lack of rhizines. Apothecia extremely rare. Spores simple, colourless, 13–18 x 7–8 µm.
Medulla: C+ red.
Habitat: Not uncommon, on hard smooth siliceous rocks in upland areas, frequently in nutrient-enriched rain-tracks. Often with *U. polyrrhiza*.

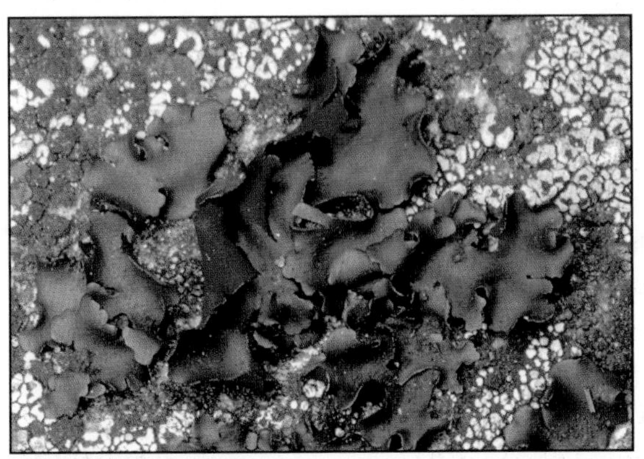

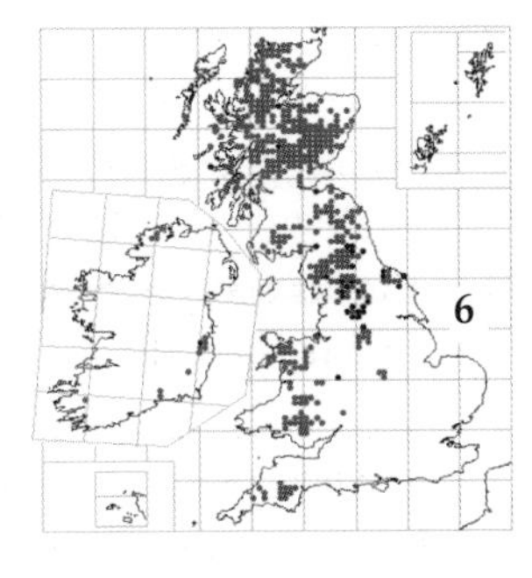

U. polyphylla x 3.

3. U. polyrrhiza Thallus deep copper to dark brown, smooth, often shiny and lacking pruina, the lobes often becoming much distorted and imbricate, the edges turning down and breaking up into small lobules and rhizines which may also grow from cracks in the surface. Under-surface black and rather granular with black forked rhizines forming a dense felt-like mass that protrudes beyond the edges of the lobes. Apothecia very rare, black, superficial, not gyrose but with radiating ridges and no margin. Spores colourless, simple, 8–11 x 4–5 µm.
Medulla: C+ red.
Habitat: Common, in upland regions on more or less nutrient-enriched, hard, siliceous rocks and exposed boulders.

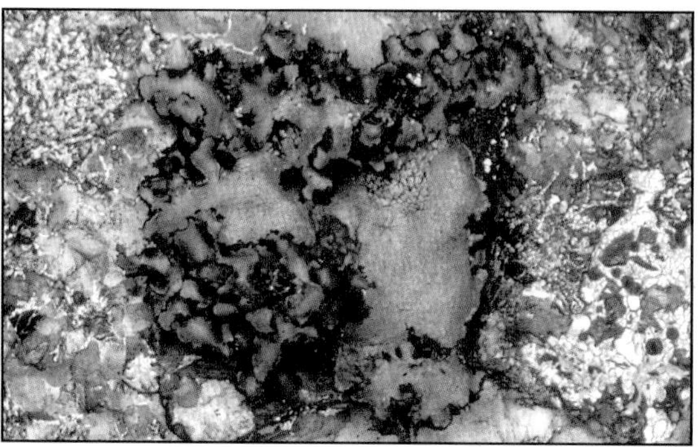

U. polyrrhiza x 3.

4. U. proboscidea Thallus very dark brown, sometimes dark grey, single-lobed, up to 5 cm wide and wrinkled. These wrinkles become stronger towards the raised centre where they form a pronounced, sharp-edged network. Centre usually more or less pruinose. Lower surface light to dark brown with only a few rhizines. Frequently fertile, discs black, gyrose. Spores colourless, simple, 12–18 x 6–8 µm.
Medulla: C+ red, P+ yellow or P–.
Habitat: Frequent in the Scottish Highlands but rarer further south. Occurs on well-lit, coarse-grained siliceous rocks and boulders.

5. U. torrefacta Thallus single-lobed, dark brown, slightly shiny, the margins irregular, perforated, becoming lace-like. In well-developed specimens the surface becomes tessellated, almost appearing to be covered in flat lobules. Lower surface lighter brown with few to many coarse rhizines and radiating, perforated trabecula. Apothecia frequent, black and gyrose. Spores colourless, simple, 8–12 x 4–7 µm.

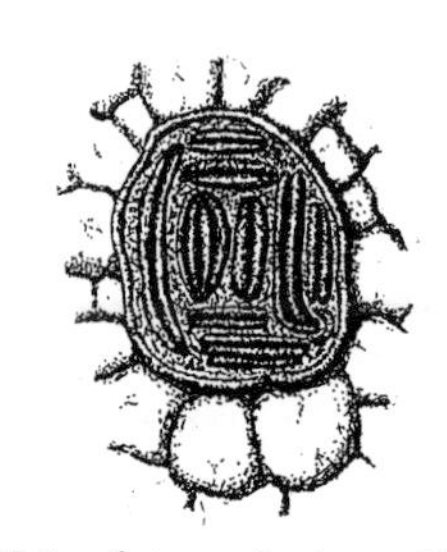

U. torrefacta apothecium x 20.

Medulla: K+ yellow, C+ red, P+ orange or P–.
Habitat: Locally abundant on ± nutrient-enriched, hard siliceous rocks in mainly upland regions.

U. torrefacta x 3.

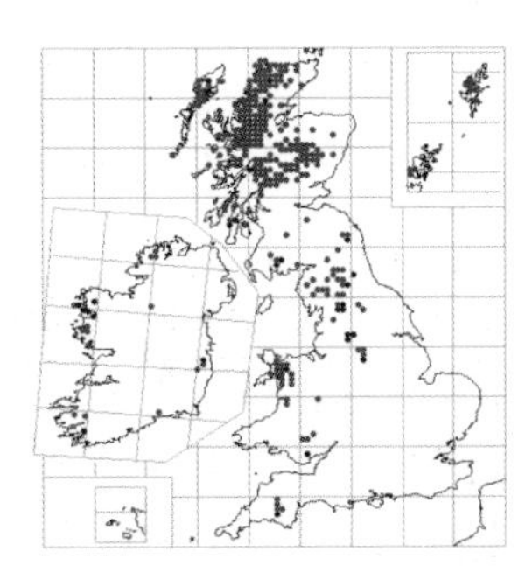

USNEA ('rope-like' – or from the Arabic for moss). **Thallus** fruticose, much branched, bushy, erect, pendent or trailing, often with a distinct holdfast, terete with a tough central core (this is usually visible if the cortex is broken or the thallus stretched; *this core is an important distinguishing characteristic of the genus).* **Photobiont** trebouxioid. **Apothecia** lecanorine, sub-terminal or terminal. **Ascus** 8-spored, *Lecanora*-type. **Spores** colourless, simple. The genus has had many uses in the past including the hair powder 'cyprus powder' for uterine complaints, to arrest haemorrhaging, and even as a source of glucose. Many of the species are morphologically variable and can be difficult to identify. The medullary tests are useful in separating some species, but in many cases thin layer chromotography is needed to be certain.

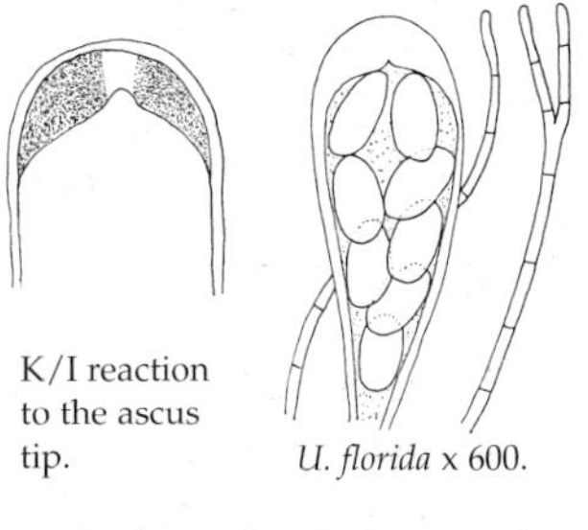

K/I reaction to the ascus tip. *U. florida* x 600.

Useful features to look for in identifying *Usnea*:

1. The colour of the basal region and absence or extent of blackening at the holdfast.
2. When looking for isidia first examine the younger branches as the isidia on the mature branches frequently break or fall off, often leaving ± sorediate areas.
3. Make a tranverse section of the main branches to ascertain whether the medulla is broad and cottony or narrow and compact.
4. Are the main branches narrowed at the point of branching from the main stem (Fig. 1, p. 390)?
5. Are there pale annular rings present on the main stems (Fig. 7)?
6. What is its growth habit; pendulous, sub-pendulous or erect?
7. Is the surface of the main stem smooth, rough or warted?

8. All specimens should be chemically tested. To check the medulla, make an oblique section through a main branch to expose a reasonable area of the medulla, then apply test under a hand-lens.

Note: (use a hand-lens to observe the following finer details). Sorediate areas in some common species such as *U. cornuta, U. flammea, U. rubicunda* and *U. subfloridana* (Fig. 2), are derived from initial, brittle isidia on the younger or smaller branches. These isidia often break off and are then replaced by a further succession of fragile, isidiate outgrowths on the older parts of the thallus. Where isidia are absent these areas often appear to be entirely sorediate.
In truly sorediate species, such as *U. esperantiana, U. fragilescens* and *U. glabrescens* and ± excavate soralia develop ***without any trace of isidia*** (Fig. 4). These soralia are often appear as ulcer-like depressions on the branches.
In truly isidiate species (e.g. *U. hirta, U. filipendula*) there is no secondary development of soredia.
Some species, such as *U. florida,* have neither soredia or isidia but develop fibril-like spines and papillate warts (Fig. 3).

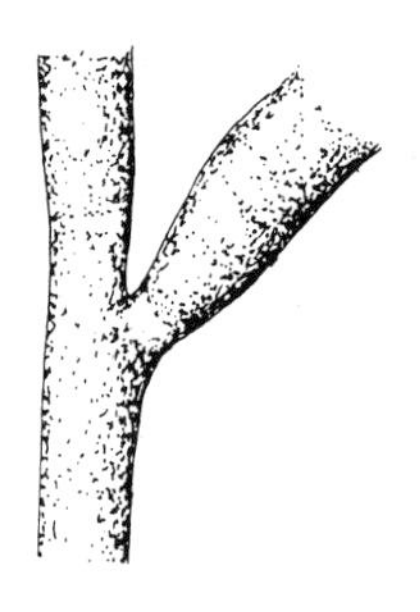

Fig. 1 Side branch constricted at junction with main branch: *U. cornuta, U. fragilescens*

Fig. 2 Soredia and isidia: *U. cornuta, U. flammea U. rubicunda U. subfloridana*

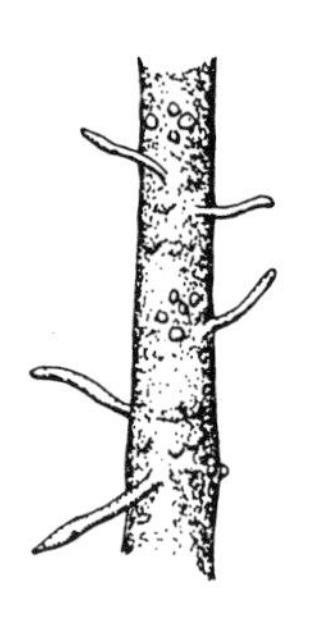

Fig. 3 Spines and warts: *U. florida*

Fig. 4 Soredia at tips: *U. esperantiana*

Fig. 5 Constrictions at the joints expose the central core *U. articulata*

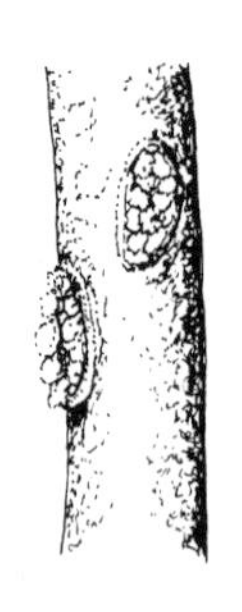

Fig. 6 Ulcerate soralia as in the *U. glabrescens* group and *U. esperantiana*

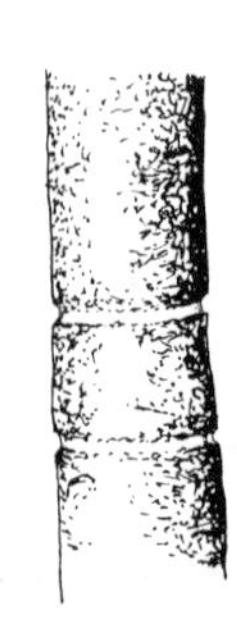

Fig. 7 Pale annular rings as found in *U. flammea*

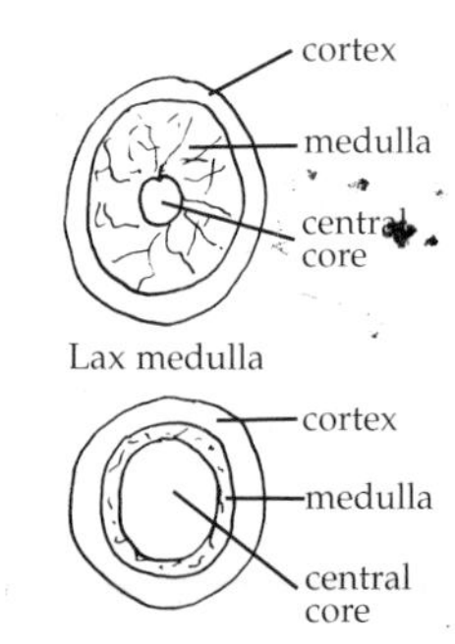

Fig. 8 Lax and compact medullas

1. Thallus long , inflated with tight constrictions (like a string of sausages) usually unattached. Soralia absent. Medulla P+ red, K– **1. U. articulata**
– Thallus not strongly inflated or sausage-shaped, having a persistent base, firmly attached. Reactions various 2

2. Thallus yellow-green to grey-green 3
– Thallus part or all reddish or brownish. Medulla K+o, P+o **11. U. rubicunda**

3. Central core pink. Medulla C+ deep yellow **2. U. ceratina**
– Central core white. Medulla C– 4

4. Sorediate and/or isidiate. Usually without apothecia 5
– Not sorediate or isidiate but with small pointed branchlets usually in fruit with fringed margins. Medulla K+o, P+o (mainly on branches and in the tree canopy) **7. U. florida**

5. With both soredia and isidia 6
– With either soralia or isidia, not both 9

6. Medulla more or less lax, constricted at junction of branches (Fig. 1) 7
– Medulla not lax, not constricted at junctions of main branches 8

7. Thallus soft and flexible even when dry, yellowish green, pendent. Holdfast blackened and shiny (mainly on trees) **8. U. fragilescens**
– Thallus firm, grey-green to olive. Fine isidia breaking down to soredia. Holdfast usually pale (common on tree branches) **3. U. cornuta**

8. Concave patches of soralia and isidia, bushy bottle-brush appearance, holdfast blackened (common on trees) **12. U. subfloridana**
– Soralia and isidia on warts, soft feel with even 'mown' appearance at top of thallus, holdfast pale (common on rocks) **6. U. flammea**

9. Sorediate 10
– Isidiate 11

10a Soralia scattered, some branches extended, hanging, flexuose **9. U. glabrescens**
b. Soralia abundant, granular soredia in eroded pits on branch tips. Apical branches recurved, twisted, skeletal-like **4. U. esperantiana**
c. Soralia flat, dot-like, widely spaced. Thallus soft and flexible even when dry, yellowish green, pendent, branchlets constricted at junctions. Holdfast blackened and shiny **8. U. fragilescens**

11. Cortex and/or medulla K+ yellow to red 12
– Medulla K– 13

12. Thallus long and pendent, consisting of a few long interwoven main branches with short secondary branches near holdfast. Main branches often densely isidiate, rigid when wet **5. U. filipendula**
– Thallus bushy, more or less erect, with scattered isidia **3. U. cornuta**

13. Main branches smooth, ± ridged, long isidia, often yellowish green. Patches of long isidia. Flaccid when wet. Central axis white **10. U. hirta**
– Main branches with coares white tubercules. Dull grey-green. Isidia short and scattered (or absent), stiff even when wet. Central axis pale pink **2. U. ceratina**

1. Usnea articulata Thallus grey-green (yellow-green to brownish yellow when dry in an herbarium), often without a distinct attachment, draped over the substratum. Up to l metre or more in length. Main branches up to 3 mm or more in diameter, generally smooth but sometimes fluted and with delicate spinulose branchlets. The older branches have scattered, comma-like pseudocyphellae. The branches are sharply constricted down to the central core, to give the appearance of an uneven string of sausages (Fig. 5). Cortex is very thin, medulla wide, lax and cottony. Not known fertile in Britain. When very young it resembles *U. flammea*, but in that species the medulla is K+ orange.
Medulla: Pd+ red, K–, KC–. (There are other chemical races which do not occur in Britain.)
Habitat: A locally common species in the extreme South and West where it festoons well-lit hedges, tree canopies and, more rarely, dunes (including north-east Norfolk) and rocks. It is probably mainly distributed by wind. One of the most SO_2 pollution-sensitive species known, formerly widespread in England; it even used to grow near London. It still occurs as far north as the Isle of Man.

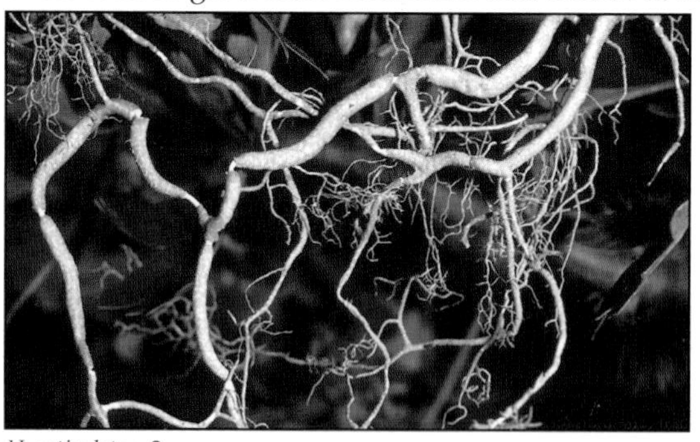

U. articulata x 2.

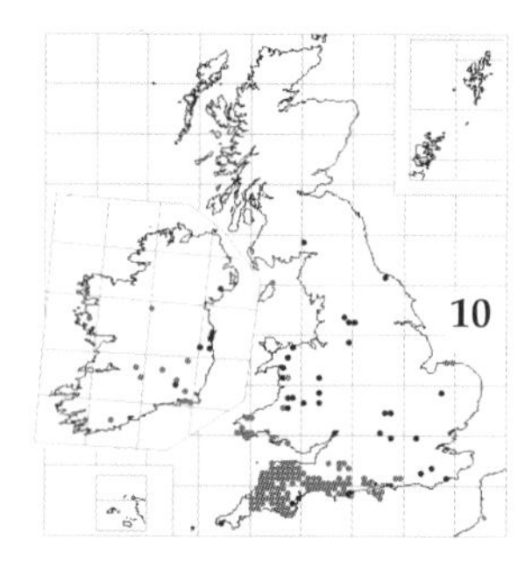

2. U. ceratina Thallus grey-green, coarsely pendent or sub-pendent, up to nearly 1 metre long. Consisting of relatively few coarse, scrawny, main branches which only taper towards the tips, often rather angular in cross-section. Not blackened at the base. Side branches sparse and mixed with scattered long fibrils, usually at right angles to the main stem. Branches not constricted where they join the main stem. Main branches often fractured with pale annular rings. Central axis usually pink (stretch plant to break the cortex; it is easier to see the pink colour on the broken end). Cortex thick, medulla compact, narrow. Branches smooth at first but usually developing small white warts, bursting with coarse granular soredia. In polluted areas it may never develop beyond a sub-pendent form that resembles *U. cornuta* which, however, has a lax medulla.

Medulla: K–, KC–, CK+ yellow-orange, P–, C+ deep yellow.
Habitat: Locally abundant, on well-lit, often old, trees, mainly on the trunks and main branches. Uncommon in the North or near the sea. It is now less widespread due to the increase in air pollution.

U. ceratina x 1.

Pale tipped warts that may develop granular soredia.

3. U. cornuta (U. inflata) Thallus dull grey- to pale olive-green often with a waxy blue tinge, coarse, more or less tufted or sub-pendent, up to 6 cm long. Very variable. Base persistent and not blackened. Main branches rather stout. Medulla lax and cottony (yields if squashed between finger-nails). Side branches markedly constricted and often fractured where they join the main branches, without pale annulations elsewhere (Fig. 1). The cortex of the main branches is smooth and somewhat shiny with small, white, punctiform dots scattered over the branches. These develop isidia and areas of granular soredia which tend to become confluent (Fig. 2).
Medulla: either K+ yellow or orange-red, P+ orange or K+ red, P+ orange to red (two chemical races).
Habitat: Common, may occur in more shaded situations than other species in the genus. On trees and, less frequently, on rocks in the South and West (where it is often the commonest *Usnea* species), extending into western Scotland, where it is not rare. Moderately pollution-resistant.

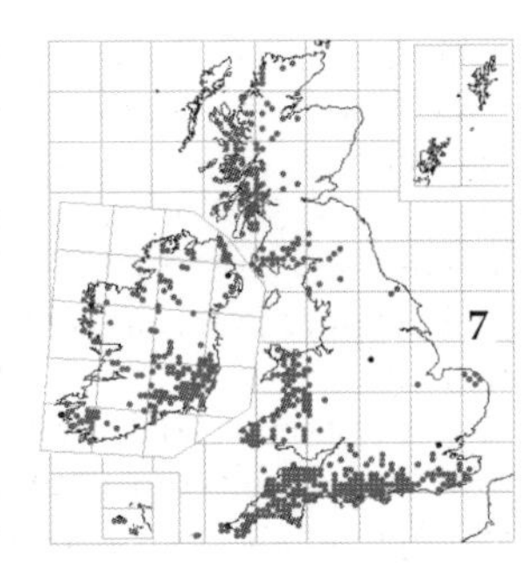

U. cornuta x 3.

4. U. esperantiana Thallus dull grey to grey-green, tufted, compact, erect, rarely sub-pendent, small (usually much less than 5 cm), surface scabrid or rough, base not blackened. Medulla lax. Branchlets numerous, not or slightly attenuated at joints, long, thin and twisted, tips characteristically and conspicuously twisted and recurved, covered with excavate soralia giving the appearance of skeletal fingers (Fig. 4). Isidia absent. Medulla ± lax. Main branches covered in warts and numerous short fibrils mixed with true soredia. Apothecia are very rare.
Medulla: K+ red, P+ red.
Habitat: A local species of the extreme South and West on deciduous trees, especially on well-lit twigs and shrubs in hedgerows in windy situations.

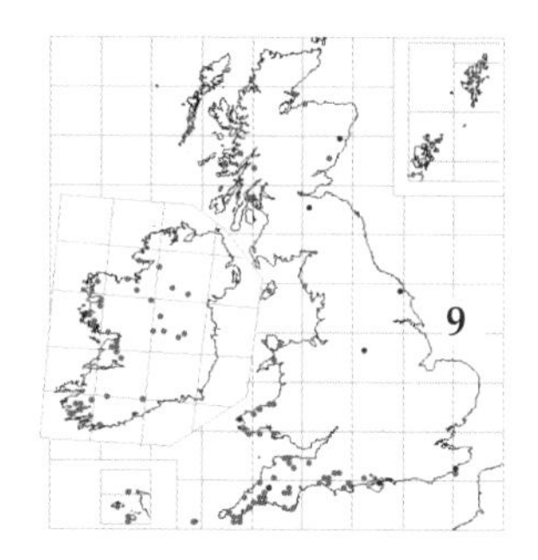

U. esperantiana x 4.

5. U. filipendula Thallus grey-green, to pale yellowish green, pendulous, up to 30 cm long, consisting of a few long, straggling, intertwined, main branches and many short branches (up to 1 cm long), diverging at right angles from the main branches, resembling a fish-bone. Above a blackened holdfast, the main branches have dense isidia in clusters on the top of coarse warts. Isidia are usually less abundant on the minor branches which may become broken into cylindrical tubes around the central core.
Medulla: K+ red, P+ orange.
Habitat: Not uncommon in upland woods (especially on conifers) in the North, more rarely, in boggy woodland sites in the South.

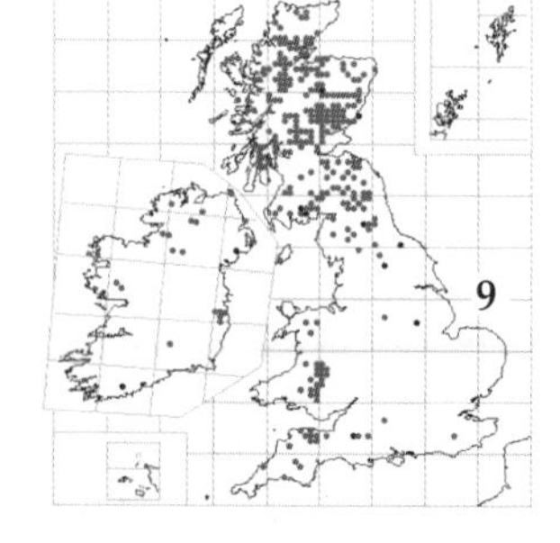

U. filipendula x 2.

6. U. flammea Thallus pale yellow-green to green, often sub-pendulous, up to 6 cm long. Soft in texture and seldom branched for about 4 mm above the short, unblackened base which usually has several pale, annular rings. Near the base the main stems are smooth or with only a few small warts. Medulla more or less lax. The main branches are slightly undulating with scattered, pale annular rings (Fig. 7), abruptly tapering towards the tips. The thin lateral branches tend mainly to grow from one side of the branch and terminate at the same height, often with a tassel of finer branches at the tip. These smaller branches have isidiate papillae which become eroded and ± sorediate.
Medulla: K+ yellow turning red, P+ orange.
Habitat: The commonest species to be found on exposed rocks and is most frequent near the coast. It also occurs on mossy trees and heather stems.

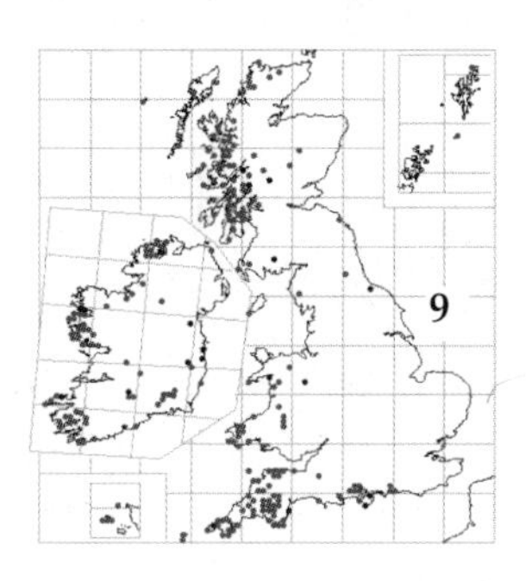

U. flammea x 3.

7. U. florida Thallus yellow- to grey-green, bushy, more or less erect, up to about 5 cm tall. The base persistent and generally blackened with horizontal cracking. The main branches coarse with minute warts and small spines, to 1 cm long. There are no soredia or isidia. Medulla narrow, with a stout central core. Both the main and, often contorted, secondary branches have many pointed branchlets, not attenuated at the junction with the main stems. It is the species most likely to be richly fertile and mature specimens are almost always found with fruits on the ends of both main and secondary branches. Apothecia frequent, large (up to 1 cm), fawn-coloured, surrounded by ray-like spinulose branchlets to 5 mm long. These large-rayed apothecia form a particularly distinctive feature, but also occur more sparingly in other species of *Usnea*. Discs concave, becoming flat and often slightly wrinkled. Spores 7–11 x 6–7 µm.
Medulla: K+ deep yellow, P+ orange-red.
Habitat: Common on tree-canopy twigs and branches but rarely on tree boles. It especially occurs in old woods. Most easily found on fallen branches and also on fence posts. Occurs mainly in the South and West, becoming rarer northwards. It is a declining species in the South.

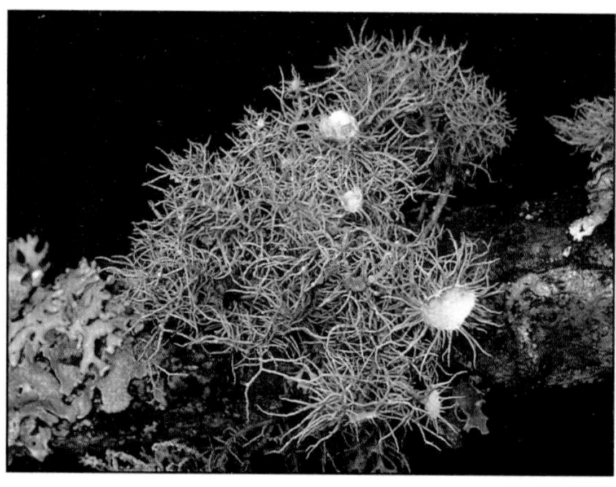

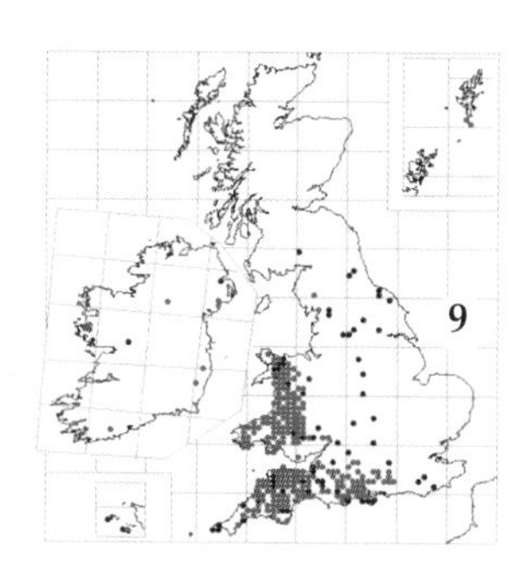

U. florida x 2.

8. U. fragilescens var. **mollis** Thallus pale yellowish green to straw-coloured, rather translucent when wet, more or less pendulous, up to about 8 cm long, soft and flexible even when dry, central core not stout. It often has a combed appearence. Base persistent, shiny and blackened. Main branches have minute punctifom warts. Branchlets constricted at the junction with the main branches due to the very lax medulla. Groups of small pointed isidia are scattered over the warted branches which become isidiate-sorediate and just sorediate towards the tips. This is the only British species with an inflated, lax medulla and a blackened base. **U. fragilescens** var. **fragilescens** is known only from a single collection from a tree in Cumberland.
Medulla: K+ orange, P+ red.
Habitat: A local species on trees (often in the canopy) in damp woodland, fence posts and rarely on rocks. Mainly occurs in the North and West of Britain, becoming more common northwards.

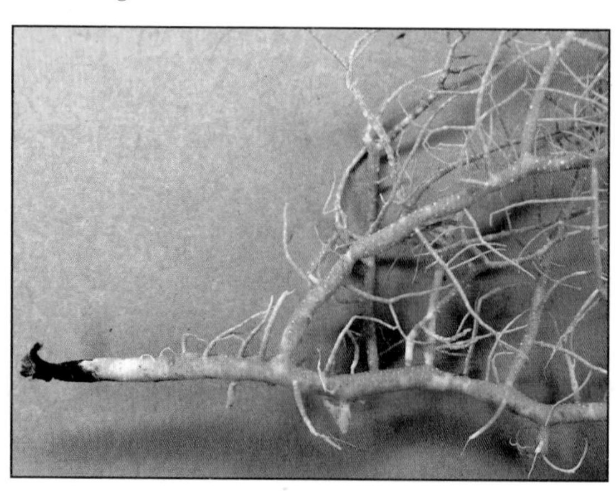

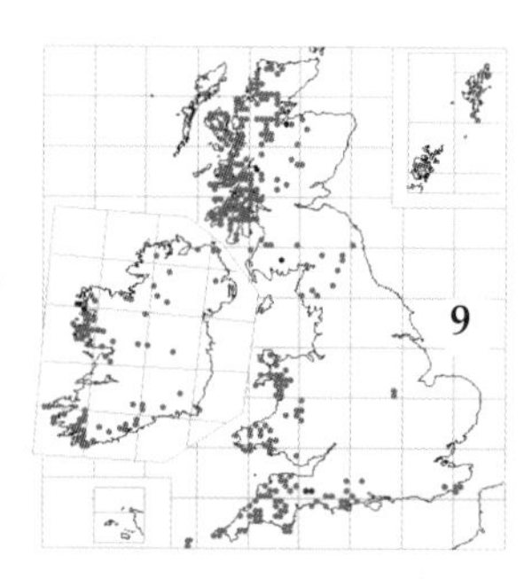

U. fragilescens x 2.

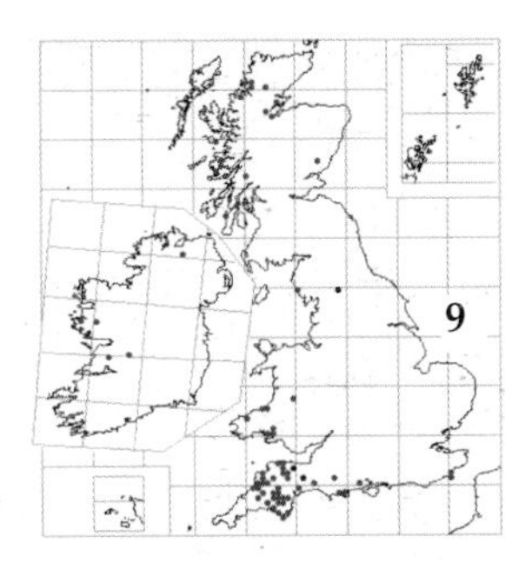

9. U. glabrescens This species resembles a robust *U. subfloridana* except for the abundance of pale ulcer-like soralia and a total lack of isidia. A few twisted main branches often extend and hang beyond the main thallus.
Medulla: K+ red or K–, P+ yellow or orange. There are three chemical races.
Habitat: Less common than *U. subfloridana*, preferring humid sites, especially boggy willow carrs. It occurs mostly on young trees.

10. U. hirta Thallus dark green-grey, often almost olive-green, bushy or slightly pendent, up to about 4 cm long with few main braches but often densely tufted. Very soft and flaccid when wet, rough when dry. Base persistent, not blackened. Main branches angular and irregular in section, ridged and very pitted, covered in long thin isidia. Soredia absent. Lateral branches constricted where they join the main stems. Medulla lax.
Medulla: K–, P–, or very rarely P+ orange, K+ red, (there are 2 chemical races).
Habitat: A locally abundant species of conifers and fences, often on exposed sites, especially in the Scottish Highlands. Prefers more acid sites than the other British species, except for *U. filipendula*. Recently recorded from Kew Gardens.

U. hirta x 3.

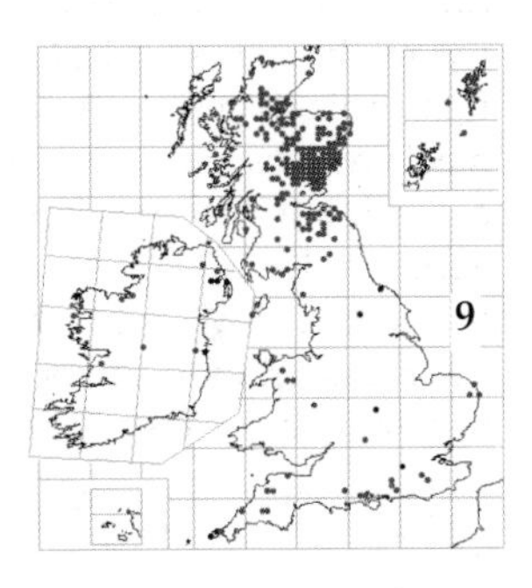

11. U. rubicunda Thallus a distinctive dull brownish or greyish red, red colour patchy in shade. Take care not to confuse the red colour found in some other species in a poor condition (e.g. *U. cornuta*) due to the decomposition of salazinic acid (the colour then includes the medulla and core). Thallus coarse, tufted to pendent, up to 20 cm long. Base persistent, not blackened. Side branches rather sparse to numerous, ± at right angles to the main stem with long attenuated tips. The stems warted, with clusters of isidia which may entirely cover the base of the main stem eroding to become sorediate. Medulla compact.
Medulla K+ orange, P+ orange.
Habitat: Common on trees in unpolluted regions, especially in the NorthWest. Rarely on mossy rocks.

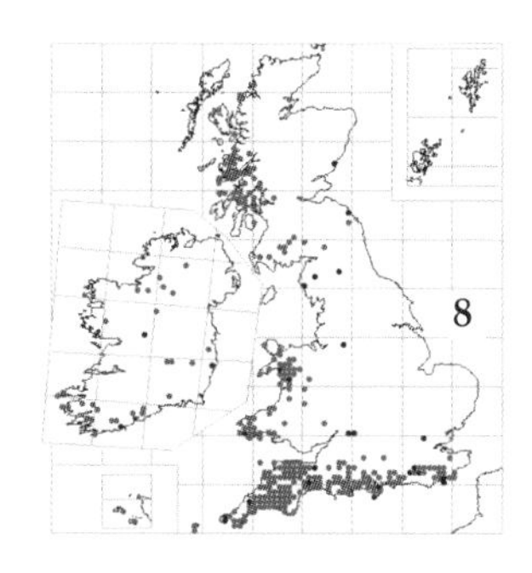

U. rubicunda x 3.

11. U. subfloridana Thallus very variable, yellow-green to grey-green, erect and bushy, sometimes sub-pendulous. Large, up to 10 cm long. Distinctly blackened near the coarse, persistent holdfast which has only transverse cracking (the similar **U. wasmuthii** has both transverse and vertical cracking). It mainly differs from *U. florida* in the rounded, concave patches of soredia and isidia (Fig. 2) and the lack of wart-like nodules. Much less frequently fertile than *U. florida* with similar but usually smaller apothecia.
Medulla: K+ yellow or orange, P+ yellow to orange-red.
Habitat: Common and widespread. On trees, fences and more rarely on rock. Mainly a twig species. If found on tree trunks, check for *U. cornuta*, less often a tree canopy species than *U. florida*. In Britain, it is the most tolerant species of the genus to air pollution. It largely disappeared from the London area and the Midlands up to 1970 but, together with *U. cornuta,* is now returning.

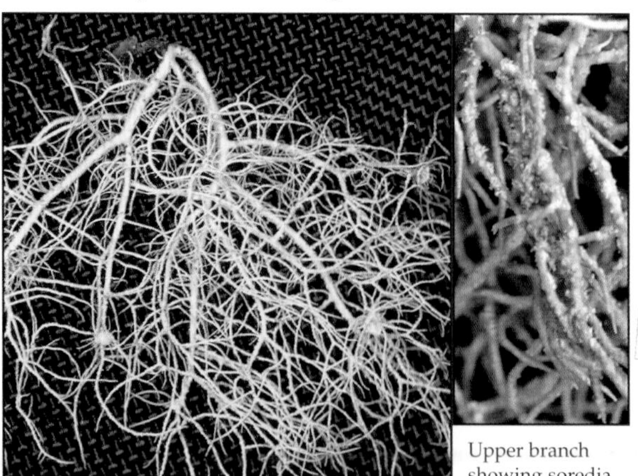

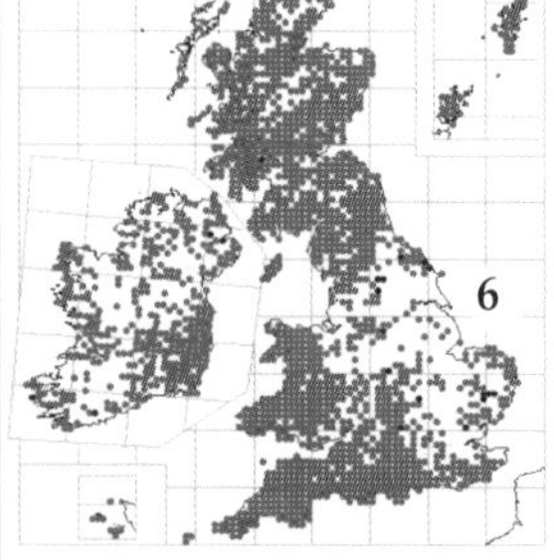

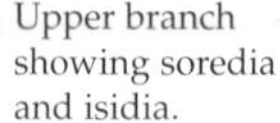
Upper branch showing soredia and isidia.

U. subfloridana x 3 (fertile).

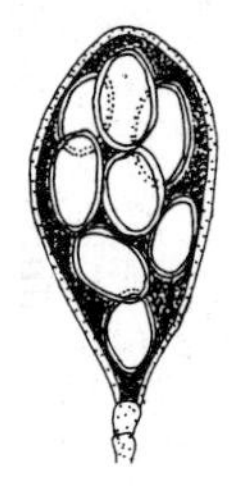
V. maura x 500.

VERRUCARIA ('wart-like'). **Thallus** crustose. **Photobiont** various. **Perithecia** either immersed or prominent, single or sometimes grouped together. **Paraphyses** and associated filaments absent at maturity. **Ascus** 8-spored, double-walled. **Spores** colourless, simple. **Chemical reactions** all negative. All the British species are saxicolous or rarely occur on very compacted sand and soil. They are found in a wide range of habitats, from well below the high-water mark to mountain summits. The lack of periphyses and the simple spores assist in separating the genus from other species with similar-looking perithecia such as *Acrocordia, Porina, Thelidium* (all 1-septate), and *Polyblastia, Staurothele* (both muriform). Identification to species level is difficult and spore size may vary in many specimens. To assist identification the species included here are grouped under habitat.

1.	Found near or below high-water mark, or in freshwater streams	2
–	Found on basic rock, not necessarily near water	13
2.	Maritime	3
–	In or very near freshwater streams	9
3.	Thallus thick. At or below high-water mark	4
–	Thallus thin or evanescent. Above the splash zone	**6. V. prominula**
4.	Thallus thick, black. Perithecia up to 0.5 mm. Around high-water mark	5
–	Thallus thin or not black. Perithecia up to 0.3 mm. Below high-water mark	6
5.	Thallus regularly cracked. Perithecia conical	**4. V. maura**
–	Thallus with minute ridges. Perithecia with depressed and/or crenulate ostioles	**1. V. amphibia**
6.	Thallus with black grains or ridges	7
–	Thallus without black grains or ridges	8
7.	Thallus dark green with black ridges	**7. V. striatula**
–	Thallus brown with minute black grains	**2. V. ditmarsica**
8.	Thallus oily, green, perithecia innate when wet. White prothallus	**5. V. mucosa**
–	Thallus green-brown to dark brown, perithecia small but prominent even when wet. Black or no prothallus	**3. V. halizoa**
9.	Thallus white, grey or pink contrasting with dark perithecia	**11. V. praetermissa**
–	Thallus green, green-black, brown-green or red brown	10
10	Thallus green to green-black	11
–	Thallus brown or reddish brown	**8. V. aethiobola**
11.	Spores 6–12 x 5–8 µm	12
–	Spores 12–28 x 6–10 µm	**10. V. funckii**

12. Thallus with black spots about 30 µm diam. Ostiole flush **12. V. rheitrophila**
– Thallus without back spots. Ostiole raised above thallus **9. V. aquatilis**

13. Thallus green, pale to chocolate-brown or black 14
– Thallus white or grey 16

14. Thallus green to green-brown or shades of brown, wide cracks (like dried mud). Perithecia to almost 1 mm, immersed **21. V. viridula**
– Thallus dark brown to black, often with a black prothallus. Perithecia to 0.5 mm, partially immersed 15

15. Perithecia up to 0.4 mm diam. Spores 20–28 x 8–15 µm **20. V. nigrescens**
– Perithecia larger. Spores 25–37 x 10–15 µm **18. V. macrostoma**

16. Thallus leaden-grey, with rather regular areoles partitioned into tiny islets by a black prothallus **16. V. glaucina**
– Thallus white to pale grey, smooth or powdery or evanescent 17

17. Perithecia with a depressed ostiole, up to half-immersed **15. V. dufourii**
– Perithecia flat or slightly conical, more than half-immersed 18

18. Thallus smooth or evanescent. Perithecia sunken, up to about 0.3 mm wide 19
– Thallus evanescent or powdery. Perithecia 0.4 mm or more wide 20

19 Thallus smooth to cracked, blue-grey **14. V. caerulea**
– Thallus immersed or very thin film, white to pale grey **13. V. baldensis**

20. Perithecia to 1 mm wide, leaving empty pits when they fall out **19. V. muralis**
– Perithecia to 0.5 mm, often leaving black remains in pits **17. V. hochstetteri**

MARITIME

1. Verrucaria amphibia Thallus black, greenish in shade, green and slightly translucent when wet, thin to thick, almost lobate. Numerous, narrow, radiating ridges (use hand-lens) scattered over the surface of the thallus. Surface is less regularly cracked and often more glossy than in *V. maura*. A seaweed-brown, thin prothallus sometimes present. Often forming neat patches up to 5 cm diam. Usually fertile, perithecia about 0.4 mm, with a flat or more usually dimpled and/or crenulate, volcano-like top. Spores 10–15 x 7–10 µm.
Habitat: Common, mainly in the West, on exposed, often vertical rocks just below the *V. maura* zone.

V. amphibia x 4.

2. V. ditmarsica Thallus very thin, brown, gelatinous, translucent with tiny black papillae which, on well-lit sites, may join together to form larger blackened, scabrid areas. Prothallus absent or very weak. Perithecia almost sessile, small, to 0.2 mm diam. Spore a distinctive kidney-shape or with one flat side, 7–10 x 4–8 µm.
Habitat: A frequent but overlooked species on sheltered rocks and shingle in the lower littoral zone, often occurring in estuaries.

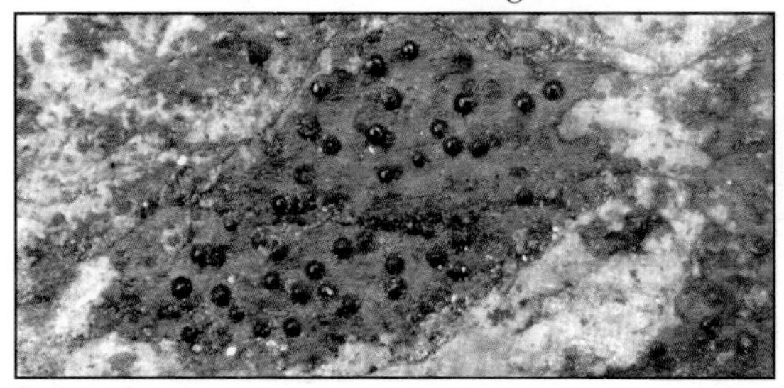
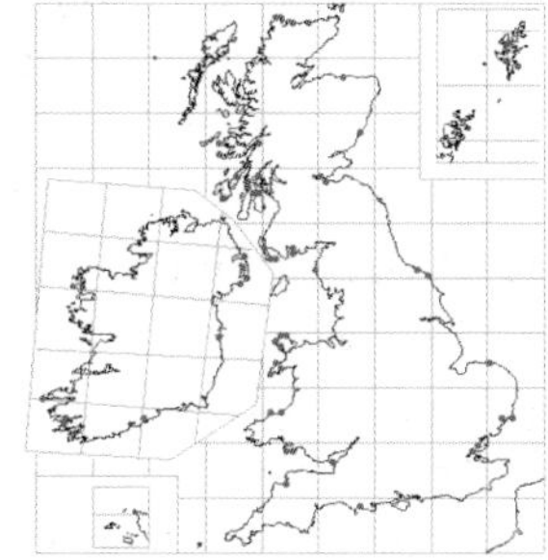

V. ditmarsica x 8.

3. V. halizoa (V. microspora) Thallus olive-green to brown-green, smooth or only slightly cracked. Translucent when wet. Black prothallus usually present. Perithecia dark and prominent, small (less than 0.3 mm diam). Spores 7–10 x 4–7 µm. It is sometimes parasitized by *Stigmidium marinum* (see under *V. mucosa*).
Habitat: Common on most rocky, exposed coasts but in crevices, etc. out of the main force of the sea and away from rapid drying-out. Generally not very abundant. It is only found below high-water mark where it forms small patches of 1–2 cm diam among other *Verrucaria* species and the red alga *Hildenbrandia*.

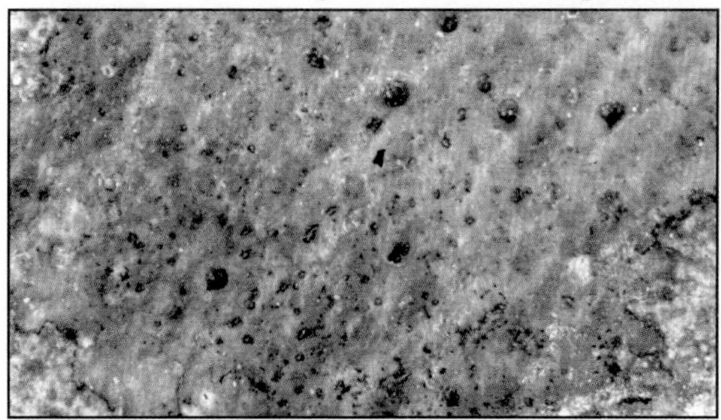
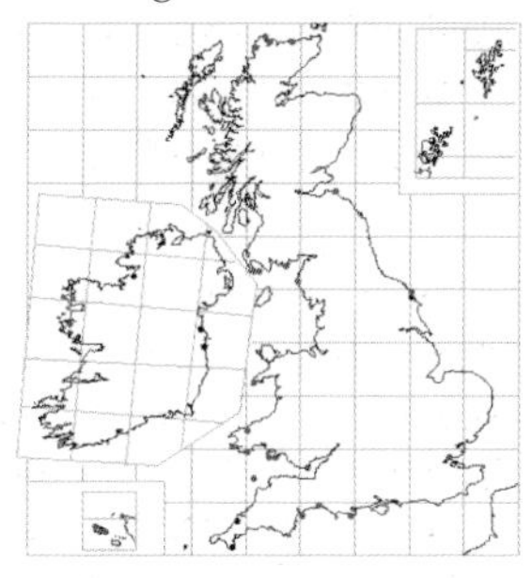

V. halizoa x 5.

4. V. maura Thallus black, up to 1 mm thick. Often confused with a layer of thick oil washed ashore. Under a lens the thallus is seen to be cracked into rather neat rectangular areoles (like dried mud). Surface scabrid, matt, with numerous black dots. These features are less noticeable when the thallus is wet. Usually with many conical perithecia about 0.5 mm diam with distinct ostioles, almost immersed, up to half-immersed in a dry thallus. Spores 10–17 x 6–10 µm.
Habitat. Very common on rocky coasts, occurs from below, to some distance well above, high-water mark. It usually forms the main constituent of the upper part of the black zone found on coastal rocks and shingle. It prefers exposed shores where it is usually best developed.

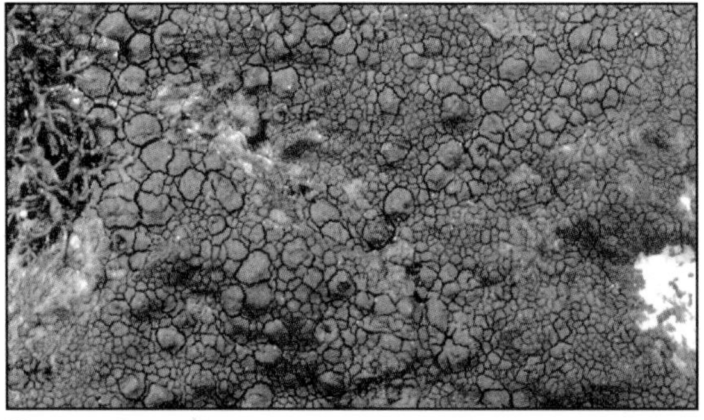

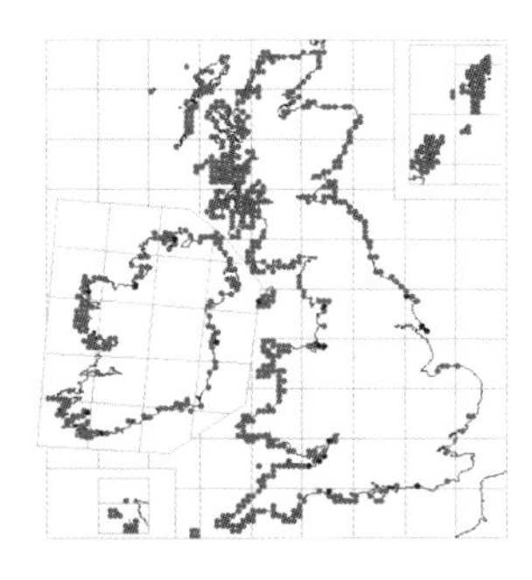

V. maura x 5

5. V. mucosa Thallus green to dark olive-green, to 1 mm thick, smooth, oily, not or slightly irregularly cracked, usually limited by a white prothallus which may also be present around cracks in the thallus. Perithecia black, immersed but becoming slightly more prominent when dry, very small (less than 0.2 mm diam). Spores 8–12 x 4–6 µm. In the South it is often parasitized by the lichenicolous fungus *Stigmidium marinum*. This has no thallus and minute (up to 0.2 mm), immersed, black perithecia. Spores are clavate, 1-septate, but may appear 3-septate.
Habitat. Common on well-lit rocks mainly in the centre of the littoral zone but extending to low-water mark. Somewhat rarer on sheltered shores.

V. mucosa x 5.

6. V. prominula Thallus grey, usually slightly mauve, thin or almost absent. Prothallus poorly developed. Perithecia prominent, up to 1 mm diam with a flat or depressed top, often two or three are fused together. Spores 12–15 x 6–8 µm with rather blunt ends.
Habitat: Frequent on soft siliceous rocks such as schist. It occurs in shaded, dry crevices and under overhangs above the splash zone.

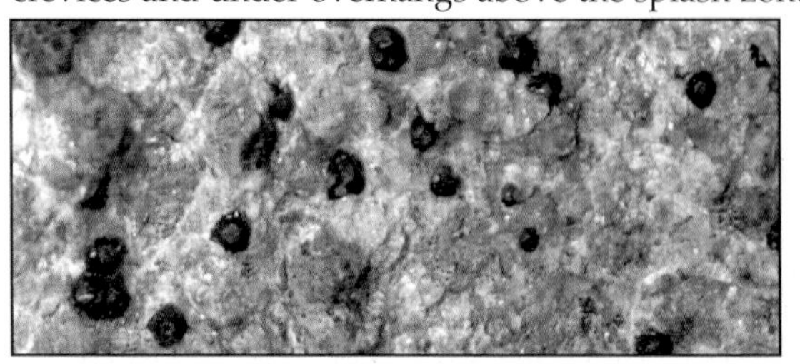

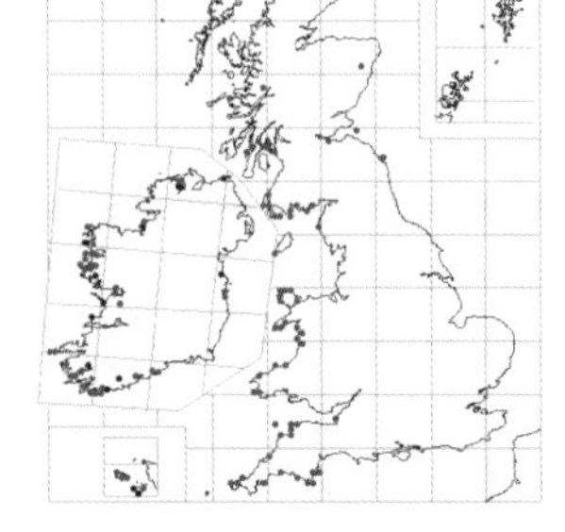

V. prominula x 5 .

7. V. striatula Thallus bright green to dark green, smooth, continuous, translucent, gelatinous. Elevated black dots and ridges (up to 0.2 mm wide) occur, especially on specimens from exposed coasts where they may almost cover the surface of the thallus, a feature that distinguishes this species from the others treated here. Perithecia very prominent, up to 0.3 mm diam, black, usually with a large irregular ostiole. Spores 7–11 x 4–6 µm.
Habitat: Common on hard rocks between *V. maura* and *V. mucosa/V. halizoa* zones.

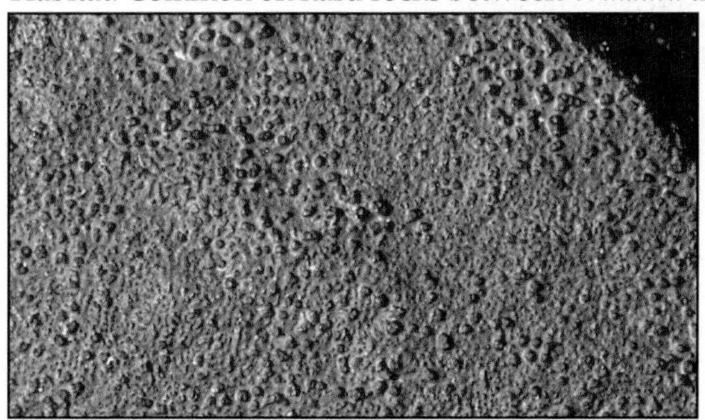

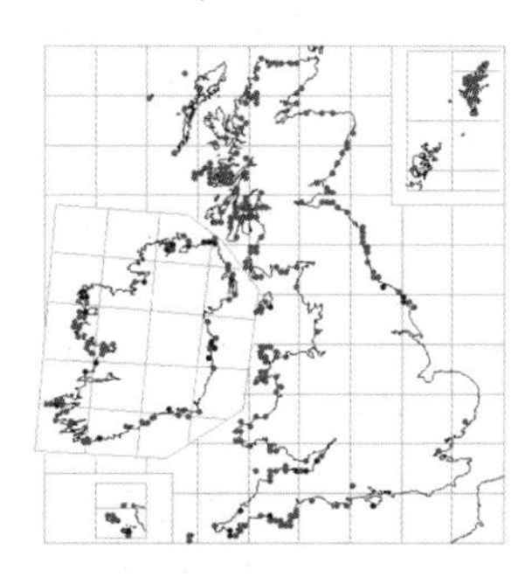

V. striatula x 4.

AQUATIC (freshwater)

8. V. aethiobola Thallus thick, reddish brown to shades of brown, rarely partially grey-brown, smooth to cracked, often becoming areolate. Prothallus normally absent. Perithecia black, up to 0.4 mm diam, almost immersed. Spores ellipsoid, 18–30 x 8–12 µm.
Habitat: Fairly common, on frequently inundated acid rocks, rarely on basic rock, by lakes and streams. Mainly on ± horizontal surfaces, often with *Hymenelia lacastris* and *Rhizocarpon lavatum*.

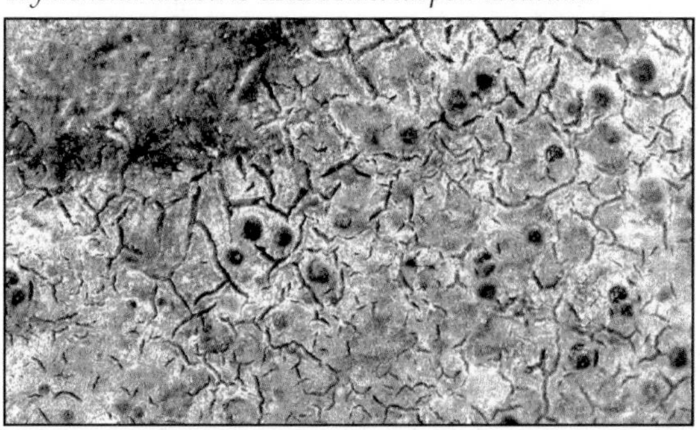

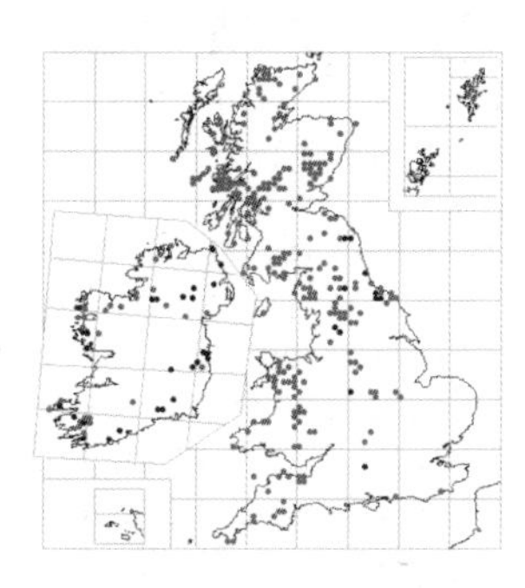

V. aethiobola x 5.

9. V. aquatilis Thallus brown to dark green-black, thin, smooth, continuous. No prothallus. Many immersed, black perithecia (up to 0.3 mm) are scattered over the surface, with only the ostiole protruding abve the thallus. Spores 6–10 x 4–7 µm, often almost globose.
Habitat: In many lakes and rivers, the commonest of the freshwater *Verrucaria* species. It occurs submerged, in clear water on hard, mainly siliceous rocks.

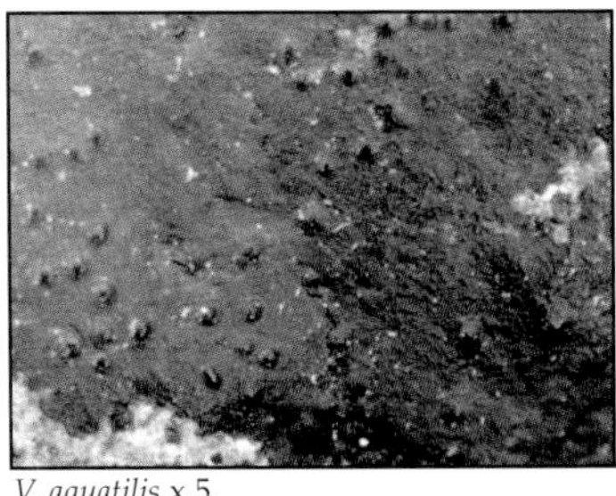

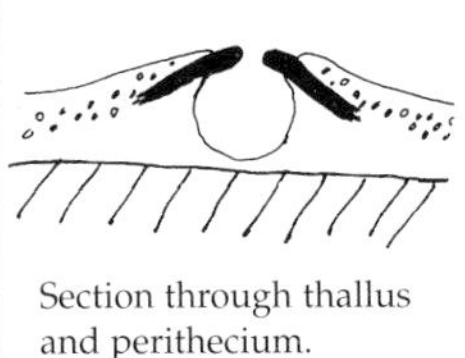

Section through thallus and perithecium.

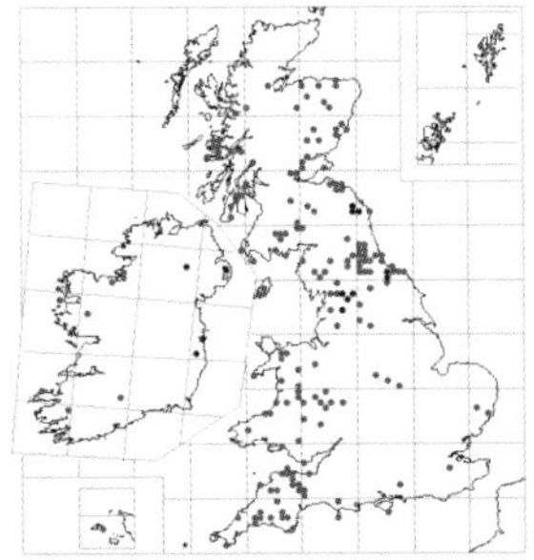

V. aquatilis x 5.

10. V. funckii Thallus green to black-green, ± gelatinous, smooth or cracked, often with pale to black prothallus. Perithecia immersed, only the ostioles visible at the surface. Small dark granules, about 0.3 mm diam, are usually present, embedded in the thallus. It resembles *V. mucosa.* Spores 12–23 x 6–9 µm.
Habitat: Frequent, on inundated or submerged acid rocks and stones in clear water in upland lakes and rivers.

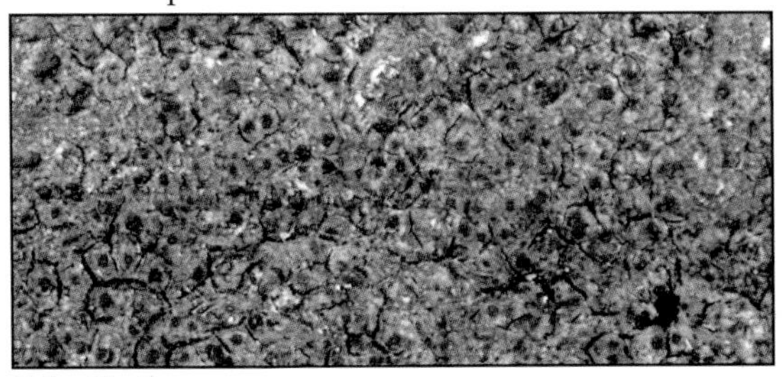

V. funckii x 5.

11. V. praetermissa Thallus white to pale brown, grey or pink, smooth to cracked, not gelatinous, often with a black-edged, pale prothallus. Perithecia black, up to 0.3 mm diam. Spores 18–25 x 7–9 µm, elongate, almost fusiform. The pale thallus dotted with small, dark, immersed perithecia, together with the elongated spores, make this a distinctive species.
Habitat: Frequent on inundated or submerged, mainly acid rocks and stones, in clear water in or by lakes and rivers. If found on basic substrata in drier situations with slightly emergent perithecia it is probably **V. elaeina**.

12. V. rheitrophila (V. kernstockii) Thallus green to a greyish green, with dispersed, sterile black spots about 30 µm diam, usually with a white or black prothallus. Perithecia immersed, up to 0.2 mm diam. Spores 8–12 x 6–8 µm. It has smaller spores than *V. funckii. V. aquatilis* lacks the small black dots and usually has more globose spores.
Habitat: Infrequent in the West, in similar sites to *V. funckii*. Especially common on slates and shales.

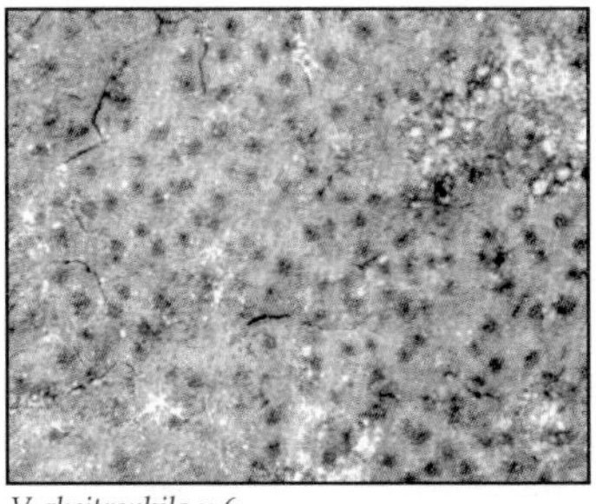
V. rheitrophila x 6.

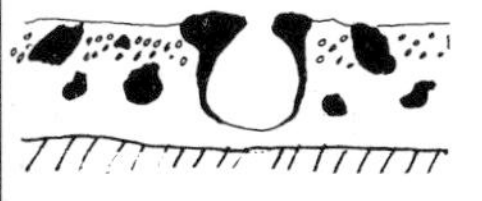
Section through thallus and perithecium.

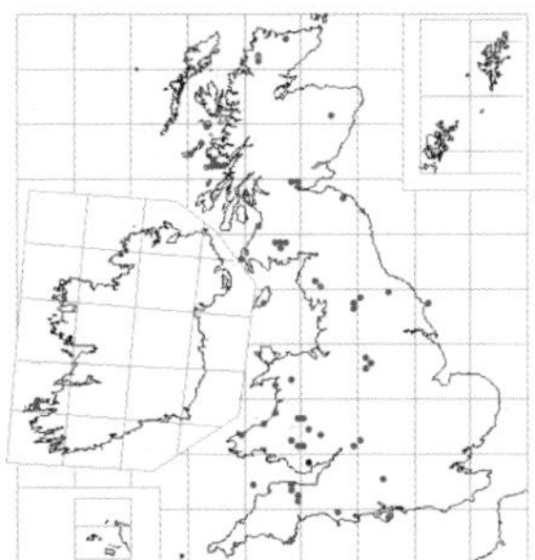

ROCKS AND WALLS
(not necessarily aquatic or maritime)

13. V. baldensis Thallus white to pale grey, thin, smooth, or immersed, usually with a dark, narrow prothallus. Thallus crowded with many small (about 0.25 mm), immersed perithecia. Up to about six very fine cracks extend from the ostiole, often resembling a hot cross bun (x 20 lens). Involucrellum almost flat, like a man-hole cover (see diagram), the perithecia leaving empty pits when they fall out. Spores 15–21 x 7–10 µm. It seems to take longer to colonize gravestones than other *Verrucaria* species. The parasitic *Opegrapha parasitica* with brownish, 3-septate spores of may often replace the perithecia.
Habitat: Very common on hard limestone, gravestones, rarely on mortar.

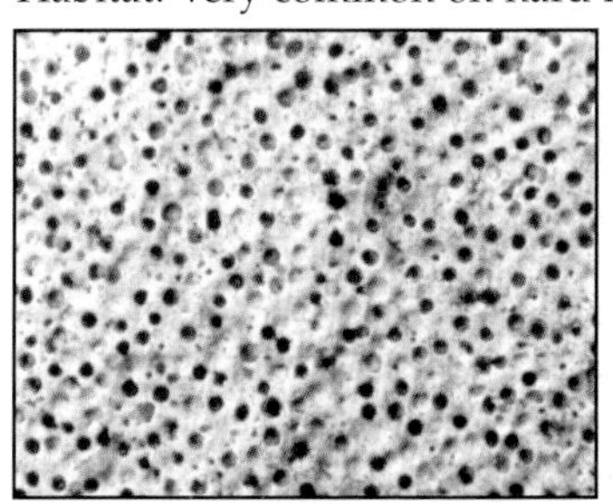
V. baldensis x 6.

Plan view of typical perithecium of *V. baldensis*.

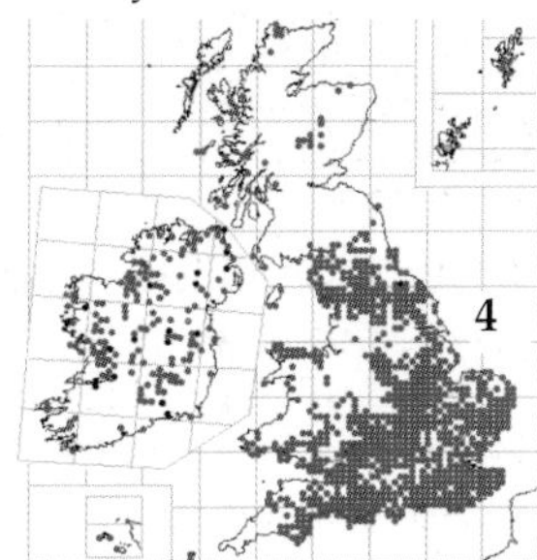

14. V. caerulea Thallus blue-grey to grey, finely cracked, somtimes with a dark brown prothallus. Perithecia numerous, almost immersed, about 0.3 mm diam, the ostiole usually in a depression on the top of the perithecium. Spores globose, 14–20 x 47 µm.
Habitat: Frequent on sheltered, hard limestone.

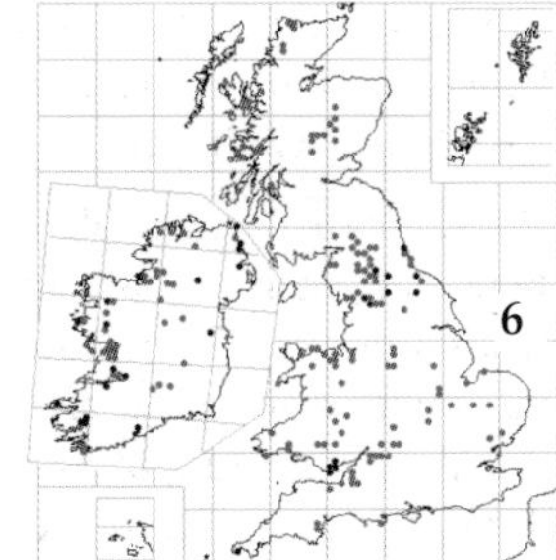

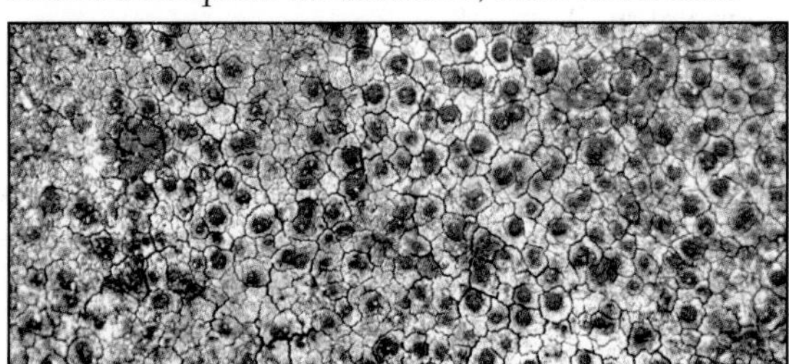
V. caerulea x 6.

15. V. dufourii Thallus pale grey to grey-brown, smooth to cracked or usually immersed, sometimes with only the brown prothallus and perithecia visible. Perithecia half-immersed, about 0.5 mm, with a marked depression at the ostiole (hand-lens), suggesting an inland version of *V. prominula*. Spores 12–20 x 6–12 µm. Habitat: Frequent on hard limestone.

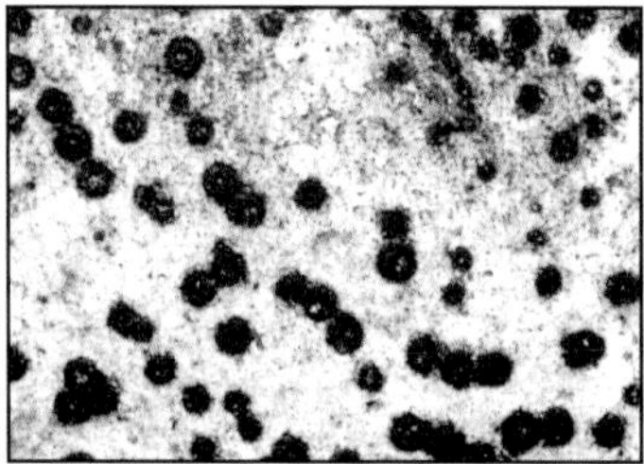

V. dufourii x 5.

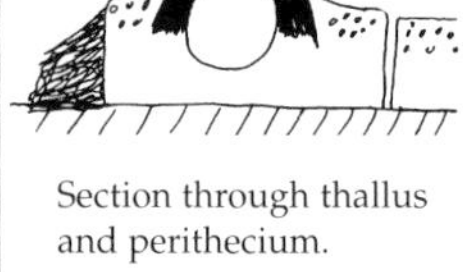

Section through thallus and perithecium.

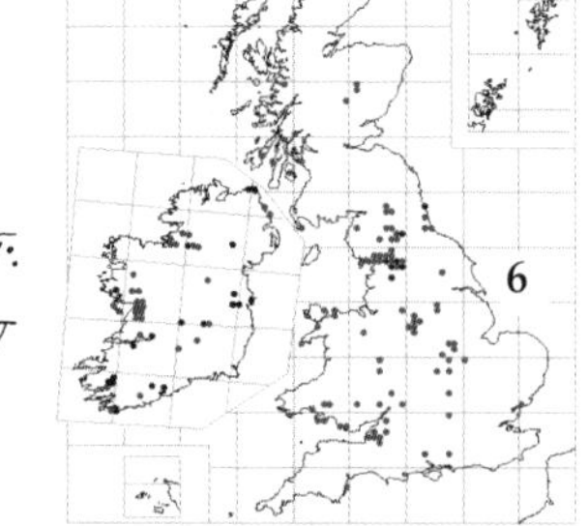

16. V. glaucina Thallus pale leaden-grey, to 1 mm thick, markedly areolate. A distinctive black, net-like prothallus is visible between the areoles and around the margin. Perithecia immersed, up to 0.25 mm diam. Spores 10–20 x 5–8 µm. Habitat: Common and widespread, often forming small islets amongst other species. On basic rocks, walls and mortar.

V. glaucina x 5.

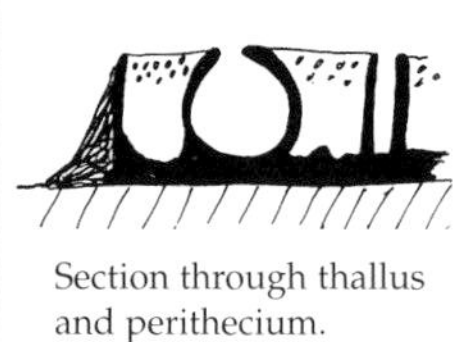

Section through thallus and perithecium.

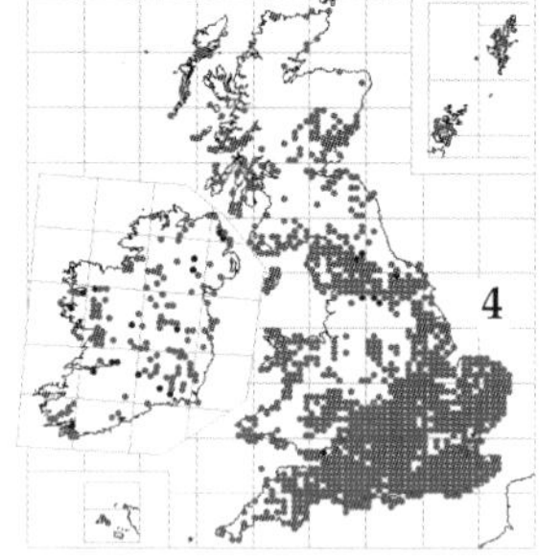

17. V. hochstetteri Thallus immersed or thin, smooth to cracked, grey-brown to grey-red, sometimes with a thin dark prothallus. Perithecia completely immersed in pits, more rarely slightly elevated, up to about 0.8 mm diam. The involucrellum is flask-shaped and the lower part frequently remains in the pit after the perithecium is shed (see *V. muralis*). Spores 23–32 x 10–20 µm. Habitat: Common on limestone and mortar.

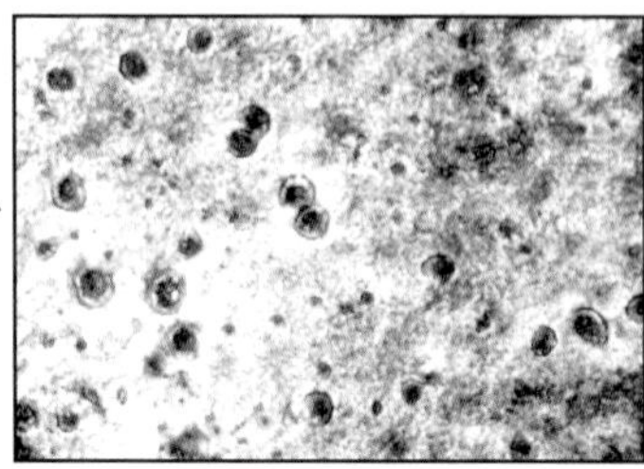

V. hochstetteri x 6

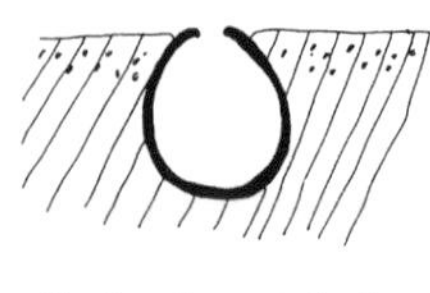

Section through thallus and perithecium.

18. V. macrostoma Thallus tan to olive-green, areolate to almost squamulose, looking like dried mud. The areole up to 1.5 mm diam, slightly convex, smooth or slightly warted. Perithecia about 0.5 mm, convex or sometimes with flattened tops, over half immersed. Spores 25–37 x 10–15 µm. The margins of the areoles are frequently sorediate (**f. furfuracea**). May be confused with *Acarospora* species, which occur on siliceous rocks, and have several hundred spores per ascus and larger areoles.

Habitat: A common species of calcareous rocks, walls, tombstones, etc., throughout the British Isles. More rarely found on acid rocks.

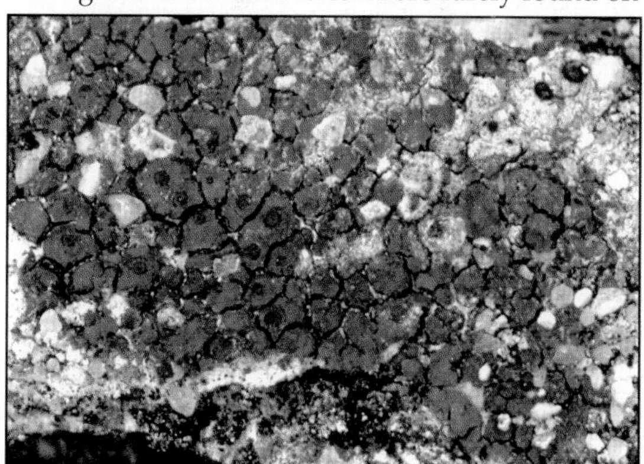

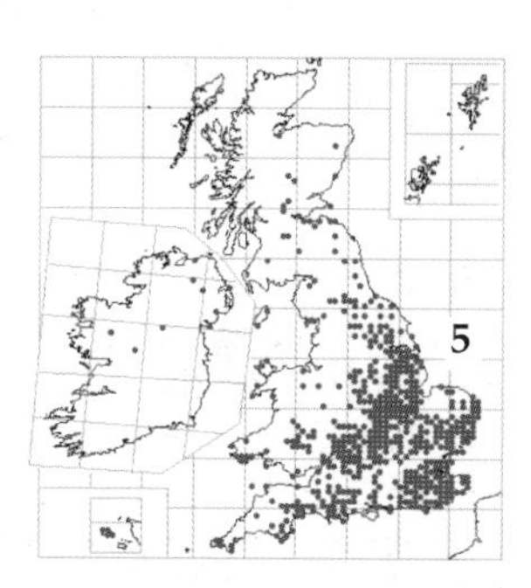

V. macrostoma x 4.

19. V. muralis Thallus pure white to pale brown-grey, powdery, slightly cracked or minutely pitted but often immersed. Perithecia black, up to 0.75 mm diam, but usually smaller, prominent to almost immersed with the ostiole clearly visible. Spores 15–25 x 8–15 µm. The apothecia fall out, leaving empty cavities in the substratum (see *V. hochstetteri*).

Habitat: Common on rather soft calcareous rocks, walls and mortar, much rarer on hard limestone.

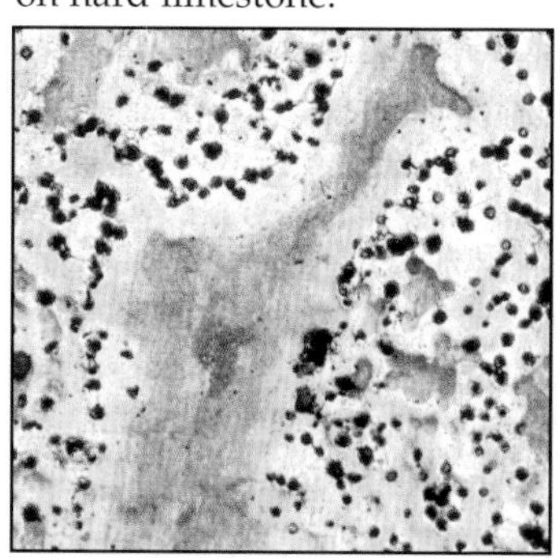

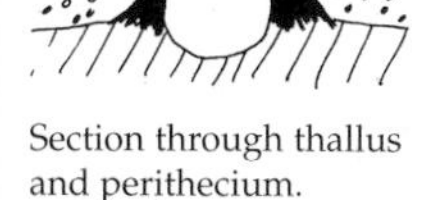

Section through thallus and perithecium.

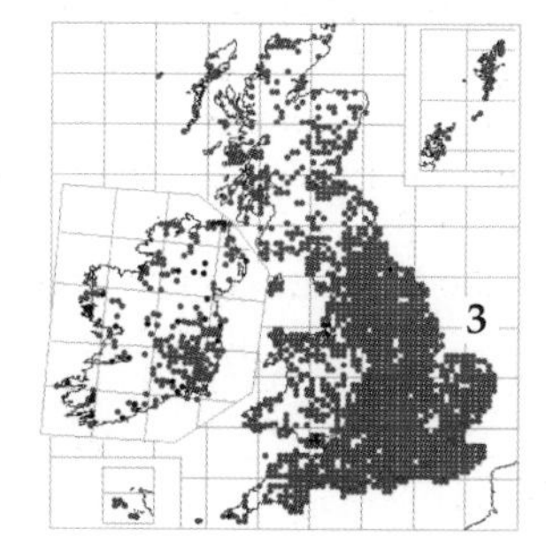

V. muralis x 3.

20. V. nigrescens Thallus chocolate-brown to black, becoming much greener when wet, usually thick and regularly cracked Areoles less than 1 mm diam. Prothallus black and continuous under the thallus. The edges of the areoles are

sometimes sorediate. Perithecia small (less than 0.4 mm), frequently in groups, over half-immersed in the thallus. Spores 20–28 x 8–15 µm.
Habitat: Common, mainly on calcareous walls, rocks and mortar. Rarely on siliceous stone. The similar **V. fusconigrescens** has half-exposed perithecia and predominantly occurs on coastal, acid rock.

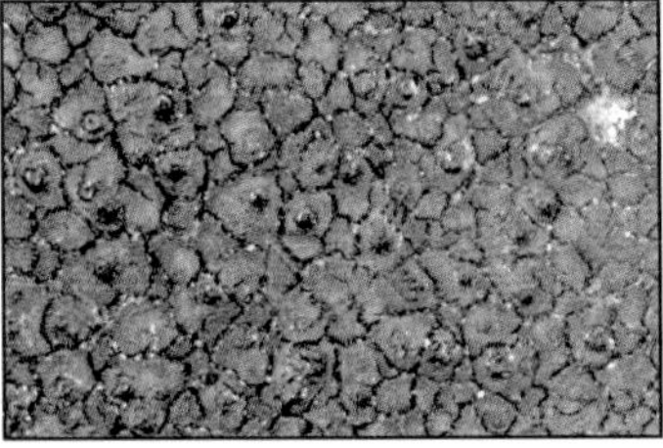

V. nigrescens x 5.

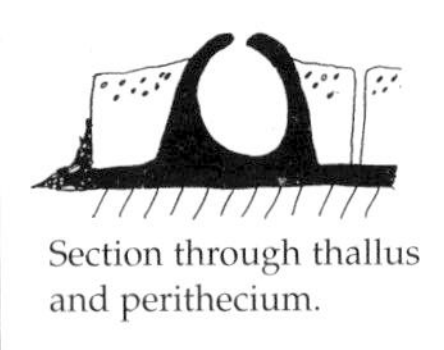

Section through thallus and perithecium.

2

21. V. viridula Thallus green to dark green-brown or shades of brown, thick, very areolate. Often surrounded by a thin prothallus but, unlike *V. nigrescens*, it does not extend under the thallus. Perithecia immersed, up to almost 1 mm diam (see *V. macrostoma*). Spores 20–35 x 10–17 µm.
Habitat: Common on basic rocks, including brick.

V. viridula x 5.

Section through thallus and perithecium.

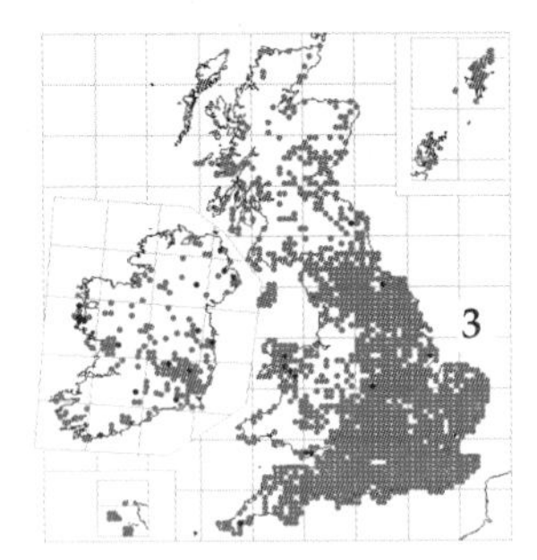

VEZDAEA (after the lichenologist Antonin Vězda, born 1920). **Thallus** crustose and granular (goniocysts) developing below the surface of mosses and lichens. These develop, burst through the cuticle of the host and are visible globose granules having a roughened surface with minute projections. **Photobiont** *Leptosira*. **Apothecia** lecideine, becoming convex. No proper margin, hypothecium or hymenial gelatine. **Ascus** 8-spored. **Spores** colourless, simple to multi-septate.

V. aestivalis x 400.

The apothecia are short-lived (3–4 months) and best seen in the winter or spring. **Chemical reactions** negative. Superficially similar to *Micarea* but the species in that genus have a proper margin, a hypothecium, hymenial gelatine and the paraphyses never coil the asci.

1. Thallus grey to greenish. Paraphyses coil around each ascus. Spores 15–19 x 5–7 µm **1. V. aestivalis**
– Thallus dark green. Paraphyses not coiled around each ascus. Spores 10–6 x 2–4 µm **2. V. leprosa**

1. V. aestivalis Thallus of crowded goniocysts with minute conical projections, grey, greenish or reddish brown, often with a fluffy surface. Apothecia usually present, up to 1 mm, grey to dull reddish brown. The paraphyses are twisted and coil around each ascus. Spores 1-septate, a few becoming 3-septate, 15–19 x 5–7 µm. It resembles *Bacidia sabuletorum* but that species has 7- or more- septate, larger spores.
Habitat: Frequent on damp, shaded mosses and plant debris mainly in calcareous situations.

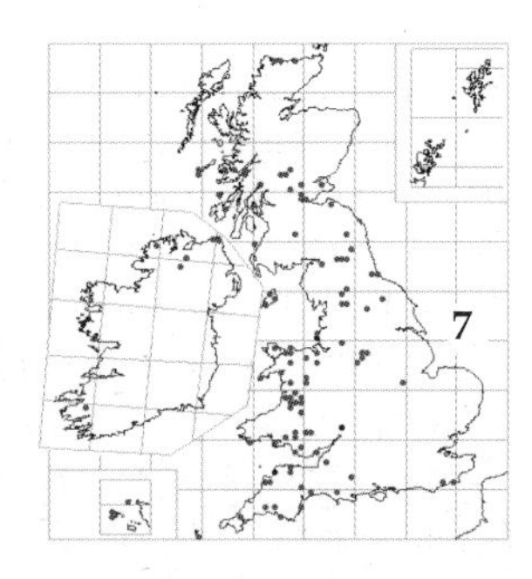

V. aestivalis x 4.

2. V. leprosa Thallus of dark green, granular goniocysts. Apothecia usually present amongst the goniocysts, pale pink to red-brown, up to 1 mm diam, globose. Paraphyses not coiled around the asci. Spores simple or becoming 1-septate, 10–16 x 2–4 µm.
Habitat: Infrequent, on old vegetation, on disturbed ground, especially near the sea or when rich in heavy metals, e.g. under galvanized wire fences.

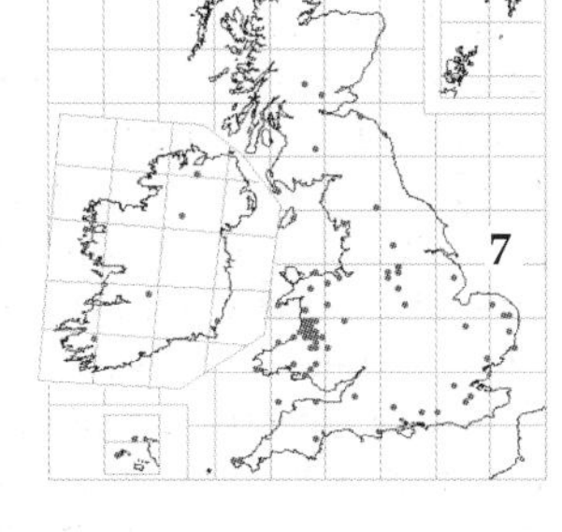

V. leprosa x 4.

WADEANA (after the British lichenologist Arthur E. Wade, 1895–1989). **Thallus** corticolous, immersed in the host. **Photobiont** *Trentepohlia.* **Apothecia** lirellate, becoming more open as they mature. **Ascus** 100- to 200-spored, K/I+ blue cap. **Spores** simple, colourless. **Paraphyses** branched, with brown tips and often anastomosing. Paraphysoid filaments also present. **Chemical reactions** negative. *Lithographa* and *Opegrapha* both have 8-spored asci.

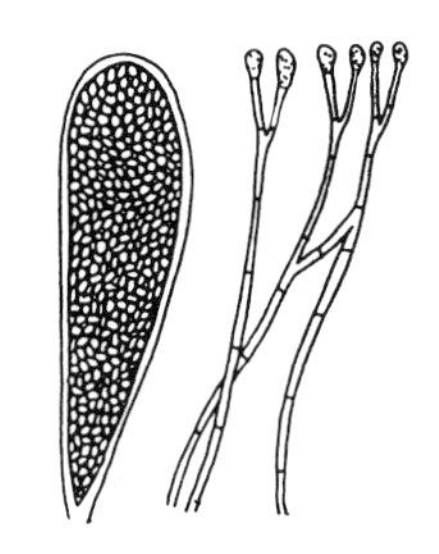

W. dendrographa x 500.

Wadeana dendrographa Thallus immersed. The lirellate apothecia are rather glossy, up to 3 mm long with pointed ends (in the common fungus *Hysterium* they are blunt), rounded in cross-section giving a lip-like apppearance, often arranged in vertical lines along the grain of the host bark. The apothecial tissues are reddish brown in a squash (less red in K). Spores 6–8 x 3–4 µm.
Thallus: often UV+ orange-yellow
Habitat: Rare on rough bark of old, nutrient-rich, deciduous trees in the South, also in West Scotland.

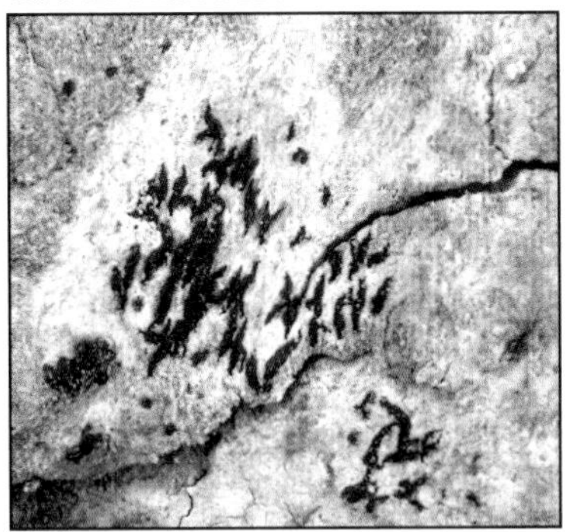

W. dendrographa x 3.

XANTHORIA ('golden yellow'). **Thallus** foliose, orange or grey in shade, under-surface white. **Photobiont** mainly trebouxioid. **Apothecia** lecanorine, often shortly stalked. **Ascus** 8-spored, *Teloschistes*-type. **Spores** colourless, polarilocular, 10–17 x 6–9 µm. The genus is characteristically found on nutrient-rich sites. In their colour and the K+ crimson reaction they resemble *Caloplaca* species, they differ in being foliose and it is possible to peel them off the substratum. The yellow colour led to them being tried as a cure for jaundice. Yellow and crimson dyes have been made from these species.

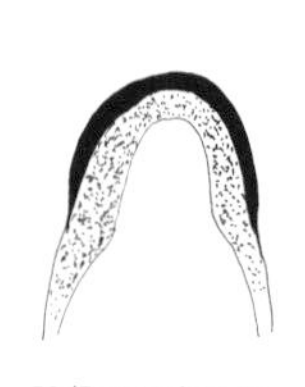

K/I reaction to the ascus tip.

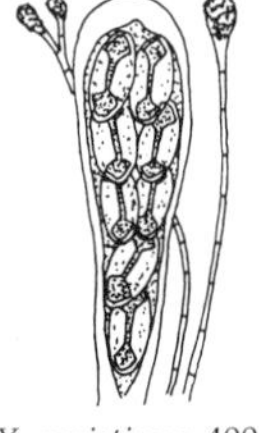

X. parietina x 400.

1.	Thallus sorediate or with coralloid, contorted or lobate isidia	2
–	Thallus not sorediate or isidiate	4

2.	Thallus of narrow lobes with sorediate tips	**2. X. candelaria**
–	Thallus with isidia or lobules	3
3.	Centre of thallus coarsely isidiate or with contorted lobules	**1. X. calcicola**
–	Lobe tips lobulate. Thallus usually covered in apothecia	**6. X. polycarpa**
4.	Thallus large with wide, rounded-tipped marginal lobes	**5. X. parietina**
–	Thallus compact, lobes long and narrow or short with abundant apothecia	5
5.	Thallus to 2 cm across, almost hidden under the apothecia	**6. X. polycarpa**
–	Thallus to 5 cm across with long narrow lobes	6
6.	Lobes overlapping and up to 2 mm wide	**3. X. ectaneoides**
–	Lobes separated and up to 1 mm wide	**4. X. elegans**

1. Xanthoria calcicola (X. aureola) Thallus large, to 20 cm, lobes to about 5 mm wide, especially at the margins of the thallus. Under-surface white with simple pale rhizinae. Similar to *X. parietina*, often deeper orange with more contorted lobes, which become densely covered in coarse, coralloid, wart-like isidia. Apothecia also similar, usually slightly stalked, but with an irregular often contorted margin, much less abundant, often entirely absent.
K+ crimson.
Habitat: Common in similar habitats to *X. parietina* but only exceptionally found on trees or acid rocks. Somewhat less common in the West.

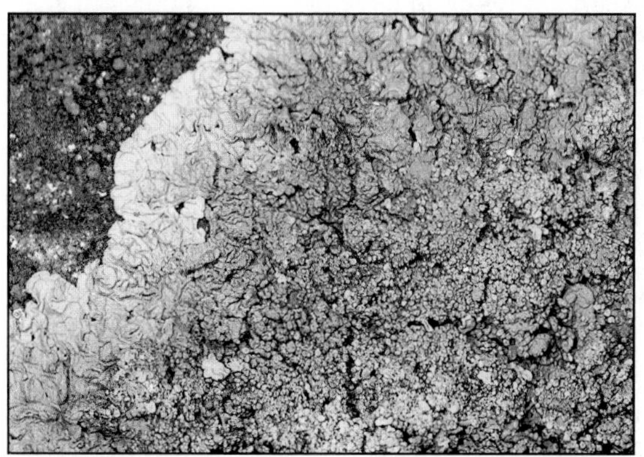

X. calcicola x 3.

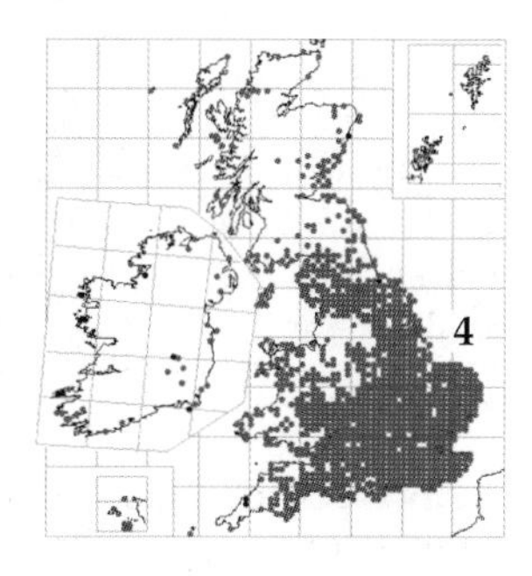

2. X. candelaria Thallus yellow-orange, consisting of a mass of ascending, crenulate lobes up to 1 mm wide, 2 mm tall. Under-surface pale, with a few short rhizines. Yellow granular soralia develop at the tips of the lobes, often spreading over the lower surface. The lobes sometimes erode to give an almost sorediate crust. Not usually fertile. Apothecia orange with a contorted margin. This species was used in Scandinavia to dye church candles yellow.
K+ crimson. This reaction and the more orange-yellow colour easily separate this species from the superficially similar *Candelaria concolor*.
Habitat: Common on nutrient-enriched (usually deciduous) trees, fences and, especially, horizontal rocks and bird-perching sites.

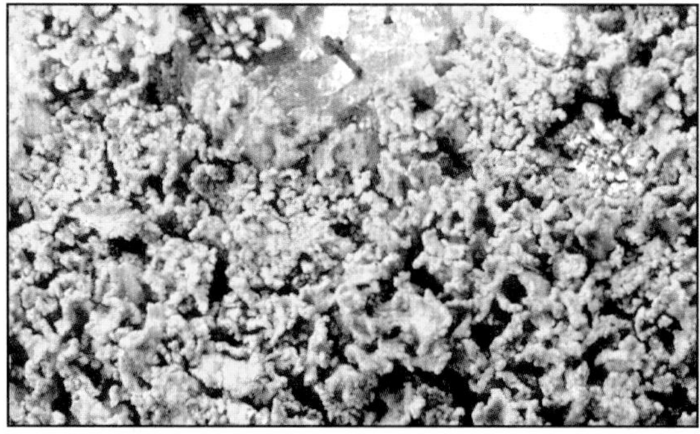

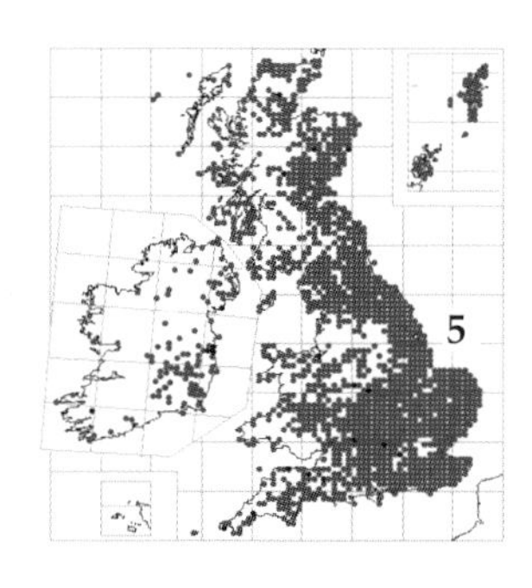

X. candelaria x 5.

3. X. ectaneoides Similar to *X. parietina* but differing in the strap-like, discrete or often overlapping lobes up to 2 mm wide. Apothecia sparse or absent.
K+ crimson.
Habitat: Occurs on exposed, nutrient-enriched shores and old buildings near or on the coast, rarely on exposed calcareous rocks at altitude.

4. X. elegans Thallus bright orange-red, closely adpressed, with narrow (up to 1 mm wide) convex, strap-like lobes, usually forming a neat orbicular patch up to about 5 cm diam. Apothecia often present in large numbers, orange-red with crenulate margins. Similar-looking *Caloplaca* species lack a lower cortex.
K+ crimson.
Habitat: Frequent on well-lit, nutrient-rich rocks in mountain and upland areas, but extending its range to concrete and slate in more lowland areas.

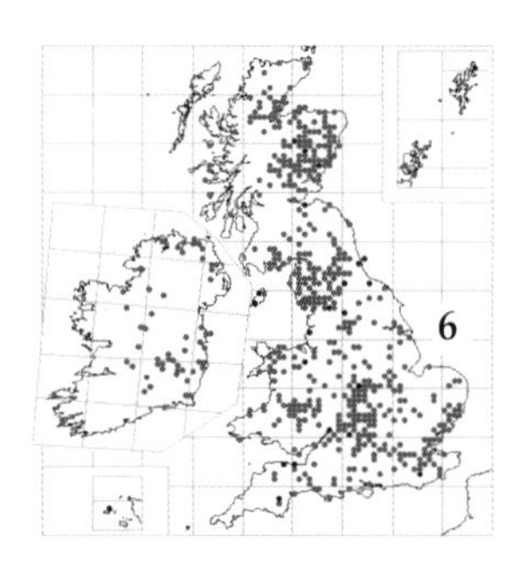

X. elegans x 3.

5. X. parietina Thallus greenish grey in shade to bright orange where exposed to strong sunlight, forming orbicular patches in which, in old specimens, the centre often dies out. Lobes long (rather narrow in very exposed situations, e.g. the seashore), wrinkled, imbricate, the edges of the lobes often turned up. The lobes may be up to 7 mm wide, especially at the margin of the thallus. Under-surface almost white with a few light-coloured rhizines. Apothecia usually abundant

towards the centre of the thallus, disc orange with a paler margin that becomes crenulate.
K+ crimson.
Habitat: Very common on nutrient-rich trees, rocks, and walls, especially bird-perching sites, e.g. on roofs under television aerials, farms, etc. This is one of the most resistant foliose species to air pollution. Commonest near the coast.

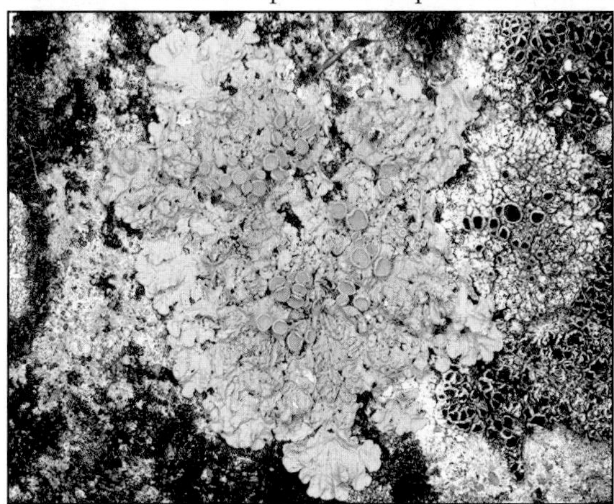

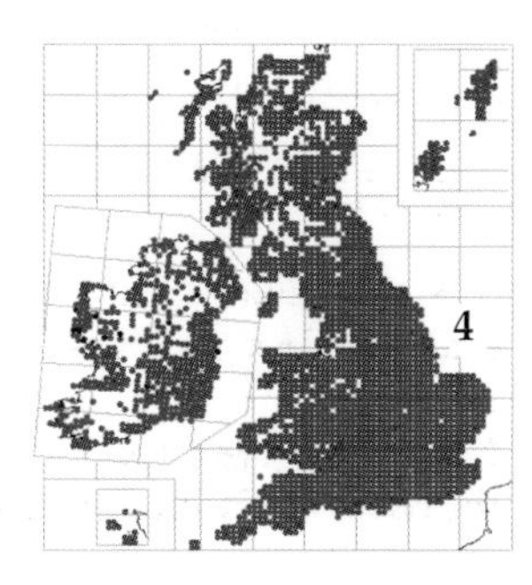

X. parietina x 1.

6. X. polycarpa Thallus greenish grey to yellow-orange, orbicular, up to 2 cm diam. Lobes convex, incised at tips to form small lobules, often almost obscured by the numerous crowded and stalked apothecia up to 4 mm diam. These have orange discs and thick pale margins which become somewhat crenulate.
K+ crimson.
Habitat: Common, especially near the sea, on nutrient-enriched trees, especially in the angles of twigs, but also found on fences and dead trees. As the levels of air pollution are reduced, it is rapidly returning to cities, where it is often very common on the internodes of small twigs.

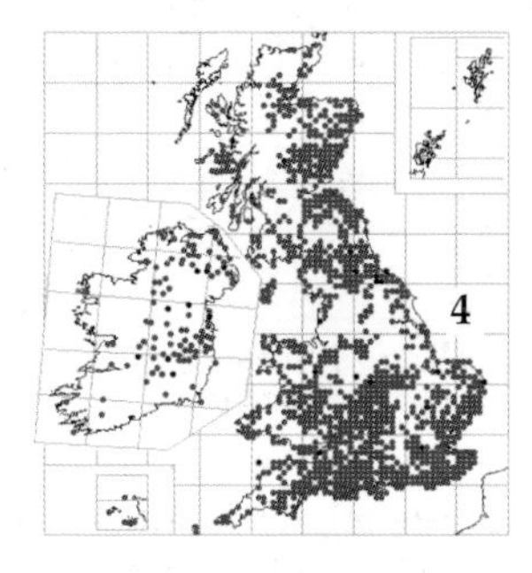

X. polycarpa x 3 (in shade).

XYLOGRAPHA ('writing on wood' – from the lirellae found on bare wood). **Thallus** crustose, often immersed. **Photobiont** chlorococcoid. **Apothecia** lecideine, becoming lirellate when mature. **Ascus** 8-spored, *Trapelia*-like but with a colourless apical cushion. **Spores** colourless (over-mature spores may become brownish), simple. **Pycnidia** very dark brown, immersed, globose.

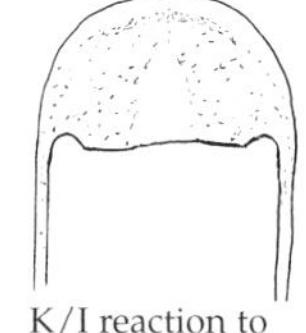
K/I reaction to the ascus tip.

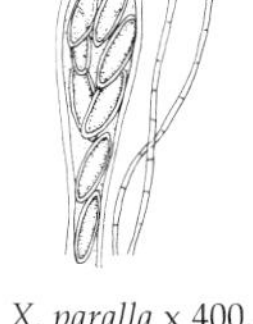
X. paralla x 400.

1. Thallus not sorediate, with minute goniocysts **1. X. parallela**
– Thallus sorediate, lacking brown goniocysts **2. X. vitiligo**

1. Xylographa parallela (X. abietina) Thallus immersed or thin, white to greenish grey with very small (20–40 µm diam) brown goniocysts scattered over the surface. Apothecia to 2 x 0.3 mm, brown, oval when young, with a thin margin and a roughened disc. They become black and lirellate, following the grain of the wood. Margins are often excluded in immature apothecia. Spores 10–16 x 5–8 µm.
Spot reactions: usually negative, rarely K+ yellow, P+ yellow.
Habitat: Locally common on slightly decayed, decorticated wood and tree stumps (especially conifers) in the North of Britain.

X. parallela x 8.

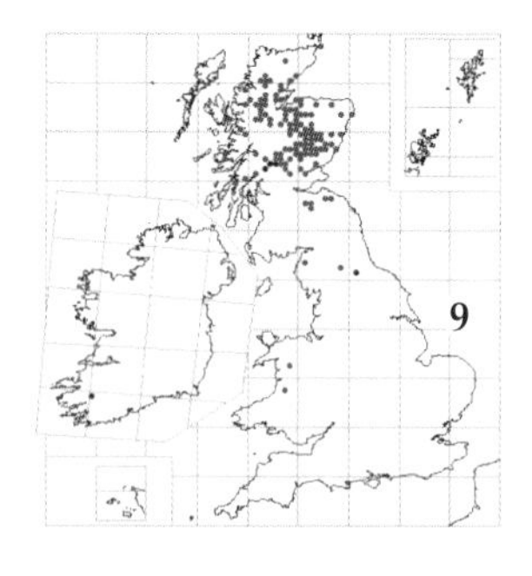

2. X. vitiligo is similar in appearance *X. parallela* but without the minute brown goniocysts. Discrete, elliptical, dark blue-grey (paler when rubbed) soralia, up to 1 x 0.5 mm, are usually present. Apothecia rare, more elliptical, up to 1 x 0.5 mm. Pycnidia usually present, immersed, inconspicuous.
Soredia: K+ yellow, P+ orange. Sterile specimens may resemble *Buellia griseovirens* but that species is K+ orange and mainly found on bark.
Habitat: Locally common on decorticated wood and tree stumps (especially conifers) in the North of Britain, rarer in the South.

X. *vitiligo* x 8.

ZAMENHOFIA (after the inventor of Esperanto, Ludwik Zamenhof, 1860–1938). **Thallus** crustose, usually densely isidiate. **Photobiont** *Trentepohlia*. **Perithecia** half- to three-quarters immersed, often infertile. **Ascus** 8-spored, thin-walled, K/I–. **Spores** colourless, 5- to 17-septate, swelling in K. **Pycnidia** unknown. **Chemical reactions** negative.

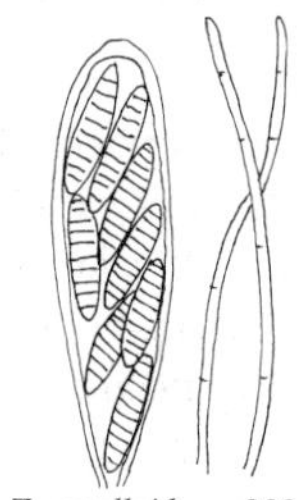

Z. coralloidea x 200.

1. Thallus purplish brown with blue-brown to brown-black isidia. Spores 40–57 x 6–9 µm, 9- to 11-septate **1. Z. coralloidea**
– Thallus orange-brown, greenish yellow or greenish brown. Infertile or spores 3- or 12- to 16-septate, sizes various 2
2. Orange-brown to greenish orange. Isidia densely packed, little branched. Spores 60–90 µm long, 12- to 16-septate **2. Z. hibernica**
– Yellowish green. Isidia much branched. Sterile in Britain. Spores 22–30 µm long, 3-septate **3. Z. rosei**

1. Zamenhofia coralloidea (Porina coralloidea) Thallus smooth, purplish grey, soon densely covered in blue-brown coralliod isidia, when not mature these isidia have paler tips (*Catillaria atropurpurea* is granular, without pale-tipped isidia). Perithecia rare, over half-immersed in the thallus, dark brown, about 0.5 mm diam. Spores 40–57 x 9–13 µm, 9- to 11-septate.
Habitat: Infrequent. An 'old forest' species of mature rough-barked trees. Most common in the New Forest.

Z. coralloidea x 6.

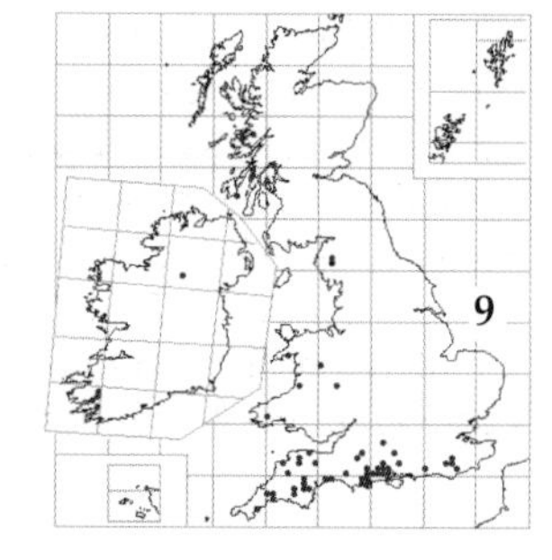

2. Z. hibernica Thallus immersed or granular, forming a thin scurfy crust that becomes covered in orange to orange-green (in shade) poorly structured, richly branched isidia. Perithecia black, up to 0.7 mm diam, often irregular in shape and clustered in groups. Spores 60–90 x 5–7 µm, 12- to 16-septate.
Habitat: A rare species of old oak trees in the South and West.

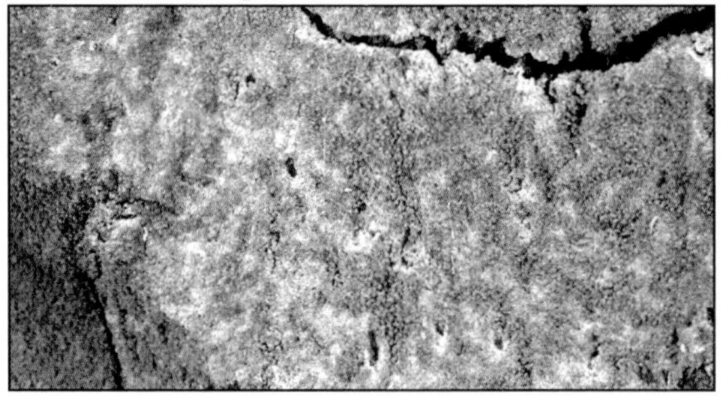

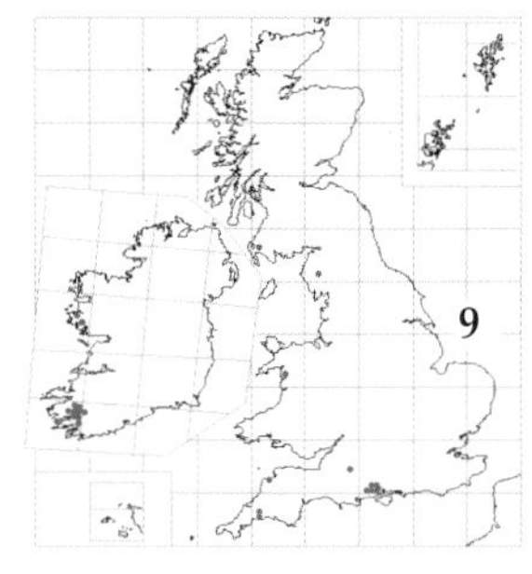

Z. hibernica x 8.

3. Z. rosei Thallus very isidiate and consisting of yellowish green, delicate, clumps of isidia. Not known fertile in Britain. Perithecia dark orange, 0.2 mm diam. Spores 22–30 x 4–6 µm, 3-septate.
Habitat: Very rare but locally frequent in the New Forest.

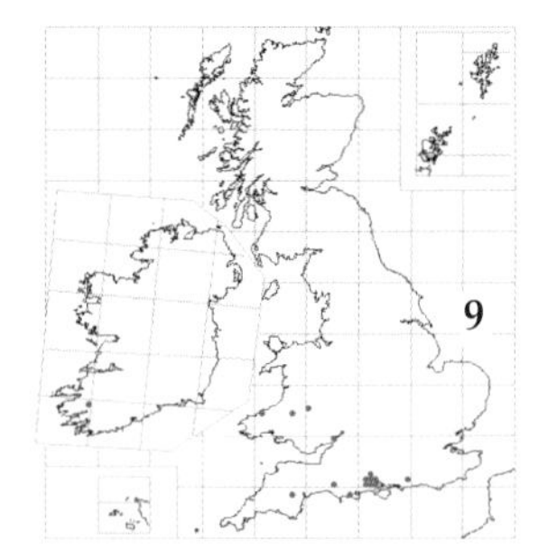

Z. rosei x 8.

SELECTED BIBLIOGRAPHY

BARON G. *Understanding Lichens* (1999) The Richmond Publishing Co. Ltd.

This book covers most areas of lichenology including lichen communities, uses, botanical classification and an extensive bibliography. It amplifies the introduction given here in this book forming an indispensible companion work.

BRITISH LICHEN SOCIETY *Identification of Parmelia Ach.* (1997) CD.

Each of the 47 British species is illustrated with several colour photographs. There are comprehensive links and extensive information about the species, habitat, chemistry, etc.

GILBERT O. *Lichens* (The New Naturalist Library) (2000) Harper Collins.

A very readable account that covers many aspects of the biology of lichens. It is especially strong on lichen habitats.

NASH T.H. *III Lichen Biology.*(1996) Cambridge University Press.

A series of detailed papers on lichen biology by various authors.

ORANGE A. *Lichens on Trees* (British Plant Life No. 3) (1994) National Museum of Wales.

A small book with good colour photographs, line drawings and accounts of some common lichens.

PURVIS O.W. *Lichens* (2000). The Natural History Museum & Smithsonian Institution.

A popular guide to lichen biology, biodiversity, ecological and economic importance, etc. Contains 150 colour photographs and diagrams.

PURVIS O.W., COPPINS B.J., HAWKSWORTH D.L., JAMES P.W., MOORE D.M. *The Lichen Flora of Great Britain and Ireland* (1992). The British Lichen Society.

The definitive flora that includes all the British and Irish species. It expands on the entries included here in this book.

RICHARDSON D.H.S. *Pollution Monitoring with Lichens* (1992) The Richmond Publishing Co. Ltd.

An indispensable book for anyone interested in investigating the relationship between lichens and pollution.

SMITH, A.L. *Lichens* (1921) Cambridge University Press. (Reprinted with new introduction 1975). The Richmond Publishing Co. Ltd.

Although now somewhat dated it contains much information and very many references that cannot be found elsewhere.

WIRTH V. *Die Flechten – Baden-Württembergs (*1995) Eugen Ulmer (2 volumes).

Contains over 500 superb colour photographs of lichens with keys in German.

All the above books (or any other in-print Botanical titles) may be obtained directly from: Retail Book Sales Dept., The Richmond Publishing Co. Ltd., PO Box 963, Slough SL2 3RS.

Information concerning membership of the British Lichen Society is obtainable from: The Secretary, c/o The Botany Department, The Natural History Museum, Cromwell Road, London, SW7 5BD or from The British Lichen Society website at: http://www.argonet.co.uk/users/jmgray/ where much information about the Society and its publications will be found together with links to a number of other selcted internet lichen sites.

GLOSSARY

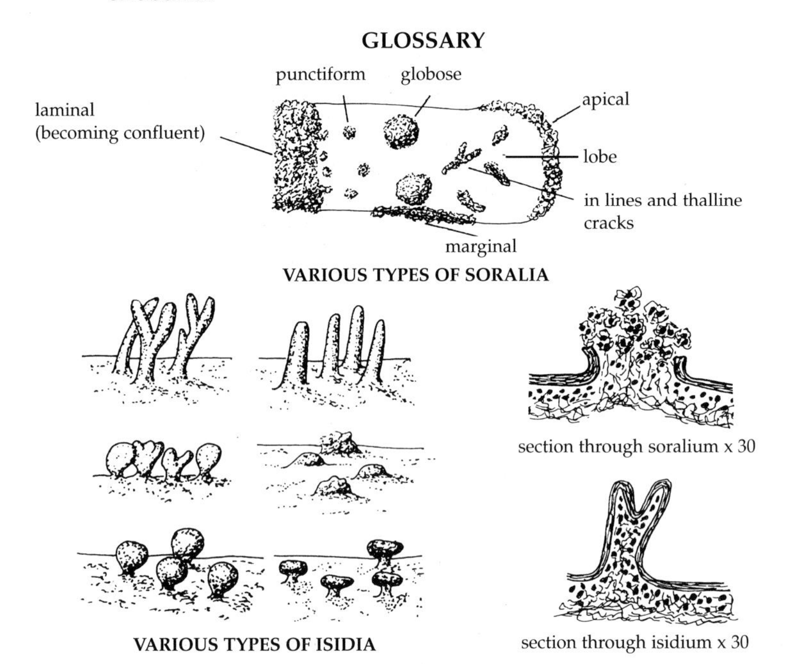

VARIOUS TYPES OF SORALIA

VARIOUS TYPES OF ISIDIA

Zone		
terrestrial zone little affected by spray	**Halophobic**	Inland species that are unable to withstand the effects of salt exposure such as *Parmelia glabratula, P. omphalodes* and *Sphaerophorus globosus*
	Halophilic	Species also found inland but able to withstand the effects of salt exposure such as *Lecanora polytropa* and *Parmelia saxatilis*
supralittoral zone only very rarely submerged in the lower region but subject to heavy spay	**xeric**	Only light spray but harsh regime of wetting and drying. Species include *Parmelia* species, *Anaptychia runcinata, Ramalina siliquosa* **'grey zone'**
	mesic	*Caloplaca* species become common in lower part with *Xantoria parietina* and *X. ectanoides* present in the upper part **'orange zone'**
littoral zone frequently submerged	**littoral fringe**	To upper limit of winkles; mainly *Verrucaria* species, especially *V. maura* also *Lichina pygmaea* **'black zone'**
	eulittoral	To upper limit of barnacles; few lichen species present eg. *Pyrenocollema halodytes* **'buff zone'**
sublittoral zone submerged except at extreme low tides		No lichens

Diagramatic representation of the main lichen zonation occuring on siliceous sea shores. (After Hawksworth 1980.)

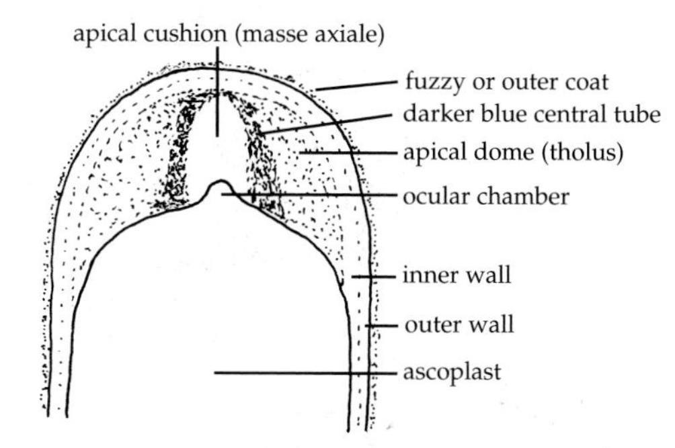

STRUCTURES WITHIN THE ASCUS TIP

Acid rocks. Siliceous, not reacting to hydrochloric acid.
Adpressed. Flat and close to the substratum.
agg. Aggregate, several similar species treated as one.
Anastomosed. Net-like.
Apical. At the tip.
Apothecium(a). Disc-shaped or elongate fruiting body containing asci.
Arachnoid. Fine; web-like.
Arctic-alpine. High montane; usually heath or heather-dominated.
Areole. Island formed by cracks in the thallus, strictly starting as separate islands that grow together to form the thallus.
Arthonioid. Type of fruiting body without a true margin. See p. 27.
Ascoma(ta). Fruit-body.
Ascospore. See Spore.
Ascus(i). Bag-shaped structure containing the spores.
Asexual. Without sex; reproducing and dispersing by means of vegatative propagules.
Atranorin. Substance produced by many lichens giving a K+ yellow reaction.
Attenuated. Drawn out to a fine point or constricted.
Axil. Junction of two branches or lobes.
Bacilliform. Rather oblong with rounded corners.
Basic bark. Bark of trees, such as sycamore, maple and elm, with a relatively high pH compared with acid-barked trees, such as oak, beech and birch.
Basidiomycete. Fungus bearing the spores on a basidium, not in an ascus.
Biatorine. Type of apothecium that lacks a proper margin and when fully developed is soft, pale coloured and often convex.
Blastidium(a). Propagules containing both partners, budded off by the lichen.
Bullate. With convex areas; blister-like.
Calcareous. Chalky, alkaline rock or soil.
Canaliculate. Channelled; trough-shaped.
Capitate. At the tip of a lobe or branch.
Capitulum. Spore-bearing area at the apex of some stalked apothecia.
Carbonaceous. Hard, black.
Chemotypes. Races of a species that differ only in their chemical constituents.
Chromatography. A sensitive method for determining chemical constituents.
Cephalodium(a). Area of the thallus of a lichen, normally with a green alga, that differs in having a blue-green cyanobacterium and may be either internal or external.
Cilia. Long hair-like structures on the ends, margins, or rarely, the surface of lobes.

Clavate. Club-shaped, wider at one end.
Concolorous. Same colour.
Confluent. Growing together to cover the surface.
Conglutinate. Stuck together.
Conidium(a). Spore produced asexually from fungal cells.
Conidiophore. A specialized hypha that produces conidia.
Coralloid. Pencil-like, or branched like coral.
Cortex. The outer layers of the thallus consisting of fungal hyphae.
Corticate. Having a cortex.
Corticolous. Growing on bark.
Crenulate. More or less regularly notched.
Crustose. Thallus type. See p. 23.
Cyphella(ae). Regular, margined perforations through the lower cortex.
Decorticate. Areas where the cortex is missing.
Decumbent. Spreading over the ground, not upright (except at the tips).
Delimited. Having clearly defined borders.
Dentate. Tooth-like.
Determinate. Having a clear edge.
Dichotomous. Divided in two, forked.
Digitate. Having finger-like projections.
Disc. The central upper surface inside the margins of the apothecium.
Discrete. In separate patches.
Dorsiventral. Upper and lower surfaces differing, sometimes used to mean vertically compressed.
Ecotype. Lichen species showing consistent variations caused by the environment.
Effuse. Spread thinly.
Endoxylic. Thallus growing within wood.
Endolithic. Thallus growing inside rock.
Endophloeodal. Thallus growing within bark.
Entire. Complete; continuous.
Epidermis. Outer cell layer of young twigs and leaves.
Epithecium(a). The upper layer of the thecium above the asci, formed by the tips of the paraphyses.
Ericaceous. Of heathers and heaths.
Erumpent. Bursting through the cortex or substratum.
Eutrophication. Nutrient-enrichment from an outside souce.
Evanescent. Disappearing early.
Exciple (excipulum). Tissue surrounding the thecium and evident as either a thalline margin (with alga) or a proper margin (without alga).
Excluded. Eliminated.
f. Form.
Farinose. Flour-like.
Fibrils. Stout hair-like growths or secondary, often perpendicular, branchlets.
Filamentous. Thallus type. See p. 22.
Fimbriate. Fringed, like a rug.
Fissural. Growing in splits in the cortex.
Flexuose. Twisted, wavy.
Foliose. Leaf-like. See p. 24.
Foveolate. Pitted.

Fruticose. Thallus type. See p. 24.
Fusiform. Long, thin and pointed at each end; spindle-shaped.
Glaucous. Pale waxy, blue-grey.
Goniocyst. Algal cell which divides to form a group of cells which become wrapped in fungal hyphae, forming a minute rounded propagule.
Gyrose. Having a serpentine, infolded margin or raised sterile tissue within the disc.
Hamathecium. All the tissues separating the asci in the fruiting body.
Hapters. Small sucker-like outgrowths that attach the lichen to the substratum.
Holdfast. Compact root-like structure fixing certain lichens to the substratum.
Homoiomerous. Thallus more or less unstructured, without an algal layer.
Hymenium. The area of a fruiting body containing the asci and paraphyses.
Hypha(ae). Fungal filament.
Hyphomycete. A group of fungi that reproduce asexually.
Hyphophore. Erect or peltate bodies that produce asexual spores.
Hypothallus. Dark, felted under-surface of *Pannaria* and *Parmeliella* species.
Hypothecium. The layer below the thecium.
Imbricate. Overlapping; like roof tiles.
Immarginate. Lacking a clearly defined margin.
Immersed. Having the fruiting bodies contained within the thickness of the thallus or substratum.
Incised. Cut.
Innate. See immersed.
Involucrellum. The external cover to some perithecia.
Isidium(a). Detachable outgrowth on the thallus containing the photobiont and externally covered by the cortex. See p. 418.
Isolichenin. A starch-like substance produced by some lichens.
Laminal. On the surface of the lobe, not on the edges.
Lateral branch. Secondary side branch growing from the main stem.
Lax. Loose and flexible.
Lecanorine. Apothecium having a thalline margin. See p. 26.
Lecideine. Apothecium without a thalline margin. See p. 26.
Lenticular. Lens-shaped.
Leprose. Thallus consisting entirelyof a powdery mass. See p. 22.
Lichenicolous. Growing on lichens.
Lignicolous. Growing on exposed or cut wood, not on living bark.
Lirella(ae). Elongate fruit, usually with a carbonaceous margin. See p. 26.
Lobate. Having lobes.
Lobule. Small secondary lobe.
Loculate. With cavities.
Maculate. Blotched and patchy.
Margin. See p. 26.
Maritime. Under the influence of sea-spray, but not or very rarely submerged.
Mazaedium. A loose dry mass of spores, formed when the asci in a fruiting body break down simultaneously.
Medulla. The inner part of the thallus lacking algae, usually of loosely packed fungal hyphae.
Monophyllus. Thallus consisting of only one lobe.
Morph. Form; used to describe the shape or form of a lichen under different stimuli such as is produced when it contains either green alga or cyanobacteria.

Mosaic. Forming a community growing together but with each thallus clearly defined.
Multi-septate. Having a number of transverse septa. See p. 21.
Muriform. Having both longitudinal and transverse septa. See p. 21.
Musicolous. Growing on moss.
Mycobiont. The fungal partner.
Nutrient-rich. Substratum, usually bark, rich in basic compounds; not acidic.
Nutrient-enriched. Enriched by bird droppings, fertilizer, etc.
Obtuse. Branching at a wide angle, or with rounded ends.
Oceanic. Pertaining to the milder, damper west coast of the British Isles.
'Old forest'. Species characteristic of a forest with a long continuity of mature trees.
Orbiculate. Circular in outline.
Ostiole. The opening at the top of a perithecium.
Ovate. Egg-shaped.
Palmate. Like the palm of the hand.
Papillate. Small wart- or finger-like projections.
Paraphysis(es). Sterile filaments growing between the asci.
Paraphysoid. Net-like filaments growing between the asci formed by stretching the original tissues.
Peltate. Plate-like and growing from a short stalk.
Periphyses. Sterile filaments found around the inside of the ostiole.
Periphysoids. Sterile filaments that grow down from above the asci.
Perispore. Sheath surrounding the spore wall.
Perithecium(a). Flask-shaped fruiting body. See p. 27.
Photobiont. Photosynthetic partner.
Phyllocladia. Small leaf-like lobes.
Placodioid. Crustose with lobed margins. See p. 23.
Plane. Flat.
Podetium(a). Lichenized stalk of a fruiting body arising from an evanescent, granular or squamulose, primary thallus. See p. 25.
Polarilocular. Spore type having a very wide septum. See p. 21.
Polyphyllous. Many-lobed.
p.p., pro parte. Indicates that only a particular part of a taxon is included.
Propagule. A reproductive or dispersal body containing both the photo- and mycobiont.
Proper margin. The margin of the disc containing fungal, but not algal cells, often concolourous with the disc.
Prostrate. Flattened against the ground, not erect.
Prothallus. Area around the edge of a crustose thallus that does not contain algal cells.
Pruina. A fine, often white, superficial powder, like the bloom on a plum.
Pseudo-. False.
Pseudocyphella(ae). Pale patch, dot or line where the cortex is thin or absent.
Punctiform. Small and sharply limited; like a pin-head.
Pustulate. With blister-like areas.
Pycnidiospore. Older name for a conidium.
Pycnidium(a). Flask-like body on the thallus that produces conidia.
Reticulate. Net-like pattern.
Revolute. Turned down, usually towards the apex.
Rhizine. Root-like outgrowth of fungal filaments from the lower cortex.
Rimose. Cracked.

Saxicolous. Growing on rock or stone.
Scabrid. Rough and scurfy.
Schizidium(a). Scale-like propagule produced by the flaking off of upper layers of the thallus.
Scyphus. A podetium in *Cladonia* species that widens at the top to form a cup.
Septum(a). Internal wall dividing cells or parts of cells.
Sessile. Fruiting body almost sitting on the surface of the thallus, not immersed.
Siliceous. Acid rocks; sand, flint, granite, etc.; not calcareous.
Sinuate. Curved and recurved, winding.
s.l., sensu lato. In a wide sense.
Sole-shaped. Shaped like the sole of a shoe.
Soralium(a). Structure producing soredia. See p. 418.
Soredium(a). Small powdery propagule containing a few algal cells and fungal hyphae.
Spinule. Small, fine, short branchlet.
Spore. Reproductive body of the fungus. For types see p. 21.
Sporochidium. Cluster of conidiophores.
Squamulose. With small scale-like structures. Lacking a lower cortex. See p. 23.
s. str., sensu stricto. in the strict sense.
Stellate. Star-shaped; radiating.
Striations. Small parallel ridges or lines.
Stroma(ta). Compact sterile fungal tissue, often containing perithecia.
subsp. Subspecies.
Substratum. Surface upon or in which the lichen grows.
Supralittoral zone. The area of the seashore well above the tide line. See p. 418.
Taxon(a). Taxonomic groups at any rank e.g. at species, generic, family etc. levels.
Terete. More or less circular in section.
Terricolous. Growing on soil, sand, peat, etc.
Tessellated. Like a tiled floor.
Tetrachotomous. Divided into fours.
Thalline margin. Outer rim found in lecanorine apothecia, containing both algal and fungal cells. See p. 26.
Thallus. The body of the lichen containing both fungal and algal cells.
Thecium. Tissues comprising the paraphyses, asci and spores.
Tholus. Inner apical tissues of many asci. See p. 419.
TLC. Thin-layer chromatography. A method used to identify chemical substances produced by a lichen.
Tomentose. Covered in fine hairs, like felt.
Trabeculum(a). Flattened 'tendon-like' rhizines.
Trichotomous. Divided into three.
Tuberculate. Wart-like.
Tumid. Thick and swollen.
Umbilicate. Attached only at a central point.
Umbonate. Having an umbo, a sterile protruding area of tissue, often found in the centre of an apothecium.
Uniseriate. In a single row.
Urceolate. Deeply concave, cup-shaped, with the margin incurved.
var. Variety.
Verrucose. Warted.

TAXONOMIC INDEX